GEOMETRY IN EASY STEPS

An Informal Approach

Philip L. Cox

ALLYN AND BACON, INC.

Boston   Rockleigh, N.J.   Atlanta   Dallas   San Jose

London   Sydney   Toronto

Author

Philip L. Cox, Mathematics Teacher
Walled Lake Central High School
Walled Lake, Michigan

Pilot Teachers

Sr. Connie Kelly
Muriel Levin
Nancy Marx
Sr. Joy Christi Przestwor
Aquinas Dominican High School
Chicago, Illinois
Phillip Kraft
Janet Maxim
Avondale Senior High School
Auburn Heights, Michigan

Richard Noteboom
Luke Powers High School
Flint, Michigan
Keith Johnson
Robert Johnson
North Chicago Community High School
North Chicago, Illinois
Art Peterson
St. Johns High School
St. Johns, Michigan

Craig Auten
Walled Lake Central High School
Walled Lake, Michigan
William Fritz
Walled Lake Western High School
Walled Lake, Michigan
Carol Youngs
Whitmer High School
Toledo, Ohio

Editing:	**Sylvia Gelb**
Technical Art:	**Lee Ames and Zak Ltd. and Anco/Boston, Inc.**
Layout:	**Lee Ames and Zak Ltd.**
Design Coordination:	**Helyn Pultz**
Cover Design:	**John Martucci Studios**
Photo Research:	**Portfolio/Mary Ruzila and Lee Ames and Zak Ltd.**
Designer:	**Beverly Fell**
Preparation Services Coordinator:	**Martha E. Ballentine**
Buyer:	**Roger Powers**

ISBN 0-205-07573-8
Library of Congress Catalog Card Number 82-70155

Printed in the United States of America

1 2 3 4 5 6 7 8 9 90 89 88 87 86 85 84 83 82

516

PREFACE

Geometry comes from two Greek words meaning "measurement of the earth." There is nothing physical that does not have shape and size. Geometry then is a mathematical study of the shapes and sizes of figures. It is made the more attractive by attention to its presence in the things around us and its application in practical ways to the solution of human problems.

Geometry in Easy Steps uses an informal approach to the study of shapes and sizes and its applications. The student begins with given facts and/or observations and induces step-wise certain and useful conclusions. In this way, the student will not only learn all the geometry content covered in most high school courses but in the process learn as well to think clearly and logically. However, because the course is based on an informal approach, it will be within the grasp of any interested student.

Some of the features which make the text more meaningful and enjoyable include the following:

> *Everyday Geometry*—consumer applications of geometry to the needs of everyday life.

> *Applications*—historical and/or technical uses of geometry in the service of humankind.

> *Geometry on the Job*—people in careers that make use of geometry.

> *Did You Know That . . .*—interesting, little known facts about geometry and related mathematics.

To assist further the learning process, the text contains the following aids:

> *Arithmetic* (or *Algebra*) *Review*—reteaching and practice of basic skills utilized in later lessons.

Test Yourself—half-page quizzes occurring after every 3 or 4 lessons.

Chapter Review—Fully-referenced three-part review consisting of Vocabulary, Skills Checklist, and Exercises.

Cumulative Review—comprehensive semester reviews.

End-of-text material—useful tables (squares and square roots, trigonometric functions, and symbols), a fully-referenced listing of constructions and major conclusions, an illustrated glossary of terms, and answers to Class Practice and Test Yourself.

Acknowledgments

The author wishes to acknowledge and thank those teachers who participated in the research for *Geometry in Easy Steps* by teaching the prototype version and providing their comments and suggestions based thereon. Special thanks are extended to the principals and supervisors of the participating schools for authorizing the use of their classes in the field-testing program.

Other persons who deserve special thanks include: Don Junak and Gary Lundquist of the L'Anse Public Schools, Mt. Clemens, Michigan, who sparked the author's interest in an informal geometry course; Gerald Wallace, principal of Walled Lake Central High School, for his support; staff members of Oakland Schools, Pontiac, Michigan; Art Coxford, Professor of Mathematics Education, University of Michigan, for his patient guidance; and Sylvia Gelb, the book's editor, for her competent editing and cooperative spirit.

Most of all, I wish to thank my wife Judy for her continual assistance and my daughter Andrea for her understanding. Without their support and encouragement, this text could not have been completed.

Philip L. Cox

CONTENTS

BUILDING A FIRM FOUNDATION

Points, Lines, and Planes; Polygons; and Prisms

1-1

Points, Lines, and Planes

In this book you will learn about geometric figures on a flat surface. These properties are useful even though Earth's surface is curved. Any small part of Earth's surface is almost flat.

Geometric figures are sets or collections of points.
Three basic geometric figures are described and pictured below.

Point •	*Line* ⟵⟶	*Plane* ▱
has no size.	is straight.	is a flat surface.
indicates a definite location.	has no thickness.	has no thickness.
	extends indefinitely in two opposite directions.	extends indefinitely in all directions.

The two terms defined next will be useful in describing other geometric figures and their properties.

Collinear points are points that are on the same line.
Points A, B, and C are collinear.
Points A, B, and D are noncollinear.
Points D and C are collinear. *If a line can be drawn through some points, they are collinear even though the line is not shown.*

Coplanar points are points that are in the same plane.
In the drawing you see two planes that *intersect*, or meet.
Points B, D, and E are coplanar.
Points A, B, D, and E are noncoplanar.
Points D, E, and G are coplanar. These three points are contained in both planes.
Points A, C, and F are coplanar. *If a plane can be drawn through some points, they are coplanar even though the plane is not shown.*

DISCUSS

1. Is there a real object that has the properties of a point? of a line? of a plane?
2. Look at the three drawings at the beginning of this lesson. In what way is the drawing of a point different from a point? the drawing of a line different from a line? the drawing of a plane different from a plane?
3. Name some objects that represent a point, a line, and a plane.

State whether each set of points is collinear.

1. D, E, F
2. C, B, D
3. D, C, F
4. A, C, B

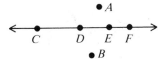

For Exercises 5–13, look at the drawing of two intersecting planes.

Identify the labeled points contained in the indicated plane(s).

5. Horizontal plane 6. Vertical plane 7. Both planes

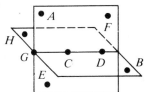

State whether each set of points is coplanar.

8. B, E, F
9. A, C, F
10. A, H, F, B
11. A, E, F, D
12. B, C, E, D
13. H, C, D

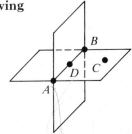

Look at the drawing of two intersecting planes and answer the following questions for each set of points.

  a. Are the points coplanar?
  b. How many planes shown contain all the points?
  c. How many other planes can be drawn that contain all the points?

14. A, B
15. A, B, C
16. A, B, D

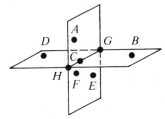

— A —

1. Look at the drawing of two intersecting lines. State whether each set of points is collinear.

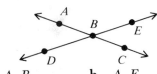

  a. A, B b. A, E
  c. D, E d. D, B, E
  e. A, B, C f. A, D, B
  g. E, C h. D, C

2. Can two points be noncollinear?
3. Can three points be collinear? non-collinear?

4. Can two different lines be drawn through two different points?
5. Look at the drawing of two intersecting planes. State whether each set of points is coplanar.

  a. A, F, E b. A, C, G
  c. H, C, G d. B, F, E
  e. A, G, H, B f. A, C, G, E

6. Six planes are shown in the drawing of a box. How many of the six planes contain all points of each set listed?

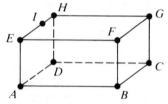

a. A, B
b. A, B, C
c. A, B, D
d. A, B, C, D
e. A, B, C, G
f. E, A
g. E, A, F
h. E, A, B
i. $E, A, B, F,$
j. E, A, B, C
k. E, I, H, G
l. E, I, H, G, F

Classify each statement as sometimes true, always true, or never true.

7. Two distinct points are collinear.
8. Three distinct points are collinear.
9. Two distinct points are coplanar.
10. Three distinct points are coplanar.
11. Four distinct points are coplanar.

— **B** —

Draw a figure to fit each description, *if possible*.

12. Two points that are collinear
13. Two points that are noncollinear
14. Three points that are collinear
15. Three points that are noncollinear
16. Four points that are collinear
17. Three points that are coplanar
18. Three points that are not coplanar
19. Three points that are coplanar and are contained in exactly one plane

— **C** —

20. Look at the picture of two intersecting planes. Which of these four phrases best describes each set of points?

collinear coplanar
neither collinear nor coplanar
both collinear and coplanar

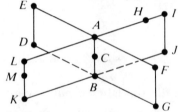

a. A, C, E
b. A, C, B
c. A, H, I
d. K, A, C
e. M, H, E, F
f. M, H, I, J
g. D, C
h. G, B, F
i. G, B, C, A, F
j. E, L, M, K

21. a. Can collinear points be noncoplanar? Why or why not?
    b. Can coplanar points be noncollinear? Why or why not?

22. Use one or more of these words— *collinear, coplanar, noncollinear,* or *noncoplanar*—to complete each statement.
    a. Any two points are ? .
    b. Any three points are ? .
    c. Three ? points lie in many planes.
    d. Three ? points lie in exactly one plane.

23. Two points determine one line. That is, exactly one line can be drawn containing both points. The figures show the number of lines determined by three noncollinear points and by four points, no three of which are collinear.

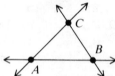

3 noncollinear points determine 3 lines. $(\overleftrightarrow{AB}, \overleftrightarrow{BC}, \overleftrightarrow{AC})$

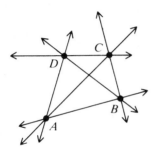

4 points, no 3 of which are collinear, determine 6 lines. ($\overleftrightarrow{AB}$, $\overleftrightarrow{BC}$, $\overleftrightarrow{CD}$, $\overleftrightarrow{DA}$, $\overleftrightarrow{AC}$, $\overleftrightarrow{BD}$)

    a. Draw 5 points, no 3 of which are collinear. Draw all lines determined by the points. How many are there?

    b. Repeat step a for 6 points, no 3 of which are collinear.

    c. Predict how many lines are determined by 7 points, no 3 of which are collinear. Check your prediction.

24. Do an activity like that in Exercise 23 but remove the restriction that no three points are collinear. Find all possibilities for the number of lines determined by each given number of points. (Hint: There are two different possibilities for 3 points.)

    a. 3 points   **b.** 4 points
    c. 5 points   **d.** 6 points
    e. 7 points

Applications

Stability in Design

As you know, when it is placed on an uneven or slanted surface, any four-legged table will wobble. To support something that must be kept absolutely steady, three legs are used for stability. The reason for this is as follows: Think of the end of each leg as a point. Any three points that are noncollinear lie in exactly one plane.

This property is used in designing many commonly used objects. Tripods are used by photographers to steady their camera. Surveyors also use a tripod to steady their transit. Some other objects whose design is based upon this property include a stand for a movie projection screen, a painter's easel, and a tricycle.

1-2
Segments and Rays

The drawings represent segments and rays.
A *segment* is part of a line with two endpoints.
A *ray* is part of a line with only one endpoint.
A ray extends indefinitely in one direction.

Special symbols are used to represent geometric figures.

Geometric Figure	Identified by:	Drawing	Symbol
Point	a capital letter	$A \bullet$	A
Line	any two points on the line or a lowercase letter		$\overleftrightarrow{AB}$ or $\overleftrightarrow{BA}$ l
Segment	its endpoints		$\overline{AB}$ or $\overline{BA}$
Ray	its endpoint and any other point on the ray (The symbol for the endpoint is given first.)		$\overrightarrow{AB}$
Plane	three noncollinear points or a capital letter (which does not represent a point)		plane ABC plane X

The *midpoint of a segment* is the point that divides the segment into two segments of equal length. A segment has exactly one midpoint.

M is the midpoint of $\overline{AB}$.

A *bisector of a segment* is a line, segment, or ray that passes through the midpoint of the segment. A segment has many bisectors.

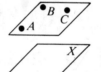

$\overline{SM}$, $\overrightarrow{MR}$, and $\overleftrightarrow{RM}$ are bisectors of $\overline{AB}$.

Opposite rays are two rays that have the same endpoint and form a line.

$\overrightarrow{OM}$ and $\overrightarrow{OR}$ are opposite rays.

═══════════════ *DISCUSS* ═══════════════

1. Is there a real object that has the properties of a segment? of a ray?
2. Name some objects that represent a segment and a ray.

1. $\overrightarrow{XY}$ is a correct symbol for the ray shown. Why is $\overrightarrow{YX}$ an incorrect symbol for this ray?

Look at line $\overleftrightarrow{CB}$.

2. $\overrightarrow{CA}$ and $\overrightarrow{BC}$ form a line. Are they opposite rays? Why or why not?

Look at the figure. M is the midpoint of $\overline{CD}$.

3. Identify two segments that have the same length.
4. Identify three different bisectors of $\overline{CD}$.
5. How many midpoints does a segment have? How many bisectors?

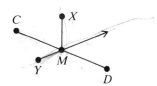

Symbols often suggest properties of geometric figures.

6. How many points are needed to determine a segment? a ray? a line?
7. In what ways do the symbols for segment, ray, and line suggest properties of each figure?
8. How many points are needed to determine a plane?
9. Will any three points always determine exactly one plane?

===== **EXERCISES** =====

_ **A** _

1. Look at this line:

   a. Are points $A, B,$ and C collinear?
   b. Write six different correct symbols for the line.
2. Name all segments shown in the drawing. (There are three.)

3. Look at this line:

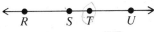

   a. Name the endpoints of $\overline{ST}$.
   b. Name three different segments with an endpoint of S.
4. Look at this line:

   a. Does $\overrightarrow{AR}$ pass through B?
   b. Is A on $\overrightarrow{RB}$? on $\overrightarrow{BR}$?
   c. Write a symbol for the ray through A with endpoint R.

5. Identify five different rays in the figure shown.

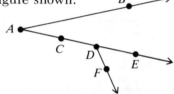

Look at the intersecting line and segment. M is the midpoint of $\overline{AB}$. Classify each statement as true or false.

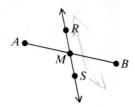

6. R and A are collinear.

7. $R, A,$ and M are collinear.

8. $R, A,$ and M are coplanar.

9. $\overleftrightarrow{RM}$ is a bisector of $\overline{AB}$.

10. $\overleftrightarrow{RS}$ is a bisector of $\overline{AB}$.

11. $\overrightarrow{SR}$ is a bisector of $\overline{AB}$.

12. $\overline{AM}$ and $\overline{MB}$ are the same length.

13. $\overrightarrow{RM}$ and $\overrightarrow{RS}$ are the same ray.

14. $\overrightarrow{MR}$ and $\overrightarrow{MS}$ are opposite rays.

15. $\overrightarrow{RS}$ and $\overrightarrow{SR}$ are opposite rays.

Classify each statement as true or false. ($A, B,$ and C are different points.)

16. $\overleftrightarrow{AB}$ and $\overleftrightarrow{BA}$ are the same line.

17. $\overline{AB}$ and $\overline{BA}$ are the same segment.

18. $\overrightarrow{AB}$ and $\overrightarrow{BA}$ are the same ray.

19. Two rays with the same endpoint must be opposite rays.

20. Points $A, B,$ and C are located in only one plane.

21. Each segment has exactly one midpoint.

22. Each segment has exactly one bisector.

_ B _

Draw and label a figure to fit each description.

23. $\overleftrightarrow{HI}$ **24.** $\overline{HI}$

25. $\overrightarrow{HI}$ **26.** $\overrightarrow{IH}$

27. $\overleftrightarrow{IH}$

28. $\overleftrightarrow{RT}$ intersecting $\overleftrightarrow{RS}$ (Identify the point of intersection.)

29. Opposite rays $\overrightarrow{OR}$ and $\overrightarrow{OT}$ (Write a symbol for the figure formed.)

30. Two rays that are not opposite rays but have the same endpoint (What kind of figure is formed?)

31. Point C on both $\overleftrightarrow{AB}$ and $\overrightarrow{AB}$

32. Point C on $\overleftrightarrow{AB}$ but not on $\overrightarrow{AB}$

33. Two lines bisecting $\overline{AB}$

34. $\overline{AB}$ and $\overline{CD}$ bisecting each other

_ C _

35. Two points determine one segment. The figures show the number of segments determined by 3 collinear points and by 4 collinear points. (Some segments overlap.)

$\bullet\!\!-\!\!-\!\!-\!\!\bullet\!\!-\!\!-\!\!-\!\!\bullet$
$A \qquad B \qquad C$
$(\overline{AB}, \overline{BC}, \overline{AC})$

3 collinear points determine 3 segments.

$\bullet\!\!-\!\!\bullet\!\!-\!\!\bullet\!\!-\!\!\bullet$
$A \quad B \quad C \quad D$

4 collinear points determine 6 segments.
$(\overline{AB}, \overline{BC}, \overline{CD}, \overline{AC}, \overline{AD}, \overline{BD})$

a. Draw 5 collinear points. Name all segments determined by the points. How many are there?

b. Repeat step a for 6 collinear points.

c. Predict how many segments are determined by 7 collinear points. Check your prediction.

d. State how the results of this activity compare with the results of Exercise 23 on page 4. Explain why this is true.

1-3
Parallel and Intersecting Lines and Planes

The concept of parallel lines is an important one in mathematics. *Parallel lines* are lines that are in the same plane and that do not intersect. $l \| m$ is read "line l is parallel to line m." Segments and rays are parallel if the lines they are part of are parallel.

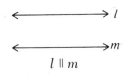
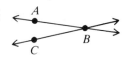

$l \| m$

If two lines are in the same plane and are not parallel, then the lines must intersect. $\overleftrightarrow{AB}$ and $\overleftrightarrow{BC}$ are *intersecting lines*. The point of intersection is B.

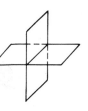

> **If two lines intersect, their intersection is always a point.**

If two planes do not intersect, they are parallel.

These are parallel planes.   These are intersecting planes.

          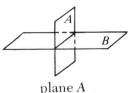   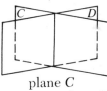

plane $A \| $ plane B plane $C \| $ plane D plane A intersects plane B plane C intersects plane D

> **If two planes intersect, their intersection is always a line.**

══════════════ CLASS PRACTICE ══════════════

1. Look at the drawing of intersecting planes. What is the meaning of the dashed segments?
2. Draw two intersecting lines.
3. Complete the statement: If two lines intersect, their intersection is a(n)?.
4. How many planes contain two intersecting lines? Why?
5. Can two different lines have two points of intersection? Why or why not?

Look around you. Name some objects that suggest each of the following.

6. Intersecting lines
7. Intersecting planes
8. Parallel lines
9. Parallel planes

Look at the figure. Point X is in both plane A and plane B.

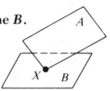

10. Do the planes have other points in common?
11. What kind of figure is the intersection of planes A and B?
12. Complete the statement: If two planes intersect, their intersection is a(n)?.

EXERCISES

— **A** —

In each figure, which point is on both lines?

1.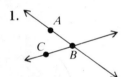

2.

3.

4.

Classify each pair of lines as parallel or intersecting.

5.

6.

7.

8.

9.

10.

Find the indicated information.

11. Look at the drawing of intersecting lines. Identify each of the following.

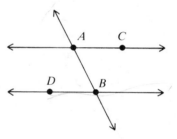

a. Pair of parallel lines
b. Two points of intersection
c. Two pairs of intersecting lines
d. Line that intersects two lines

Classify each pair of planes as parallel or intersecting.

12. 13.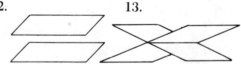

14. 15.

Find the indicated information.

16. Look at the drawing of plane A intersecting plane B. Identify each of the following.

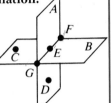

   a. Three points that are in both planes
   b. Four points in plane A
   c. Four points in plane B
   d. Three collinear points
   e. Three noncollinear points
   f. Intersection of planes A and B

17. Look at the drawing of a box. Identify each of the following.

   a. Three segments parallel to $\overline{AB}$
   b. Three segments parallel to $\overline{AD}$
   c. Three pairs of intersecting segments
   d. Three segments that intersect at a point
   e. Plane parallel to plane ABC
   f. Plane parallel to plane ADH

_ **B** _

Draw and label a figure to fit each description.

18. $\overleftrightarrow{AB} \parallel \overleftrightarrow{CD}$
19. $\overleftrightarrow{XY}$ intersects $\overleftrightarrow{XZ}$ (Name the point of intersection.)

Write a description of each drawing.

   Example:

$\overleftrightarrow{RM}$ bisects $\overline{AB}$.

or

$\overleftrightarrow{RM}$ and $\overline{AB}$ intersect at point M.

20.

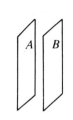

21.

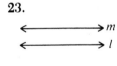

22.

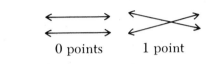

23.

_ **C** _

24. Two lines may have either one point of intersection or no points of intersection. Three lines may have either one, two, three, or no points of intersection.

0 points   1 point

0 points   1 point   2 points   3 points

   a. Draw four lines. Count the number of points of intersection. As illustrated for two and three lines, find all possibilities. (There are six different possibilities for four lines.)
   b. Draw five lines. Find all possibilities for the number of points of intersection. (There are nine possibilities.)

25. Using planes, do an activity similar to that in Exercise 24. Find all possibilities for the number of lines of intersection for each of the following.
   a. Two planes   b. Three planes
   c. Four planes

1-4

Angles

In this lesson you will be introduced to the angle and learn how to identify and name it and its parts.

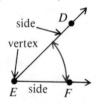

An *angle* is formed by two rays with a common endpoint. The two rays that form an angle are the *sides*. The common endpoint of the rays is called the *vertex* of the angle.

Vertex: E
Sides: $\overrightarrow{ED}$ and $\overrightarrow{EF}$

The size of an angle depends on the amount of opening between its sides. The amount of opening is indicated by a double-headed curved arrow ($\leftrightarrow$).

There are three ways to name an angle:

1. Use the capital letter for the vertex. The angle shown is angle A and its symbol is $\angle A$. (The symbol $\angle$ is read "angle.")

2. Use a lowercase letter or a number written inside the drawing of an angle. The angles shown are angle b and angle 1. Their symbols are $\angle b$ and $\angle 1$.

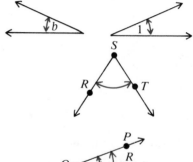

3. Use three capital letters, one for the vertex and two for points on the sides. The angle shown is angle RST (or angle TSR). Its symbol is $\angle RST$ (or $\angle TSR$). The middle letter is *always* the letter for the vertex.

The figure shown here shows why three letters are sometimes needed to identify an angle. If you write $\angle Q$, it is not clear which of the *three* angles you mean.

CLASS PRACTICE

Look at the drawing of an angle.

1. Name the angle in four different ways.
2. Identify the vertex of the angle.
3. Identify the sides of the angle.

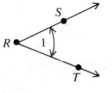

4. Look at the drawing of three angles. Why is $\angle A$ an *incorrect* name for any of the angles?
5. Look around you. Name some objects that suggest an angle.

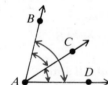

_ A _

For each angle, identify the vertex and sides of the angle.

1.

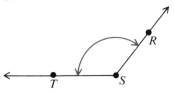

2.

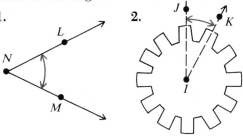

3.

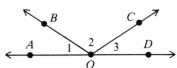

Find the indicated information.

4. Name in four different ways the angle shown.

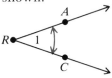

5. Look at the figure. Identify each of the following.

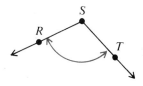

   a. All angles
   b. All angles with $\overrightarrow{OB}$ as one side
   c. Two other names for ∠3
   d. Two opposite rays

For each angle indicated by a double-headed arrow (↔), select correct names for that angle from the list given. (Each exercise has more than one answer.)

6. ∠O   ∠OMB   7. ∠CAB ∠CAD
    ∠BOM ∠B   ∠CAE ∠DAB
    ∠MOB ∠BMO   ∠A   ∠EAD

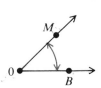

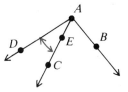

8. ∠1   ∠B   9. ∠DRT ∠R
    ∠O   ∠BOX   ∠DRS ∠SRT
    ∠OXB ∠OBX   ∠SDR ∠D

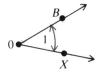

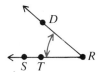

10. ∠X   ∠TXR   11. ∠M ∠X
    ∠1   ∠RXS   ∠t   ∠MNX
    ∠TXS ∠RXT   ∠N ∠MXN

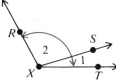

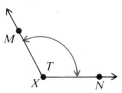

12. ∠1   ∠RAN   13. ∠S   ∠SRT
    ∠2   ∠NAR   ∠RST ∠RTS
    ∠RAP ∠A   ∠TSR ∠STR

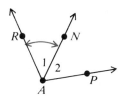

— B —

Draw and label a figure to fit each description.

14. Angle whose symbol is ∠RAT
15. Angle with sides $\overrightarrow{OR}$ and $\overrightarrow{OB}$
16. Angle whose vertex is B

Select the larger angle in each pair.

17.

18.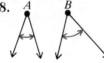

19. **20.**

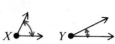

For each group of three angles, select the two angles having the same size.

21.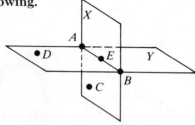

22.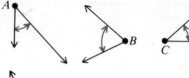

23.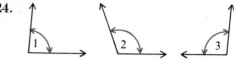

For each group of three angles, list the angles in order from the smallest to the largest.

24.

25.

26.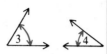

Test Yourself

Look at the figure in which plane X intersects plane Y. Identify each of the following.

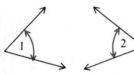

1. Three collinear points
2. Three noncollinear points
3. Four points in plane X
4. Intersection of planes X and Y

Classify each statement as true or false.

5. Two points are always collinear.
6. Three points are always coplanar.
7. Each segment has many bisectors.
8. Any two rays with the same endpoint are opposite rays.

Draw and label a figure to fit each description.

9. $\overrightarrow{XY}$
10. $l \parallel m$
11. ∠BXR
12. $\overleftrightarrow{AB}$ bisecting $\overline{RS}$
13. $\overrightarrow{OR}$ with midpoint M
14. Opposite rays $\overrightarrow{AB}$ and $\overrightarrow{AC}$

1-5
Polygons

A *polygon* is a special kind of geometric figure. The word "polygon" comes from the Greek words meaning "many angled." The figures below show how polygons differ from figures that are not polygons.

These figures are polygons.

These figures are *not* polygons.

Polygons are either *convex* or *concave*. The figures below show how convex and concave polgons differ.

These polygons are convex.

These polygons are concave.

Polygons are classified by the number of sides. In the table below you will find some of the types of polygons. An * indicates the types that will be used most often in this book.

Polygon	Number of Sides	Polygon	Number of Sides
*Triangle	3	Nonagon	9
*Quadrilateral	4	Decagon	10
*Pentagon	5	Dodecagon	12
*Hexagon	6	19-gon	19
Septagon(or Heptagon)	7	n-gon	n
*Octagon	8		

Most of the work in this book will be with convex polygons. Unless stated otherwise, "polygon" means "convex polygon."

It is not easy to write a good definition of a polygon, a convex polygon, or a concave polygon. However, the following questions will help you learn to recognize them:

1. In what way(s) are polygons different from other geometric figures? In what way(s) are they like them?

2. In what way(s) are convex polygons different from concave polygons? In what way(s) are they like them?

3. Which figures are polygons? Which are convex polygons? Which are concave polygons?

A   B   C   D

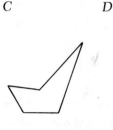

E   F   G   H

EXERCISES

_ A _

1. Which figures are polygons? (Hint: There are four polygons shown.)

2. Which polygons are convex and which are concave?

A   B

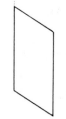

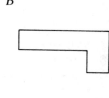

C   D   E

C   D   E

F   G

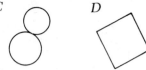

H   I

Count the number of sides and then classify each polygon.

3.

4.

5.
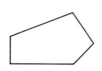

6.

7.

8.

9.

10.

11.

12.

Draw a polygon to fit each description.
13. Septagon   14. Decagon
15. Hexagon
16. Quadrilateral with no sides equal in length
17. 5-gon (What is a more common name for this figure?)
18. Convex quadrilateral
19. Concave quadrilateral
20. Polygon with the least possible number of sides

_ C _

Many traffic signs are in the shape of a polygon. Name the polygon represented by each sign.
21. Stop sign
22. Speed-limit sign
23. Yield sign
24. Point A is in the interior (inside) of a convex polygon. Point B is another point in the interior of the same polygon. Can $\overline{AB}$ intersect the polygon?
25. Point A is in the interior of a concave polygon. Point B is another point in the interior of the same polygon. Can $\overline{AB}$ intersect the polygon?

══════ *MORE EXPLORING* ══════
Prefixes and Suffixes

The names for polygons are easier to remember if you know the meaning of some Greek and Latin prefixes and suffixes. These prefixes and suffixes are also used in common words.

For each prefix and suffix listed below, use a dictionary to find (a) the meaning of the prefix or suffix, and (b) at least two words that contain the prefix or suffix.

1. *penta-*   2. *-lateral*   3. *hexa-*   4. *nona-*
5. *quad-*   6. *deca-*   7. *-gon*   8. *tri-*

1-6

Naming Polygons

A *vertex* of a polygon is any point where two of its sides intersect. The plural of "vertex" is "vertices" (pronounced "ver-ti-sees"). A polygon is named by listing its vertices in any *consecutive* order.

Consecutive angles of a polygon are angles that have one side that contains the same side of the polygon.

Opposite (nonconsecutive) angles of a polygon are angles whose sides contain different sides of the polygon.

Consecutive (adjacent) sides of a polygon are sides that intersect.

Opposite (nonconsecutive) sides of a polygon are sides that do not intersect.

Consecutive (adjacent) vertices of a polygon are endpoints of the same side.

Opposite (nonconsecutive) vertices of a polygon are not endpoints of the same side.

Some Consecutive Angles: $\angle A$ and $\angle B$, $\angle D$ and $\angle E$

Some Opposite Angles: $\angle A$ and $\angle C$, $\angle E$ and $\angle B$

Some Consecutive Sides: $\overline{AB}$ and $\overline{BC}$, $\overline{AE}$ and $\overline{ED}$

Some Opposite Sides: $\overline{AB}$ and $\overline{CD}$, $\overline{AB}$ and $\overline{ED}$

Some Consecutive Vertices: A and B, B and C

Some Opposite Vertices: A and C, A and D

Sides: $\overline{AB}, \overline{BC}, \overline{CD}, \overline{DE}, \overline{EA}$ Vertices: A, B, C, D, E

Some Names: polygon $ABCDE$, polygon $CDEAB$, polygon $EDCBA$

A *diagonal* of a polygon is a segment joining a pair of opposite vertices. Some of the diagonals for two polygons are shown below.

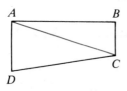

$\overline{AC}$ is a diagonal.

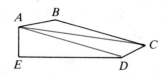

$\overline{AC}$ and $\overline{AD}$ are diagonals.

CLASS PRACTICE

Identify each of the following for each polygon shown.

a.   All vertices   b.   All sides

c.   Pair of consecutive sides   d.   Pair of opposite sides

e. Pair of consecutive vertices
f. Pair of opposite vertices
g. Pair of consecutive angles
h. Pair of opposite angles
i. Two different names for the polygon
j. Number of diagonals that can be drawn from each vertex

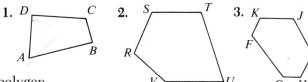

EXERCISES

_ **A** _

1. Identify each of the following for the hexagon shown.
   a. Six vertices
   b. Six sides
   c. Two different names for the hexagon, each starting with A
   d. Two sides adjacent to $\overline{BC}$
   e. Three sides opposite $\overline{BC}$
   f. Two vertices adjacent to B
   g. Three vertices opposite B
   h. Three angles opposite $\angle D$
   i. Two angles consecutive to $\angle D$
   j. All diagonals with endpoint A

2. Identify each of the following for the pentagon shown.
   a. Five vertices
   b. Five sides
   c. Two different names for the pentagon, each starting with P
   d. All sides adjacent to $\overline{PA}$
   e. All sides opposite $\overline{PA}$
   f. All vertices adjacent to P
   g. All vertices opposite P
   h. All angles consecutive to $\angle P$
   i. All angles opposite $\angle P$
   j. All diagonals with endpoint A

3. Which are correct names for the pentagon shown?
   ABCDE
   BCEDA
   CBAED
   DCABE

4. Which are correct names for the hexagon shown?
   OPQRMN
   POMNRQ
   MRQOPN
   QRMNOP

_ **B** _

Draw and label a figure to fit each description.

5. Polygon $FGHI$
6. Polygon $ABCDE$
7. Quadrilateral with two pairs of opposite sides that are parallel
8. Polygon with three vertices
9. Pentagon
10. Octagon
11. Quadrilateral with exactly one pair of opposite sides that are parallel

_ **C** _

12. Answer the following questions for each type of polygon shown.

Triangle   Quadrilateral

Pentagon

Hexagon

a. How many sides are adjacent to any one side of the polygon?

b. How many sides are opposite that side?

c. How many vertices are adjacent to any one vertex of the polygon?

d. How many vertices are opposite that vertex?

e. How many diagonals can be drawn from that vertex?

f. Study your answers to parts a–e.

Do you see any patterns? If so, write a description of these patterns.

Draw and label a figure to fit each description.

13. Polygon with $\overline{RS}$ as a side and with 2 sides adjacent to $\overline{RS}$

14. Polygon with $\overline{RS}$ as a side and with 3 sides opposite $\overline{RS}$

Look at your drawings for Exercises 13 and 14.

15. What kind of polygon did you draw? Is that the only kind of polygon that could have been drawn? Why or why not?

MORE EXPLORING
How Many Diagonals Will a Polygon Have?

1. Draw a triangle, a quadrilateral, a pentagon, a hexagon, a septagon, and an octagon.

2. Draw all possible diagonals for each polygon.

3. Use your results to complete a table like this:

Number of Sides (n)	Number of Diagonals (d)	Number of Vertices Opposite Each Vertex ($n-3$)	$(n-3) \cdot n$

4. Look at your completed table.

   a. Which polygon has no diagonals? Why?

   b. Compare the second and fourth columns. Look for a pattern.

   c. Write a formula for the number of diagonals (d) in a polygon with n sides. Why does this formula work?

   d. Use your formula. How many diagonals does a 12-gon have?

Classifying Polygons

Many things, including geometric figures, may be classified in more than one way. For example, in the rectangle shown, $\overline{AB}$ is a segment as well as a side of the rectangle and a set of points. Can you think of any other ways to correctly classify $\overline{AB}$?

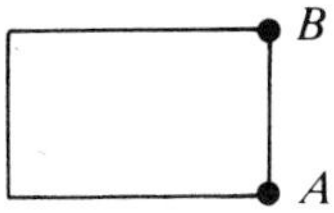

In this lesson we will discuss different types (classes) of quadrilaterals and another way to classify polygons. Shown below are some special types of quadrilaterals.

Special Types of Quadrilaterals

Trapezoid
Quadrilateral with exactly one pair of parallel sides.

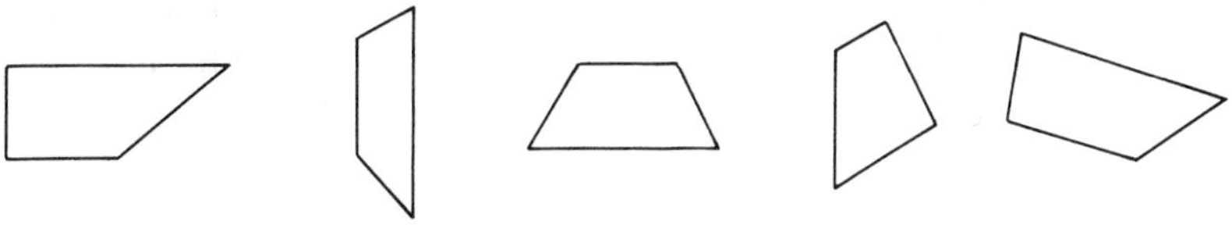

Parallelogram
Quadrilateral with two pairs of parallel sides.

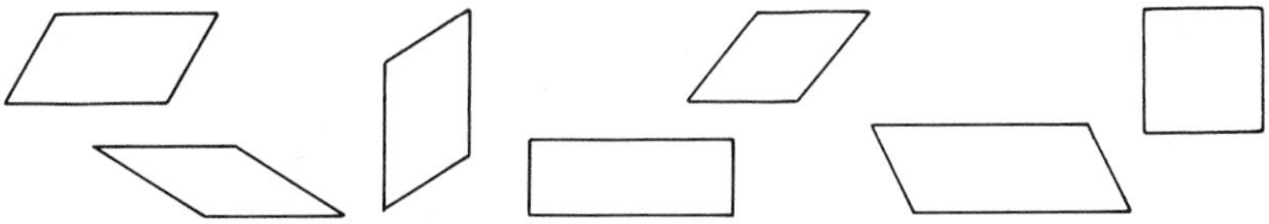

Rhombus
Parallelogram with all sides the same length.

Rectangle
Parallelogram with right angles.

Square
Rhombus with right angles.
Rectangle with all sides the same length.

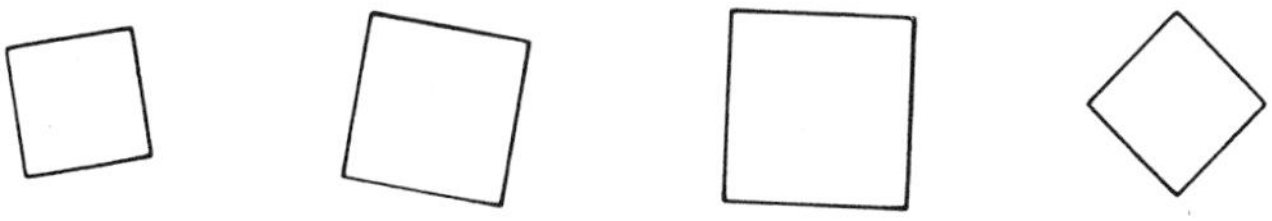

Some of the quadrilaterals shown above have angles that are right angles. A *right angle* is an angle that can be described as a square corner.

Four right angles are shown here.

Some quadrilaterals can be classified in more than one way. The figure below the right angles is a quadrilateral, a parallelogram, and a rectangle.

- It is a quadrilateral because it is a polygon with four sides.
- It is a parallelogram because it is a quadrilateral with opposite sides parallel.
- It is a rectangle because it is a parallelogram with right angles.

It is common practice to use the name of the type that gives the most information about the figure. For the figure shown, this is "rectangle."

A *regular polygon* is a polygon in which all sides have the same length and all angles have the same size. The figures at the right illustrate this definition.

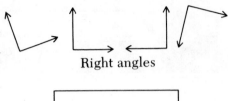

Right angles

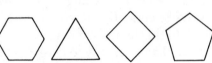

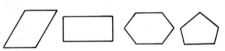

These are regular polygons.

These are *not* regular polygons.

Look at these quadrilaterals. Which are parallelograms? rectangles? rhombuses? squares? trapezoids?

1.
2.
3.
4.
5.

6.
7.
8.
9.
10.

Find the indicated information.

11. Look at the figures on page 22 that are *not* regular polygons. State *why* each is not a regular polygon.

12. People also can be classified in many ways. Someone may be an American citizen, a male (female), a brother (sister), student (worker), and so on. Think of as many ways as possible in which you can classify yourself.

— A —

1. Draw a regular quadrilateral.
2. State other correct ways, besides calling it a "regular quadrilateral," of classifying the figure you drew for Exercise 1. What is that figure more commonly called?
3. Which are regular polygons?

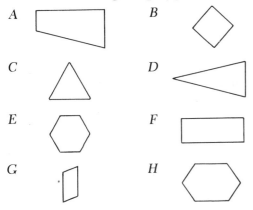

A   B

C   D

E   F

G   H

— B —

Draw a figure to fit each description.
4. Quadrilateral that is not a parallelogram
5. Parallelogram that is also a rectangle
6. Quadrilateral that is not a regular polygon but has all sides of the same length
7. Hexagon that is not a regular polygon
8. Parallelogram that is not a rectangle
9. Trapezoid with two sides of the same length
10. Rectangle that is also a square

Classify each statement as true or false. Explain each answer.
11. Every parallelogram is a quadrilateral.
12. Every quadrilateral is a parallelogram.
13. Every parallelogram is a rectangle.
14. Every rectangle is a parallelogram.
15. Every rhombus is a square.
16. Every square is a rhombus.
17. Every rhombus is a rectangle.
18. Every rectangle is a rhombus.
19. Every square is a rectangle.
20. Every rectangle is a square.

From the five classes listed, choose the correct ones for each figure. (Each exercise has more than one answer.)
21. hexagon
    polygon
    octagon
    parallelogram
    regular polygon

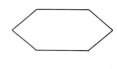

22. rhombus
    parallelogram
    quadrilateral
    regular polygon
    polygon

23. pentagon
    polygon
    hexagon
    regular polygon
    octagon

24. quadrilateral
    parallelogram
    square
    rectangle
    polygon

MORE EXPLORING
What Kind of Figure is Formed by Connecting the Midpoints
of the Sides of a Quadrilateral?

1. Draw 5 or 6 different quadrilaterals. Include at least one rectangle, one square, one trapezoid, and one rhombus.
2. For each figure, mark the midpoint of each side.
3. For each figure, draw segments joining the midpoints of adjacent sides.
4. What kind of figure is formed by connecting the midpoints? Write a conclusion based on your results.
5. Test your conclusion. Draw two or three other quadrilaterals. Make some of them strangely shaped. Follow steps 1–3 for these new quadrilaterals. Do you get the same result?

Everyday Geometry
Tile Shapes

Tiles for a floor or wall have to fit together without gaps between them. Most people use square tiles, but for creative decorating other shapes can be used. Tiles do not have to be regular polygons, or even all the same shape, as the examples show.

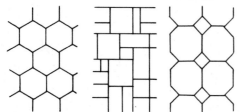

EXERCISES

1. Draw a regular pentagon as accurately as you can (each angle measures 108°). Use it as a pattern. Cut out several regular pentagons from paper. Can regular pentagons be used to tile a floor?
2. Draw two different tile patterns. Be creative!

DID YOU KNOW THAT....

September, October, and December were the 7th, 8th, and 10th months of the early Roman calendar. In 46 B.C. Julius Caesar revised the calendar so that September, October, and December became the 9th, 10th, and 12th months, as they are today.

1-8
Prisms

So far we have discussed properties of *two-dimensional* or flat figures. Now we will discuss some properties of *three-dimensional* or space figures. The diagram illustrates some of the terms used to describe some three-dimensional figures.

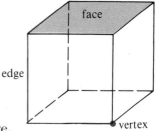

A *face* is a part of a plane forming a side of a three-dimensional figure.

An *edge* is a segment formed by the intersection of two faces.

A *vertex* is the point of intersection of at least three edges.

A *prism* is a special kind of three-dimensional figure.

These are prisms.

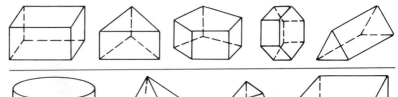

These are *not* prisms.

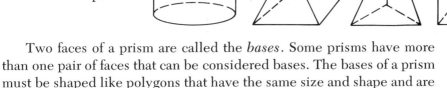

Two faces of a prism are called the *bases*. Some prisms have more than one pair of faces that can be considered bases. The bases of a prism must be shaped like polygons that have the same size and shape and are parallel (lie in parallel planes).

The *lateral faces* of a prism are the faces that are not bases. The lateral faces of any prism are shaped like parallelograms.

The bases of the prisms shown below are shaded, while the lateral faces are not.

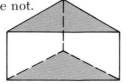 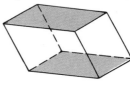

A *right prism* is a prism in which all the lateral faces are rectangular. In a right prism, each edge of a lateral face is at a right angle to the bases. Prisms that are *not* right prisms are called *oblique prisms*. Most of the prisms in this book are right prisms.

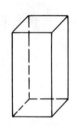

These are right prisms.　　　These are oblique prisms.

Prisms are classified by the shape of their bases. For example, a prism with triangular bases is called a triangular prism.

Prisms with square bases have special names, though, as shown at right.

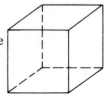

Rectangular prism

DISCUSS

Look at the drawings on page 25 of three-dimensional figures that are prisms and those that are not prisms.
1. How are the prisms like those that are not prisms?
2. How are the prisms different from those that are not prisms?

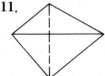

Cube

Look at the prisms illustrated at the top of page 25.
3. Describe the shape of the bases of each prism.
4. Describe the shape of the lateral faces of each prism.
5. Which prisms have more than one pair of faces that can be considered bases?
6. Classify each prism.
7. For each prism, state the number of faces, edges, and vertices.

Explain why each of the following figures is not a prism.

8. 　9. 　10. 　11.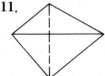

EXERCISES

_ A _

For each prism shown, find the following information.
    a. Number of faces
    b. Number of edges
    c. Number of vertices
    d. Shape of the bases

1. 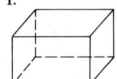　2.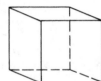

3. 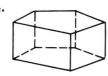 **4.**   **9.**   **10.**

5.   **6.**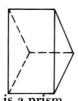

State whether each figure is a prism.

7.   **8.**

Classify each statement as true or false. Explain each answer.

11. Every right prism has a rectangular base.

12. The lateral faces of all prisms are parallelograms.

13. Every right prism has two bases.

14. A triangular prism has three faces.

MORE EXPLORING
Euler's Formula

A *polyhedron* is a three-dimensional figure in which all faces are polygons. A prism is a special kind of polyhedron.

1. Look at the polyhedrons shown. Count the number of faces, vertices, and edges of each.

A 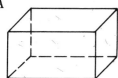 B 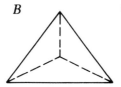 C 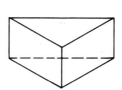 D

E 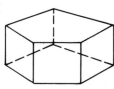 F   G 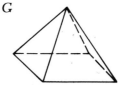 H

2. Leonard Euler (pronounced "Oy'-ler"), an 18th century Swiss mathematician, discovered a relationship among the number of faces, vertices, and edges of any polyhedron. Can you find it? (Hint: Compare the number of faces and number of vertices with the number of edges.) Write a formula for this relationship.

Look at the pentagon. Identify each of the following.

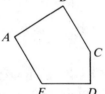

1. All sides opposite $\overline{AE}$
2. All vertices adjacent to E
3. All diagonals with an endpoint of B

Classify each statement as true or false.

4. Every rectangle is a square.
5. Every rectangle is a parallelogram.
6. Every rectangular prism has four faces.

Draw a figure to fit each description.

7. Polygon with four sides
8. Concave hexagon
9. Regular polygon
10. Quadrilateral and all its diagonals

Find the indicated information.

11. Count the number of faces, edges, and vertices of the prism shown.

12. State several ways to classify the figure shown.

1-9

Drawing Prisms

Suppose you wish to draw a picture of a cube. The problem is this: Your writing surface is flat (two-dimensional) but you want your picture to show three dimensions—length, width, and height. With a little care, you can overcome this problem.

These four steps can be used in drawing a cube seen from the right.

Step 1   Step 2   Step 3   Step 4

If you draw all edges lightly, it will be easier to erase in order to make the dashed edges in Step 4. An alternative method is to dash all edges through Step 3 and then trace over the edges that are visible (not hidden).

If you wish to draw a cube seen from the left, follow these steps.

Step 1   Step 2   Step 3   Step 4

If you wish to draw a box, or rectangular prism, you can follow these four steps.

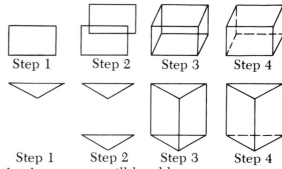

Step 1   Step 2   Step 3   Step 4

These steps show how a triangular prism can be drawn. Other types of prisms can be drawn in a similar manner.

Step 1   Step 2   Step 3   Step 4

If you follow the steps outlined in this lesson, you will be able to draw a fairly good picture of almost any prism. Your drawings should be neat and accurate. Use a pencil and straightedge.

CLASS PRACTICE

To draw a good picture of a cube, you should take a point of view that shows *all* the cube's dimensions—length, width, and height.

Look at the three drawings of a cube. Each was made from a different point of view.
1. Describe the point of view (the point from which the cube is being seen) for each drawing.
2. Which is the best drawing of a cube? Why?

A   B   C

Find the indicated information.
3. Suppose that no segments have been dashed in the drawing of a cube, as shown here. Look at the cube. Blink your eyes or turn away for a few seconds and look at the drawing again. What happened? Did the cube look the same when you looked at it for the second time? Why should some edges be dashed? Which ones should be dashed?
4. Consider these five drawings of a cube. All were made with segments of the same length. Describe the different appearances created by dashing different segments.

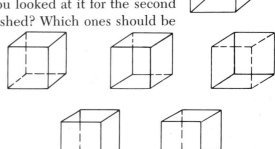

Look at the steps shown on page 29 for drawing a rectangular prism.
5. In what way(s) are these steps like those used for drawing a cube? In what way(s) are they different?

6. How would you change that drawing to make a rectangular prism that looks longer? wider(deeper)? higher(taller)?

Look at the steps shown on page 29 for drawing a triangular prism. What changes would you make to draw the prisms described below?

7. Triangular prism in which only one (instead of two) rectangular faces are showing
8. Triangular prism that is lying on its side
9. Triangular prism that is shorter (not as high)
10. Triangular prism that is wider (deeper)
11. Pentagonal prism

EXERCISES

1. Draw three cubes, each from a different point of view.

Look at the drawing of a rectangular prism. Draw a rectangular prism to fit each description.

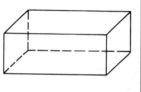

2. Like the one shown
3. Like the one shown except that the front face is open

4. Like the one shown but viewed from the left corner
5. Wider (deeper) than the one shown
6. Higher (taller) than the one shown

Draw a prism to fit each description.

7. Triangular prism
8. Triangular prism taller than Ex. 7
9. Hexagonal prism
10. Pentagonal prism
11. Cube with the front face open

MORE EXPLORING
Cube Patterns

Each of the patterns shown can be folded into a cube. Altogether there are eleven different patterns, all made up of six squares, that can be folded into a cube. Find all eleven patterns. For each pattern, each square must share at least one side with at least one other square. Two patterns are *not* different if one can be produced by flipping or turning the other.

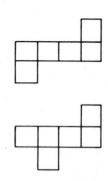

1-10
Drawing Planes and Lines

A rectangular prism contains three pairs of parallel faces. One such pair is indicated by the shading in the figure shown here.

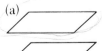

You can draw parallel planes by drawing a rectangular prism and then erasing either (a) the four vertical edges, (b) the four horizontal edges, or (c) the four slanting edges. This is illustrated by the three drawings at the right:

(a)

Some faces of a rectangular prism intersect and so are not parallel. One such pair is indicated by the shading in the figure shown below.

(b)

Suppose you start with a drawing of a rectangular prism, like that above, and erase some of the edges so you are left with two faces that intersect, as in the middle figure shown below. The right-hand figure shows how this drawing of two intersecting planes can be improved.

(c)

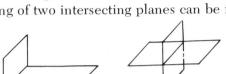

Here are three different pictures of two intersecting planes.

Study the following drawings and their descriptions. The terms that are highlighted are often used to describe the relationships among points, lines, and planes.

Notice that the word *intersects* is used to mean either "meets" or "cuts." Dashed segments indicate the hidden parts of lines.

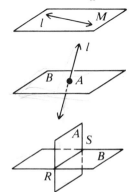

Plane *M contains* line *l*.
Line *l lies in* plane *M*.

Line *l intersects* plane *B*.
Line *l* and plane *B intersect* at point *A*.

Planes *A* and *B intersect*.
$\overleftrightarrow{RS}$ is the *intersection* of planes *A* and *B*.
$\overleftrightarrow{RS}$ *lies in* both planes.
$\overleftrightarrow{RS}$ is *contained in* planes *A* and *B*.
Planes *A* and *B contain* $\overleftrightarrow{RS}$.

Look at figures (a), (b), and (c) on page 31.
1. What kind of figure is used to represent a plane?
2. How would you draw a picture to represent two parallel vertical planes? to represent two parallel horizontal planes?

Look at the pictures of intersecting planes on page 31.
3. What kind of figure is formed by the intersection of two planes?
4. Why do you think the "improved" figure is a better drawing of two intersecting planes than the ones at the left?
5. Why are some segments dashed?

Look at the figures labeled *A–C* on page 31.
6. How are these drawings alike?
7. How are these drawings different?

EXERCISES

Look at the drawing of intersecting planes. Classify each statement as true or false.

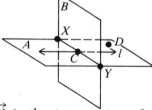

1. $\overleftrightarrow{XY}$ is the intersection of planes *A* and *B*.
2. Line *l* lies in plane *A*.
3. *l* and $\overleftrightarrow{XY}$ intersect at point *C*.
4. Line *l* lies in plane *A*.
5. Line *l* intersects plane *A*.
6. Line *l* intersects plane *B*.
7. Plane *B* does not contain point *D*.
8. All the lines in plane *A* intersect plane *B*.
9. Planes *A* and *B* have exactly three points in common.
10. Planes *A* and *B* are intersecting planes.

Look at the drawing of intersecting planes *X* and *Y*.

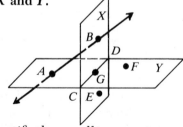

11. Identify three collinear points.
12. Identify three noncollinear points.
13. Identify five points in plane *X*.
14. Identify five points in plane *Y*.
15. Identify three coplanar points that are collinear.
16. Identify three coplanar points that are not collinear.
17. Are points *A*, *B*, and *G* coplanar?
18. What is the intersection of planes *X* and *Y*?
19. Is $\overleftrightarrow{AB}$ in either plane *X* or plane *Y*?
20. What is the intersection of $\overleftrightarrow{AB}$ and plane *X*?

Look at the drawing. Plane A is a vertical plane.

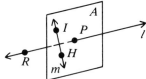

21. Does line *l* intersect line *m*?
22. Is line *l* parallel to line *m*?
23. State another name for line *l*.
24. State another name for line *m*.
25. Does line *l* lie in plane A?
26. Does line *m* lie in plane A?
27. Identify three coplanar points.

Draw and label a figure to fit each description. Use dashed segments to indicate hidden parts of lines.
28. Two intersecting planes
29. Three parallel planes
30. Two horizontal planes that do not intersect
31. Line *l* intersecting parallel planes A and B
32. Line *m* in plane C
33. Line *n* intersecting plane D

34. Two parallel lines
35. Two perpendicular planes

Write a description for each drawing. Be as specific as possible.

36.

37.

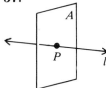

38.

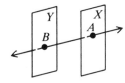

39.

40.

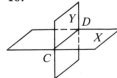

41.

DID YOU KNOW THAT....

Although there are infinitely many regular polygons, there are only five regular solids—tetrahedron (4 faces), cube (6 faces), octahedron (8 faces), dodecahedron (12 faces), and icosahedron (20 faces). A *regular solid* is a convex three-dimensional figure in which all faces are regular polygons of the same size and shape and in which the same number of edges intersect at each vertex.

1-11
Perspective Drawing

If you stand on a long, straight country road and look straight into the distance, you will see its sides appear to come together in one point. They appear to meet at some *vanishing point* on the *horizon*.

Artists often use *one-point perspective* to draw realistic pictures. The drawing of the country road is an example.

In one-point perspective, parallel lines that intersect the horizon line seem to meet at a point, called the *vanishing point*, on the *horizon line*, which is at the eye level of the viewer. The pictures at the right were drawn by using the one-point perspective method.

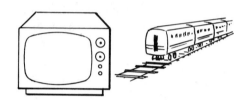

The diagrams at the right show how a rectangular prism can be drawn with one-point perspective.

Step 1 involves drawing a horizon line, selecting a vanishing point, and drawing a rectangle (front face of the prism). Step 2 involves connecting the corners of the rectangle to the vanishing point. Step 3 completes the prism by drawing the other visible faces of the prism. Dashed lines inside the figure are erased. Notice that each back edge is parallel to one of the front edges.

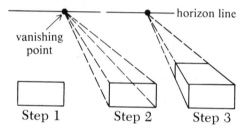

The location of the horizon line and the vanishing point depends on the point of view (perspective) from which the object is seen. The drawings at the right illustrate this for a cube.

The *two-point perspective method* is used more often than the one-point method in perspective drawing. This method uses two vanishing points. Pictures such as an aerial view of a city or a corner of a building often involve two-point perspective.

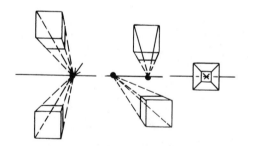

When using one-point perspective, you began with a face of the object parallel to the horizon line. In two-point perspective drawings, you begin with an edge of the object. From this edge, lines come

together to the right and left toward the two vanishing points. The pictures at the bottom of page 34 were drawn by using two-point perspective.

The diagrams below show how a rectangular prism can be drawn with two-point perspective.

As with one-point perspective drawings, the location of the horizon line and vanishing points depends on the point of view (perspective) from which the object is seen. The drawings at the right illustrate this for a cube.

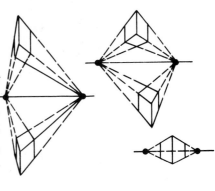

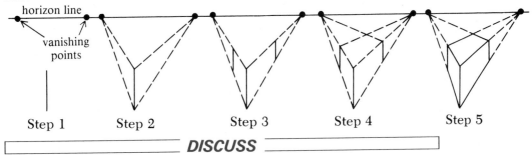

Step 1   Step 2   Step 3   Step 4   Step 5

DISCUSS

Look at the steps for drawing a rectangular prism with one-point perspective (page 34).
1. How many faces of the prism are visible in Step 3?
2. How many faces of the prism would be visible if the vanishing point were centered above the prism? directly in back of the prism? to the right of the prism?
3. Suppose the prism were not solid but, instead, a wooden frame. Draw a figure for Step 3 showing the other edges of the frame.

Look at the steps for drawing a rectangular prism with two-point perspective (page 35).
4. How many steps of the prism are visible in Step 5?
5. How many faces of the prism would be visible if both vanishing points were to the right of the prism?

EXERCISES

Draw a figure to fit each description.
1. Rectangular prism—horizon line above the prism; one-point perspective
2. Rectangular prism—horizon line below the prism; one-point perspective
3. Rectangular prism—horizon line above the prism; two-point perspective
4. Rectangular prism—horizon line below the prism; two-point perspective

Geometry on the Job

COMMERCIAL ARTIST

In his work as a commercial artist, Pablo Hurtado applies many geometric ideas. He uses both one-point and two-point perspective drawings to represent three-dimensional objects on a flat surface.

The photograph shows Pablo at work on a newspaper advertisement for a large department store. Some of his completed drawings are shown here.

Notice that examples of both one-point and two-point perspective are included.

EXERCISES

1. Collect some examples of both one-point and two-point perspective drawings from newspapers or magazines.

2. Select two or three one-point perspective drawings. Draw lines to locate the vanishing point for each drawing.

3. Select two or three two-point perspective drawings. Draw lines to locate the vanishing points for each drawing.

4. Make a classroom bulletin-board display showing examples of one-point and two-point perspective drawings.

5. Select some object and draw a one-point or two-point perspective drawing of it.

ARITHMETIC REVIEW — *Equivalent Fractions/ Simplest Form*

Equivalent fractions represent the same amount. Five equivalent fractions are shown below.

$\frac{1}{2}$ $\frac{2}{4}$ $\frac{3}{6}$ $\frac{4}{8}$ $\frac{5}{10}$

> To find a fraction equivalent to a given fraction, multiply or divide both the numerator and denominator by the same number.

Examples
Write an equivalent fraction for each given fraction.

1. $\frac{2}{3} = \frac{2 \times 4}{3 \times 4} = \frac{8}{12}$

2. $\frac{3}{4} = \frac{3 \times 6}{4 \times 6} = \frac{18}{24}$

3. $\frac{10}{15} = \frac{10 \div 5}{15 \div 5} = \frac{2}{3}$

4. $\frac{24}{30} = \frac{24 \div 6}{30 \div 6} = \frac{4}{5}$

5. $\frac{8xy}{16x} = \frac{8xy \div 8x}{16x \div 8x} = \frac{y}{2}$

6. $\frac{4 \times a}{5x \times a} = \frac{4a}{5ax}$

A fraction is in *simplest form* when the only whole number that is a common factor of (divides into) the numerator and denominator is 1.

Examples
Express each fraction in simplest form.

1. $\frac{6}{10} = \frac{6 \div 2}{10 \div 2} = \frac{3}{5}$

2. $\frac{100}{360} = \frac{100 \div 20}{360 \div 20} = \frac{5}{18}$

3. $\frac{4x}{10xy} = \frac{4x \div 2x}{10xy \div 2x} = \frac{2}{5y}$

EXERCISES
Write three fractions equivalent to each given fraction.

1. $\frac{3}{5}$ 2. $\frac{1}{4}$ 3. $\frac{3}{8}$ 4. $\frac{15}{20}$ 5. $\frac{18}{24}$ 6. $\frac{3}{12}$

7. $\frac{10}{16}$ 8. $\frac{3}{10}$ 9. $\frac{25}{100}$ 10. $\frac{2a}{3a}$ 11. $\frac{3xy}{4x}$ 12. $\frac{8a}{10a}$

Express each fraction in simplest form.

13. $\frac{6}{9}$ 14. $\frac{18}{30}$ 15. $\frac{12}{16}$ 16. $\frac{8}{10}$ 17. $\frac{10}{30}$ 18. $\frac{15}{45}$

19. $\frac{8}{12}$ 20. $\frac{6}{12}$ 21. $\frac{10}{16}$ 22. $\frac{21}{24}$ 23. $\frac{16}{20}$ 24. $\frac{10}{25}$

25. $\frac{12}{60}$ 26. $\frac{75}{100}$ 27. $\frac{70}{100}$ 28. $\frac{45}{100}$ 29. $\frac{60}{360}$ 30. $\frac{30}{360}$

31. $\frac{50}{360}$ 32. $\frac{135}{360}$ 33. $\frac{3y}{4y}$ 34. $\frac{3xy}{6x}$ 35. $\frac{8a}{12ab}$ 36. $\frac{10s}{15s}$

Chapter 1 Review

Vocabulary

The following terms and symbols were introduced in this chapter. You should be able to write a brief description, draw a picture, or give an example to illustrate the meaning of each.

angle (p. 12)
bisector of a segment (p. 6)
collinear points (p. 2)
coplanar points (p. 2)
intersect (p. 2)
line (p. 2)

midpoint of a segment (p. 6)
opposite rays (p. 6)
parallel lines (planes) (p. 9)
plane (p. 2)
point (p. 2)

polygon (p. 15)
prism (p. 25)
ray (p. 6)
segment (p. 6)
side (of an angle) (p. 12)
vertex (of an angle) (p. 12)

Polygons

Types
concave polygon (p. 15)
convex polygon (p. 15)
regular polygon (p. 22)
triangle (p. 15)
quadrilateral (p. 15)
pentagon (p. 15)
hexagon (p. 15)
octagon (p. 15)

Types of Quadrilaterals
parallelogram (p. 21)
rectangle (p. 21)
rhombus (p. 21)
square (p. 21)
trapezoid (p. 21)

Terms
consecutive sides
(vertices) (angles) (p. 18)
diagonal (p. 18)
opposite sides (vertices)
(angles) (p. 18)
vertex (p. 18)

Prisms

Types
cube (p. 26)
oblique prism (p. 25)
rectangular prism (p. 26)
right prism (p. 25)

Terms
base (p. 25)
edge (p. 25)
face (p. 25)
lateral face (p. 25)
vertex (p. 25)

Symbols
$\angle ABC$ (angle) (p. 12)
$\overleftrightarrow{AB}$ (line) (p. 6)
∥ (parallel to) (p. 9)
$\overrightarrow{AB}$ (ray) (p. 6)
$\overline{AB}$ (segment) (p. 6)

Perspective Drawing   horizon line (p. 34)   two-point perspective (p. 34)
                        one-point perspective (p. 34)   vanishing point (p. 34)

Skills Checklist

In Chapter 1 you learned terms and symbols needed for the study of geometry; some basic relationships among points, lines, and planes; and how to make and interpret drawings of 2- and 3-dimensional figures.

The following list indicates the major skills, facts, and results you should have mastered in this chapter:

- Know and use the proper notation for points, lines, segments, rays, planes, and angles. (**1-2**, pp. 6–8; **1-4**, pp. 12–14)
- Know and use these results about points, lines, segments, and planes:
  - Two different points determine exactly one line. (**1-1**, pp. 2–5)
  - If two lines intersect, their intersection is a point. (**1-3**, pp. 9–11)
  - If two planes intersect, their intersection is a line. (**1-3**, pp. 9–11)
  - Three noncollinear points determine exactly one plane. (**1-1**, pp. 2–5; **1-2**, pp. 6–8)
  - Each segment has exactly one midpoint and many bisectors. (**1-2**, pp. 6–8)
- Recognize a polygon. (**1-5**, pp. 15–17)
- Classify a polygon as convex or concave. (**1-5**, pp. 15–17)
- Identify the type of polygon given the number of sides. (**1-5**, pp. 15–17)
- Identify the sides (vertices) (angles) that are (a) consecutive to and (b) opposite a side (vertex) (angle) of a polygon. (**1-6**, pp. 18–20)
- Recognize differences and likenesses among different types of quadrilaterals. (**1-7**, pp. 21–24)
- Recognize a regular polygon. (**1-7**, pp. 21–24)
- Recognize a prism. (**1-8**, pp. 25–27)
- State the number of faces, edges, and vertices of a prism. (**1-8**, pp. 25–27)
- Identify the type of prism given the shape of the base. (**1-8**, pp. 25–27)
- Make an accurate drawing of a prism. (**1-9**, pp. 28–30)
- Make accurate drawings of (a) parallel planes, (b) intersecting planes, and (c) the intersection of lines and planes. (**1-10**, pp. 31–33)
- Make an accurate one-point or two-point perspective drawing of a prism. (**1-11**, pp. 34–35)

Exercises

Classify each statement as true or false. For Exercises 5–8, look at the figure.

1. Any two points are collinear. (**1-1**)
2. Any three points determine exactly one plane. (**1-1**)
3. Each segment has exactly one bisector. (**1-2**)
4. The intersection of two nonparallel planes is a line. (**1-3**)

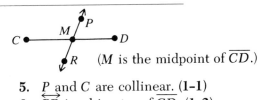

(M is the midpoint of $\overline{CD}$.)

5. P and C are collinear. (**1-1**)
6. $\overleftrightarrow{PR}$ is a bisector of $\overline{CD}$. (**1-2**)
7. $\overline{PR}$ is a bisector of $\overline{CD}$. (**1-2**)
8. CM and DM are the same length. (**1-2**)

Draw and label a figure to fit each description.

9. $\overleftrightarrow{AB}$ (1-1)
10. $\overline{AB}$ (1-2)
11. $\overrightarrow{AB}$ (1-2)
12. $\overrightarrow{AR}$ bisecting $\overline{CD}$ (1-2)
13. Opposite rays $\overrightarrow{OR}$ and $\overrightarrow{OB}$ (1-2)
14. $\overleftrightarrow{AB}$ and $\overleftrightarrow{CD}$ intersecting at point X (1-3)
15. Three noncollinear points (1-1)
16. Look at the angle shown. Identify each of the following. (1-4)

   a. Vertex   b. Sides
   c. Four different names for the angle

Draw and label a figure to fit each description. (1-4)

17. Angle named $\angle BRT$
18. Angle with sides $\overrightarrow{RX}$ and $\overrightarrow{RY}$

Find the indicated information.

19. Look at the octagon. Identify each of the following. (1-6)

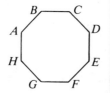

   a. All vertices adjacent to H
   b. All vertices opposite H
   c. All sides adjacent to $\overline{DE}$
   d. All sides opposite $\overline{DE}$
   e. Two different names for the octagon, each starting with G

Classify each figure in several ways. (1-7)

20.

21.

22.

23.

Draw a figure to fit each description. (1-7)

24. Hexagon
25. Concave quadrilateral
26. Pentagon and all its diagonals
27. Parallelogram that is *not* a rectangle

Count the number of faces, edges, and vertices for each prism. (1-8)

28.   29.

Draw a figure to fit each description. (1-9)

30. Rectangular prism that is not a cube
31. Cube   32. Triangular prism

Classify each statement as true or false. The intersection of planes A and B shown is $\overleftrightarrow{CD}$. (1-10)

33. Point I is in plane B.
34. Point F is in both planes A and B.
35. Point G is on $\overleftrightarrow{FE}$.
36. Point G is on $\overrightarrow{FE}$.
37. The line through points D and G is in plane A.
38. The line through points D and G intersects $\overleftrightarrow{HI}$.

Draw a figure to fit each description.

39. Line intersecting a horizontal plane in exactly one point (1-10)
40. Two parallel vertical planes (1-10)
41. Two intersecting planes (1-10)
42. Line l that lies in plane P (1-10)

LOOKING AT
ALL THE ANGLES

Angles and Circles

2-1
Circles

In this lesson you will learn some basic facts about circles. These facts will be helpful when discussing angles and their properties. The following diagrams illustrate some of the terms used to describe circles.

A *circle* is the set of all points in a plane that are the same distance from some point called the *center*. A circle is named by its center. The circle shown is called circle C (in symbols, ⊙ C), since C is its center.

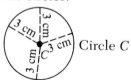
Circle C

A *radius* is a segment whose endpoints are the center of a circle and any point on the circle. ("Radius" also refers to the length of such a segment.) The plural of "radius" is "radii" (pronounced "ray-dee-eye").

A *chord* is a segment whose endpoints are any two points on a circle.

A *diameter* is a chord that passes through the center of a circle. ("Diameter" also refers to the length of such a segment.)

In this book the symbol BC is read "the measure of segment BC." For the circle here, BC = 6 cm is read "the measure of segment BC is 6 centimeters."

Radii: $\overline{AC}$, $\overline{BC}$, $\overline{DC}$

Chords: $\overline{AB}$, $\overline{EF}$

Diameter: $\overline{AB}$

The radius of ⊙ C is 6 cm.

The diameter of ⊙ C is 12 cm.

CLASS PRACTICE

Look at ⊙ X.
1. Identify all radii.
2. Identify all chords.
3. Identify all diameters.
4. If BX = 3 cm, AC = ? cm.
5. If AC = 16 cm, XC = ? cm.
6. If BX = 3 cm, what can be said about the length of $\overline{ED}$?

EXERCISES

— A —

For each circle, identify (a) all radii, (b) all chords, and (c) all diameters.

1.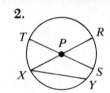

2.

3.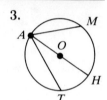

Find the indicated information.

4. How many chords does a circle have? How many diameters? How many radii?

5. If a radius of a circle is 4 cm, how long is each diameter?

6. If a diameter of a circle is 10 cm, how long is each radius?

— **B** —

Classify each statement as true or false.

7. Every diameter of a circle is a chord.
8. Every radius of a circle is a chord.
9. Every circle has an infinite number of chords.
10. In every circle the radius is twice the diameter.
11. The longest chord of any circle is a diameter.
12. Every chord of a circle is a diameter.
13. A circle with a radius of 6 cm can have a chord of 10 cm.

Find the indicated information.

14. The radius of a circle is 8 cm. What is the length of its longest chord?

15. Draw a circle and label its center R. Then draw each of the following.
    a. Radius $\overline{RA}$
    b. Diameter $\overline{BC}$
    c. Chord $\overline{DE}$ (*not* a diameter)

16. Circle D has a radius of 5 cm.
    a. Suppose point X is 6 cm from point D. Is point X inside, outside, or on circle D?
    b. Suppose point Y is 4 cm from point D. Is point Y inside, outside, or on circle D?
    c. Suppose point Z is 5 cm from point D. Is point Z inside, outside, or on circle D?

d. Draw and label a figure that represents the information in each of parts a–c. Use a compass.

17. Point A is on circle O. How many radii can be drawn that contain A? How many chords? How many diameters?

18. Point B is inside circle O. How many radii can be drawn that contain B? How many chords? How many diameters?

— **C** —

For each exercise, draw a circle like the one shown.

19. A and B are any two points inside the circle.
    a. Does $\overline{AB}$ intersect $\odot O$?
    b. Is $\overline{AB}$ located entirely inside $\odot O$?
    c. Can *any* two points inside a circle be the endpoints of a segment located entirely inside the circle?
    d. What can be said about the length of any segment whose endpoints are any two points inside $\odot O$?

20. C and D are any two points outside the circle.
    a. Can $\overline{CD}$ intersect $\odot O$?
    b. Is CD located entirely outside $\odot O$?
    c. Can *any* two points outside a circle be the endpoints of a segment located entirely outside the circle?
    d. What can be said about the length of any segment whose endpoints are any two points outside $\odot O$?

21. *E* and *F* are any two points where *E* is inside the circle and *F* is outside the circle.
    a. Does $\overline{EF}$ intersect $\odot O$?
    b. Can *any* point inside a circle and *any* point outside the circle be the endpoints of a segment that does not intersect the circle?
    c. What can be said about the length of any segment whose endpoints are any point inside $\odot O$ and any point outside $\odot O$?

22. A set of points is said to be *convex* if any segment whose endpoints are a pair of points in the set is located entirely inside the set.
    a. Is the inside (interior) of a circle convex?
    b. Is the outside (exterior) of a circle convex?

=== *MORE EXPLORING* ===

How Many Regions Are Formed by a Given Number of Chords of a Circle?

Suppose you have a given number of chords of a circle. Into how many regions can these chords divide the circle?

Example:

0 chords divide a circle into 1 region.

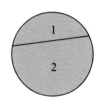
1 chord divides a circle into 2 regions.

2 chords divide a circle into at most 4 regions.

1. Make a table like the one shown.
2. Do you see a pattern? Predict the maximum number of regions formed by 3 chords, 4 chords, and 5 chords.
3. Check your predictions by drawing circles and chords. (*Note:* The chords should cross whenever possible. No more than two chords should intersect at any one point.)
4. Now predict how many regions can be formed by 6 chords. Check your prediction. Describe the pattern in words or by writing a formula.

No. of Chords	Max. No. of Regions
0	1
1	2
2	4
3	?
4	?
5	?

2-2
Amount of Turn

You constantly use your hands to turn things. For example, you turn a doorknob to open a door, a knob or lever to get water, and a knob to turn on a radio or television.

In some situations, it is necessary to determine accurately how much an object is turned. Scales of numbers are usually used to determine the amount of turn. Some examples include the numbers on a TV dial, a telephone dial, and an oven knob.

In Chapter 1 an angle was viewed as two rays with a common endpoint, and the size of the angle was determined by the amount of opening between its sides. Another way to think of an angle is to view it as *the figure produced by turning a ray about its endpoint.*

For example, $\angle CAB$ can be obtained by turning $\overrightarrow{AC}$ about the point A. A single-headed curved arrow is used to indicate the direction and amount of turn.

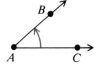

This second view of an angle will be emphasized in this chapter. The amount of turn will be used to measure an angle.

These angles are measured by the amount of turn.

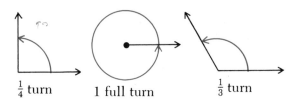

$\frac{1}{4}$ turn   1 full turn $\frac{1}{3}$ turn

An angle with its vertex at the center of a circle is a *central angle*. In this lesson angles will be drawn as central angles so that it is easier to measure the amount of turn.

These are central angles.

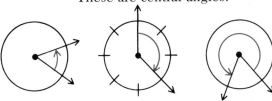

The four examples on the next page illustrate how a circle is useful for measuring the amount of turn. The symbol $m\angle 1$ is read "the measure of angle 1."

Example 1: What is the measure of ∠1?

Solution:

The circle is divided into 8 equal-size pieces. Each piece is $\frac{1}{8}$ of the circle. Therefore, $m\angle 1 = \frac{3}{8}$ of a turn.

Sometimes the measure of an angle does not come out even. Then the measure is given to the nearest part of a turn.

Example 2:
What is the measure
of ∠2?

Solution:
$m\angle 2 = \frac{3}{8}$ turn

Example 3:
What is the measure
of ∠3?

Solution:
$m\angle 3 = \frac{11}{16}$ turn

If no arrow is shown, more than one measure can be given for the same angle, as indicated by the figure here.

In cases where there is no arrow to indicate the direction and amount of turn, assume that the angle is (a) less than 1 turn, and (b) the smaller of the two angles. Using these assumptions, in the figure at the right, $m\angle A = \frac{3}{8}$ turn.

Although it is possible to have angles of more than 1 turn, your work in this chapter will be limited to angles of 1 turn or less.

$m\angle A = \frac{3}{8}$ turn

or

$m\angle A = \frac{5}{8}$ turn

─────── **CLASS PRACTICE** ───────

State the amount of turn for each indicated angle.

1. 2. 3. 4. 5. 6.

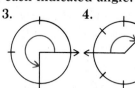

7. Which angles in Exercises 1–6 are measured in a clockwise direction? Which in a counterclockwise direction?

Find the measure of each indicated angle.

8. 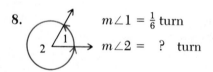 $m\angle 1 = \frac{1}{6}$ turn

$m\angle 2 = \ ?\ $ turn

9. 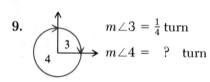 $m\angle 3 = \frac{1}{4}$ turn

$m\angle 4 = \ ?\ $ turn

_ A _

Find the amount of turn of each indicated central angle.

1. ∠AOB

2. ∠TIN

3. ∠POW

4. ∠KEN

5. ∠CAD

6. ∠TRY

7. Which of Exercises 1–6 show an angle formed by a clockwise turn?

For each measure and direction, draw a circle with a central angle as indicated.

8. $\frac{3}{8}$ turn (clockwise)

9. $\frac{3}{12}$ turn (counterclockwise)

10. $\frac{5}{16}$ turn (counterclockwise)

11. $\frac{1}{6}$ turn (clockwise)

For each angle in Ex. 12–14, select the phrase that best describes its measure.
  less than $\frac{1}{4}$ turn $\frac{1}{4}$ turn
  between $\frac{1}{4}$ and $\frac{1}{2}$ turn $\frac{1}{2}$ turn

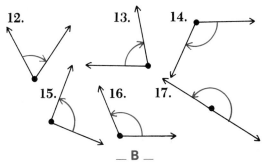

12.   13.   14.   15.   16.   17.

_ B _

Find the amount of turn of each indicated central angle.

18. ∠SAD

19. ∠NED

Find the indicated information.

20. The hour and minute hands on a circular clock can be thought of as forming a central angle.
  a. The hour markings on a circular clock divide a circle into 12 equal-size pieces. Each is what fractional part of the circle?
  b. The minute markings on a circular clock divide a circle into 60 equal-size pieces. Each is what fractional part of the circle?

Through what size angle does the hour hand of a clock move in each period?

21. 1 hour   22. 2 hours
23. 4 hours   24. 6 hours

Through what size angle does the minute hand of a clock move in each period?

25. 1 minute   26. 2 minutes
27. 5 minutes   28. 30 minutes

2-3
Degree Measure

One of the most important of all angles is a *right angle*. A right angle has a measure of $\frac{1}{4}$ turn. The sides of a right angle are perpendicular.

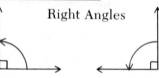
Right Angles

A square, or box, at a vertex indicates a right angle.

$\overrightarrow{BA} \perp \overrightarrow{BC}$

The symbol $\perp$ is read "is perpendicular to."

Straight Angle

The angle made by $\frac{1}{2}$ turn also has a special name. It is called a *straight angle*.

From your previous work in mathematics you may remember that *the measure of a right angle is 90 degrees*. A *degree* is the most commonly used unit for measuring angles. The following statements give the relationship between the amount of turn and the degree measure of an angle:

> $\frac{1}{360}$ **turn = 1 degree (symbol, 1°)**
>
> **1 full turn = 360°**

The following five examples show how to convert the amount of turn of an angle to degree measure, and vice versa.

Example 1:

$100° = \ ?\ $ turn

Solution:

$1° = \frac{1}{360}$ turn

$100° = \frac{100}{360}$ turn

$= \frac{10}{36}$ turn

$= \frac{5}{18}$ turn

Example 2:

$60° = \ ?\ $ turn

Solution:

$1° = \frac{1}{360}$ turn

$60° = \frac{60}{360}$ turn

$= \frac{6}{36}$ turn

$= \frac{1}{6}$ turn

Example 3:

$\frac{1}{3}$ turn $= \ ?°$

Solution:

1 turn $= 360°$

$\frac{1}{3}$ turn $= \frac{1}{3} \times \frac{360°}{1}$

$= \frac{360°}{3}$

$= 120°$

or

$\frac{1}{3}$ turn $= 360° \div 3$

$= 120°$

Example 4:

$\frac{3}{8}$ turn = $?°$

Solution:

1 turn = $360°$

$\frac{3}{8}$ turn = $\frac{3}{8} \times \frac{360°}{1}$

$= \frac{1080°}{8}$

$= 135°$

or

$\frac{3}{8}$ turn = $3 \times (\frac{1}{8}$ turn$)$

$= 3 \times 45°$

$= 135°$

Example 5: The hour divisions on a circular clock can be located by drawing 12 equal-size central angles. What is the size of each angle?

Solution:

1 turn = $360°$

$m\angle 1 = \frac{1}{12}$ turn

$m\angle 1 = \frac{1}{12} \times 360° = 360° \div 12 = 30°$

CLASS PRACTICE

1. How many right angles are in one full turn? How many straight angles?
2. How many right angles are in a straight angle?

Convert each measure from degrees to amount of turn.
3. $40°$
4. $75°$
5. $135°$

Convert each measure from amount of turn to degrees.
6. $\frac{1}{5}$ turn
7. $\frac{2}{5}$ turn
8. $\frac{3}{4}$ turn

EXERCISES

— A —

Complete each statement.
1. 1 turn = $?°$ 2. $1° = ?$ turn
3. An angle with a measure of $\frac{1}{4}$ turn is called a(n) $?$ angle.
4. An angle with a measure of $\frac{1}{2}$ turn is called a(n) $?$ angle.
5. The sides of a right angle are $?$ to each other.
6. The sides of a straight angle are $?$ rays.

For each angle, select the phrase that *best* describes its measure.

less than a right angle
between a right and a straight angle
right angle
straight angle

7.

8.

9.

10.    **11.**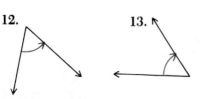

12.   **13.**

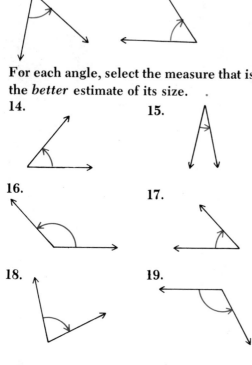

For each angle, select the measure that is the *better* estimate of its size.

14.   **15.**

16.   **17.**

18.   **19.**

— **B** —

Convert each measure from degrees to amount of turn.

20. 1°   **21.** 30°
22. 270°   **23.** 45°
24. 10°   **25.** 180°
26. 20°   **27.** 15°

Convert each measure from amount of turn to degrees.

28. 1 turn   **29.** $\frac{1}{2}$ turn
30. $\frac{1}{4}$ turn   **31.** $\frac{1}{6}$ turn
32. $\frac{1}{3}$ turn   **33.** $\frac{2}{3}$ turn
34. $\frac{1}{8}$ turn   **35.** $\frac{5}{8}$ turn

Find the measure of the indicated angle (a) in amount of turn and (b) in degrees.

36. ∠*MAD*   **37.** ∠*MIT*

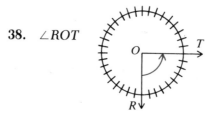

38. ∠*ROT*

Find the indicated information.

39. A circle is divided into 8 equal-size pieces. A central angle of this circle cuts off 3 of the 8 pieces.
   a. What is the measure of the angle in amount of turn?
   b. What is the measure of the angle in degrees?

40. A circle is divided into 24 equal-size pieces. A central angle of this circle cuts off 18 of the 24 pieces.
   a. What is the measure of the angle in amount of turn?
   b. What is the measure of the angle in degrees?

For each measure, draw a circle and a central angle having the given measure. Use any direction of turn. (Hint: It may help to first convert each degree measure to amount of turn.)

41. 60°   **42.** 240°
43. 330°

Applications

The Origin of the Degree

The use of the degree as a unit of angle measure dates back thousands of years to the ancient Sumerians, who lived along the Tigris and Euphrates Rivers in what is today called the Near East. We also owe our system for dividing time—the 60-minute hour—to the Sumerians.

The Sumerians divided the *year*—which is defined as the length of time it takes Earth to make one complete revolution around the sun—into 360 days. They assumed that the path of Earth around the sun is circular and that Earth travels along this path at a constant speed. This means that in its annual passage around the sun the part of a circle through which Earth would travel in one day, which they defined as a *degree*, is $\frac{1}{360}$ of a circle.

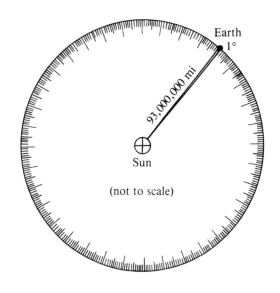

Earth 1°

93,000,000 mi

Sun

(not to scale)

DID YOU KNOW THAT....

The type of geometry presented in this book is called *Euclidean* geometry after the Greek mathematician Euclid, who lived about 300 B.C. Among the books written by Euclid is a series of 13 books called *The Elements*, a compilation and organization of the mathematical knowledge known at that time. Except for the Bible, no book has been more widely used or printed in the Western world. More than 1000 editions have appeared since the invention of printing. The teaching of geometry today is still largely based on Euclid's work of over 2000 years ago.

2-4

Measuring Angles with a Protractor

A *protractor* is an instrument used to measure angles. Most protractors are either circular or semicircular. A circular protractor is convenient for angle measures greater than 180° and for navigation or locating distant objects.

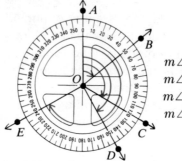

$m\angle AOB = 50°$
$m\angle AOC = 120°$
$m\angle AOD = 150°$
$m\angle AOE = 240°$

The circular protractor shown has been used to find the measure of some angles.

When using a protractor, keep in mind the following:
- The center point of the protractor is placed on the vertex of the angle.
- One side of the angle passes through the zero point on the protractor scale.
- The measure of the angle is the number on the protractor scale through which the *other* side of the angle passes.

$m\angle PXR = 30°$
$m\angle PXS = 120°$
$m\angle PXT = 150°$

Most protractors you have seen or used were probably semicircular. The semicircular protractor shown has been used to find the measure of some angles. Notice that it is used in the same way as a circular protractor.

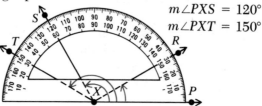

Some protractors, such as the semicircular protractor, have more than one scale of numbers. The following example shows how making an estimate before measuring will help you use the correct scale.

Example: $m\angle 1 = \quad ?°$

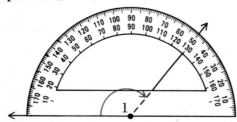

Solution:
Estimate the measure of $\angle 1$. ($\angle 1$ is larger than a right angle so its measure is between 90° and 180°.)
Line up the protractor as shown.
Use the scale that gives a measure greater than 90°.
$m\angle 1 = 130°$

The ability to make reasonable estimates is not a skill that can be mastered in one lesson. Keep in practice by estimating whenever possible. Learning to make reasonable estimates will enable you to check the reasonableness of any measurement you make.

In the remainder of this book most angles will be measured in degrees. Therefore, unless otherwise noted, for angles the word "measure" will mean "degree measure," not "amount of turn."

DISCUSS

1. Look at the first diagram on page 52 showing how to use a semicircular protractor. Why was the outer scale of numbers used to find the measures of the three angles?
2. Look at the second diagram on page 52 showing how to use a semicircular protractor. How did the estimate help determine the correct scale to use for finding the measure of ∠1?
3. Tell how a semicircular protractor can be considered one half a circular protractor.
4. Tell how to use a semicircular protractor to measure an angle whose measure is between 180° and 360°.
5. How does making an estimate help you check your measurement of an angle?
6. Tell how you estimate the measure of angles.
7. Tell the measures of some angles that would serve as useful estimation guides.

CLASS PRACTICE

Draw four or five angles with measures between 0° and 360°. (At least one angle should have a measure between 180° and 360°.)
1. Estimate the measure of each angle.
2. Using both a circular and a semicircular protractor, measure each angle to the nearest degree.
3. Did you get the same measure regardless of which type of protractor you used? Why or why not?

EXERCISES

For exercises 1-12, record your answers in a table like this:

Angle	Esti-mate	Measure-ment	Dif-ference
1	?	?	?
2	?	?	?

a. Estimate the measure of each angle shown.
b. Measure each angle to the nearest degree. (Extend the sides if necessary.) Use both a circular and a semicircular protractor, if available, to measure some angles.
c. Check the closeness of your esti-

mates by computing the difference between your estimate and the measurement for each angle.

1.
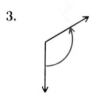

2.
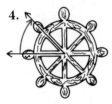

3.

4.
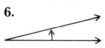

5.
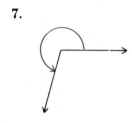

6.
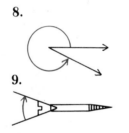

7.

8.

9.

10. **11.** **12.**
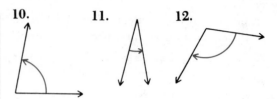

Select the angle whose measure is closest to the measure given. Do not use a protractor.

13.
25°
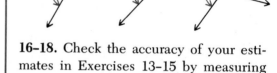

14.
60°
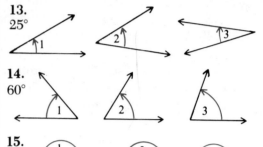

15.
240°
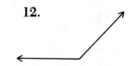

16–18. Check the accuracy of your estimates in Exercises 13–15 by measuring each angle.

Test Yourself

Look at ⊙ C. Identify each of the following.

1. All radii
2. All chords
3. All diameters
4. If XY = 10 cm, CZ = ? cm.

Complete the following.

5. $1°$ = ? turn
6. $60°$ = ? turn
7. $150°$ = ? turn
8. 1 turn = ?°
9. $\frac{1}{10}$ turn = ?°
10. $\frac{3}{8}$ turn = ?°

For each angle, (a) estimate the measure and (b) measure the angle to the nearest degree.

11. **12.**

Draw a figure to fit each description.

13. Central angle with a measure of $\frac{1}{3}$ turn
14. Right angle
15. Straight angle

2-5
Drawing Angles with a Protractor

The diagrams here show $\angle PQR$ being measured in two ways. In both cases, $m\angle PQR = 60°$.

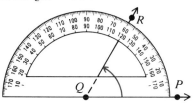 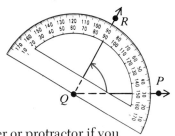

Any point may be used as the zero point on a ruler or protractor if you are careful. Here are two examples:

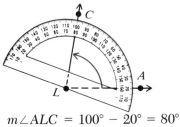 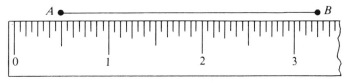

$$m\angle ALC = 100° - 20° = 80° \qquad\qquad AB = 3\tfrac{1}{4} \text{ in.} - \tfrac{1}{2} \text{ in.} = 2\tfrac{3}{4} \text{ in.}$$

Up to now you have used a protractor to measure a given angle. In the next example you will see that a protractor can also be used to draw an angle of a given size.

Example: Use a protractor to draw a 67° angle.

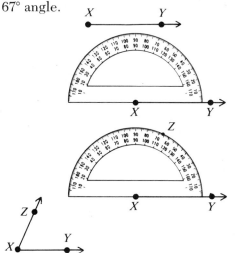

Solution:

Step 1 Draw a ray and label it $\overrightarrow{XY}$.

Step 2 Place the center point of the protractor on the endpoint (X) of the ray and line up the ray with the straight edge of the protractor.

Step 3 Locate 67° on the protractor scale and make a dot (call it **Z**) at that point.

Step 4 Remove the protractor and draw $\overrightarrow{XZ}$. $m\angle YXZ = 67°$

1. When measuring an angle with a protractor, is it necessary for one of the rays of the angle to pass through the zero point on the protractor scale? Why or why not?
2. Tell how a semicircular protractor can be used to draw a 240° angle.
3. Tell how a circular protractor can be used to draw angles which measure (a) 120° and (b) 220°.

CLASS PRACTICE

Find the measure of each angle.

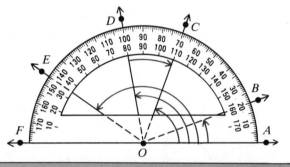

1. ∠AOB	2. ∠AOC
3. ∠AOD	4. ∠AOE
5. ∠BOC	6. ∠BOD
7. ∠BOE	8. ∠BOF
9. ∠COD	10. ∠COE
11. ∠COF	12. ∠DOE

EXERCISES

— A —

For Exercises 1–14, refer to the drawing of a semicircular protractor.
Identify each of the following.

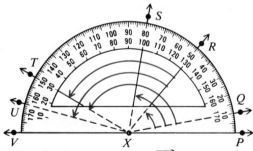

1. Six angles with side $\overrightarrow{XP}$
2. Six angles with side $\overrightarrow{XS}$

Find the measure of each angle.

3. ∠PXQ	4. ∠PXR
5. ∠PXS	6. ∠PXT
7. ∠PXU	8. ∠PXV
9. ∠QXR	10. ∠QXS
11. ∠QXT	12. ∠QXV
13. ∠RXT	14. ∠RXU

Find the measure of each angle shown in the drawing of a circular protractor.

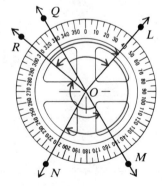

15. ∠QOL
16. ∠LON
17. ∠QOR
18. ∠NOM
19. ∠ROL
20. ∠MOR

Use a protractor and straightedge to draw angles with these measures.

21. 78°   22. 254°   23. 323°
24. 35°   25. 127°   26. 155°

For Exercises 27–32 record your results in a table:

a. Estimate the measure of each angle shown.
b. Measure each angle to the nearest degree.
c. Check the closeness of your estimates by computing the difference between your estimate and the measurement for each angle.

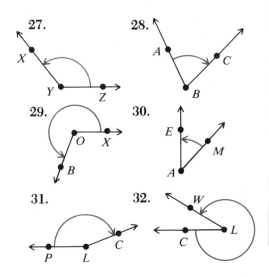

27.

28.

29.

30.

31.

32.

Using only a straightedge, draw an angle that you think has each indicated measure.

33. 50°   34. 300°
35. 140°   36. 70°

37–40. Check the closeness of your estimates in Exercises 33–36. Measure each angle drawn and compute the difference between the actual size and the desired size. (If you came within 10°, you did a very good job!)

The United States Army uses a unit of angle measure called a *mil*. A mil is defined by the U.S. Army as $\frac{1}{6400}$ of a circle or full turn. The semicircular protractor shown here is marked in mils.

Find the number of mils in each angle.

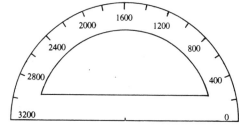

41. 90° angle   42. 135° angle
43. 45° angle   44. Straight angle

DID YOU KNOW THAT....

Although a very small unit of measure, the degree is sometimes divided into still smaller units—*minutes* (') and *seconds* (")—to express angle measures that are not whole numbers. There are 60 minutes in a degree and 60 seconds in a minute. Therefore, $1' = \frac{1}{60}^\circ$ and $1'' = \frac{1}{3600}^\circ$. Another unit of angle measure sometimes used is the *radian*, which is defined in terms of arc length on a circle with a radius of one.

2-6

Adding and Subtracting Angle Measures

The diagrams show how we can find the measures of some angles by adding and subtracting measures. Recall that one full turn measures 360°, a straight angle ($\frac{1}{2}$ turn) measures 180°, and a right angle ($\frac{1}{4}$ turn) measures 90°.

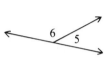

$$m\angle 1 + m\angle 2 = m\angle AOB$$
$$m\angle 1 = m\angle AOB - m\angle 2$$
$$m\angle 2 = m\angle AOB - m\angle 1$$

$$m\angle 3 + m\angle 4 = 360°$$
$$m\angle 3 = 360° - m\angle 4$$
$$m\angle 4 = 360° - m\angle 3$$

$$m\angle 5 + m\angle 6 = 180°$$
$$m\angle 5 = 180° - m\angle 6$$
$$m\angle 6 = 180° - m\angle 5$$

$$m\angle 7 + m\angle 8 = 90°$$
$$m\angle 7 = 90° - m\angle 8$$
$$m\angle 8 = 90° - m\angle 7$$

CLASS PRACTICE

Use the given information to find the measure of the indicated angles.

1. $m\angle BAC = 40°$
    $m\angle CAD = 55°$
    $m\angle BAD = $?°

2. $m\angle YWZ = 120°$
    $m\angle YWX = 230°$
    $m\angle ZWX = $?°
    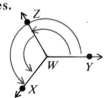

3. $m\angle BAC = 40°$
    $m\angle BAD = 110°$
    $m\angle DAC = $?°
    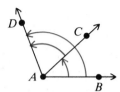

4. $m\angle 1 = 60°$
    $m\angle 2 = $?°
    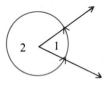

5. $m\angle MEO = 35°$
    $m\angle GEO = $?°
    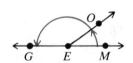

6. $\angle UTR$ is a right angle.
    $m\angle VTR = 25°$
    $m\angle UTV = $?°

Use the given information to find the measure of the indicated angles.

1. $m\angle RXS = 70°$
   $m\angle SXT = 50°$
   $m\angle RXT = $?°

2. $m\angle 1 = 40°$
   $m\angle 2 = $?°

3. $m\angle YTZ = 65°$
   $m\angle XTY = $?°

4. $\angle HKL$ is a right angle.
   $m\angle MKL = 55°$
   $m\angle HKM = $?°

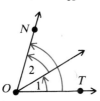

5. $m\angle 1 = 30°$
   $m\angle 2 = 45°$
   $m\angle NOT = $?°

6. $m\angle 1 = 30°$
   $m\angle 2 = 100°$
   $m\angle 4 = 130°$

   a. $m\angle 3 = $?°
   b. $m\angle 1 + m\angle 2 + m\angle 3 = $?°
   c. $m\angle 3 + m\angle 4 = $?°

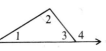

7. $\angle 3$ is a right angle.
   $m\angle RAT = 130°$
   $m\angle 4 = $?°

8. $m\angle XYZ = 155°$
   $m\angle XYW = 70°$
   $m\angle WYZ = $?°

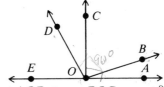

Look at the diagram. $\angle AOC$ is a right angle.

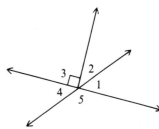

9. $m\angle AOB + m\angle BOC = m\angle$?
10. $m\angle AOB + m\angle BOD = m\angle$?
11. $m\angle BOC + m\angle COE = m\angle$?
12. $m\angle AOC + m\angle COD = m\angle$?
13. $m\angle BOE - m\angle DOE = m\angle$?
14. $m\angle AOD - m\angle BOD = m\angle$?
15. $m\angle AOD + m\angle DOE = $?°
16. $m\angle COD + m\angle DOE = $?°

Find the indicated information.
17. Look at the diagram.

   a. $m\angle 1 + m\angle 2 = $?°
   b. $m\angle 1 + m\angle 2 + m\angle 3 = $?°
   c. $m\angle 4 + m\angle 5 = $?°
   d. $m\angle 1 + m\angle 2 + m\angle 3 + m\angle 4 + m\angle 5 = $?°

18. Point X is in the interior (inside) of $\angle ABC$. If $m\angle ABX = 30°$ and $m\angle ABC = 110°$, what is $m\angle XBC$?

2-7

Compass Bearings

The position of ships, planes, forest fires, and tornadoes is often given in terms of the direction and distance from an observation point. This direction is usually determined by a magnetic compass, such as the one shown here.

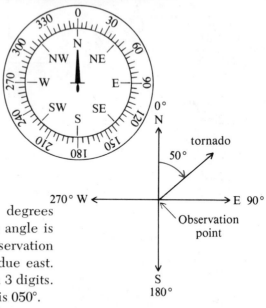

A magnetic compass is used to establish the north line. The direction of an object is found by measuring the angle between the north line and the line joining the observation point to the object.

The direction angle is measured in degrees from north in a *clockwise* direction. This angle is called the *bearing* of the object from the observation point. Thus a bearing of 090° would be due east. Note that bearings are always written with 3 digits. In the figure, the bearing of the tornado is 050°.

Large national or state forests have lookout towers for spotting forest fires. When a fire is spotted, the bearing is immediately taken from the lookout tower. The ranger then calls a second tower. The ranger at the second tower takes the fire's bearing from that tower. These two readings are plotted on a map and the location of the fire is pinpointed, as shown in the figure.

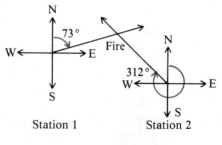

Station 1   Station 2

Radar is used to obtain the distance and direction of ships, planes, tornadoes, and so on. The radar set sends out radio waves that bounce off objects they meet and return to the set.

A bearing is found from the direction of the radar antenna at the moment the waves return. The distance is computed by using the time it takes the wave to reach the object and return to the set. Radio waves travel 186,272 miles per second.

An object picked up by radar appears on the radar screen as a bright spot in a position corresponding to its actual position. The bearing of the object on the screen shown is about 145°.

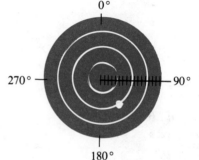

1. What is a bearing? What uses are made of bearings?

State the bearing represented by each of the following directions.

2. east   3. south   4. west   5. northeast

6. southeast   7. southwest   8. northwest

EXERCISES

— A —

Draw two intersecting perpendicular lines to represent the directions N, S, E, and W. Then draw rays to indicate the following bearings.

1. 010°   2. 317°
3. 135°   4. 248°
5. 275°   6. 068°
7. 210°   8. 170°

What is the bearing after each turn described?

9. Clockwise 100° from S
10. Clockwise 300° from E
11. Counterclockwise 45° from SW
12. Counterclockwise 80° from NE
13. Clockwise 20° from W
14. Clockwise 50° from N
15. Counterclockwise 25° from NW
16. Counterclockwise 60° from SE

Use a protractor to find the bearing of the indicated points.

17.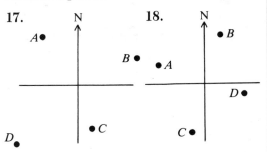
18.

Find the indicated information.

19. Find the bearing of each thunderstorm picked up on the radar screen shown.

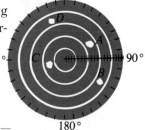

— B —

20. Rangers from two lookout towers have phoned in information about a forest fire. The fire's bearing from Tower No. 1 is 110° and that from Tower No. 2 is 263°. Copy the diagram shown and plot the location of the fire with the help of a protractor and straightedge.

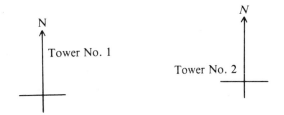

Plot each course, starting at point *A*. Mark point *A* as shown here. Connect consecutive points with segments.

21. a. From point *A* move 3 in. at a bearing of 045°. Label point *B*.

b. From point B move $1\frac{1}{2}$ in. at a bearing of 350°. Label point C.

c. From point C move $2\frac{1}{4}$ in. at a bearing of 130°. Label point D.

d. What is the bearing of point D from point A?

22. **a.** From point A move 6 cm at a

bearing of 110°. Label point B.

b. From point B move 4 cm at a bearing of 350°. Label point C.

c. From point C move 6 cm at a bearing of 225°. Label point D.

d. What is the bearing of point D from point A?

Everyday Geometry

Positioning Solar Collectors

Many people put solar collectors on the roof of their home to use energy from the sun to heat water. To trap the most energy, the collector should face south, plus or minus 20°.

A solar collector should be tilted so that it is at a right angle to the rays of the sun. On Earth, the *latitude* of a place is its angle north or south of the equator. At the North Pole, 90° north latitude, a collector should be at a 90° angle to the ground. In general, the angle of a collector should be equal to the latitude, plus or minus 10°.

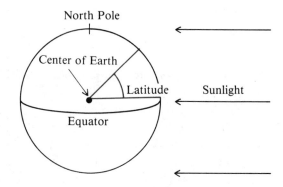

EXERCISES

1. Between what bearings should a solar collector face?

2. Find out the latitude of your home. What is the ideal range for the angle between a solar collector and the ground?

DID YOU KNOW THAT....

The word "chord" comes from the Latin word *chorda*, meaning bowstring, and the word "arc" comes from *arcus*, meaning bow. The resemblance of the geometric terms to their namesakes can be seen in the diagram.

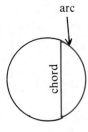

2-8

Arcs and Central Angles

There are several important relationships among segments, arcs, and angles associated with a circle. In this lesson, you will learn some properties of central angles and arcs of circles.

First, recall that in Lesson 2-2 of this chapter we defined a central angle as an angle whose vertex is the center of a circle.

∠*RVT* is a central angle.

An *arc* is part of a circle. Any two points on a circle determine two arcs. With one exception, the two arcs do not have the same size. (Can you name the exception?)

For example, points *B* and *R* on the circle here determine two arcs that do not have the same size. The larger arc determined by any two points on a circle is the *major arc* and the smaller arc is the *minor arc*.

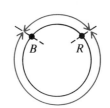

An arc is named by its endpoints. To distinguish between the minor arc and the major arc determined by two points on a circle, a third point is used.

Suppose point *T* is located on the major arc of the circle shown. Then the symbol $\overset{\frown}{BR}$ refers to the minor arc while $\overset{\frown}{BTR}$ refers to the major arc. The symbol ⌢ is read "arc."

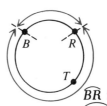

$\overset{\frown}{BR}$ is a minor arc.
$\overset{\frown}{BTR}$ is a major arc.

Before discussing arc measure, we should review some assumptions in our work. First, recall that there are 360° in one full turn. In this book the word "arc" will always refer to the minor arc. $m\,\overset{\frown}{AB}$ is read "the measure of arc *AB*."

The degree is commonly used as a unit of measure for arcs as well as for angles. The measure of an arc depends on the relationship of the arc's length to the distance around the circle of which the arc is a part. This is illustrated by the following examples.

Examples 1 and 2: Find the measure of each arc. (Notice that each circle is divided into a *different* number of equal-size arcs.)

1.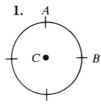

Solution:
The length of $\overset{\frown}{AB}$ is $\frac{1}{4}$ of the circle.

$$m\,\overset{\frown}{AB} = \frac{1}{4} \times 360°$$
$$= \frac{360°}{4}$$
$$= 90°$$

2.

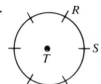

Solution:

The length of $\overset{\frown}{RS}$ is $\frac{1}{6}$ of the circle.

$$m\,\overset{\frown}{RS} = \frac{1}{6} \times 360°$$
$$= \frac{360°}{6}$$
$$= 60°$$

The sides of a central angle intersect a circle in two points. In the figure shown, the sides of $\angle TOR$ intersect the circle in points R and T. These two points determine $\overset{\frown}{RT}$, which is the *intercepted arc* for central angle TOR.

How does the measure of the central angle ($\angle TOR$) compare to the measure of its intercepted arc ($\overset{\frown}{RT}$)? This relationship is illustrated by the following examples.

Examples 3 and 4: Find the measure of each central angle and its intercepted arc. (The fractions show what part of the circle each arc is.)

3.

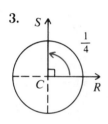

Solution:

$$m\,\overset{\frown}{RS} = \frac{1}{4} \times 360°$$
$$= \frac{360°}{4}$$
$$= 90°$$
$$m\angle RCS = \frac{1}{4}\text{ turn}$$
$$= \frac{1}{4} \times 360°$$
$$= 90°$$

4.

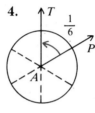

Solution:

$$m\,\overset{\frown}{PT} = \frac{1}{6} \times 360°$$
$$= \frac{360°}{6}$$
$$= 60°$$
$$m\angle PAT = \frac{1}{6}\text{ turn}$$
$$= \frac{1}{6} \times 360°$$
$$= 60°$$

The examples above illustrate the following conclusion:

> **The measure of a central angle is equal to the measure of its intercepted arc.**

This conclusion is very useful and has many applications. Many dials and gauges either are circular or have a scale that is based on a circular design. The relationship between the measure of a central angle and that of its intercepted arc can be used to guarantee that scale markings are equally spaced.

For example, when the hour markings on the timer shown are extended, the smaller central angle formed by adjacent markings has a measure of 15°.

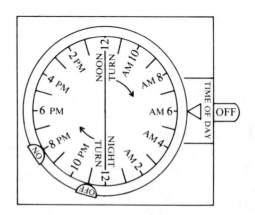

On the speedometer shown, part of the needle that indicates speed is hidden from view. The needle turns on a point so the end of the needle follows a circular path as it moves. For example, as the needle moves from 0 to 20 mi/h, the measure of the central angle formed in the speedometer shown is 20°.

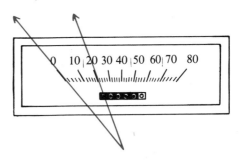

CLASS PRACTICE

For Exercises 1–12, look at ⊙ C.

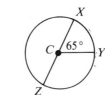

Identify each of the following.
  1. Two minor arcs
  2. Major arc
  3. Three central angles
  4. Three radii
  5. Diameter
  6. Intercepted arc for ∠XCY

Find the indicated measures.
  7. $m\angle YCZ$
  8. $m\angle XCZ$
  9. $m\ \overarc{XY}$
  10. $m\ \overarc{YZ}$
  11. $m\ \overarc{XZ}$
  12. $m\ \overarc{XZY}$

Use the given information to find the indicated measures.

13. $\overarc{RT}$ is $\frac{1}{2}$ of the circle.

  a. $m\ \overarc{RT}$ = ?°
  b. $m\angle RBT$ = ?°

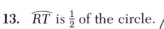

14. $\overarc{LQ}$ is $\frac{1}{8}$ of the circle.

  a. $m\ \overarc{LQ}$ = ?°
  b. $m\angle LMQ$ = ?°

15. a. $m\ \overarc{AB}$ = ?°
    b. $m\angle 1$ = ?°

290°

16. a. $m\angle 2$ = ?°
    b. $m\ \overarc{XRY}$ = ?°

60°

17. a. $m\ \overarc{AB}$ = ?°
    b. $m\angle 1$ = ?°
    c. $m\ \overarc{AC}$ = ?°
    d. $m\ \overarc{CDA}$ = ?°
    e. $m\angle AOC$ = ?°

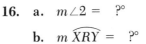

18. a. $m\angle AOB$ = ?°
    b. $m\angle COB$ = ?°
    c. $m\angle AOC$ = ?°
    d. $m\ \overarc{AC}$ = ?°
    e. $m\ \overarc{CDA}$ = ?°
    f. $m\ \overarc{BCA}$ = ?°

80°   70°

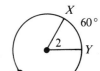

Look at the series of different-size circles. The length of each arc is $\frac{1}{4}$ of its circle.

   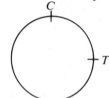

19. What is the measure of each arc shown?
20. How do the measures of these arcs compare? Why?
21. How do the lengths of these arcs compare?
22. Must arcs having the same measure also have the same length? Why or why not?

Find the indicated information.

23. Suppose you were given a blank circular face and were told to design a timer like the one shown on page 64. How would you use the relationship between the measures of a central angle and its intercepted arc to guarantee that the markings on the dial are equally spaced?

24. Explain how to design a speedometer dial with markings like the one shown on page 65.

25. The dials and gauges shown in this lesson are only a sample of the many that could have been used. Bring in dials and gauges (or pictures of them) whose scales are based on a circular design. Explain how the dials could be designed so that the markings are equally spaced.

EXERCISES

_ A _

For Exercises 1–2, look at ⊙ O.

1. Identify each of the following.
   a. Two minor arcs
   b. Major arc
   c. Three central angles
   d. Three radii
   e. Diameter
   f. Intercepted arc for ∠LOP

2. Find the indicated measures.
   a. $m\angle COL$ b. $m\angle LOP$

   c. $m \overset{\frown}{PL}$ d. $m\angle POC$
   e. $m \overset{\frown}{PC}$ f. $m \overset{\frown}{PCL}$

3. Suppose the measure of an arc is 60°. The arc's length is what fractional part of the circle?

4. The measure of $\overset{\frown}{BR}$ shown is 45°. This arc is $\frac{45}{360}$ or $\frac{1}{8}$ of the circle. If the circle is 48 inches around, how long is the arc?

Use the given information to find the indicated measures.

5. $m\angle ROB = 45°$
   $m \stackrel{\frown}{RB} = $?°

6. $m\angle MOP = 100°$
   $m \stackrel{\frown}{PM} = $?°

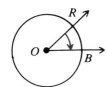

7. $m \stackrel{\frown}{HP} = 120°$
   $m\angle HIP = $?°

8. $m \stackrel{\frown}{AB} = 70°$
   $m\angle AOB = $?°

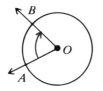

9. $m \stackrel{\frown}{XY} = 110°$
   a. $m\angle 1 = $?°
   b. $m \stackrel{\frown}{XAY} = $?°

10. $m\angle 1 = 70°$
   a. $m\angle 2 = $?°
   b. $m \stackrel{\frown}{RS} = $?°

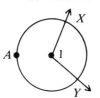

11. $m\angle 1 = 60°$
   a. $m \stackrel{\frown}{XY} = $?°
   b. $m \stackrel{\frown}{XZY} = $?°

12. $m \stackrel{\frown}{BX} = 70°$
   $m \stackrel{\frown}{BTX} = $?°

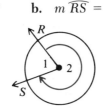

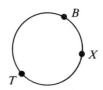

13. $\overline{AB}$ is a diameter of circle O.
   a. $m \stackrel{\frown}{AYB} = $?°
   b. $m \stackrel{\frown}{AXB} = $?°

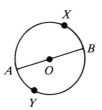

14. $m \stackrel{\frown}{DC} = 140°$
   a. $m\angle 3 = $?°
   b. $m \stackrel{\frown}{BC} = $?°
   c. $m\angle 1 = $?°
   d. $m \stackrel{\frown}{AD} = $?°
   e. $m\angle 2 = $?°
   f. $m \stackrel{\frown}{ACB} = $?°

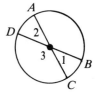

15. O is the center of the circle. $m \stackrel{\frown}{AB} = 50°$
   a. $m\angle 1 = $?°
   b. $m \stackrel{\frown}{BC} = $?°
   c. $m\angle 2 = $?°
   d. $m\angle 1 + m\angle 2 = $?°

— **B** —

16. a. $m\angle AOB = $?°
   b. $m \stackrel{\frown}{BC} = $?°
   c. $m\angle AOC = $?°
   d. $m \stackrel{\frown}{AC} = $?°
   e. $m \stackrel{\frown}{ADC} = $?°
   f. $m \stackrel{\frown}{BCA} = $?°

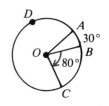

17. a. $m\angle XCY = $?°
   b. $m\angle YCZ = $?°
   c. $m\angle XCZ = $?°
   d. $m \stackrel{\frown}{XZ} = $?°
   e. $m \stackrel{\frown}{XWZ} = $?°
   f. $m \stackrel{\frown}{YWZ} = $?°

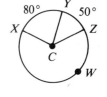

Find the indicated information.

18. The fractions show what part of $\odot P$ each arc is. Find the measure of the indicated arcs and central angles.
   a. $m \stackrel{\frown}{DE} = $?°
   b. $m \stackrel{\frown}{CB} = $?°
   c. $m \stackrel{\frown}{CE} = $?°
   d. $m \stackrel{\frown}{DA} = $?°
   e. $m\angle CPB = $?°
   f. $m\angle APB = $?°
   g. $m\angle DPE = $?°

19. Were any of your results in Exercise 18 the same? Why or why not?

20. Three circles with the same center are shown.

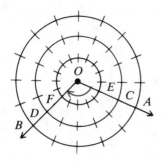

a. How many equal-size arcs are marked off on each circle?

b. How do the lengths of the arcs on the three circles compare?

c. Find the measure of each central angle:

$m\angle AOB = $?° $m\angle COD = $?°
$m\angle EOF = $?°

d. Find the measure of each intercepted arc:

$m\,\overset{\frown}{AB} = $?° $m\,\overset{\frown}{CD} = $?°
$m\,\overset{\frown}{EF} = $?°

21. The timer shown will time intervals up to 60 minutes long. It has been set for an interval of 40 minutes.

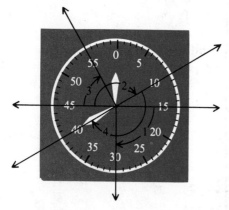

a. The circular dial on the timer is divided into how many equal-size arcs?

b. The length of each of the equal-size arcs is what fractional part of the circle?

c. What is the measure of each arc?

d. Find the measure of each angle:

$m\angle 1 = $?° $m\angle 2 = $?°
$m\angle 3 = $?° $m\angle 4 = $?°

_ **C** _

22. Explain how two different arcs, one with a length of 3 cm and another with a length of 2 cm, can both have a measure of 60°.

23. Any two points on a circle determine two different arcs. Under what conditions will the two arcs have the same length and the same measure?

Look at the diagram.

The positions of the five lugs on an automobile wheel could be located by drawing five equal-size central angles. The central angle for each lug would be $\frac{1}{5}$ turn, or 72°. The lugs would be located at the same distance from the center along the sides of the angles.

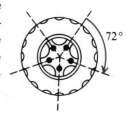

For each number of points, draw a circle with a radius of at least 5 cm (or 2 in.). Using a protractor to draw the central angles, locate the given number of equally-spaced points around the circle.

24. 3 points **25.** 6 points

26. 8 points

2-9

Inscribed Angles

In Lesson 2-8 you learned that the measure of a central angle is equal to the measure of its intercepted arc. Look at ⊙ O.

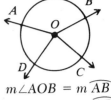

$m\angle AOB = m\,\overarc{AB}$
$m\angle AOD = m\,\overarc{AD}$
$m\angle COD = m\,\overarc{CD}$
$m\angle COB = m\,\overarc{CB}$

In this lesson you will learn the relationship between the measure of an inscribed angle and the measure of its intercepted arc. An *inscribed angle* of a circle is an angle whose vertex is on the circle and whose sides intersect the circle.

These angles are inscribed angles.

These angles are *not* inscribed angles.

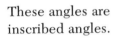   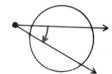

There is a direct relationship between the *measure of an inscribed angle* and that of its intercepted arc. The EXPLORING describes a way to discover this relationship. You will need a compass, straightedge, and protractor.

EXPLORING
Inscribed Angles and Their Intercepted Arcs

1. Draw $\angle ABC$ inscribed in circle O.
   $\overarc{AC}$ is the intercepted arc for $\angle ABC$.
2. Use a protractor to measure $\angle ABC$.
3. Draw central angle AOC.
   $\overarc{AC}$ is the intercepted arc for $\angle AOC$.
4. Use a protractor to measure $\angle AOC$.
5. Compare $m\angle ABC$ and $m\angle AOC$.
   Does $m\angle AOC = m\,\overarc{AC}$? Why?
   Does $m\angle ABC = \frac{1}{2}m\angle AOC$?
   Does $m\angle ABC = \frac{1}{2}m\,\overarc{AC}$?

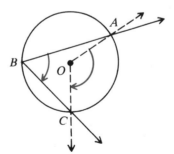

6. What seems to be the relationship between the measure of the inscribed angle, $\angle ABC$, and the measure of its intercepted arc, $\overarc{AC}$?
7. Test your conclusion in step 6 by repeating steps 1–5 with an inscribed angle of a different size. Do you get the same result?

If you did the preceding EXPLORING carefully, you discovered the following conclusion:

> **The measure of an inscribed angle is equal to one half the measure of its intercepted arc.**

Here are two examples.

Example 1:

$m \overset{\frown}{BC} = 120°$

$m \angle A = \ ?°$

Solution:

$m \angle A = \frac{1}{2} \times 120°$
$= 60°$

Example 2:

$m \angle DEF = 80°$

$m \overset{\frown}{DF} = \ ?°$

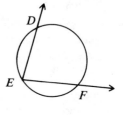

Solution:

$m \overset{\frown}{DF} = 2 \times 80°$
$= 160°$

In the figure shown, $\angle OTX$ is an inscribed angle whose sides intersect the circle at the endpoints of the diameter $\overline{OX}$. Such an angle is said to "intercept a semicircle" or "to be inscribed in a semicircle" (a *semicircle* is half a circle).

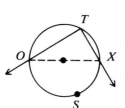

The intercepted arc for $\angle OTX$ is $\overset{\frown}{OSX}$. Since $m \overset{\frown}{OSX} = 180°$, $m \angle OTX = 90°$ and so is a right angle. This example illustrates the following conclusion, which is a special case of the one listed above:

> **An inscribed angle that intercepts a semicircle is a right angle.**

================= CLASS PRACTICE =================

For Exercises 1–13, look at $\odot C$. Identify each of the following.

1. Three central angles
2. Inscribed angle
3. Two semicircles
4. Intercepted arc for $\angle XCY$
5. Intercepted arc for $\angle ZWY$

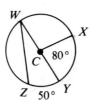

Find the indicated measures.

6. $m \overset{\frown}{XY}$
7. $m \angle WCX$
8. $m \overset{\frown}{WX}$
9. $m \angle ZWY$
10. $m \overset{\frown}{WZY}$
11. $m \overset{\frown}{WZ}$
12. $m \overset{\frown}{XZ}$
13. $m \overset{\frown}{XZY}$

Use the given information to find the indicated measures.
O is the center of the circle.

14. $m \overarc{ACB} =$?°

15. $m \angle ACB =$?°

16. $m \overarc{CD} =$?°

17. $m \overarc{CTD} =$?°

18. $m \angle 1 =$?°

19. $m \angle 2 =$?°

20. $m \angle 3 =$?°

21. $m \angle 1 + m \angle 2 + m \angle 3 =$?°

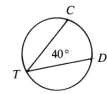

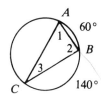

EXERCISES

— A —

1. Identify each of the following.
   a. All radii
   b. All chords
   c. Diameter
   d. Three central angles
   e. Inscribed angle
   f. Intercepted arc for $\angle LIP$
   g. Intercepted arc for $\angle HOP$

For each exercise, draw a figure like ⊙ C.

2. Draw a central angle whose intercepted arc is AB.

3. Draw two inscribed angles whose intercepted arc is AB.

For each circle, tell whether the angle is an inscribed angle, a central angle, or neither.

4.

5.

6.

7.

8.

9.

Use the given information to find the indicated measures. (Be careful: not all the angles are inscribed angles.)

10. $\overline{RB}$ is a diameter.
    $m \angle ROB =$?°

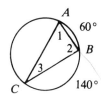

11. $\overline{AT}$ is a diameter.
    a. $m \angle ART =$?°
    b. $m \overarc{AST} =$?°

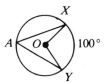

12. a. $m \angle XOY =$?°
    b. $m \angle XAY =$?°
    c. $m \overarc{XAY} =$?°

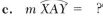

13. $m\angle CRT = $?°

14. $m\,\overset{\frown}{MT} = $?°

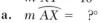

15. $m\,\overset{\frown}{PN} = $?°

16. $m\,\overset{\frown}{CU} = $?°

17. X is the center of the circle.
$m\,\overset{\frown}{PS} = $?°

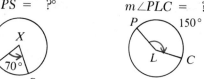

18. L is the center of the circle.
$m\angle PLC = $?°

19. $m\,\overset{\frown}{AB} = 60°$
  a. $m\angle 1 = $?°
  b. $m\angle 2 = $?°

20.
  a. $m\angle 1 = $?°
  b. $m\,\overset{\frown}{RAS} = $?°

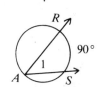

21. $m\,\overset{\frown}{AX} = m\,\overset{\frown}{BX}$
  $m\angle 1 = 25°$
  a. $m\angle 2 = $?°
  b. $m\,\overset{\frown}{BX} = $?°
  c. $m\,\overset{\frown}{AB} = $?°

Find the indicated information.

22. Look at $\odot X$.
  a. How many central angles could have $\overset{\frown}{CD}$ as the intercepted arc?

b. How many inscribed angles could have $\overset{\frown}{CD}$ as the intercepted arc?

— B —

Use the given information to find the indicated measures.

23. O is the center of the circle.
  $m\,\overset{\frown}{YZA} = 260°$
  $m\,\overset{\frown}{XY} = 40°$
  a. $m\,\overset{\frown}{AX} = $?°
  b. $m\,\overset{\frown}{ABZ} = $?°
  c. $m\,\overset{\frown}{YZ} = $?°
  d. $m\angle 1 = $?°
  e. $m\angle 2 = $?°
  f. $m\angle XAZ = $?°

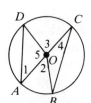

24. $m\,\overset{\frown}{AB} = 70°$
  $m\,\overset{\frown}{BC} = 90°$
  a. $m\angle 1 = $?°
  b. $m\angle 2 = $?°
  c. $m\angle 3 = $?°
  d. $m\angle 1 + m\angle 2 + m\angle 3 = $?°

25. $m\angle 1 = 70°$
  $m\,\overset{\frown}{UA} = 55°$
  a. $m\,\overset{\frown}{UD} = $?°
  b. $m\,\overset{\frown}{AD} = $?°
  c. $m\,\overset{\frown}{UQD} = $?°

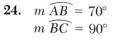

26. $m\,\overset{\frown}{QDA} = 160°$
  $m\,\overset{\frown}{QUA} = 200°$
  a. $m\angle 1 = $?°
  b. $m\angle 2 = $?°
  c. $m\angle 1 + m\angle 2 = $?°

27. $\overline{AC}$ is a diameter.
  $m\,\overset{\frown}{AB} = 50°$
  $m\,\overset{\frown}{DC} = 80°$
  a. $m\angle 1 = $?°
  b. $m\angle 2 = $?°
  c. $m\angle 3 = $?°
  d. $m\angle 4 = $?°
  e. $m\angle 5 = $?°
  f. $m\,\overset{\frown}{AD} = $?°
  g. $m\,\overset{\frown}{BC} = $?°

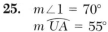

28. $\overline{DF}$ is a diameter.
$m\stackrel{\frown}{BF} = 70°$
$m\stackrel{\frown}{CD} = 50°$
$m\stackrel{\frown}{DE} = 90°$

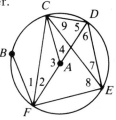

a. Find the measure of each numbered angle.
b. $m\angle BFD = $?°
c. $m\angle CDE = $?°

Look at ⊙ X. Identify each of the following.

1. Three central angles
2. Inscribed angle
3. Two semicircles
4. Five minor arcs
5. Three major arcs
6. Intercepted arc for ∠BAC.

Use the given information to find the indicated measures.

$m\stackrel{\frown}{XZ} = 140°$
7. $m\stackrel{\frown}{XY} = $?°
8. $m\angle XOY = $?°
9. $m\stackrel{\frown}{XWZ} = $?°
10. $m\stackrel{\frown}{XWY} = $?°

$m\angle CBA = 140°$
11. $m\angle DBA = $?°
12. $m\angle 1 = $?°

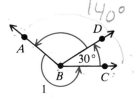

$\overline{AC}$ is a diameter.
13. $m\angle 1 = $?°
14. $m\stackrel{\frown}{CDA} = $?°
15. $m\angle 2 = $?°
16. $m\stackrel{\frown}{BC} = $?°

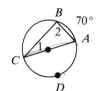

DID YOU KNOW THAT....

In the introduction to Book 1 of *The Elements*, Euclid defined an angle as follows: "A plane angle is the inclination to one another of two lines in a plane which meet one another but which do not lie in the same line." Notice that Euclid's definition of angle from over 2000 years ago has some similarities to the manner in which angles are described in this text. This is just one example of the influence that Euclid's work still has on the teaching of geometry today.

2-10

Some Special Angles

In Lesson 2-3 you learned about right angles and straight angles. In this lesson, you will learn about other kinds of angles.

An *acute angle* has a measure less than 90°, or less than $\frac{1}{4}$ turn.

 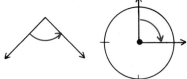 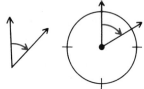

A *right angle* has a measure of 90°, or $\frac{1}{4}$ turn.

An *obtuse angle* has a measure between 90° and 180°, or between $\frac{1}{4}$ and $\frac{1}{2}$ turn.

A *straight angle* has a measure of 180°, or $\frac{1}{2}$ turn.

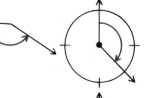

DISCUSS

1. A dictionary defines the words "acute" and "obtuse" as follows:
   Acute—sharp at the end; ending in a point.
   Obtuse—blunt in form; not sharp or acute.
   How are these two definitions related to the mathematical definitions of acute and obtuse angles?
2. Recall that perpendicular lines meet to form right angles.
   a. Is a horizontal line perpendicular to a vertical line?
   b. Do pairs of perpendicular lines have to be horizontal and vertical? Why or why not? Give examples.

Look at the diagram. Classify each angle as acute, right, obtuse, or straight.

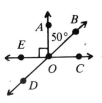

1. ∠ARB　　　　2. ∠ARC　　　　3. ∠ARD
4. ∠ARE　　　　5. ∠BRE　　　　6. ∠BRC

For Exercises 7–16, look at the diagram. Identify each of the following.

7. Three acute angles　　　8. Three obtuse angles
9. Two right angles　　　　10. Two straight angles

Find the indicated measures.

11. *m*∠BOC　　　12. *m*∠AOC　　　13. *m*∠DOC
14. *m*∠DOE　　　15. *m*∠AOD　　　16. *m*∠EOC

EXERCISES

_ A _

Classify each angle as acute, right, obtuse, or straight.

1. 　　　2. *m*∠2 = 138°

3. 　　　4. *m*∠X = 90°

5. 　　　6. *m*∠1 = 68°

7. Has a measure of $\frac{1}{4}$ turn
8. Has a measure between 0° and 90°
9. Has a measure of $\frac{1}{2}$ turn
10. Has a measure between 90° and 180°
11. Has a measure between $\frac{1}{4}$ and $\frac{1}{2}$ turn

Find the indicated measures.
12. *m*∠1 = ?°　　13. *m*∠2 = ?°

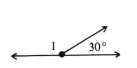　　

14. a. *m*∠TOM = ?°
　　b. *m*∠NOB = ?°
　　c. *m*∠BOT = ?°

_ B _

Draw and label a figure to fit each description, *if possible*.
15. Obtuse angle named ∠RST
16. Acute angle named ∠RDX
17. Straight angle named ∠BHT
18. Right angle named ∠XYZ
19. Triangle with exactly one acute angle
20. Quadrilateral with exactly two right angles
21. Quadrilateral with exactly three right angles

Draw a circle and an angle to fit each description.
22. Inscribed angle that is a right angle
23. Obtuse central angle
24. Acute inscribed angle

2-11

Some Special Angle Relationships

In this lesson you will learn some important relationships between two angles. The following figures illustrate some definitions.

Adjacent angles are two angles in the same plane that have the same vertex and a common side but do not have any interior points in common.

∠1 and ∠2 are adjacent angles.
∠1 and ∠ABC are *not* adjacent angles. (Why not?)

Vertical angles are two angles whose sides form two pairs of opposite rays. (Opposite rays form a straight line.)

∠1 and ∠3 are vertical angles.
∠2 and ∠4 are vertical angles.

Complementary angles are two angles whose measures add up to 90°.

∠A and ∠B are complementary
angles.
∠A is the complement of ∠B,
and vice versa.

∠ROB and ∠BOT are complementary
angles.
∠ROB is the complement of ∠BOT,
and vice versa.

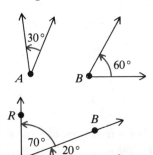

Supplementary angles are two angles whose measures add up to 180°.

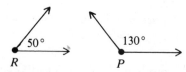

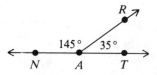

∠R and ∠P are supplementary
angles.
∠R is the supplement of ∠P,
and vice versa.

∠RAT and ∠RAN are supplementary
angles.
∠RAT is the supplement of ∠RAN,
and vice versa.

Measures of Vertical Angles

Look at the lines that intersect and form two pairs of vertical angles.

Do not use a protractor in steps 1–4.
1. Is ∠1 supplementary to ∠2?
2. Is ∠3 supplementary to∠2?
3. How do the measures of ∠1 and ∠3 compare? Why?
4. How do the measures of ∠2 and ∠4 compare? Why?
5. Now use a protractor to measure ∠1, ∠2, ∠3, and ∠4.
6. Do your measurements agree with your answers in steps 1–4?
7. How are the measures of vertical angles related?

   If you did the preceding EXPLORING carefully, you discovered the following conclusion:

> **The measures of vertical angles are equal.**

CLASS PRACTICE

For Exercises 1–4, look at the figure.

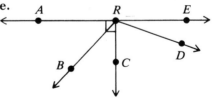

1. ∠ARB and ∠ARC have a common vertex (R) and a common side ($\overrightarrow{RA}$). Are they adjacent angles? Why or why not?
2. Identify three pairs of adjacent angles.
3. Identify two pairs of complementary angles. How many pairs are shown?
4. Identify two pairs of supplementary angles. How many pairs are shown?
5. Can two acute angles be complementary? supplementary? Why or why not?
6. Can two acute angles be both complementary and adjacent?
7. Must complementary angles be adjacent? Why or why not?
8. Suppose ∠X and ∠Y are supplementary angles. What kinds of angles can they be?
9. Must supplementary angles be adjacent? Why or why not?

Look at the figure.

10. Identify a pair of vertical angles.
11. Which two angles are supplements of ∠*DOC*?
12. Are ∠*AOE* and ∠*DOC* vertical angles?
13. Are ∠*AOB* and ∠*BOC* complementary angles?
14. Are ∠*AOB* and ∠*DOE* complementary angles?
15. *m*∠*AOB* = ?°   16. *m*∠*DOC* = ?°
17. *m*∠*DOE* = ?°   18. *m*∠*AOD* = ?°

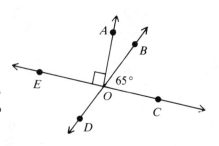

EXERCISES

— A —

Classify each statement as true or false.

1. Complementary angles must be adjacent.
2. Supplementary angles must be adjacent.
3. Vertical angles must have the same measure.
4. Any two right angles are supplementary.
5. Two obtuse angles can be supplementary.
6. Two acute angles can be supplementary.
7. Two acute angles can be complementary.
8. Two right angles can be supplementary.

Match each term with its definition.

9. Acute angle
10. Obtuse angle
11. Right angle
12. Straight angle
13. Complementary angles
14. Supplementary angles
15. Central angle
16. Inscribed angle
17. Vertical angles

a. An angle with a measure of 90°.
b. Two angles whose measures add up to 90°.
c. An angle with a measure between 90° and 180°.
d. An angle with its vertex at the center of a circle.
e. Two angles whose measures add up to 180°.
f. An angle with a measure of 180°.
g. Two angles whose sides form a pair of opposite rays.
h. An angle with a measure less than 90°.
i. An angle whose vertex is on a circle and whose sides intersect the circle.

Classify each pair of angles as complementary, supplementary, or neither.

18. 75°, 20°   19. 111°, 89°

20.   21. 130°, 50°

22. 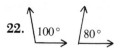   23.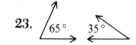

Find the indicated information.

24. If $m\angle A = 55°$, what is the measure of a complement of $\angle A$? of a supplement of $\angle A$?

25. If $m\angle B = 76°$, what is the measure of a complement of $\angle B$? of a supplement of $\angle B$?

26. Look at the figure.

   a. Are $\angle 3$ and $\angle 5$ vertical angles? Why or why not?

   Identify each of the following.
   b. One pair of complementary angles
   c. Two pairs of supplementary angles
   d. Two angles adjacent to $\angle 2$
   e. One pair of vertical angles
   f. Two angles complementary to $\angle 5$

— **B** —

27. Two angles are equal in measure and complementary. What is the measure of each angle?

28. Two angles are equal in measure and supplementary. What is the measure of each angle?

Draw and label a figure to fit each description.

29. Two adjacent angles, $\angle MON$ and $\angle NOR$

30. Two angles, $\angle BHT$ and $\angle THE$, that are both supplementary and adjacent

31. Two adjacent central angles

32. Two angles, $\angle ABC$ and $\angle CBD$, that are both complementary and adjacent

Find the indicated information.

33. Use a protractor and straightedge to draw each angle.

   a. Angle complementary to the one shown

   b. Angle supplementary to the one shown

Use the given information to find the indicated measures.

34. a. $m\angle 1 = $?°
   b. $m\angle 2 = $?°
   c. $m\angle 3 = $?°
   d. $m\angle 1 + m\angle 2 = $?°

35. a. $m\angle 1 = $?°
   b. $m\angle 2 = $?°
   c. $m\angle 3 = $?°

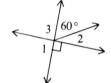

36. a. $m\angle 1 = $?°
   b. $m\angle 2 = $?°
   c. $m\angle 3 = $?°

37. a. $m\angle 1 = $?°
   b. $m\ \overset{\frown}{AB} = $?°
   c. $m\ \overset{\frown}{ACB} = $?°
   d. $m\angle 2 = $?°
   e. $m\angle 1 + m\angle 2 = $?°

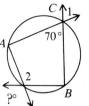

38. a. $m\angle AXB = $?°
   b. $m\angle CXN = $?°
   c. $m\angle AXC = $?°
   d. $m\angle BXN = $?°

Geometry on the Job

AIR-TRAFFIC CONTROLLER

Joseph Martinelli monitors a radar screen on his job as an air-traffic controller. He must know the exact location of planes approaching or leaving the airport.

The location of a plane displayed on the radar screen is read as *polar coordinates*, the distance from the origin (in this case, the control tower) and a bearing. For example, on the radar screen shown below, the distance

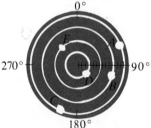

between the circles is 10 miles. Aircraft *A* is 40 miles from the control tower (located at the center of the scope) where Joseph works. The bearing of aircraft *A* is 065°. Therefore its location is represented by the polar coordinates (40, 065°).

Polar coordinates and/or bearings are also used extensively by persons

such as weather forecasters and navigators to describe the location of objects like thunderstorms and ships.

EXERCISES

State the polar coordinates—(distance, bearing)—for the location of each aircraft.

1. Aircraft *B*
2. Aircraft *C*
3. Aircraft *D*
4. Aircraft *E*
5. Could more than one airplane have the same bearing from the tower?
6. Could more than one airplane be the same distance from the tower?
7. Will each distance and bearing describe the location of only one aircraft?
8. Obtain a map of your state or region. Select a city as the origin. Using the map scale, use polar coordinates to describe the location of several cities.
9. Navigators usually make a distinction between *magnetic course*, *compass course*, and *true course*. Do some research to find the differences among these three terms.

ARITHMETIC REVIEW — *Multiplying Fractions*

The following rule is used for multiplying fractions:

> **The numerator of the product is the product of the numerators of the factors. The denominator of the product is the product of the denominators of the factors.**

Examples
Multiply. Write answers in simplest form.

1. $\frac{2}{3} \cdot \frac{4}{5} = \frac{8}{15}$

2. $\frac{3}{5} \cdot \frac{5}{3} = \frac{15}{15} = 1$

3. $\frac{5}{6} \cdot \frac{2}{3} = \frac{10}{18} = \frac{5}{9}$

4. $\frac{3}{8} \cdot \frac{6}{7} = \frac{18}{56} = \frac{9}{28}$

5. $\frac{1}{3} \cdot 360 = \frac{1}{3} \cdot \frac{360}{1} = \frac{360}{3} = 120$

6. $\frac{3}{4} \cdot 2\frac{1}{2} = \frac{3}{4} \cdot \frac{5}{2} = \frac{15}{8}$, or $1\frac{7}{8}$

EXERCISES
Multiply. Write answers in simplest form.

1. $\frac{1}{2} \cdot \frac{1}{5}$ **2.** $\frac{3}{4} \cdot \frac{2}{3}$ **3.** $\frac{1}{2} \cdot \frac{1}{8}$ **4.** $\frac{3}{5} \cdot \frac{2}{4}$

5. $\frac{5}{8} \cdot \frac{2}{5}$ **6.** $\frac{4}{5} \cdot \frac{1}{3}$ **7.** $\frac{2}{3} \cdot \frac{2}{5}$ **8.** $\frac{3}{4} \cdot \frac{5}{8}$

9. $\frac{3}{5} \cdot \frac{3}{4}$ **10.** $\frac{1}{6} \cdot \frac{1}{2}$ **11.** $\frac{9}{16} \cdot \frac{5}{6}$ **12.** $\frac{3}{4} \cdot \frac{6}{15}$

13. $\frac{3}{8} \cdot \frac{4}{5}$ **14.** $\frac{3}{2} \cdot \frac{5}{4}$ **15.** $\frac{5}{6} \cdot \frac{2}{3}$ **16.** $\frac{8}{9} \cdot \frac{3}{5}$

17. $\frac{5}{8} \cdot 8$ **18.** $\frac{2}{3} \cdot 6$ **19.** $8 \cdot \frac{1}{4}$ **20.** $12 \cdot \frac{1}{3}$

21. $\frac{1}{2} \cdot 3$ **22.** $\frac{3}{4} \cdot 5$ **23.** $9 \cdot \frac{2}{3}$ **24.** $3 \cdot \frac{1}{4}$

25. $\frac{2}{3} \cdot \frac{1}{4} \cdot \frac{1}{2}$ **26.** $3 \cdot \frac{2}{3} \cdot \frac{1}{2}$ **27.** $6 \cdot \frac{3}{4} \cdot 2\frac{2}{3}$ **28.** $\frac{1}{2} \cdot \frac{6}{15} \cdot \frac{5}{6}$

29. $4 \cdot 2\frac{1}{2}$ **30.** $3 \cdot 1\frac{2}{3}$ **31.** $5\frac{1}{2} \cdot 5$ **32.** $2\frac{1}{4} \cdot 3$

33. $4\frac{1}{2} \cdot \frac{2}{3}$ **34.** $3\frac{1}{3} \cdot \frac{1}{2}$ **35.** $\frac{2}{3} \cdot 3\frac{1}{2}$ **36.** $\frac{3}{4} \cdot 2\frac{2}{5}$

37. $2\frac{1}{2} \cdot \frac{1}{4}$ **38.** $\frac{3}{4} \cdot 3\frac{1}{3}$ **39.** $1\frac{1}{2} \cdot 1\frac{1}{4}$ **40.** $1\frac{3}{8} \cdot \frac{1}{2}$

41. $\frac{3}{4} \cdot \frac{4}{3}$ **42.** $8 \cdot \frac{1}{8}$ **43.** $\frac{4}{9} \cdot \frac{9}{4}$ **44.** $\frac{4}{9} \cdot \frac{4}{9}$

Chapter 2 Review

Vocabulary

The following terms and symbols were introduced in this chapter. You should be able to write a brief description, draw a picture, or give an example to illustrate the meaning of each.

Angles

Measurement of	*Special Types*	*Special Angle Relationships*
amount of turn (p. 45)	acute angle (p. 74)	adjacent angles (p. 76)
degree (p. 48)	obtuse angle (p. 74)	complementary angles (p. 76)
protractor (p. 52)	right angle (p. 48)	supplementary angles (p. 76)
	straight angle (p. 48)	vertical angles (p. 76)

Circles

arc (p. 63)	inscribed angle (p. 69)	radius (p. 42)
center (p. 42)	intercepted arc (p. 64)	semicircle (p. 70)
central angle (p. 45)	major arc (p. 63)	
chord (p. 42)	minor arc (p. 63)	bearing (p. 60)
diameter (p. 42)		perpendicular lines (p. 48)

Symbols

$\overparen{AB}$ (arc) (p. 63)	BC (length of $\overline{BC}$) (p. 42)	$m\,\overparen{AB}$ (measure of arc AB)
$\odot O$ (circle) (p. 42)	$\overparen{DEF}$ (major arc) (p. 63)	(p. 63)
40° (degrees) (p. 48)	$m\angle ABC$ (measure of angle	$\perp$ (perpendicular to) (p. 48)
d (diameter) (p. 42)	ABC) (p. 45)	r (radius) (p. 42)

Skills Checklist

In Chapter 2 you learned terms and symbols associated with angles, circles, and arcs; some special relationships between pairs of angles; how to estimate and measure the size of angles; and how to use a protractor to draw and measure angles. In addition, you were introduced to some applications of angle measure.

The following list indicates the major skills, facts, and results you should have mastered in this chapter:

- Recognize special segments associated with a circle (radius, diameter, and chord) and use relationships among the lengths of these segments. (**2-1,** pp. 42–44)
- Make accurate estimates and measurements of angle size using amount of turn and degrees. (**2-2—2-4,** pp. 45–54)
- Convert angle measures from degrees to amount of turn and vice versa. (**2-3,** pp. 48–50)

- Use a protractor to draw an angle of a given size. (**2–5**, pp. 55–57)
- Solve problems involving the addition and subtraction of angle measures. (**2–6**, pp. 58–59)
- Determine compass bearings for given objects. (**2–7**, pp. 60–62)
- Recognize central and inscribed angles and use the relationship of their measures to the measures of their intercepted arcs. (**2–8—2–9**, pp. 63–73)
- Recognize and classify angles according to size (acute, right, obtuse, and straight). (**2–3**, pp. 48–50; **2–10**, pp. 74–75)
- Recognize and use special relationships between pairs of angles. These include adjacent angles, complementary angles, supplementary angles, and vertical angles. (**2–11**, pp. 76–79)

Exercises

1. Look at ⊙ O. Identify each of the following. (**2–1**)
   a. All radii
   b. All chords
   c. All diameters

Classify each statement as true or false. (2–1)

2. A diameter of a circle is also a chord.
3. In every circle the diameter is twice the radius.
4. A circle with a diameter of 4 cm can have a chord of 6 cm.

Complete each statement. (2–3)

5. $80° =$? turn
6. $120° =$? turn
7. $\frac{1}{12}$ turn = ?°
8. $\frac{2}{5}$ turn = ?°
9. If the diameter is 8 cm, then the radius of the same circle is ? cm.

(a) Estimate the measure of each angle and (b) use a protractor to find its measure to the nearest degree. (2–4)

10.

11.

Draw a figure to fit each description.

12. Angle whose measure is 125° (**2–5**)
13. Ray with a bearing of 165° (**2–7**)

Use the given information to find the indicated measures. (2–6)

14. $m\angle 1 = 75°$
    $m\angle 2 =$?°

15. $m\angle 1 = 20°$
    $m\angle CBA = 100°$
    $m\angle 2 =$?°

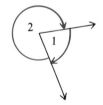

16. $m\angle AXB =$?°
17. $m\angle AXC =$?°
18. $m\angle BXC =$?°
19. $m\angle BXD =$?°

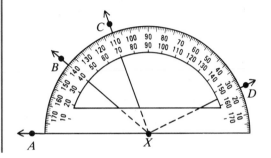

20. $m\angle AOB = $?° **21.** $m\angle AOC = $?°
22. $m\angle BOC = $?° **23.** $m\angle BOD = $?°

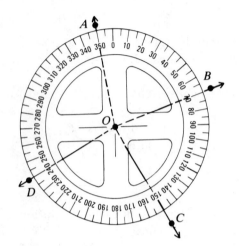

Find the indicated information.

24. Look at $\odot O$.
Identify each
of the following.

   a. Three central
   angles **(2–8)**
   b. One inscribed
   angle **(2–9)**
   c. Two semicircles **(2–9)**
   d. Five minor arcs **(2–8)**
   e. Four major arcs **(2–8)**
   f. Intercepted arc for $\angle AOD$ **(2–8)**

Use the given information to find the indicated measures.

25. $m\,\widehat{AB} = 80°$
(2–9) a. $m\,\widehat{AXB} = $?°
   b. $m\angle AXB = $?°

26. $m\,\widehat{XY} = 130°$
(2–8) a. $m\angle XOY = $?°
   b. $m\,\widehat{XWY} = $?°

27. $\overline{AB}$ is a diameter.
(2–9) a. $m\angle 1 = $?°
   b. $m\,\widehat{ACB} = $?°

28. a. $m\,\widehat{WXY} = $?°
(2–9) b. $m\angle 1 = $?°
   c. $m\,\widehat{WZY} = $?°
   d. $m\,\widehat{YZ} = $?°

Draw a figure to fit each description.
29. Central angle **(2–8)**
30. Inscribed angle **(2–9)**

For Exercises 31 and 32,
look at the drawing of
intersecting lines.

31. Identify each of the
   following.
   a. One pair of
   (2–11) vertical angles
   b. All acute angles **(2–10)**
   c. All obtuse angles **(2–10)**
   d. All right angles **(2–10)**
   e. Five pairs of adjacent angles
   (2–11)
   f. Two angles supplementary to
   $\angle 2$ **(2–11)**

32. a. Are $\angle 5$ and $\angle 3$ vertical angles?
   b. Are $\angle 5$ and $\angle 3$ complementary
   angles? **(2–11)**

Find the indicated measures. **(2–11)**
33. a. $m\angle 1 = $?°
   b. $m\angle 2 = $?°

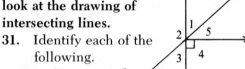

Draw a figure to fit each description.
34. Acute angle **(2–10)**
35. Two perpendicular lines **(2–3)**
36. Two complementary angles **(2–11)**
37. Two adjacent angles that are not
   supplementary **(2–11)**

REFLECTING ON PROPERTIES

Congruence and Properties of Polygons

3-1
Metric Units of Length

The first two lessons of this chapter review metric units of length and the use of a metric ruler in measuring distance.

You may be more familiar with customary units of length—such as inches, feet, and yards—than with metric units of length. However, as metric units are becoming more widely used in the U.S., it is important to know how to use them. Most of the measurements in this book will be metric.

In the metric system, the basic unit of length is the meter. The height of a kitchen counter is about 1 meter. Distances in Olympic and other international sporting events have been measured in meters for several years, since almost all countries of the world use the metric system.

Another important metric unit of length is the *centimeter*. The prefix *centi-* means 0.01, or $\frac{1}{100}$. Therefore one centimeter is $\frac{1}{100}$ of a meter and there are 100 centimeters in one meter.

Shown below are two segments being measured to the nearest centimeter. The symbol cm is read "centimeter."

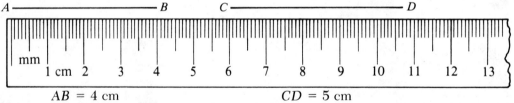

$AB = 4$ cm $\qquad\qquad\qquad\qquad CD = 5$ cm

Another common metric unit of length is the *millimeter*. The prefix *milli-* means 0.001 or $\frac{1}{1000}$. Therefore one millimeter is $\frac{1}{1000}$ of a meter and there are 1000 millimeters in one meter.

Shown below are two segments being measured to the nearest millimeter. The symbol mm is read "millimeter."

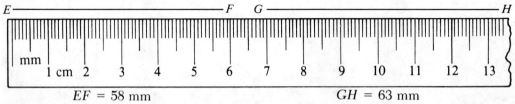

$EF = 58$ mm $\qquad\qquad\qquad\qquad GH = 63$ mm

In the metric system, longer distances, such as the distance between two cities, are measured in *kilometers*. Speedometers on automobiles now have markings in both miles per hour and kilometers per hour and some highway signs give distances in kilometers.

The prefix *kilo-* means 1000. Therefore a kilometer is equivalent to 1000 meters. The symbol km is read "kilometer."

The following table shows the prefixes and symbols for some common metric units of length. An * indicates those units that will be used most often in this book.

Prefix	Meaning	Unit	Symbol	Distance
kilo-	thousand	*kilometer	km	1000 meters
hecto-	hundred	hectometer	hm	100 meters
deka-	ten	dekameter	dam	10 meters
		*meter	m	1 meter
deci-	tenth	decimeter	dm	0.1 meter
centi-	hundredth	*centimeter	cm	0.01 meter
milli-	thousandth	*millimeter	mm	0.001 meter

DISCUSS

1. Why is the ability to measure length useful?
2. Why is the ability to estimate length useful?

CLASS PRACTICE

Complete each statement.
1. 1 m = ? cm   2. 1 m = ? mm   3. 1 cm = ? mm   4. 1 km = ? m

Find the indicated information.
5. One millimeter is what part of a centimeter? what part of a meter?
6. One centimeter is what part of a meter?

Estimate the length of each segment (a) to the nearest centimeter and (b) to the nearest millimeter.

7.

8.   9.

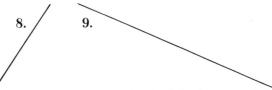

10–12. Measure the length of each segment in Exercises 7–9 (a) to the nearest centimeter and (b) to the nearest millimeter.

Draw a segment having each given length.
13. 2 cm   14. 5 cm   15. 34 mm   16. 62 mm

What metric unit of length would most likely be used to measure each of the following?

17. Drapes for a living room or bedroom
18. Lumber for building a picnic table
19. Fencing for a yard
20. Distance traveled on a vacation trip
21. Name some tools or instruments that are used to measure length.

EXERCISES

_ A _

Estimate the length of each segment (a) to the nearest centimeter and (b) to the nearest millimeter.

1.———
2.————————
3.—————
4.————————
5.—————————
6.———————
7.——————————
8.————————

9–16. Measure the length of each segment in Exercises 1–8 (a) to the nearest centimeter and (b) to the nearest millimeter.

Complete each statement.

17. 1 cm = ? mm   18. 1 m = ? cm
19. 1 mm = ? m   20. 1 cm = ? m
21. 1 m = ? mm   22. 1 mm = ? cm

Draw a segment having each given length.

23. 1 cm   24. 8 cm
25. 6 cm   26. 3 cm
27. 10 cm   28. 13 cm
29. 3 mm   30. 7 mm
31. 15 mm   32. 20 mm
33. 70 mm   34. 53 mm

Name the larger unit in each pair.

35. centimeter, millimeter
36. kilometer, meter
37. kilometer, millimeter

_ B _

Name the metric unit of length that would most likely be used to measure each given length.

38. Width of Lake Michigan
39. Length of an automobile
40. Your height
41. Size (width) of film for a camera
42. Width of a classroom

Find the indicated information.

43. Arrange the following units in order from shortest to longest.

    meter   centimeter
    kilometer   millimeter

_ C _

Use a meter stick or a piece of string one meter long to make the following measurements.

44. Look around you. Choose some distances—such as, from desk to window—that you estimate have the following measures: 1 meter, 2 meters, 3 meters, 4 meters, and 5 meters.

a. Measure each distance to the nearest meter.

b. Record your results in a table.

45. Look around you. Choose some other distances that you estimate are more than one meter long.

a. Estimate each distance to the nearest meter.

b. Measure each distance to the nearest meter.

c. Record your results in a table.

MORE EXPLORING
Metric Prefixes

Metrix prefixes are used with various units of measure and in the names of various objects. For example, the prefix *mega-* means one million and a megavolt is equivalent to 1,000,000 volts.

State the meaning of the following words:

1. decade
2. decathlon
3. micrometer
4. centigrade
5. mill (money)
6. millipede
7. Find other words that contain a metric prefix. State the meaning of each word.

Everyday Geometry

Pacing Distances

Often people want to know a distance but do not need an exact measurement. For example, someone planting a garden may want to know the length of a row in order to buy the right amount of seed.

Pacing is a quick way to estimate such distances. First, measure the length of your step: (1) Find a fairly long distance such as the length of a large room. (2) Measure the length. (3) Walk the distance, using normal steps. (4) Count how many steps you take and divide to find the distance per step. (5) Make a record of the measurement. To estimate a distance, pace it off and use the length of your step to find the distance.

EXERCISES

Give an example of a situation in which pacing would give a good enough estimate. Give an example of a situation in which it would not.

3-2

Equivalent Lengths

In Lesson 3–1 you learned that 1 cm = 10 mm and 1 mm = 0.1 cm. This allows you to write some measurements in more than one way, as illustrated by the examples below.

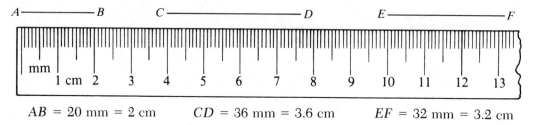

AB = 20 mm = 2 cm CD = 36 mm = 3.6 cm EF = 32 mm = 3.2 cm

The following examples show how to write a length given in one metric unit of length in terms of another metric unit of length.

Examples:	Solutions:	Answers:
1. 3 cm = ? mm	1 cm = 10 mm 3 × 10 = 30	30 mm
2. 80 mm = ? cm	10 mm = 1 cm 80 ÷ 10 = 8	8 cm
3. 3.7 cm = ? mm	1 cm = 10 mm 3.7 × 10 = 37	37 mm
4. 89 mm = ? cm	10 mm = 1 cm 89 ÷ 10 = 8.9	8.9 cm
5. 6 m = ? cm	1 m = 100 cm 6 × 100 = 600	600 cm
6. 400 cm = ? m	100 cm = 1 m 400 ÷ 100 = 4	4 m

To convert a given measure from a larger unit to a smaller unit (see Examples 1, 3, and 5), you first find the number of smaller units that is equivalent to one of the larger units. Multiplication is used to find the result.

To convert a given measure from a smaller unit to a larger unit (see Examples 2, 4, and 6), you first find the number of smaller units that is equivalent to one of the larger units. Division is used to find the result.

Measure the length of each segment (a) to the nearest millimeter and (b) to the nearest tenth of a centimeter.

1.

3.

4.

2.

Draw a segment having each given length.

5.   3.6 cm   6.   47 mm   7.   5.3 cm   8.   74 mm

Complete each statement.

9.   8.9 cm = ? mm   10.   11.2 cm = ? mm   11.   6.3 cm = ? mm

12.   38 mm = ? cm   13.   54 mm = ? cm   14.   147 mm = ? cm

EXERCISES

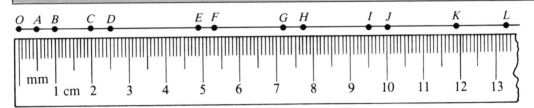

_ A _

Refer to the ruler shown to find the length of each segment (a) to the nearest millimeter and (b) to the nearest tenth of a centimeter.

1. $\overline{OA}$ 2. $\overline{OB}$
3. $\overline{OC}$ 4. $\overline{OD}$
5. $\overline{OE}$ 6. $\overline{OF}$
7. $\overline{OG}$ 8. $\overline{OH}$
9. $\overline{OI}$ 10. $\overline{OJ}$
11. $\overline{OK}$ 12. $\overline{OL}$

Measure the length of each segment (a) to the nearest millimeter and (b) to the nearest tenth of a centimeter.

13. _____

14. _____

15. _____

16. _____

17. _____

18. _____

19. _____

20. _____

Draw a segment having each given length.

21.   6.7 cm   22.   35 mm
23.   4 cm   24.   82 mm
25.   4.8 cm   26.   7.0 cm

_ B _

Complete each statement.

27.   1.7 cm = ? mm
28.   6 cm = ? mm
29.   82 mm = ? cm
30.   13.6 cm = ? mm
31.   98 mm = ? cm
32.   320 mm = ? cm
33.   4.0 cm = ? mm
34.   3 m = ? cm

35. 173 mm = ? cm
36. 8 mm = ? cm
37. 1 km = ? m
38. 1 cm = ? mm

Name the metric unit of length that would most likely be used to measure each of the following.
39. Length of a dollar bill
40. Thickness of a quarter
41. Length of the Ohio River
42. Altitude of an airplane
43. Width of a picture frame

State whether each statement is reasonable.
44. My foot is 15 millimeters long.
45. My height is 175 centimeters.
46. I live 100 meters from school.
47. My textbook is 20 centimeters wide.
48. The width of my thumb is 2.5 meters.
49. The door is 2 kilometers high.

— C —
Suppose that metric prefixes were used with units of time.
50. If your class period were a *deci*day long, would you like it better? Why or why not?
51. About how many *centi*days would it take to make an hour (nearest whole number)?

52. A *kilo*day would be about how many years (nearest whole number)?
53. What is a more common name for a *centi*dollar? for a *deci*dollar?

Metric prefixes are used with units of measure other than length. For example, electricity is measured in watt-hours (W·h) or kilowatt-hours (kW·h), each of which is 1000 watt-hours.

An appliance rated 40 watts will use 40 watts of electricity per hour. Therefore, a 100-watt bulb will use 1 kW·h of electricity in 10 hours (100 watts × 10 hours = 1000 watt-hours = 1 kW·h).

54. How many hours will it take for two 100-watt bulbs to use 1 kW·h of electricity?
55. An electric fan is marked "40 watts." How many hours will it take the fan to use 2 kW·h of electricity?
56. Choose some measures such as 2 m, 30 cm, and 1.20 m.
   a. Find some distances in your classroom that have these measures.
   b. Record your results in a table.
57. Look around you. Choose some distances, such as from your desk to the door.
   a. Estimate each distance to the nearest centimeter.
   b. Measure each distance to the nearest centimeter.
   c. Record your results in a table.

DID YOU KNOW THAT....

The metric system of weights and measures is the only system that has been legalized for general use in the United States. Legislation legalizing the use of the metric system was passed by the U.S. Congress in July 1866.

3-3

Congruent Figures and Corresponding Parts

Geometric figures that are exactly the same size and shape are called *congruent figures*. The symbol ≅ is read "is congruent to." A statement asserting that two figures are congruent is called a *congruence statement*. Some examples of congruent figures are shown below. Notice the use of hatch marks to indicate segments and angles that are congruent to each other.

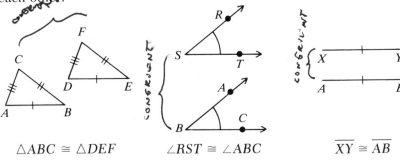

$$\triangle ABC \cong \triangle DEF \qquad \angle RST \cong \angle ABC \qquad \overline{XY} \cong \overline{AB}$$

When two polygons are congruent, one polygon will fit exactly over the other. The angles and sides that match each other are called *corresponding angles* and *corresponding sides*.

For example, $\triangle ABC$ and $\triangle XYZ$ shown are congruent. If you slide one triangle to fit over the other, the following vertices are matched with each other: A with X; B with Y; C with Z. This matching of vertices also determines the sides and angles that *correspond to*, or match, one another.

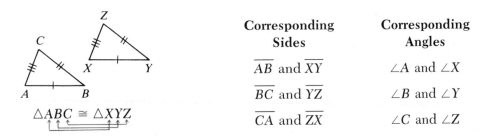

Corresponding Sides	Corresponding Angles
$\overline{AB}$ and $\overline{XY}$	$\angle A$ and $\angle X$
$\overline{BC}$ and $\overline{YZ}$	$\angle B$ and $\angle Y$
$\overline{CA}$ and $\overline{ZX}$	$\angle C$ and $\angle Z$

Corresponding sides and corresponding angles of congruent polygons are referred to as the *corresponding parts* of the polygons.

> The corresponding parts of congruent polygons must also be congruent.

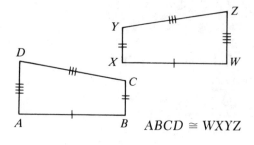

Corresponding Parts

$\overline{AB} \cong \overline{WX}$	$\angle A \cong \angle W$
$\overline{BC} \cong \overline{XY}$	$\angle B \cong \angle X$
$\overline{CD} \cong \overline{YZ}$	$\angle C \cong \angle Y$
$\overline{DA} \cong \overline{ZW}$	$\angle D \cong \angle Z$

$ABCD \cong WXYZ$

DISCUSS

1. Look at the way each pair of congruent figures has been named above. What is the relationship between the order of the vertices in the polygon names and the corresponding vertices?
2. Look at the way corresponding parts of each pair of congruent figures have been named above. What is the relationship between the order of the vertices in the names of corresponding parts and the corresponding vertices?
3. What advantages does this special way of naming congruent figures and corresponding parts have?
4. State some words or phrases that mean the same as "congruent."
5. Which of the keys shown will unlock the same door as the unlabeled key?
6. How could you prove that your selection is correct?
7. State reasons for not selecting the other keys.
8. Name three pairs of objects in your classroom that appear to be congruent.

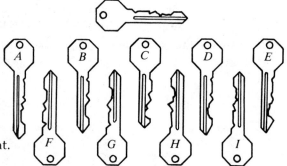

What applications would the idea of congruence have for the following items or fields?

9. Assembly line
10. Rubber stamps
11. Sports
12. Gaskets
13. Printing
14. Fingerprints
15. Name at least five situations from everyday life in which congruence is important. (Example: duplicate keys)

Look at congruent triangles XYZ and JKL.

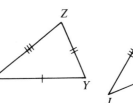
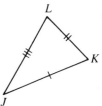

1. What segment in △JKL is congruent to $\overline{XY}$? to $\overline{YZ}$? to $\overline{XZ}$?

2. What angle in △JKL is congruent to ∠X? to ∠Y? to ∠Z?

Look at congruent triangles ABC and DEF. Complete each statement.

3. $\overline{AC} \cong$?   4. $\overline{AB} \cong$?   5. $\overline{BC} \cong$?

6. ∠A ≅ ∠ ?   7. ∠B ≅ ∠ ?   8. ∠C ≅ ∠ ?

9. △CBA ≅ △ ?   10. △ACB ≅ △ ?   11. △BAC ≅ △ ?

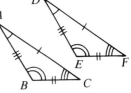

Suppose you know that △RST ≅ △GHI.

12. Identify the three pairs of corresponding angles.

13. Identify the three pairs of corresponding sides.

14. Does the congruence statement △SRT ≅ △HGI correctly identify the corresponding vertices? Does the statement △TRS ≅ △IGH?

_ A _

State whether each pair of figures are congruent.

1.
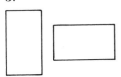

2.

3.
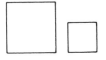

4.

5.

6.

Find the indicated information.

7. Identify all pairs of congruent figures by writing a congruence statement. (Example: fig. A ≅ fig. D)

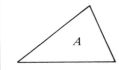
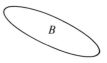

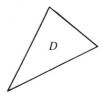

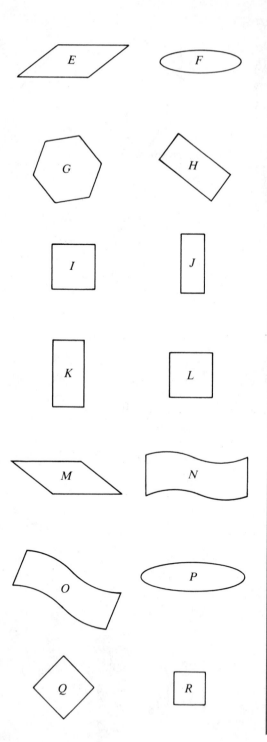

Name the corresponding parts (sides and angles) for each pair of congruent figures. (Remember: The order of the letters naming the vertices is important.)

8.

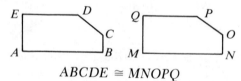

$$ABCDE \cong MNOPQ$$

$\overline{AB} \cong \overline{MN}$		$\angle A \cong \angle M$	
$\overline{BC} \cong$?		$\angle B \cong \angle$?	
$\overline{CD} \cong$?		$\angle C \cong \angle$?	
$\overline{DE} \cong$?		$\angle D \cong \angle$?	
$\overline{EA} \cong$?		$\angle E \cong \angle$?	

9.

$$\triangle WXY \cong \triangle DEF$$

10.

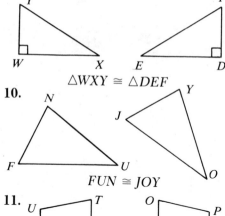

$$FUN \cong JOY$$

11.

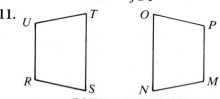

$$RSTU \cong MNOP$$

12.

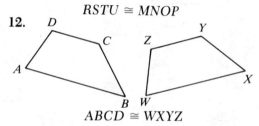

$$ABCD \cong WXYZ$$

13–17. For each pair of congruent figures in Exercises 8–12, write two other congruence statements that will match up the corresponding vertices.

_ **B** _

18. Suppose that $PQRS \cong ABCD$.
  a. Identify the four pairs of corresponding angles.
  b. Identify the four pairs of corresponding sides.
  c. Does the congruence statement $RQPS \cong CBAD$ correctly identify the corresponding vertices? Does the statement $PSRQ \cong ADBC$?

19. Look at $\overline{AB}$ and $\overline{CD}$. When measured to the nearest centimeter, both $\overline{AB}$ and $\overline{CD}$ have a measure of 3 cm. Is $\overline{AB} \cong \overline{CD}$?

A —————————— B
C ———————————— D

20. In the figure shown, $\triangle ADC \cong \triangle BCD$. Complete each statement by matching up corresponding parts of these triangles.

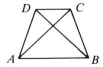

  a. $\angle DAC \cong \angle$?   **b.** $\overline{BD} \cong$?
  c. $\angle ADC \cong \angle$?   **d.** $\overline{DC} \cong$?

For each given congruence statement, draw and label a pair of figures and list all pairs of corresponding sides.
21. $\triangle ABC \cong \triangle XYZ$
22. $\triangle ABC \cong \triangle ABD$
23. $MNOP \cong ABCD$
24. $TVRS \cong XYRS$

_ **C** _

Look at pentagon ABCDE.

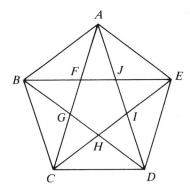

25. Identify four triangles congruent to $\triangle BGF$.
26. Identify four triangles congruent to $\triangle ABC$.
27. Identify four triangles congruent to $\triangle AFB$.
28. Identify nine triangles congruent to $\triangle AGB$.
29. There are 35 different triangles in this figure. Identify as many as you can. (Remember: $\triangle ABC$ is the same triangle as $\triangle CBA$.)

DID YOU KNOW THAT....

In 1893 the meter and kilogram were designated as the standards of length and mass in the United States. Customary units such as the yard and pound are defined in terms of these metric standards.

———————————————

3-4

Symmetric Figures

Symmetry is a kind of balance that many figures have. In this lesson you will learn about one kind of symmetry—folding or line symmetry.

The square shown is said to have *line symmetry* because if you fold the figure on the dashed line the two halves of the figure match exactly. Figures having line symmetry are called *symmetric figures*. The folding line (indicated by a dashed line) is a *line of symmetry* for the square.

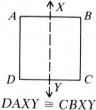

Square *ABCD* has line symmetry. $\overleftrightarrow{XY}$ is a line of symmetry.

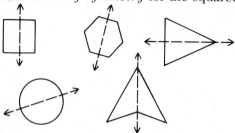

These figures have line symmetry. (Each dashed line is a line of symmetry.)

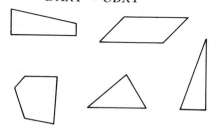

These figures do *not* have line symmetry.

When a figure is folded on a line of symmetry, the two halves that match are congruent. That is, they have the same size and shape.

A line of symmetry divides a geometric figure into two congruent halves.

The corresponding parts of the two halves formed by a line of symmetry are congruent to each other, as shown by the following example.

$\overleftrightarrow{XY}$ is a line of symmetry for trapezoid *ABCD*.

Congruent Halves

Corresponding Parts of Congruent Halves

$ADXY \cong BCXY$

$\overline{AD} \cong \overline{BC}$	$\angle A \cong \angle B$
$\overline{DX} \cong \overline{CX}$	$\angle D \cong \angle C$
$\overline{XY} \cong \overline{XY}$	$\angle DXY \cong \angle CXY$
$\overline{YA} \cong \overline{YB}$	$\angle AYX \cong \angle BYX$

For each figure, state whether the dashed line is a line of symmetry.

1.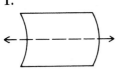

2.

3.

4.

5.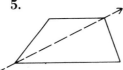

6.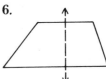

Look at rhombus *ABCD*. $\overleftrightarrow{AC}$ is a line of symmetry.
Complete each statement.

7. $\triangle ADC \cong \triangle$?
8. $\angle DAC \cong \angle$?
9. $\angle D \cong \angle$?
10. $\overline{AD} \cong$?
11. $\overline{CD} \cong$?
12. $\overline{AC} \cong$?

EXERCISES

— A —

Each figure shows a shape folded along the line of symmetry. For each figure draw a picture showing how it looks unfolded.

1.

2.

3.

4.

5.

6.

7.

8.

9.

10.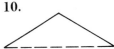

11.

12.

For each figure, tell whether the dashed line is a line of symmetry.

13.
a. b. c.

14.
a. b. c.

15.
a. b. 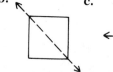 c.

16.
a. b. c.

17.
a. 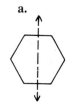 b. c.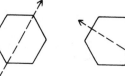

18.
a. b. 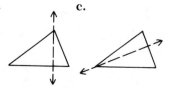 c.

19.
a. 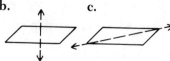 b. c.

20.
a. b. c.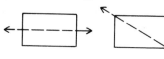

— **B** —

Look at the figures in Exercises 13–20.

21. Which figures seem to have no line of symmetry?

22. Which figures seem to have exactly one line of symmetry?

23. Which figures seem to have more than one line of symmetry?

24. Look around you. Name some objects that seem to be symmetric.

Complete each statement. Each dashed line is a line of symmetry.

25.
a. $XCBA \cong$?
b. $\angle ABC \cong \angle$?
c. $\overline{AB} \cong$?
d. $\overline{AX} \cong$?
e. $\angle BAX \cong \angle$?

26.
a. $\triangle YZW \cong \triangle$?
b. $\angle YZW \cong \angle$?
c. $\overline{YZ} \cong$?
d. $\angle ZWY \cong \angle$?
e. $\overline{YW} \cong$?

27.
a. $XDAY \cong$?
b. $\overline{DX} \cong$?
c. $\overline{AD} \cong$?
d. $\angle DXY \cong \angle$?
e. $\angle DAY \cong \angle$?

Find the indicated information.

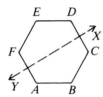

$ABCXY \cong FEDXY$

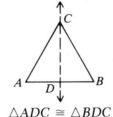

$\triangle ADC \cong \triangle BDC$

28. You have learned that a line of symmetry divides a figure into two congruent halves, as shown in these figures. The congruent halves are sometimes called *reflection images* or *mirror images* of each other. Why are these terms accurate descriptions of the congruent halves?

Test Yourself

Measure each segment (a) to the nearest centimeter and (b) to the nearest millimeter.

1. ——————————————

2. ———————

3. ——————————————————

Draw a segment having each given length.

   4. 5 cm   5. 7.4 cm
   6. 87 mm

Complete each statement.

   7. 6.8 cm = ? mm
   8. 80 mm = ? cm
   9. 7 m = ? cm
  10. 4 km = ? cm
  11. 8000 m = ? km
  12. 17 cm = ? mm

State whether each pair of figures are congruent.

13. 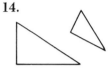   14.

For each figure, state whether the dashed line is a line of symmetry.

15. a.   b.

16. a. 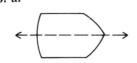   b.

DID YOU KNOW THAT....

The shortest metric unit of length is the *attometer*, which is one ten-quadrillionth of a centimeter. In decimal form, this is 0.0000000000000001 cm.

3-5

Finding Lines of Symmetry

Bisect means to divide into two congruent parts. In Chapter 1 you learned that a segment is bisected by any line, segment, or ray passing through its midpoint. The bisector of a segment that is perpendicular to the segment is the *perpendicular bisector*.

In the figure shown, M is the midpoint of $\overline{AB}$. $\overleftrightarrow{LM}$ bisects $\overline{AB}$ because it divides $\overline{AB}$ into two congruent parts. $\overleftrightarrow{KM}$ is a perpendicular bisector of $\overline{AB}$.

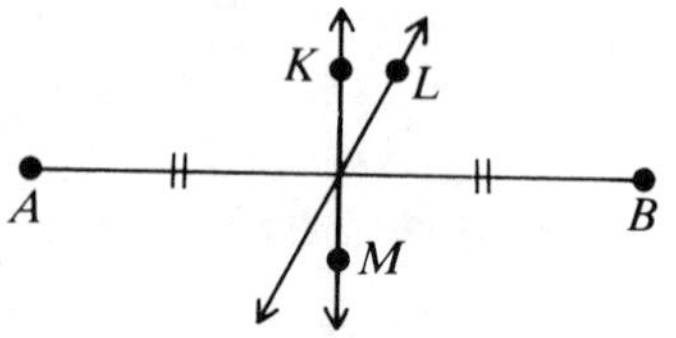

The ray that bisects an angle is called an *angle bisector*. In the figure shown, $\overrightarrow{AR}$ is the angle bisector of $\angle CAB$ because it divides $\angle CAB$ into two congruent parts.

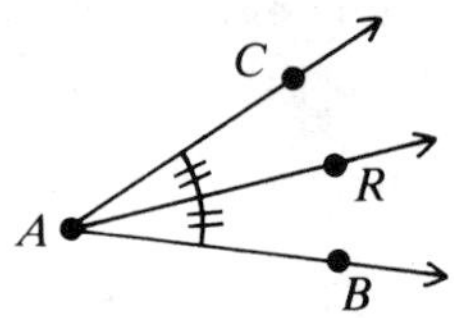

Any angle also has only one line of symmetry. If $\angle CAB$ is folded along $\overrightarrow{AR}$, the two smaller angles, $\angle CAR$ and $\angle BAR$, will match and be congruent to each other. Therefore $\overleftrightarrow{AR}$ is a line of symmetry for $\angle CAB$. The angle bisector determines a line of symmetry.

In contrast, every segment has more than one line of symmetry. One of these lies along the segment. In addition, the perpendicular bisector of a segment is also a line of symmetry. This can be illustrated by folding any segment along its perpendicular bisector.

The following statements summarize some properties of bisectors and lines of symmetry for angles and segments.

The dashed line is a line of symmetry for $\overline{AB}$.

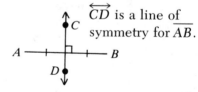
$\overleftrightarrow{CD}$ is a line of symmetry for $\overline{AB}$.

Every angle has exactly one line of symmetry and exactly one angle bisector.

For every angle, the angle bisector determines the line of symmetry.

Every segment has exactly two lines of symmetry.

The line passing through a segment and the perpendicular bisector of the segment are lines of symmetry.

---

1. How many lines of symmetry does a segment have? How many bisectors?

2. How many lines of symmetry does an angle have? How many bisectors?

Copy or trace each figure. Draw all the lines of symmetry. Then state whether the figure is symmetric.

3.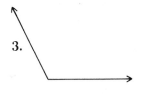

4.

5.

6.

7.

8.

EXERCISES

— A —

Classify each statement as true or false.

1. Each angle has exactly one line of symmetry.
2. Each angle has exactly one bisector.
3. The bisector of any angle is also a line of symmetry.
4. A line of symmetry for any angle also bisects the angle.
5. Each segment has exactly one line of symmetry.
6. Each segment has an infinite number of bisectors.
7. Any bisector of a segment is also a line of symmetry.
8. The perpendicular bisector of any segment is also a line of symmetry.
9. Each segment has exactly one perpendicular bisector.

Copy or trace each figure. Draw all the lines of symmetry. Then state whether the figure is symmetric.

10.

11.

12.

13.

14.

15.

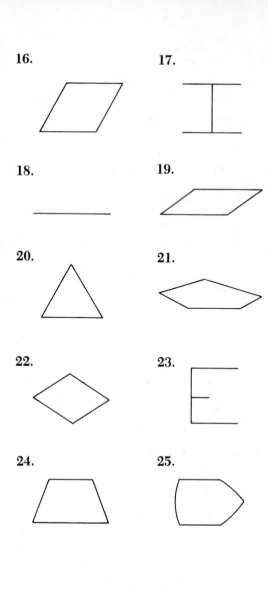

16.

17.

18.

19.

20.

21.

22.

23.

24.

25.

_ B _

26. a. Draw two intersecting lines, as in the figure shown. Draw all lines of symmetry for the angles.

b. Describe the relationship of the lines of symmetry. Why is this true?

27. a. Draw a figure like the one shown. Draw the line of symmetry for ∠*ROS* and the one for ∠*TOS*.

b. How does the size of the angle formed by the lines of symmetry compare with the size of ∠*TOR*? Why is this true?

_ C _

28. The word "DOCK" has a horizontal line of symmetry. Print three other words that have a horizontal line of symmetry.

29. The word "MOUTH" when printed vertically has a vertical line of symmetry. Vertically print three other words that have a vertical line of symmetry.

Draw a figure to fit each description.

30. Hexagon that has no lines of symmetry

31. Hexagon that has at least one line of symmetry

32. Triangle that has no lines of symmetry

33. Triangle that has exactly one line of symmetry

34. Triangle that has more than one line of symmetry

35. Quadrilateral that has exactly two lines of symmetry

36. Quadrilateral that has exactly four lines of symmetry

37. Look at hexagon *ABCDEF*. $\overleftrightarrow{XY}$ is a line of symmetry. When *ABCDEF* is folded along $\overleftrightarrow{XY}$, the points which fall on top of each other and the cor-

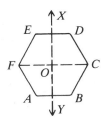

responding parts of the congruent halves (*AFEXY* and *BCDXY*) are called *images* of each other.

a. Identify the image of each of points A, F, E, X, and Y.

b. Identify the image of each of $\overline{FE}, \overline{EX}$, and $\overline{AY}$.

c. Identify the image of each of $\angle EFA, \angle EXY$, and $\angle AYX$.

d. What kind of angles are $\angle EXY$ and $\angle DXY$? $\angle XOF$ and $\angle XOC$? $\angle AYX$ and $\angle BYX$?

e. Why is $\overline{EX} \cong \overline{DX}$? $\overline{OF} \cong \overline{OC}$? $\overline{AY} \cong \overline{BY}$?

f. What is the relationship between $\overleftrightarrow{XY}$ and $\overline{ED}$? $\overleftrightarrow{XY}$ and $\overline{FC}$? $\overleftrightarrow{XY}$ and $\overline{AB}$?

Applications

Symmetry in Architecture

Many buildings and other structures are symmetric. One reason for this is that people are usually more comfortable looking at symmetric figures—perhaps because so many natural objects, including the human body, are basically symmetric. In addition, a symmetric design distributes weight more evenly over the foundation. However, some modern structures are asymmetric, either for *other* structural reasons or out of a desire to break with tradition.

3-6

Classifying Triangles by Sides and Angles

Triangles are classified by the number of congruent sides.

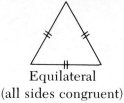

Equilateral
(all sides congruent)

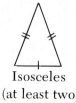

Isosceles
(at least two
sides congruent)

Scalene
(no sides congruent)

The parts of an isosceles triangle have special names, which are listed and illustrated below.

legs   Two congruent sides of an isosceles triangle.

vertex angle   The angle formed by the two congruent sides.

base angles   The angles other than the vertex angle.

base   The side whose endpoints are the vertices of the base angles.

△ABC is an isosceles triangle.

Legs: $\overline{AC}$ and $\overline{BC}$ Vertex Angle: ∠C

Base: $\overline{AB}$ Base Angles: ∠A and ∠B

Triangles are also classified by their angles.

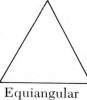

Equiangular
(all angles are
congruent)

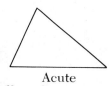

Acute
(all angles are acute)

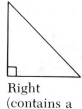

Right
(contains a
right angle)

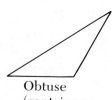

Obtuse
(contains an
obtuse angle)

CLASS PRACTICE

△**DEF** shown is an isosceles triangle. Identify each of the following:

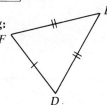

1. Legs
2. Base
3. Vertex angle
4. Base angles

Identify all triangles shown that fit each description.

5. Right triangle
6. Obtuse triangle
7. Acute triangle
8. Equiangular triangle
9. Scalene triangle
10. Isosceles triangle
11. Equilateral triangle
12. Isosceles obtuse triangle
13. Isosceles acute triangle
14. Acute obtuse triangle

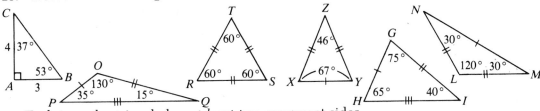

Each isosceles triangle has *at least* two congruent sides.

15. Must an equilateral triangle have at least two congruent sides?
16. Is each equilateral triangle also an isosceles triangle?
17. Is each isosceles triangle also an equilateral triangle?

EXERCISES

_ A _

Identify all triangles shown that fit each description.

1. Isosceles triangle
2. Equilateral triangle
3. Scalene triangle

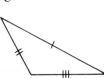

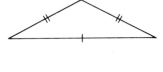

For each isosceles triangle, identify each of the following.

a. Legs
b. Base
c. Vertex angle
d. Base angles

4.

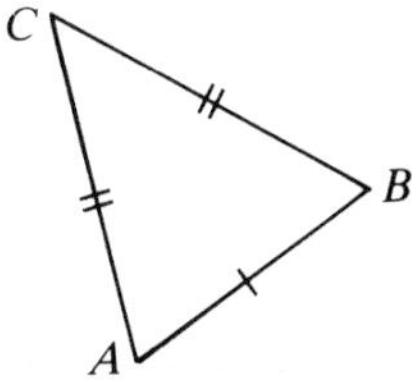

5.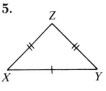

6.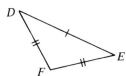

Identify all triangles shown that fit each description.

7. Equiangular triangle
8. Acute triangle   9. Right triangle
10. Obtuse triangle

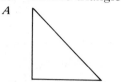

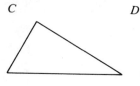
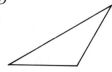
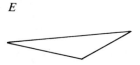

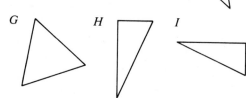

Classify each triangle as equilateral, isosceles, or scalene.

11. $\triangle XYZ$ with $XY = 8$, $YZ = 10$, and $ZX = 8$
12. $\triangle JKL$ with $JK = 10$, $KL = 8$, and $LJ = 5$
13. $\triangle RST$ with $RS = 7$, $ST = 7$, and $TR = 7$

Classify each triangle as acute, right, or obtuse.

14. $\triangle MNO$ with $m\angle M = 132°$, $m\angle N = 35°$, and $m\angle O = 13°$
15. $\triangle GHI$ with $m\angle G = 55°$, $m\angle H = 90°$, and $m\angle I = 35°$
16. $\triangle PQR$ with $m\angle P = 65°$, $m\angle Q = 58°$, and $m\angle R = 57°$

_ B _

Draw and label a triangle to fit each description.

17. Isosceles triangle with legs $\overline{FG}$ and $\overline{FH}$
18. Isosceles triangle with vertex angle $\angle A$ and base angles $\angle R$ and $\angle S$
19. Isosceles triangle with base $\overline{XY}$ and vertex angle $\angle B$
20. Obtuse triangle with obtuse angle $\angle S$ and side $\overline{AM}$ opposite the obtuse angle

Classify each triangle by its sides (scalene, isosceles, or equilateral) *and* by its angles (acute, right, obtuse, or equiangular).

21.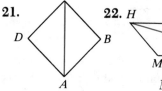

ABCD is a square.

22.

MATH is a parallelogram.

Draw a triangle to fit each description.

23. Acute triangle   24. Obtuse triangle
25. Isosceles obtuse triangle
26. Isosceles right triangle
27. Isosceles acute triangle
28. Scalene right triangle

_ C _

29. $\overline{AC}$ and $\overline{BD}$ are diagonals of square ABCD. Identify four isosceles right triangles.
30. Look at the triangle shown. Identify the following.
    a. Eight triangles
    b. Four right triangles
    c. Three obtuse triangles $\overline{AB} = \overline{CB}$
    d. Two isosceles triangles
    e. Five scalene triangles

3-7

Properties of Isosceles and Equilateral Triangles

The ideas you have learned about symmetric figures lead to some properties of isosceles and equilateral triangles. The two EXPLORINGs here develop some of these properties.

Recall that a line of symmetry divides a polygon into congruent halves and that corresponding parts of congruent figures are congruent.

EXPLORING

Properties of Isosceles Triangles

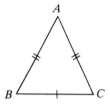

1. Draw a large isosceles triangle, △ABC, with only two congruent sides.
2. Fold △ABC to find all lines of symmetry. How many are there?
3. Draw the line of symmetry through A intersecting $\overline{BC}$. Label the point of intersection D.
4. Identify the vertex angle and the base angles of △ABC.
5. Why is △BAD ≅ △CAD?

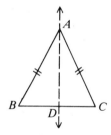

6. Why are the following pairs of angles or segments congruent—∠B and ∠C; ∠BAD and ∠CAD; ∠ADB and ∠ADC; and $\overline{BD}$ and $\overline{CD}$?
7. Why are ∠ADB and ∠ADC right angles?
8. What is the relationship between the line of symmetry and the vertex angle? between the line of symmetry and the base? How do the measures of the base angles compare?
9. Repeat steps 1–8 for an isosceles triangle (with only two congruent sides) of a different size. Do you get the same results?

Recall that an equilateral triangle is a special kind of isosceles triangle. Therefore all properties of an isosceles triangle are also true for an equilateral triangle.

Properties of Equilateral Triangles

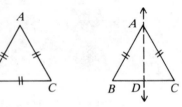

1. Draw a large equilateral triangle, △ABC.
2. Fold △ABC to find all the lines of symmetry. How many are there?
3. Draw the line of symmetry through A intersecting $\overline{BC}$. Label the point of intersection D.

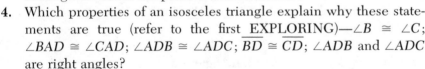

4. Which properties of an isosceles triangle explain why these statements are true (refer to the first EXPLORING)—∠B ≅ ∠C; ∠BAD ≅ ∠CAD; ∠ADB ≅ ∠ADC; $\overline{BD}$ ≅ $\overline{CD}$; ∠ADB and ∠ADC are right angles?

5. Draw an equilateral triangle congruent to the one drawn in step 1. Label its vertices in the same way.

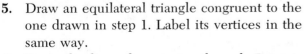

6. Draw the line of symmetry through B intersecting $\overline{AC}$. Label the point of intersection E.

7. Why are the following statements true—∠A ≅ ∠C; ∠CBE ≅ ∠ABE; ∠BEA ≅ ∠BEC; $\overline{AE}$ ≅ $\overline{CE}$; ∠BEA and ∠BEC are right angles?

8. Draw an equilateral triangle congruent to the one drawn in step 1. Label its vertices in the same way.

9. Draw the line of symmetry through C intersecting $\overline{AB}$. Label the point of intersection F.

10. Why are the following statements true—∠B ≅ ∠A; ∠BCF ≅ ∠ACF; ∠CFB ≅ ∠CFA; $\overline{BF}$ ≅ $\overline{AF}$; ∠CFB and ∠CFA are right angles?

11. Look at your results in steps 4, 7, and 10. What is the relationship between each line of symmetry and the angle it intersects? between each line of symmetry and the side it intersects? How do the measures of the angles of △ABC compare?

12. Repeat steps 1–11 for an equilateral triangle of a different size. Do you get the same results?

If you did the preceding EXPLORINGs carefully, you discovered the following properties:

Properties of an Isosceles Triangle

1. Exactly one line of symmetry.
2. The base angles are congruent.
3. The line of symmetry bisects the vertex angle and is the perpendicular bisector of the base.

Properties of an Equilateral Triangle

1. Exactly three lines of symmetry.
2. All angles are congruent.
3. Each line of symmetry bisects an angle of the triangle and is the perpendicular bisector of the side opposite that angle.

CLASS PRACTICE

1. Draw an isosceles triangle. Draw all lines of symmetry for this triangle.
2. Draw an equilateral triangle. Draw all lines of symmetry for this triangle.

Use the given information to find the indicated measures.

3. $m\angle 1 =$?°
4. $m\angle 2 =$?°
5. $BC =$? cm

6. $LK =$? cm
7. $m\angle 1 =$?°

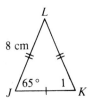

$m\angle XYZ = 40°$ $XZ = 10$ cm
$\overleftrightarrow{YW}$ is a line of symmetry.

$\triangle RST$ is equilateral.
$\overleftrightarrow{TX}$ is a line of symmetry.

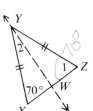

8. $m\angle 1 =$?°
10. $XW =$? cm
12. $m\angle 1 =$?°
14. $m\angle 3 =$?°
16. $SX =$? cm

9. $m\angle 2 =$?°
11. $ZW =$? cm
13. $m\angle 2 =$?°
15. $RX =$? cm
17. $RS =$? cm

EXERCISES

Classify each statement as true or false.

1. Each equilateral triangle is also equiangular.
2. Each equilateral triangle is also an acute triangle.
3. Each isosceles triangle is also equiangular.

4. In $\triangle ABC$ shown, if $\overline{AB} \cong \overline{AC}$, then $\angle A \cong \angle B$.

5. Each isosceles triangle has exactly three lines of symmetry.

6. Each equilateral triangle has exactly three lines of symmetry.

7. In △DEF shown, if $\overleftrightarrow{FG}$ is a line of symmetry for △DEF, then $\overleftrightarrow{FG}$ is the perpendicular bisector of $\overline{DE}$.

8. In △DEF shown, $\overleftrightarrow{FG}$ is the only bisector of $\overline{DE}$.

9. Each isosceles triangle is also equilateral.

10. Each equilateral triangle is also isosceles.

11. A scalene triangle cannot have a right angle.

12. An isosceles triangle cannot have an obtuse angle.

13. A scalene triangle can be isosceles.

14. An isosceles triangle can have a right angle.

For each figure, identify the angles that must be congruent.

15.

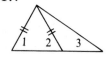

16.

17.

Use the given information to find the indicated measures.

18. $\overleftrightarrow{KN}$ is a line of symmetry for isosceles △KET.
$m\angle TKE = 46°$
$KE = 10$ cm
$m\angle E = 67°$
$NE = 3$ cm

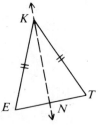

a. $m\angle T = $?°   b. $m\angle TKN = $?°
c. $m\angle KNE = $?° d. $m\angle EKN = $?°
e. $NT = $? cm   f. $KT = $? cm

19. △ABC is an equilateral triangle. $\overleftrightarrow{CD}$ is a line of symmetry.
a. $m\angle 1 = $?°
b. $m\angle 2 = $?°
c. $m\angle BDC = $?°
d. $m\angle CAD = $?°
e. $AB = $? cm
f. $BC = $? cm   g. $AD = $? cm

Find the indicated information.

20. Identify three pairs of congruent angles in the figure shown. △PLC is an isosceles triangle with $\overline{PC} \cong \overline{LC}$. $\overleftrightarrow{CD}$ is a line of symmetry.

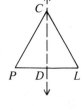

21. Look at figure GEOM. $\overline{ME}$ bisects ∠GEO.
a. Identify two isosceles triangles.
b. Identify three pairs of congruent angles.
c. If $m\angle 1 = 50°$, then $m\angle 2 = $?°.
d. If $m\angle O = 65°$, then $m\angle 4 = $?°.
e. If $m\angle 1 = 50°$, then $m\angle GEO = $?°
f. If $GM = 6$ and $ME = 8$, then $GE = $? and $OE = $?.

22. Look at △ACD. Identify each of the following.

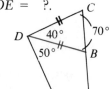

a. Three triangles
b. Obtuse triangle
c. Right triangle
d. Isosceles triangle
e. Acute triangle
f. Two scalene triangles

Copy or trace each figure. Draw all lines of symmetry.

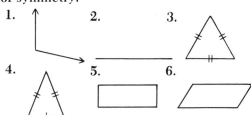

1.   2.   3.

4.   5.   6.

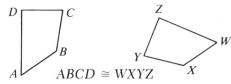

Look at the two congruent figures.

$ABCD \cong WXYZ$

7. Write two other correct congruence statements for the figures.
8. $\overline{DA} \cong$?   9. $\overline{BA} \cong$?
10. $\angle BCD \cong \angle$?

Suppose you know that $\triangle GHI \cong \triangle JKL$. Identify each of the following.
11. Three pairs of corresponding angles
12. Three pairs of corresponding sides

Draw a figure to fit each description.
13. Obtuse triangle
14. Isosceles right triangle
15. Acute triangle
16. Scalene triangle

$\triangle RST$ shown is an isosceles triangle. $\overleftrightarrow{TY}$ is a line of symmetry. $m\angle RTS = 48°$
17. Identify the legs.
18. Identify the base angles.
19. $m\angle RTY =$?°
20. $m\angle RYT =$?°
21. $m\angle R =$?°
22. $ST =$? cm

3-8
Properties of Parallelograms

In Chapter 1 you studied likenesses and differences among different types of quadrilaterals. Some properties of the quadrilaterals were discussed informally so that you could recognize and use them. In the next four lessons you will develop some of these properties in greater detail.

The first figure to be considered is the parallelogram. Recall that a parallelogram is a quadrilateral with two pairs of parallel sides.

A *diagonal* of a polygon is a segment joining a pair of opposite vertices. The following EXPLORING develops some properties of the diagonals of a parallelogram.

EXPLORING

Properties of the Diagonals of Parallelograms

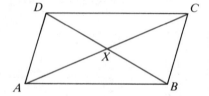

1. Draw a parallelogram that is not a rhombus, rectangle, or square. Draw its diagonals. Label your drawing as shown.

2. Measure the following segments to the nearest millimeter—$\overline{AX}$, $\overline{CX}$, $\overline{BX}$, $\overline{DX}$, $\overline{AC}$, and $\overline{BD}$.

3. Look at your results in step 2. Do the diagonals bisect each other? Are the diagonals congruent?

4. Does either diagonal ($\overline{AC}$ or $\overline{BD}$) determine a line of symmetry for the parallelogram? (Test this by folding.)

5. Measure angles 1–12. (See the picture.) Do the diagonals bisect the angles whose vertices are their endpoints? Are the diagonals perpendicular to each other?

6. Repeat steps 1–5 for a parallelogram of a different size. Do you get the same results?

Additional properties true for any parallelogram can be illustrated by drawing a parallelogram and comparing the measures of its angles and sides. The following statements summarize these properties and the properties of diagonals developed in the preceding EXPLORING.

Properties of a Parallelogram

1. Opposite sides are congruent.
2. Opposite angles are congruent.
3. Consecutive angles are supplementary.
4. Diagonals bisect each other.

Notice that although the diagonals of a parallelogram bisect each other, they are neither congruent nor perpendicular to each other and they do not bisect the angles whose vertices are their endpoints. Furthermore, the lines determined by the diagonals are not lines of symmetry.

ABCD shown is a parallelogram. Use the given information to find the indicated measures.

1. $m\angle ABC =$?°
2. $m\angle BCD =$?°
3. $m\angle CDA =$?°
4. $DC =$? cm
5. $BC =$? cm
6. $BO =$? cm
7. $CO =$? cm
8. $DB =$? cm
9. $AC =$? cm

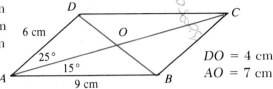

$DO = 4$ cm
$AO = 7$ cm

10. In parallelogram $PQRS$ shown, identify four pairs of congruent segments.

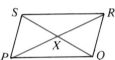

EXERCISES

Classify each statement as true or false.

1. All parallelograms are symmetric.
2. All parallelograms have exactly two diagonals.
3. Each diagonal of any parallelogram is also a line of symmetry.
4. Opposite angles of any parallelogram are supplementary.
5. Consecutive angles of any parallelogram are supplementary.
6. The diagonals of any parallelogram are congruent.
7. The diagonals of any parallelogram bisect each other.
8. The diagonals of any parallelogram are perpendicular.

Look at parallelogram GEOM. Classify each statement as true or false.

9. $\angle 1 \cong \angle 2$
10. $\overline{ME} \cong \overline{GO}$
11. $\overline{GX} \cong \overline{OX}$
12. $\overline{MX} \cong \overline{EX}$
13. $\overline{MX} \cong \overline{GX}$
14. $\overline{ME} \perp \overline{GO}$

For each parallelogram use the given information to find the indicated measures.

15. a. $m\angle T =$?°
    b. $m\angle A =$?°
    c. $m\angle U =$?°
    d. $UA =$? cm
    e. $TU =$? cm

16. a. $BX =$? cm
    b. $BD =$? cm
    c. $AC =$? cm
    d. $m\angle 1 =$?°
    e. $m\angle 2 =$?°
    f. $m\angle 3 =$?°
    g. $m\angle ADC =$?° h. $m\angle DAB =$?°

    $m\angle ABC = 120°$ $DX = 4$ cm $AX = 6$ cm

17. Identify each of the following for parallelogram $RUST$.
    a. Two pairs of congruent angles
    b. Four pairs of supplementary angles
    c. Two pairs of congruent segments

3-9

Properties of Rhombuses

In the preceding lesson, the following properties of parallelograms were developed.

> **Properties of a Parallelogram**
>
> 1. Opposite sides are congruent and parallel.
> 2. Opposite angles are congruent.
> 3. Consecutive angles are supplementary.
> 4. Diagonals bisect each other.

Since rhombuses, rectangles, and squares are special types of parallelograms, the properties above are also true for them. However, these special parallelograms have additional properties that are not true for all parallelograms. Some will be developed in the next three lessons.

Unlike many other parallelograms, all of these special parallelograms—rhombus, rectangle, and square—are symmetric. Properties of symmetric figures will be used to develop many of the conclusions in the next three lessons.

This lesson will develop properties of rhombuses. A *rhombus* is a parallelogram with four congruent sides.

EXPLORING

Properties of Rhombuses

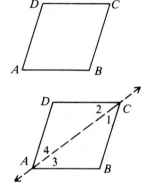

PART A

1. Draw a rhombus that is not a square. Label it as shown.
2. Draw $\overleftrightarrow{AC}$. $\overleftrightarrow{AC}$ is a line of symmetry. (Check by folding.) Why is $\triangle ADC \cong \triangle ABC$? Why is $\angle 1 \cong \angle 2$ and $\angle 3 \cong \angle 4$? Why is $\overline{AC}$ a diagonal?
3. Draw a rhombus congruent to the one drawn in step 1. Label it as shown.
4. Draw $\overleftrightarrow{BD}$. $\overleftrightarrow{BD}$ is a line of symmetry. (Check by folding.) Why is $\triangle BCD \cong \triangle BAD$? Why is $\angle 5 \cong \angle 6$ and $\angle 7 \cong \angle 8$? Why is $\overline{BD}$ a diagonal?
5. How is each diagonal related to the two angles whose vertices are its endpoints?

6. Repeat steps 1–5 for a rhombus of a different size. Do you get the same results?

PART B

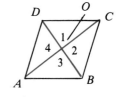

1. Draw a rhombus that is not a square. Draw the diagonals and label the figure as shown.
2. $\overline{AC}$ and $\overline{BD}$ divide the rhombus into four nonoverlapping congruent triangles. Why is $\overline{DO} \cong \overline{BO}$ and $\overline{AO} \cong \overline{CO}$? Why are $\angle 1$, $\angle 2$, $\angle 3$, and $\angle 4$ right angles?
3. Measure $\overline{AC}$ and $\overline{BD}$ to the nearest millimeter. Is $\overline{AC} \cong \overline{BD}$?
4. Describe the relationship between $\overline{AC}$ and $\overline{BD}$.
5. Repeat steps 1–4 for a rhombus (that is not a square) of a different size. Do you get the same results?

If you did the preceding EXPLORING carefully, you discovered the following properties:

Properties of a Rhombus

1. Opposite angles are congruent.
2. Consecutive angles are supplementary.
3. Exactly two lines of symmetry.
4. Each diagonal bisects the angles whose vertices are its endpoints.
5. Each diagonal determines a line of symmetry.
⋇6. Each diagonal is the perpendicular bisector of the other.

Notice that although the diagonals of a rhombus are perpendicular bisectors of each other, they are not congruent.

═══════════════ **CLASS PRACTICE** ═══════════════

For each rhombus use the given information to find the indicated measures.

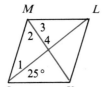

1. $m\angle 1 = $?°
2. $m\angle 2 = $?°
3. $m\angle 3 = $?°
4. $m\angle 4 = $?°
5. $m\angle JML = $?°
6. $m\angle MLK = $?°

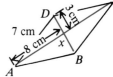

7. $BX = $? cm
8. $DB = $? cm
9. $CX = $? cm
10. $AC = $? cm
11. $BC = $? cm
12. $DC = $? cm

EXERCISES

Classify each statement as true or false.

1. Each rhombus has exactly two lines of symmetry.
2. Each rhombus has exactly two diagonals.
3. Each diagonal of a rhombus determines a line of symmetry.
4. The diagonals of any rhombus are congruent.
5. The diagonals of any rhombus are perpendicular.
6. Each rhombus is also a parallelogram.
7. Each parallelogram is also a rhombus.
8. The opposite sides of any rhombus are parallel and congruent.
9. All rhombuses are symmetric.
10. The opposite angles of any rhombus are congruent.
11. The consecutive angles of any rhombus are supplementary.
12. All sides of a rhombus are congruent.

Look at rhombus *ABCD*. Classify each statement as true or false.

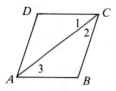

13. $\angle DAB \cong \angle BCD$
14. $\angle DAB \cong \angle ADC$
15. $\angle 1 \cong \angle 2$
16. $\angle 2 \cong \angle 3$
17. $m\angle DAB + m\angle ABC = 180°$
18. $\triangle ABC$ is isosceles.

Look at rhombus *RSTU*. Recall that in any rhombus each diagonal is the perpendicular bisector of the other. Classify each statement as true or false.

19. $\angle UOT \cong \angle SOT$
20. $\angle SOT \cong \angle SOR$
21. $\overline{US} \perp \overline{TR}$
22. $\overline{UO} \cong \overline{SO}$
23. $\overline{RO} \cong \overline{TO}$
24. $\overline{US} \cong \overline{TR}$

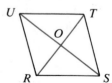

For each rhombus use the given information to find the indicated measures.

25. a. $m\angle 4 =$?°
    b. $m\angle 1 =$?°
    c. $m\angle 5 =$?°
    d. $m\angle 2 =$?°
    e. $m\angle 3 =$?°
    f. $m\angle 6 =$?°
    g. $m\angle ADC =$?°
    h. $m\angle DCB =$?°

26. a. $LN =$? cm
    b. $OP =$? cm
    c. $PN =$? cm
    d. $MP =$? cm
    e. $m\angle 1 =$?°
    f. $m\angle 2 =$?°
    g. $m\angle 3 =$?°
    h. $m\angle 4 =$?° $\quad LP = 4$ cm
    $\quad MO = 6$ cm

27. Look at parallelogram *KENT*.
    $m\angle KTN = 102°$
    a. $m\angle 1 =$?°
    b. $m\angle 2 =$?°
    c. $m\angle 3 =$?°
    d. $m\angle 4 =$?°
    e. Is $\overline{TE} \cong \overline{KN}$?
    f. Does $\overline{TE}$ bisect $\overline{KN}$?

3-10

Properties of Rectangles

A *rectangle* is a parallelogram with four right angles. Therefore every property of a parallelogram also holds for a rectangle. (Refer to the list on page 114.) Since a rectangle is also a symmetric figure, we can use properties of symmetric figures to develop some special properties of rectangles.

EXPLORING
Properties of Rectangles

PART A

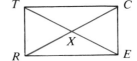

1. Look at rectangle *RECT*. $\overline{RC}$ and $\overline{TE}$ are diagonals.
2. State the property of parallelograms that explains why each statement is true: $\angle TRE \cong \angle ECT$ and $\angle RTC \cong \angle CER$; $m\angle TRE + m\angle REC = 180°$; $TX \cong EX$ and $RX \cong CX$; $TC \parallel RE$ and $TR \parallel CE$; and $TC \cong RE$ and $TR \cong CE$.

PART B

1. Draw a rectangle that is not a square. Label it as shown.
2. Draw the line of symmetry that intersects $\overline{DC}$ and $\overline{AB}$. Label the points of intersection X and Y.

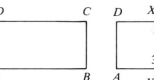

3. Why is $ADXY \cong BCXY$?
4. Why are the following pairs of angles or segments congruent—$\angle 1$ and $\angle 2$; $\angle 3$ and $\angle 4$; $\overline{DX}$ and $\overline{CX}$; $\overline{AY}$ and $\overline{BY}$? Why are $\angle 1$, $\angle 2$, $\angle 3$, and $\angle 4$ right angles?
5. Draw the line of symmetry that intersects $\overline{AD}$ and $\overline{BC}$. Label the points of intersection W and Z.

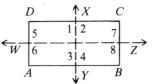

6. Why is $CDWZ \cong BAWZ$?
7. Why are the following pairs of angles or segments congruent—$\angle 5$ and $\angle 6$; $\angle 7$ and $\angle 8$; $\overline{DW}$ and $\overline{AW}$; $\overline{CZ}$ and $\overline{BZ}$? Why are $\angle 5$, $\angle 6$, $\angle 7$, and $\angle 8$ right angles?
8. Look at your results in steps 4 and 7. What is the relationship between each line of symmetry and the sides they intersect?
9. Repeat steps 1–8 with a rectangle (that is not a square) of a different size. Do you get the same results?

PART C

1. Draw a rectangle that is not a square. Label it as shown.
2. Draw diagonals $\overline{AC}$ and $\overline{BD}$ and both lines of symmetry. Label your figure as shown.
3. $\overline{AC}$ and $\overline{BD}$ are diagonals. Are $\overleftrightarrow{AC}$ and $\overleftrightarrow{BD}$ lines of symmetry? Why or why not?
4. $\overleftrightarrow{WZ}$ and $\overleftrightarrow{XY}$ are lines of symmetry. Why is $\triangle DOC \cong \triangle AOB$ and $\triangle DOA \cong \triangle COB$? (Hint: What is the *image* of $\triangle DOC$ and of $\triangle DOA$ when the rectangle is folded over $\overleftrightarrow{WZ}$ and $\overleftrightarrow{XY}$, respectively? See Ex. 28 on p. 101 and Ex. 37 on p. 104.)
5. Why are the following pairs of segments congruent—$\overline{DO}$ and $\overline{AO}$; $\overline{DO}$ and $\overline{CO}$; $\overline{CO}$ and $\overline{BO}$; $\overline{AO}$ and $\overline{OB}$; $\overline{DB}$ and $\overline{AC}$?
6. Repeat steps 1–5 for a rectangle (that is not a square) of a different size. Do you get the same results?

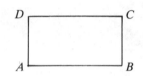

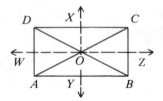

If you did the preceding EXPLORING carefully, you discovered the following properties:

Properties of a Rectangle

1. Exactly two lines of symmetry.
2. Each line of symmetry is the perpendicular bisector of the sides it intersects.
3. Diagonals bisect each other and are congruent.

Notice that although the diagonals of a rectangle bisect each other and are congruent, they are not perpendicular to each other and they do not bisect the angles whose vertices are their endpoints. Furthermore, the lines determined by the diagonals are not lines of symmetry.

CLASS PRACTICE

For each rectangle, use the given information to find the indicated measures.

1. $XB = $? cm
2. $AX = $? cm
3. $DB = $? cm
4. $AC = $? cm
5. $AB = $? cm
6. $BC = $? cm

$DX = 6.5$ cm

7. $m\angle 1 = $?°
8. $m\angle 2 = $?°
9. $m\angle 3 = $?°
10. $m\angle 4 = $?°
11. $m\angle 5 = $?°
12. $m\angle 6 = $?°

Classify each statement as true or false.

1. Each rectangle has exactly two lines of symmetry.
2. Each line of symmetry of a rectangle is the perpendicular bisector of two sides of the rectangle.
3. The diagonals of any rectangle are congruent.
4. The diagonals of any rectangle bisect each other.
5. Each diagonal of a rectangle determines a line of symmetry.
6. Each line of symmetry of a rectangle determines a diagonal.
7. The opposite sides of any rectangle are congruent.
8. All rectangles are symmetric.
9. Each rectangle is also a parallelogram.
10. Each parallelogram is also a rectangle.

Look at rectangle *ABCD*. Classify each statement as true or false.

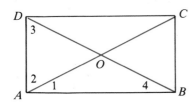

11. $\overline{AD} \cong \overline{DC}$
12. $\overline{AO} \cong \overline{CO}$
13. $\overline{AO} \cong \overline{BO}$
14. $\overline{AC} \cong \overline{BD}$
15. $\overline{AC} \perp \overline{BD}$
16. $\angle 1 \cong \angle 2$
17. $\angle 2 \cong \angle 3$
18. $\angle 1 \cong \angle 4$
19. $\triangle AOB \cong \triangle DOC$
20. $\triangle AOB \cong \triangle AOD$

21. O is the midpoint of $\overline{AC}$ and $\overline{BD}$.
22. $\triangle AOB$ is isosceles.

Look at rectangle *MNOP*. Use the given information to find the indicated measures.

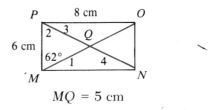

$$MQ = 5 \text{ cm}$$

23. $QO = $? cm
24. $MN = $? cm
25. $ON = $? cm
26. $QN = $? cm
27. $m\angle 1 = $?°
28. $m\angle 2 = $?°
29. $m\angle 3 = $?°
30. $m\angle 4 = $?°

Look at rectangle *RSTU*. Identify the following.

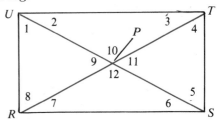

31. Segments congruent to $\overline{UR}$
32. Segments congruent to $\overline{RP}$
33. Segments congruent to $\overline{UT}$
34. Segments congruent to $\overline{RT}$
35. Segments congruent to $\overline{US}$
36. Angles congruent to $\angle 7$
37. Angles congruent to $\angle 8$
38. Angles supplementary to $\angle 10$
39. Triangles congruent to $\triangle RPS$
40. Triangles congruent to $\triangle UPR$
41. Right triangles
42. Isosceles triangles

3-11

Properties of Squares

A *square* is a quadrilateral that is both a rectangle and a rhombus. In Lessons 3-10 and 3-11 you developed some additional properties of rectangles and rhombuses. Some properties of these figures are summarized below.

Properties of a Rectangle

1. Opposite sides are parallel and congruent.
2. All angles are right angles.
3. Exactly two lines of symmetry.
4. Each line of symmetry is the perpendicular bisector of the sides it intersects.
5. Diagonals bisect each other and are congruent.

Properties of a Rhombus

1. Opposite sides are parallel.
2. All sides are congruent.
3. Opposite angles are congruent.
4. Consecutive angles are supplementary.
5. Exactly two lines of symmetry.
6. Each line of symmetry bisects the two angles it intersects.
7. Each diagonal is the perpendicular bisector of the other.
8. Each diagonal determines a line of symmetry.

Since a square is both a rectangle and a rhombus, all of the above properties are also properties of a square. Therefore the following properties are true for every square.

Properties of a Square

1. Opposite sides are parallel.
2. All sides are congruent.
3. All angles are right angles.
4. Exactly four lines of symmetry.

5. Two of the lines of symmetry are the perpendicular bisectors of the sides they intersect.
6. Two of the lines of symmetry bisect the angles they intersect.
7. Diagonals are the perpendicular bisectors of each other and are congruent.
8. Each diagonal determines a line of symmetry.

Some of these properties are illustrated by the squares shown.

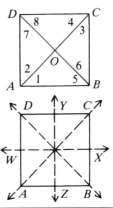

$\overline{AB} \cong \overline{BC} \cong \overline{CD} \cong \overline{DA}$

$\angle A$, $\angle B$, $\angle C$, and $\angle D$ are right angles.

$\angle 1 \cong \angle 2$, $\angle 3 \cong \angle 4$, $\angle 5 \cong \angle 6$, and $\angle 7 \cong \angle 8$

$\overline{AC}$ is the perpendicular bisector of $\overline{BD}$.

$\overline{AC} \cong \overline{BD}$

$\overleftrightarrow{WX}$ is the perpendicular bisector of $\overline{AD}$ and $\overline{BC}$.
$\overleftrightarrow{YZ}$ is the perpendicular bisector of $\overline{AB}$ and $\overline{DC}$.
$\overleftrightarrow{WX}$, $\overleftrightarrow{XZ}$, $\overleftrightarrow{AC}$, and $\overleftrightarrow{BD}$ are lines of symmetry.

―――――――――― **CLASS PRACTICE** ――――――――――

For each square use the given information to find the indicated measures.

1. $BX = $? cm
2. $AX = $? cm
3. $DB = $? cm
4. $AC = $? cm
5. $AB = $? cm
6. $BC = $? cm

$DX = 8.5$ cm

7. $m\angle 1 = $?°
8. $m\angle 2 = $?°
9. $m\angle 3 = $?°
10. $m\angle 4 = $?°
11. $m\angle 5 = $?°
12. $m\angle 6 = $?°

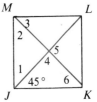

EXERCISES

― A ―

Classify each statement as true or false.

1. Each square has exactly two lines of symmetry.
2. Each square has exactly 2 diagonals.
3. Each diagonal of a square determines a line of symmetry.
4. Each line of symmetry of a square determines a diagonal.
5. The diagonals of any square are congruent.
6. The diagonals of any square bisect each other.
7. The diagonals of any square are perpendicular.
8. The opposite sides of any square are congruent.
9. All squares are symmetric.

10. Each square is also a rectangle.
11. Each square is also a rhombus.
12. Each square is also a parallelogram.

Look at square *ABCD*. Classify each statement as true or false.

13. $\overline{DO} \cong \overline{BO}$
14. $\overline{DO} \cong \overline{AO}$
15. $\overline{AO} \cong \overline{CO}$
16. $\overline{AC} \cong \overline{BD}$
17. $\overline{AC} \perp \overline{BD}$
18. $\angle 1 \cong \angle 2$
19. $\angle 2 \cong \angle 3$ 20. $\triangle AOB \cong \triangle DOC$
21. $\angle 1 \cong \angle 4$ 22. $\triangle AOB \cong \triangle AOD$
23. O is the midpoint of $\overline{AC}$ and $\overline{BD}$.
24. $\triangle AOB$ is isosceles.

Look at square *MNOP*. Use the given information to find the indicated measures.

25. $QO = $? cm
26. $QN = $? cm
27. $PN = $? cm   3 cm
28. $MN = $? cm
29. $m\angle 1 = $?°
30. $m\angle 2 = $?°
31. $m\angle 3 = $?°
32. $m\angle 4 = $?°

$MQ = 2.1$ cm

Look at square *RSTU*. Identify each of the following.

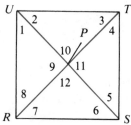

33. Segments congruent to $\overline{UR}$
34. Segments congruent to $\overline{RP}$
35. Segments congruent to $\overline{RT}$
36. Angles congruent to $\angle 7$

37. Angles supplementary to $\angle 10$
38. Triangles congruent to $\triangle RPS$
39. Right triangles
40. Isosceles triangles

— **B** —

State which quadrilaterals have each property stated.

  parallelogram rhombus
  rectangle   square

41. The figure is symmetric.
42. There are exactly two lines of symmetry.
43. All angles are congruent.
44. The diagonals are congruent.
45. The diagonals are perpendicular.
46. The diagonals bisect each other.
47. The diagonals are perpendicular bisectors of each other.
48. Opposite angles are congruent.
49. Consecutive angles are supplementary.
50. Each diagonal determines a line of symmetry.
51. Each diagonal bisects two angles.

Draw a figure to fit each description.
52. Rhombus that is also a square
53. Rectangle that is not a square
54. Quadrilateral in which the diagonals are congruent but not perpendicular
55. Quadrilateral in which the diagonals are perpendicular but not congruent
56. Quadrilateral in which each diagonal determines a line of symmetry
57. Quadrilateral with exactly four lines of symmetry
58. Parallelogram that is not symmetric
59. Regular quadrilateral

Geometry on the Job

TOOL-AND-DIE MAKER

As a tool-and-die maker, Wayne Richardson makes tools, molds, and special measuring devices that are used to mass-produce metal parts for automobiles. He has to be able to measure very accurately. Also, because parts made from a mold should be exactly like the original, he must be able to recognize congruent figures.

EXERCISES

1. A machine part is to be 124.336 mm long. What is its length in centimeters?

2. A machine part is to be 16.583 mm wide *plus or minus* 0.005 mm. Which of these finished widths is within the acceptable range?

    a. 16.589 mm   **b.** 16.579 mm
    c. 16.538 mm

3. Which of these gears is congruent to the gear shown?

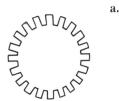
a.

b.

c.

ARITHMETIC REVIEW — *Rewriting Fractions as Decimals*

> To rewrite a fraction as a decimal, divide the numerator by the denominator.

Examples

Rewrite each fraction as a decimal.

1. $\frac{3}{4}$

$$4\overline{)3.00}$$
$$\begin{array}{r} 0.75 \\ \underline{2\,8} \\ 20 \\ \underline{20} \\ 0 \end{array}$$

$\frac{3}{4} = 0.75$

2. $\frac{5}{8}$

$$8\overline{)5.000}$$
$$\begin{array}{r} 0.625 \\ \underline{4\,8} \\ 20 \\ \underline{16} \\ 40 \\ \underline{40} \\ 0 \end{array}$$

$\frac{5}{8} = 0.625$

3. $\frac{7}{11}$

$$11\overline{)7.0000}$$
$$\begin{array}{r} 0.6363 \\ \underline{6\,6} \\ 40 \\ \underline{33} \\ 70 \\ \underline{66} \\ 40 \\ \underline{33} \\ 7 \end{array}$$

$\frac{7}{11} = 0.\overline{63}$

The division does not come out even. Notice that the remainders, and the quotient digits, repeat. The bar over "63" indicates that these digits repeat over and over.

Fractions with denominators such as 10, 100, 1000, and so on can be rewritten directly as decimals. Those whose denominators are factors of these numbers can be rewritten as a decimal by first writing an equivalent fraction.

Examples

Rewrite each fraction as a decimal.

4. $\frac{8}{10} = 0.8$

5. $\frac{9}{100} = 0.09$

6. $\frac{6}{25} = \frac{24}{100} = 0.24$

EXERCISES

Rewrite each fraction as a decimal.

1. $\frac{1}{2}$ 2. $\frac{3}{10}$ 3. $\frac{1}{8}$ 4. $\frac{3}{8}$ 5. $\frac{3}{5}$ 6. $\frac{16}{100}$

7. $\frac{23}{1000}$ 8. $\frac{1}{16}$ 9. $\frac{3}{16}$ 10. $\frac{3}{25}$ 11. $\frac{7}{50}$ 12. $\frac{2}{5}$

13. $\frac{3}{100}$ 14. $\frac{798}{1000}$ 15. $\frac{9}{20}$ 16. $\frac{2}{11}$ 17. $\frac{1}{9}$ 18. $\frac{1}{3}$

19. $\frac{2}{3}$ 20. $\frac{5}{9}$ 21. $\frac{7}{10}$ 22. $\frac{13}{40}$ 23. $\frac{7}{8}$ 24. $\frac{17}{50}$

25. $\frac{5}{12}$ 26. $\frac{53}{100}$ 27. $\frac{9}{10}$ 28. $\frac{321}{1000}$ 29. $\frac{1}{6}$ 30. $\frac{9}{16}$

Chapter 3 Review

Vocabulary

The following terms and symbols were introduced in this chapter. You should be able to write a brief description, draw a picture, or give an example to illustrate the meaning of each.

angle bisector (p. 103)
congruence statement (p. 93)
congruent (p. 93)
corresponding parts (p. 93)
line of symmetry (p. 98)
line symmetry (p. 98)
perpendicular bisector
  (p. 102)
symmetric (p. 98)

Symbols
cm (centimeter) (p. 86)
≅ (congruent to) (p. 93)
km (kilometer) (p. 86)
m (meter) (p. 86)
mm (millimeter) (p. 86)
△ABC (triangle ABC) (p. 93)

Units of Length
centimeter (p. 86)
kilometer (p. 86)
meter (p. 86)
millimeter (p. 86)

Classes of Triangles
acute (p. 106)
equiangular (p. 106)
equilateral (p. 106)
isosceles (p. 106)
  base (p. 106)
  base angles (p. 106)
  legs (p. 106)
  vertex angle (p. 106)
obtuse (p. 106)
right (p. 106)
scalene (p. 106)

Skills Checklist

In Chapter 3 you learned some common metric units of length; some properties of isosceles and equilateral triangles, parallelograms, rhombuses, rectangles, and squares; how to recognize congruent and symmetric figures; and how to classify triangles by their sides and angles.

The following list indicates the major skills, facts, and results you should have mastered in this chapter:

- Estimate and measure distances to the nearest centimeter, millimeter, or meter. (**3-1**, pp. 86–89)
- Convert measurements from one metric unit of length to another. (**3-2**, pp. 90–92)
- Recognize congruent figures and use the fact that the corresponding parts of congruent figures must also be congruent. (**3-3**, pp. 93–97)
- Recognize symmetric figures and use the fact that a line of symmetry divides a figure into two congruent halves. (**3-4**, pp. 98–101)
- Draw all lines of symmetry for a given figure. (**3-5**, pp. 102–105)
- Recognize and use some properties of segments and angles. (**3-5**, pp. 102–105)

- Classify triangles by their sides (scalene, isosceles, and equilateral) and by their angles (acute, obtuse, right, and equiangular). (**3-6**, pp. 106-108)
- Identify the legs, base, vertex angle, and base angles of any isosceles triangle. (**3-6**, pp. 106-108)
- Recognize and use some properties of isosceles and equilateral triangles. (**3-7**, pp. 109-113)
- Recognize and use some properties of parallelograms, rhombuses, rectangles, and squares. (**3-8—3-11**, pp. 113-124)

Property	Parallelogram	Rhombus	Rectangle	Square
Opposite sides are parallel.	X	X	X	X
Opposite sides are congruent.	X	X	X	X
All sides are congruent.		X		X
Opposite angles are congruent.	X	X	X	X
Consecutive angles are supplementary.	X	X	X	X
All angles are right angles.			X	X
Exactly two diagonals.	X	X	X	X
Diagonals bisect each other.	X	X	X	X
Diagonals are congruent.			X	X
Diagonals are perpendicular.		X		X
Each diagonal bisects two angles.		X		X
Each diagonal determines a line of symmetry.		X		X
Exactly two lines of symmetry.		X	X	
Exactly four lines of symmetry.				X

Exercises

(a) Estimate the length of each segment to the nearest centimeter and (b) measure its length to the nearest centimeter and nearest millimeter. (3-1)

1.————————————————

2.——————————

3.——————————————

Complete each statement. (3-2)

4. 6 cm = ? mm
5. 30 mm = ? cm
6. 1 m = ? mm
7. 6.7 cm = ? mm
8. 1 m = ? cm
9. 1 cm = ? mm

10. 3000 m = ? km

11. 5 km = ? m

Draw a segment with each given measure. (3–1, 3–2)

12. 4 cm   13. 7.1 cm

14. 65 mm

Name the metric unit of length that would most probably be used to measure the given length. (3–1)

15. Distance between Chicago and New York City

16. Width of your math textbook

17. Thickness of a contact lens

Find the indicated information.

18. Answer these questions about the congruent pentagons. (3–3)

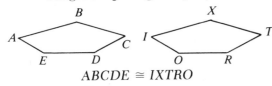

$$ABCDE \cong IXTRO$$

a. $\overline{AB} \cong$?   b. $\angle D \cong \angle$?

c. $\overline{DE} \cong$?   d. $\angle I \cong \angle$?

e. Write two other congruence statements different from the one given.

19. Look at pentagon $ABCDE$. $\overleftrightarrow{AX}$ is a line of symmetry. (3–4)

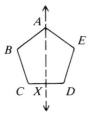

a. Identify the congruent halves.

b. $\overline{AB} \cong$?   c. $\angle BCX \cong \angle$?

d. $\angle BAX \cong \angle$?

Copy or trace each figure. Draw all lines of symmetry. (3–5)

20.   21.

22.   23.

Classify each statement as true or false. (3–5)

24. Each segment has an infinite number of bisectors.

25. Each segment has exactly one line of symmetry.

26. The line of symmetry of any angle is also its bisector.

27. Any bisector of a segment is also a line of symmetry.

Find the indicated information.

28. $\triangle ART$ shown is an isosceles triangle. Identify each of the following. (3–6)

a. Legs

b. Base

c. Vertex angle

d. Base angles

29. $\triangle ABC$ shown is an isosceles triangle. $\overleftrightarrow{CD}$ is a line of symmetry. (3–7)

$m\angle A = 65°$ $m\angle ACB = 50°$

$AC = 7$ cm $AD = 3$ cm

a. $BC =$? cm

b. $BD =$? cm

c. $m\angle B =$?°

d. $m\angle ACD =$?°

e. $AB =$? cm

f. $m\angle ADC =$?°

Draw and label a figure to fit each description. (3-7)

30. Isosceles triangle with legs $\overline{RB}$ and $\overline{RA}$

31. Two triangles such that $\triangle ARC \cong \triangle DEG$

32. Obtuse scalene triangle

33. Isosceles right triangle

Classify each statement as true or false. (3-7)

34. Each isosceles triangle is also equilateral.

35. Each equilateral triangle is also equiangular.

36. Each equiangular triangle is also an acute triangle.

37. An obtuse triangle cannot be isosceles.

Copy or trace each figure. Draw all the diagonals. (3-8)

38.

39.

40.

41.

Find the indicated information.

42. Answer these questions about rectangle $ABCD$. (3-10)
    a. $BC = $? cm
    b. $BO = $? cm
    c. $AC = $? cm
    d. $DB = $? cm
    e. $CO = $? cm
    f. $m\angle 1 = $?°

$AO = 4.5$ cm

g. $m\angle 2 = $?°   h. $m\angle 3 = $?°

43. Answer these questions about rhombus $ABCD$. (3-9)
    a. Is $\overline{AC} \cong \overline{BD}$?
    b. $m\angle 1 = $?°
    c. $m\angle BAD = $?°
    d. $m\angle AOB = $?°
    e. $m\angle ADC = $?°
    f. $m\angle ABC = $?°
    g. $m\angle 2 = $?°
    h. $m\angle 3 = $?°

44. Answer these questions about parallelogram $MATH$. (3-8)
    a. Is $\overleftrightarrow{MT}$ a line of symmetry?
    b. $m\angle HMA = $?°
    c. $m\angle 1 = $?°
    d. $m\angle 2 = $?°
    e. $HT = $? cm
    f. $AT = $? cm

45. Answer these questions about square $ROMA$. (3-11)
    a. $MO = $? cm
    b. $AM = $? cm
    c. $m\angle 1 = $?°
    d. $m\angle 2 = $?°
    e. Is $\overline{AX} \cong \overline{OX}$?
    f. Is $\overline{AO} \cong \overline{RM}$?

Classify each statement as true or false.

46. Each rhombus is a square. (3-11)

47. The diagonals of each parallelogram are congruent. (3-8)

48. The diagonals of each rhombus are congruent. (3-9)

49. Each parallelogram is a symmetric figure. (3-8)

50. All parallelograms have exactly two diagonals. (3-8)

51. Each diagonal of a rectangle determines a line of symmetry. (3-10)

52. Each square is a rhombus. (3-11)

Chapter 4

CONSTRUCTIVE
IDEAS

Constructions and Properties of Congruent Triangles

4-1

Constructing Congruent Triangles–SSS

It is common practice in mathematics to distinguish between a *drawing* and a *construction*. You have already made many drawings in this course, including those of angles, several kinds of polygons, and lines of symmetry. When making a drawing, you may use a ruler, protractor, compass, or whatever other instrument you wish. You may even use paper folding to locate certain lines, such as lines of symmetry.

Constructing is a kind of game that has some very specific rules. A construction is made with a limited number of tools. Only two construction tools are allowed—a straightedge for drawing lines and a compass for drawing circles and arcs and marking off distances. Measuring with a ruler or protractor and guessing are not allowed. If you use a ruler for a straightedge, you must ignore the markings on the ruler.

Your constructions will be more accurate if you follow these suggestions. Use a sharp pencil; do not use a ballpoint pen. Use one pencil for drawing lines and another in the compass. Adjust the pencil in the compass so it is at the same depth as the compass point. Do not squeeze the compass, as this may change the setting. Make construction marks lightly and do not erase them.

In the remainder of this book, when you are asked to construct, use only a compass and straightedge. When you are asked to draw, use any drawing tools that are handy *unless you are given specific instructions to use only certain ones.*

If you are careful and measure accurately, a congruent copy of $\overline{AB}$ shown can be drawn by using a ruler or by tracing. A congruent copy of a given segment can also be constructed using only a compass and straightedge. Construction 1 shows the steps for this construction.

A _____ B

Construction 1
A Segment

Problem

Construct a congruent copy of segment $\overline{AB}$.

A •_____• B

Procedure

Step 1 With a straightedge draw a segment longer than $\overline{AB}$. Label one endpoint C.

C _____

Step 2 Open your compass to the length of $\overline{AB}$. With the compass point on C, draw an arc intersecting the segment.

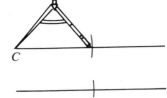

Step 3 Label the point of intersection D. $\overline{CD} \cong \overline{AB}$. You are done.

Given the lengths of the three sides, a triangle can be constructed using only a compass and straightedge. Construction 2 shows the steps for this construction.

Construction 2

A Triangle—Given Three Sides (SSS)

Problem
Construct a triangle having sides that measure $x, y,$ and z.

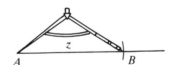

Procedure
Step 1 With a straightedge, draw a segment longer than the longest segment given.

Step 2 On that segment, construct a copy of the segment whose length is z. (Construction 1)

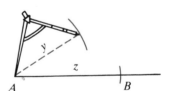

Step 3 Set your compass for length y. With the compass point on A, draw an arc above $\overline{AB}$. (This arc is part of a circle with center A and radius y.)

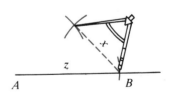

Step 4 Set your compass for length x. With the compass point on B, draw an arc above $\overline{AB}$ that intersects the arc drawn in Step 3.

Step 5 Point C, where the two arcs intersect, is the third vertex of the triangle. With a straightedge, draw $\overline{AC}$ and $\overline{BC}$. You are done.

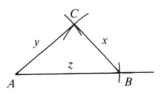

EXPLORING

The SSS Property

1. Repeat Construction 2 but in Step 3 put your compass point on B and in Step 4 put your compass point on A.
2. Again repeat Construction 2 but this time draw the arcs in Steps 3 and 4 below $\overline{AB}$ instead of above it.
3. Compare the two triangles just constructed in steps 1 and 2 above with the one originally done in Construction 2. How do they differ? How are they alike? Are they congruent?
4. Did constructing the sides in a different order change the size and shape of the triangle?

Regardless of the order in which they are constructed, the lengths of the three sides of a triangle completely determine its shape. Therefore, three given lengths will determine only one triangle. Construction 2 shows how to construct the triangle having three given lengths for its sides.

The constructions just completed and the answers to the above questions illustrate the following property, which can be used to make or show triangles to be congruent.

Side/Side/Side Property (SSS)

If three sides of one triangle are congruent to the corresponding sides of another triangle, the triangles are congruent.

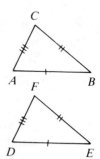

For triangles ABC and DEF shown, if $\overline{AB} \cong \overline{DE}, \overline{BC} \cong \overline{EF}$, and $\overline{CA} \cong \overline{FD}$, then $\triangle ABC \cong \triangle DEF$.

It is, however, not always possible to construct a triangle from three given lengths. In cases where we can, the SSS Property indicates that all triangles constructed from these three lengths will be congruent to each other. The next EXPLORING develops a method for determining whether three given lengths can be used to construct a triangle.

EXPLORING

The Triangle Inequality Property

1. Try to construct a triangle with sides of length a, b, and c, as shown. Can it be done? Why or why not?

$$a$$
$$b$$
$$c$$

2. Measure the three sides of each triangle shown below. For each triangle, compare the length of each side to the sum of the lengths of the other two sides.

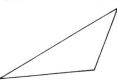 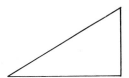 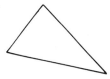

Your results from this EXPLORING should suggest the following property. This property can be thought of as another way of saying "A straight line is the shortest path between two points."

> **The Triangle Inequality Property**
>
> **The sum of the lengths of any two sides of a triangle is greater than the length of the third side.**

CLASS PRACTICE

Draw two segments that are not congruent. Use Construction 1 to construct a segment to fit each description.
1. Congruent to the shorter segment
2. Congruent to the longer segment
3. Twice as long as the shorter segment
4. Equal in length to the sum of the lengths of the segments
5. Equal in length to the difference of the lengths of the segments
6. Using the segments shown, construct a triangle with sides of length x, y, and z.

$$x$$
$$y$$
$$z$$

State whether the SSS Property could be used to prove each pair of triangles congruent.

7.   8. 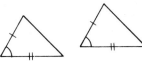   9.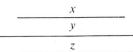

10. Look at triangles XYZ and RST. To use the SSS Property to prove $\triangle XYZ \cong \triangle RST$, you must show that $\overline{XY} \cong$? , $\overline{YZ} \cong$? , and $\overline{ZX} \cong$? .

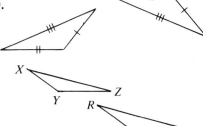

Which of the following sets of lengths can be used to construct a triangle? Explain your answers.

11. _____

12. _____

13. _____

14. 2 cm, 3 cm, 4 cm   15. 6 cm, 6 cm, 6 cm   16. 2 cm, 3 cm, 7 cm
17. 8 cm, 4 cm, 5 cm   18. 2 cm, 2 cm, 4 cm   19. 4 cm, 2 cm, 8 cm

EXERCISES

_ A _

For Exercises 1–9 use segments a, b, c, and d as needed.

a _____

b _____

c _____

d _____

Construct a segment of each length.

1. Same length as c
2. Sum of lengths of a and b
3. Difference between lengths of d and c
4. Three times as long as b

Construct a triangle to fit each description, *if possible*.

5. Sides a, b, and c
6. Sides b, c, and d
7. Sides a, b, and d
8. All sides same length as c
9. Two sides same length as c and one side same length as a
10. It is impossible to construct one of the triangles in Exercises 5–9. Which one? Why?

State which triangles constructed in Exercises 5–9 are of each type.

11. Right   12. Acute
13. Obtuse   14. Scalene
15. Isosceles   16. Equilateral

17. Construct a triangle congruent to the one shown.

State whether the SSS Property could be used to prove each pair of triangles congruent.

18. 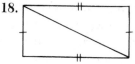   19.

State whether each set of lengths can be used to construct a triangle.

20. 3 cm, 4 cm, 5 cm   24. 3 cm, 5 cm,
21. 4 cm, 4 cm, 4 cm   9 cm
22. 3 cm, 5 cm, 6 cm   25. 6 cm, 3 cm,
23. 3 cm, 5 cm, 8 cm   4 cm

_ B _

26. Look at triangles PQR and GHI. To use the SSS Property to prove $\triangle PQR \cong \triangle GHI$, you must show that $\overline{PQ} \cong$? , $\overline{QR} \cong$? , and $\overline{RP} \cong$? .

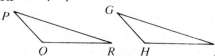

27. To use the SSS Property to prove

that $\triangle ABC \cong \triangle MNO$, you must show that $\overline{AB} \cong$? , $\overline{BC} \cong$? , and $\overline{CA} \cong$? .

28. Suppose you know that $\overline{RS} \cong \overline{GH}$ and wish to prove that $\triangle RST \cong \triangle GHI$ by using the SSS Property. What additional facts must be shown to be true?

For Exercises 29–32, look at $\triangle ABI$ and $\triangle WLC$.

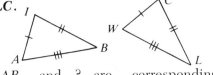

29. AB and ? are corresponding sides.

30. $\angle I$ and $\angle$? are corresponding angles.

31. Why is $\triangle ABI \cong \triangle WLC$?

32. If $m\angle A = 65°$, then $m\angle W =$?° .

33. Construct an isosceles triangle with a base 5 cm long and legs 4 cm long.

— C —

34. Draw four noncongruent segments. Using these segments as sides, construct two quadrilaterals that are not congruent.

35. Is the size and shape of a quadrilateral completely determined by the lengths of its sides? Explain your answer.

Applications

Building Rigid Structures

Architects and builders use triangular forms in construction because a triangle is a rigid form. A triangle will always hold its shape while other figures will collapse unless some additional support is added. For example, many roofs have a triangular cross section.

The geodesic dome in Montreal, Quebec, was designed by R. Buckminster Fuller. It is 200 feet high and has a spherical diameter of 250 feet. Notice the triangles used in constructing this dome, which has no interior support.

The SSS Property states that if three sides of one triangle are congruent to the corresponding sides of another triangle, then the triangles are congruent. Therefore, the length of at least one side

of a triangle must be changed before its shape changes.

In contrast, the shape of other polygons, such as quadrilaterals, which are not rigid figures, may be changed *without* changing the length of any of the sides.

4-2

Constructing Angles and Angle Bisectors

You can make a congruent copy of ∠A by tracing or by using a protractor and straightedge. You can also make a congruent copy of ∠A by constructing with a compass and straightedge according to the steps shown in Construction 3.

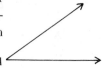

Construction 3
An Angle

Problem

Construct an angle congruent to ∠A.

Procedure

Step 1   Draw a ray with endpoint P.

Step 2   Using the same compass setting, draw arcs of equal radius from A and P.

Step 3   Adjust your compass to the length of $\overline{BC}$. Use this setting to draw an arc with center at Q and intersecting the arc drawn in Step 2 at a point R.

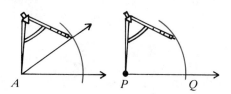

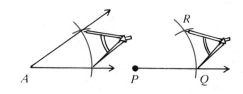

Step 4   Draw $\overrightarrow{PR}$. ∠RPQ ≅ ∠A. You are done.

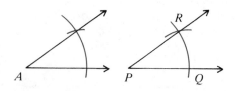

Why Construction 3 Works

∠2 has been constructed congruent to ∠1 by Construction 3. The dashed segments are not part of the construction.

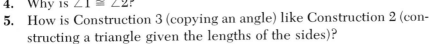

1. Why are the following pairs of segments congruent—$\overline{PR}$ and $\overline{AB}$; $\overline{RQ}$ and $\overline{BC}$; and $\overline{PQ}$ and $\overline{AC}$?
2. Why is $\triangle RPQ \cong \triangle BAC$?
3. What angle of $\triangle BAC$ corresponds to ∠1 of $\triangle RPQ$?
4. Why is ∠1 ≅ ∠2?
5. How is Construction 3 (copying an angle) like Construction 2 (constructing a triangle given the lengths of the sides)?

In Chapter 3, you folded an angle onto itself to find the bisector of the angle, which is also the line of symmetry of the angle. You can also find the bisector of an angle by constructing it with a compass and straightedge. Construction 4 shows the steps for this construction.

Construction 4

The Bisector of an Angle

Problem
Construct the bisector of ∠A.

Procedure
Step 1 With the compass point on A, draw an arc intersecting the sides of ∠A at points B and C.

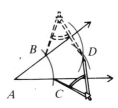

Step 2 Using the same compass setting, draw arcs of equal radius from B and C. Label the point of intersection of the arcs D.

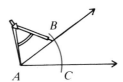

Step 3 Draw $\overrightarrow{AD}$. ∠1 ≅ ∠2. $\overrightarrow{AD}$ is the bisector of ∠A. You are done.

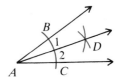

Why Construction 4 Works

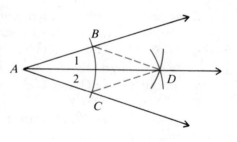

$\overrightarrow{AD}$, the bisector of $\angle BAC$, has been constructed by Construction 4. The dashed segments are not part of the construction.

1. Why are $\overline{AC}$, $\overline{AB}$, $\overline{CD}$, and $\overline{BD}$ congruent to each other?
2. $ACDB$ is a special kind of quadrilateral. What kind? Why?
3. $\overline{AD}$ is a diagonal of $ACDB$. Why is $\angle 1 \cong \angle 2$? (See page 128.)

CLASS PRACTICE

1. Draw an angle. Use Construction 3 to construct a copy of it.
2. Draw an angle. Use Construction 4 to construct its bisector.

EXERCISES

— A —

1. Draw an acute angle. Construct an angle congruent to it.
2. Draw an obtuse angle. Construct an angle congruent to it.
3. Draw an acute angle. Construct its bisector.
4. Draw an obtuse angle. Construct its bisector.

— B —

Construct an isosceles triangle to fit each description. Use $\angle 1$, $\angle 2$, and $\overline{XY}$ as needed.

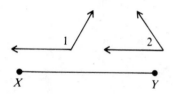

5. Vertex angle congruent to $\angle 1$ and legs congruent to $\overline{XY}$
6. Base angles congruent to $\angle 2$ and base congruent to $\overline{XY}$

— C —

Construct a triangle congruent to the one shown by constructing copies of the segments and angles given in each group.

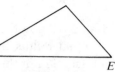

7. $\overline{DF}$, $\overline{EF}$, and $\overline{DE}$
8. $\angle D$, $\overline{DF}$, and $\overline{DE}$
9. $\overline{DE}$, $\angle D$, $\angle E$
10. Draw a straight angle. Construct its bisector.
11. Draw a large triangle and label its vertices A, B, and C. Construct an angle whose measure is the sum of the measures of $\angle A$, $\angle B$, and $\angle C$.

4-3

Other Ways to Construct Congruent Triangles—SAS and ASA

In Lesson 4-1 you constructed congruent triangles by constructing the sides of a second triangle congruent to those in the given triangle. (See Construction 2 and the SSS Property.)

In this lesson you will learn two other methods for constructing congruent triangles. (These methods were introduced in Exercises 8 and 9 on page 140.) The following discussion introduces two terms used in describing these methods.

In any triangle, each angle is *included by* two sides and each side is *included by* two angles. In △ABC shown, $\overline{AB}$ is the side included by ∠A and ∠B, and ∠A is the angle included by sides $\overline{AC}$ and $\overline{AB}$.

These other methods for constructing congruent triangles are described by Constructions 5 and 6.

Construction 5

A Triangle—Given Two Sides and the Included Angle (SAS)

Problem
Construct a triangle congruent to △ABC by constructing copies of ∠A, $\overline{AB}$, and $\overline{AC}$.

Procedure
Step 1 Draw a segment and label one endpoint P. At P, construct an angle congruent to ∠A (the angle included by $\overline{AB}$ and $\overline{AC}$).

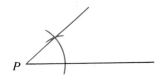

Step 2 Construct $\overline{PQ} \cong \overline{AB}$ and $\overline{PR} \cong \overline{AC}$. Draw $\overline{RQ}$. You are done.

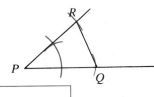

EXPLORING

The SAS Property

1. Repeat Construction 5 by constructing ∠B, $\overline{AB}$, and $\overline{BC}$ instead of ∠A, $\overline{AB}$, and $\overline{AC}$ as shown.
2. Compare the triangle constructed above with the one originally

done for Construction 5. How do they differ? How are they alike? Are they congruent?

3. Did constructing a different pair of sides and their included angle change the shape of the triangle being constructed?

Any pair of sides and their included angle will determine the shape of a triangle. Therefore two given lengths and an included angle will determine only one triangle. Construction 5 shows how to construct the triangle having two given lengths for two of its sides and the included angle for these sides.

The construction just completed and the answers to the above questions illustrate the following property, which can be used to make or show triangles to be congruent.

Side/Angle/Side Property (SAS)

If two sides and the included angle of one triangle are congruent to the corresponding sides and angle of another triangle, the triangles are congruent.

For triangles ABC and DEF shown, if $\overline{AB} \cong \overline{DE}, \overline{AC} \cong \overline{DF}$, and $\angle A \cong \angle D$, then $\triangle ABC \cong \triangle DEF$.

Construction 6

A Triangle—Given Two Angles and the Included Side (ASA)

Problem
Construct a triangle congruent to $\triangle ABC$ by constructing copies of $\overline{AB}$, $\angle A$, and $\angle B$.

Procedure
Step 1 Draw a segment longer than $\overline{AB}$. Construct $\overline{PQ} \cong \overline{AB}$.

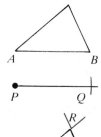

Step 2 At P, construct an angle congruent to $\angle A$. At Q, construct an angle congruent to $\angle B$. The intersection of the sides of these angles is the third vertex (R) of the triangle. You are done.

EXPLORING

The ASA Property

1. Repeat Construction 6 by constructing $\overline{AC}$, $\angle A$, and $\angle C$ instead of $\overline{AB}$, $\angle A$, and $\angle B$ as shown.

2. Compare the triangle constructed above with the one originally done for Construction 6. How do they differ? How are they alike? Are they congruent?

3. Did constructing a different pair of angles and their included side change the shape of the triangle being constructed?

Any pair of angles and their included side will completely determine the shape of a triangle. Therefore, two given angles and an included side will determine only one triangle. Construction 6 shows how to construct the triangle having two given measures for two of its angles and the included side for these angles.

The construction just completed and the answers to the above questions illustrate the following property, which can be used to make or show triangles to be congruent.

Angle/Side/Angle Property (ASA)

If two angles and the included side of one triangle are congruent to the corresponding angles and side of another triangle, the triangles are congruent.

For triangles ABC and DEF shown, if $\angle A \cong \angle D$, $\angle B \cong \angle E$, and $\overline{AB} \cong \overline{DE}$, then $\triangle ABC \cong \triangle DEF$.

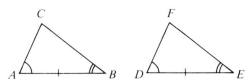

CLASS PRACTICE

Look at △XYZ. Complete each statement.
1. $\angle X$ is included by sides ? and ? .
2. $\overline{XZ}$ is included by $\angle$? and $\angle$? .
3. The included angle for $\overline{XY}$ and $\overline{ZY}$ is $\angle$? .
4. The included side for $\angle Y$ and $\angle Z$ is ? .

Use each given method and the indicated sides and angles to construct a triangle congruent to △RST shown.

5. SAS: $\overline{RT}, \overline{RS}$, and $\angle R$
6. ASA: $\overline{ST}, \angle T$, and $\angle S$

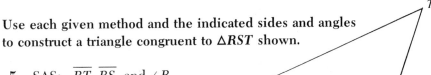

Look at △MNO and △XYZ.

7. To use the SAS Property to prove △MNO ≅ △XYZ, you could show that $\overline{MN}$ ≅ ? , $\overline{NO}$ ≅ ? , and ∠N ≅∠ ? .

8. To use the ASA Property to prove △MNO ≅ △XYZ, you could show that ∠O ≅ ∠ ? , ∠N ≅ ∠ ? , and $\overline{NO}$ ≅ ? .

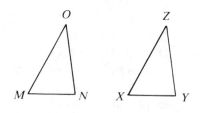

EXERCISES

— A —

Look at △ABC. Complete each statement.

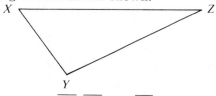

1. ∠A is opposite side ?
2. ∠A is included by sides ? and ? .
3. $\overline{AB}$ is opposite ∠ ? .
4. $\overline{AB}$ is included by ∠ ? and ∠ ? .
5. ∠C is included by sides ? and ? .
6. ∠B is opposite side ? .
7. ∠B is included by sides ? and ? .
8. $\overline{AC}$ is included by ∠ ? and ∠ ? .

Use each given method and the indicated sides and angles to construct a triangle congruent to △XYZ shown.

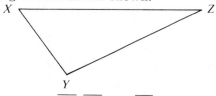

9. SSS: $\overline{XY}, \overline{XZ},$ and $\overline{YZ}$
10. SAS: $\overline{XY}, ∠X,$ and $\overline{XZ}$
11. SAS: $\overline{YZ}, ∠Y,$ and $\overline{XY}$
12. ASA: $\overline{XY}, ∠X,$ and ∠Y
13. ASA: $\overline{XZ}, ∠X,$ and ∠Z

State whether the SAS Property could be used to prove each pair of triangles congruent.

14.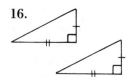

15.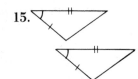

16.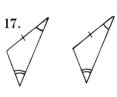

State whether the ASA Property could be used to prove each pair of triangles congruent.

17.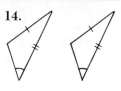

18.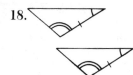

19.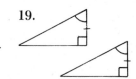

Look at △ABC and △GHI. Complete each statement.

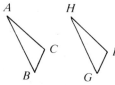

20. Suppose $\overline{AB} \cong \overline{HG}$, $\overline{AC} \cong \overline{HI}$, and $\angle A \cong \angle H$. Then $\triangle ABC \cong \triangle HGI$ by the ? Property.

21. Suppose $\angle A \cong \angle H$, $4B \cong \angle G$, and $\overline{AB} \cong \overline{HG}$. Then $\triangle ABC \cong \triangle HGI$ by the ? Property.

22. Suppose $\overline{AB} \cong \overline{HG}$, $\overline{BC} \cong \overline{GI}$, and $\overline{CA} \cong \overline{IH}$. Then $\triangle ABC \cong \triangle HGI$ by the ? Property.

23. Suppose $\overline{AC} \cong \overline{HI}$, $\angle A \cong \angle H$, and $\angle C \cong \angle I$. Then $\triangle ABC \cong \triangle HGI$ by the ? Property.

24. Suppose $\angle C \cong \angle I$, $\overline{BC} \cong \overline{GI}$, and $\overline{AC} \cong \overline{HI}$. Then $\triangle ABC \cong \triangle HGI$ by the ? Property.

— B —

Suppose you wish to prove $\triangle RST \cong \triangle XYZ$ shown. Complete each statement.

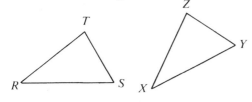

25. To use the SSS Property, you must show that $\overline{RS} \cong$? , $\overline{ST} \cong$? , and $\overline{TR} \cong$? .

26. To use the SAS Property, you could show that $\overline{RT} \cong$? , $\overline{ST} \cong$? , and $\angle T \cong \angle$? .

27. To use the ASA Property, you could show that $\overline{SR} \cong$? , $\angle R \cong \angle$? , and $\angle S \cong \angle$? .

28. To use the SAS Property, you could show that $\angle Y \cong \angle$? , $\overline{YX} \cong$? , and $\overline{YZ} \cong$? .

Find the indicated information.

29. Suppose you know that $\overline{QR} \cong \overline{KL}$ and wish to prove that $\triangle PQR \cong$ $\triangle JKL$ by using the ASA Property. What additional facts must be shown to be true?

30. Suppose you know that $\angle R \cong \angle L$ and wish to prove that $\triangle PQR \cong$ $\triangle JKL$ by using the SAS Property. What additional facts must be shown to be true?

— C —

Look at $\triangle DEF$ and $\triangle MNO$.

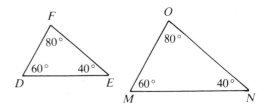

31. Identify the pairs of corresponding parts in $\triangle DEF$ and $\triangle MNO$ that are congruent.

32. Does $\triangle DEF$ appear to be congruent to $\triangle MNO$? Do you think there is an AAA Property that can be used to prove triangles congruent to each other? Explain your answer.

Look at $\triangle ABC$ and $\triangle RST$.

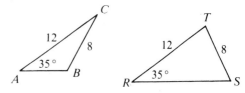

33. Identify the pairs of corresponding parts in $\triangle ABC$ and $\triangle RST$ that are congruent.

34. Does $\triangle ABC$ appear to be congruent to $\triangle RST$? Do you think there is an SSA Property that can be used to prove triangles congruent to each other? Explain your answer.

4-4

Constructing Perpendiculars

The perpendicular bisector of a segment can be found by folding a segment onto itself. The perpendicular bisector is one of the two lines of symmetry for a segment.

The perpendicular bisector of a segment can also be located by first measuring to find the midpoint of the segment and then using a square corner to draw the line through the midpoint that is perpendicular to the segment.

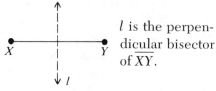

l is the perpendicular bisector of $\overline{XY}$.

A compass and straightedge can also be used to construct the perpendicular bisector of a segment. Construction 7 shows the steps for this construction.

Construction 7
The Perpendicular Bisector of a Segment

Problem

Construct the perpendicular bisector of $\overline{AB}$.

Procedure

Step 1 Open your compass to more than one half the length of $\overline{AB}$. With the compass point on A, draw an arc intersecting $\overline{AB}$.

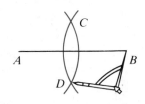

Step 2 Using the same compass setting, repeat Step 1 at point B. Label the points of intersection of the arcs C and D.

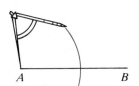

Step 3 Draw $\overleftrightarrow{CD}$. You are done.

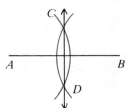

Why Construction 7 Works

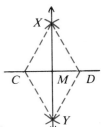

The perpendicular bisector of $\overline{CD}$ has been constructed by Construction 7. $\overleftrightarrow{XY}$ is the perpendicular bisector of $\overline{CD}$. M is the midpoint of $\overline{CD}$. The dashed segments are not part of the construction.

1. Why are $\overline{CY}$, $\overline{YD}$, $\overline{DX}$, and $\overline{CX}$ congruent to each other?
2. $CYDX$ is a special kind of quadrilateral. What kind? Why?
3. $\overline{CD}$ and $\overline{XY}$ are diagonals of $CYDX$. Why is $\overleftrightarrow{XY}$ the perpendicular bisector of $\overline{CD}$?

Given any segment, you now know how to construct its perpendicular bisector. There are two more constructions involving perpendiculars still to be learned. These are constructing the perpendicular to a line at a given point on it, and constructing the perpendicular to a line from a point not on the line. Constructions 8 and 9 show the steps for these two constructions.

======== *Construction 8* ========

The Perpendicular to a Line at a Point on the Line

Problem
Construct a line through A that is perpendicular to l.

Procedure
Step 1 With the compass point on A, draw an arc intersecting l in two points. Label these points B and C.

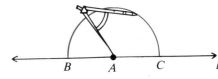

Step 2 Open your compass to more than one half the length of $\overline{BC}$. Draw arcs of equal radius from B and C. Label the point of intersection of the arcs D.

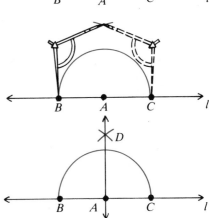

Step 3 Draw $\overleftrightarrow{DA}$. You are done.

The Perpendicular to a Line from a Point not on the Line

Problem

Construct a perpendicular from P to line l.

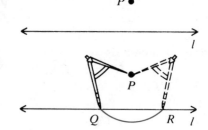

Procedure

Step 1   With the compass point on P, draw an arc intersecting l in two points. Label these points Q and R.

Step 2   Using the same compass setting, draw arcs of equal radius from Q and R. Label the point of intersection of the arcs S.

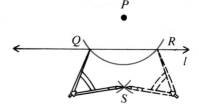

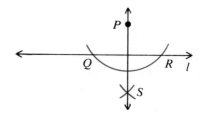

Step 3   Draw $\overleftrightarrow{PS}$. You are done.

========== *EXPLORING* ==========

A Property of Perpendiculars

1.   Draw a line l. Locate two points on the line and label them A and B.
2.   Use Construction 8 to construct a line through A that is perpendicular to l, and a line through B that is perpendicular to l.
3.   The two perpendiculars you constructed in step 2 have a special relationship to each other. What is it?

If you did the preceding EXPLORING carefully, you discovered the following property:

> **If two coplanar lines are perpendicular to the same line, then the two lines are parallel.**

Look at $\overline{AB}$. M is the midpoint of $\overline{AB}$.

1. How many lines can be drawn through M?
2. Is every line through M a bisector of $\overline{AB}$?
3. How many bisectors does $\overline{AB}$ have?
4. How many perpendicular bisectors does $\overline{AB}$ have?

Look at line l.

5. How many lines can be drawn through P?
6. How many lines through P will be perpendicular to l?

Look at line m.

7. How many lines can be drawn through R?
8. How many lines through R will be perpendicular to m?

Look at Construction 7.

9. Notice the comment in Step 1 about the compass opening. Would the construction work if the opening were not more than one half the length of $\overline{AB}$? Why or why not?

Answer the following questions.

10. Tell how Construction 8 can be considered a special case of bisecting an angle. (Hint: Think of $\angle BAC$ as a straight angle.)
11. In what ways are Constructions 8 and 9 like Construction 7?
12. Explain why Constructions 8 and 9 work.

1. Draw two noncongruent segments. Use Construction 7 to construct the perpendicular bisector of each segment. Check the accuracy of your constructions by measuring or folding.
2. Draw a line and choose any point on it. Use Construction 8 to construct a perpendicular to the line at that point.
3. Draw a line and choose any point either above or below the line. Use Construction 9 to construct a perpendicular from the point to the line.
4. In the figure shown, lines l and m are coplanar and are both perpendicular to line x. What is the relationship between l and m?

— A —

1. Draw a segment at least 8 centimeters long. Construct its perpendicular bisector.

2. Draw a segment at least 8 centimeters long. Divide it into four congruent parts, using only a compass and straightedge.

3. Draw a line l and choose any point P on it. Construct a line through P that is perpendicular to l.

4. Draw a line l and choose any point P either above or below the line. Construct a line through P that is perpendicular to l.

5. Use Construction 7 to construct a right angle.

6. Construct a 45° angle by bisecting the right angle you constructed in Exercise 5.

— B —

7. Draw $\overline{AB}$. Construct a segment whose length is $\frac{3}{4}$ that of $\overline{AB}$. (Hint: Use Construction 7 twice.)

For Exercise 8, use $\overline{AB}$ and $\overline{CD}$ as needed.

A _____ B

C _____ D

8. Construct a rectangle whose length is the same as $\overline{AB}$ and whose width is the same as $\overline{CD}$.

Draw a figure similar to, but larger than, the one shown.

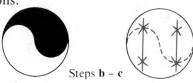

9. Construct the perpendicular from C to $\overleftrightarrow{AB}$.

10. Construct the perpendicular from A to $\overleftrightarrow{BC}$.

— C —

11. Construct a symbol like the one shown by following these directions.

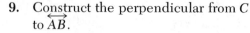

Steps **b** – **c**

a. Construct a circle and mark its center.

b. Draw a horizontal diameter. Locate the midpoints of the two radii on the diameter by constructing the perpendicular bisector for each radius. (See second figure.)

c. Using these two midpoints as centers, construct a semicircle above the left radius and a semicircle below the right radius.

d. Shade the figure as shown.

12. Draw a figure similar to, but larger than, the one shown.

A •

← ────────── → l

a. Construct the perpendicular from A to l.

b. Construct a line through A perpendicular to the line in part a.

c. What is the special relationship between the line constructed in part b and line l. Explain why this is true. (Hint: See EXPLORING on page 148.)

Use the given method and the indicated angles and sides to construct a triangle.

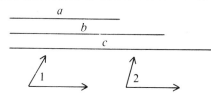

1. SSS: sides *a*, *b*, and *c*
2. SAS: sides *a* and *b*; included angle ∠1
3. ASA: included side *c*; angles ∠1 and ∠2
4. Which sets of lengths can be used to form a triangle?
   a. 6 cm, 9 cm, 10 cm
   b. 8 cm, 3 cm, 4 cm
   c. 8 cm, 5 cm, 7 cm
   d. 6 cm, 7 cm, 13 cm
5. Draw an acute angle.
   a. Construct an angle congruent to it.
   b. Construct the bisector of the angle.
6. Draw a segment. Construct its perpendicular bisector.
7. Draw a line *l* and mark a point *P* on the line. Construct a line through *P* that is perpendicular to *l*.
8. Draw a line *l* and mark a point *P* above the line. Construct a line through *P* that is perpendicular to *l*.

Everyday Geometry
Geometric Language

A knowledge of geometric terms is helpful in understanding the meaning of many common words and phrases.

EXERCISES

For each word or phrase listed below, describe how its meaning is consistent with the meaning of some geometric terms used in this text.

1. Airplane
2. Hydroplane
3. Ray of light
4. Radiant smile
5. Angle iron
6. Centerpiece
7. Out of square
8. Turning radius (of a car)
9. Adjacent house lots
10. Vertex (of a mountain)
11. Lateral pass (in football)
12. Horizontal bars (in gymnastics)
13. State some other words and phrases whose meaning is consistent with that of some geometric term.

4-5

Proving Corresponding Parts Congruent

As you may recall from Lesson 3–6, the corresponding parts of congruent figures are congruent. However, it can be time-consuming or difficult to show that *all* pairs of corresponding parts of two figures are congruent in order to prove that the two figures are congruent. In Lessons 4–1 and 4–3 you learned three shortcut methods (SSS, SAS, and ASA) for determining that two triangles are congruent. To use one of these methods, you must find only three pairs of corresponding parts congruent in order to prove that two triangles are congruent.

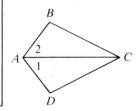

In the figure shown, the SAS Property can be used to prove that $\triangle PQR \cong \triangle STR$. Once we know that the two triangles are congruent, we can conclude that the remaining corresponding parts ($\overline{PQ}$ and $\overline{ST}$; $\angle P$ and $\angle S$; $\angle Q$ and $\angle T$) are also congruent.

One way to prove segments or angles congruent is to show that they are corresponding parts of congruent triangles. The following statements summarize this strategy.

Using Congruent Triangles to Prove Angles or Segments Congruent

1. Find two triangles in which the angles or sides are corresponding parts.
2. Prove that the triangles are congruent.
3. State that the angles or sides are congruent because corresponding parts of congruent figures are congruent.

Suppose you wished to prove $\angle 1 \cong \angle 2$, given the figure and information shown:

1. $\angle 1$ and $\angle 2$ are corresponding parts of $\triangle CDA$ and $\triangle CBA$.
2. Two pairs of corresponding sides ($\overline{DA}$ and $\overline{BA}$; $\overline{CD}$ and $\overline{CB}$) are given as congruent and $\overline{AC} \cong \overline{AC}$ since $\overline{AC}$ is a common side of the triangles. Therefore $\triangle CDA \cong \triangle CBA$ by the SSS Property.
3. Therefore $\angle 1 \cong \angle 2$ because corresponding parts of congruent figures are congruent.

Given:
$\overline{DA} \cong \overline{BA}$
$\overline{CD} \cong \overline{CB}$

Prove:
$\angle 1 \cong \angle 2$

Identify the property—SSS, SAS, or ASA—that you could use to prove each pair of triangles congruent.

1.   **2.**   **3.**

The triangles in each pair are congruent. Identify two pairs of congruent sides and one pair of congruent angles that you could use to prove each pair of triangles congruent by the SAS Property.

4. 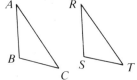   **5.** 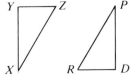   **6.**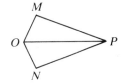

7–9. Using the triangles in Exercises 4–6, identify two pairs of congruent angles and one pair of congruent sides that you could use to prove the triangles in each pair congruent by the ASA Property.

Identify the triangles in the figure you could prove congruent in order to prove each given congruence statement.

10. $\angle 1 \cong \angle 2$ **11.** $\angle C \cong \angle D$
12. $\angle CAB \cong \angle DBA$ **13.** $\overline{CE} \cong \overline{DE}$
14. $\overline{CB} \cong \overline{DA}$ **15.** $\overline{CA} \cong \overline{DB}$

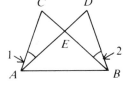

Suppose that you have proved $\triangle WXZ \cong \triangle YXZ$ in the figure shown. State whether each given congruence statement is a correct conclusion.

16. $\angle 1 \cong \angle 3$
17. $\angle 1 \cong \angle 4$
18. $\overline{WX} \cong \overline{YZ}$
19. $\overline{WZ} \cong \overline{YZ}$

— A —

Identify the property—SSS, SAS, or ASA—that you could use to prove each pair of triangles congruent.

1.   2.

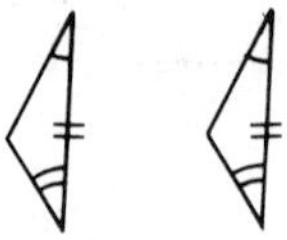

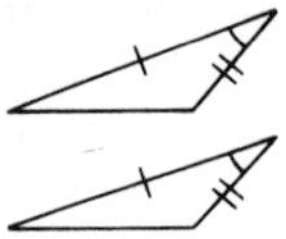

3. 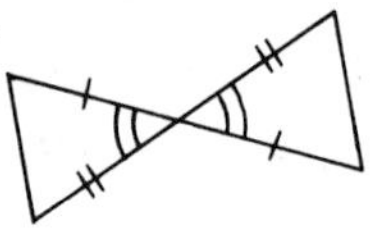   4.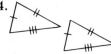

5. 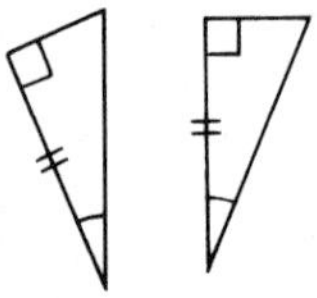   6.

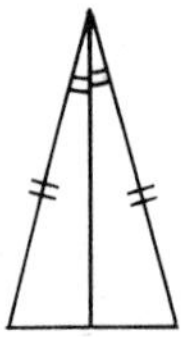

The triangles in each pair are congruent. Identify two pairs of congruent sides and one pair of congruent angles that you could use to prove each pair of triangles congruent by the SAS Property.

7. 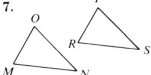   8.

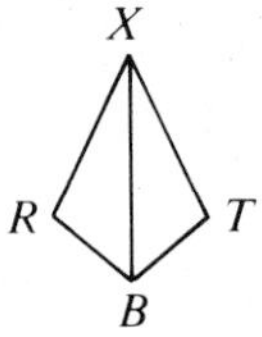

9.

10–12. Using the triangles from Exercises 7–9, identify two pairs of congruent angles and one pair of congruent sides that you could use to prove each pair of triangles congruent by the ASA Property.

— B —

Identify two triangles in the figure you could prove congruent in order to prove each congruence statement true.

13. ∠1 ≅ ∠2
14. ∠3 ≅ ∠4
15. ∠ZWX ≅ ∠YXW
16. $\overline{WZ} \cong \overline{XY}$
17. $\overline{ZX} \cong \overline{YW}$
18. $\overline{WU} \cong \overline{XU}$

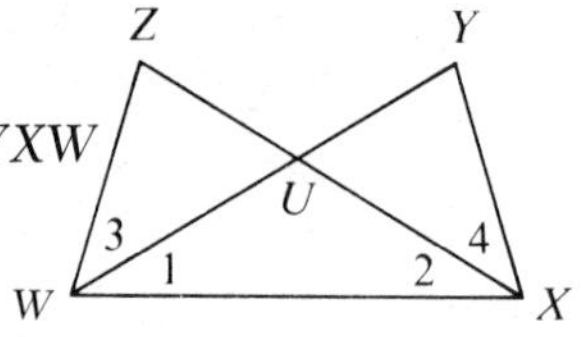

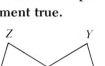

Suppose you have proved △ABC ≅ △CDA in the figure shown.

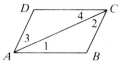

19. List the three pairs of corresponding sides for △ABC and △CDA.
20. State whether each statement is a correct conclusion.
    a. ∠1 ≅ ∠3   b. ∠2 ≅ ∠3
    c. ∠B ≅ ∠C   d. $\overline{BC} \cong \overline{DA}$

Suppose you have proved △WXY ≅ △ZYX in the figure shown.

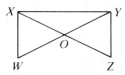

21. List the three pairs of corresponding sides for △WXY and △ZYX.

22. State whether each statement is a correct conclusion.

    a. $\angle W \cong \angle Z$ **b.** $\angle WXY \cong \angle ZYX$

    c. $\overline{WO} \cong \overline{ZO}$ **d.** $\overline{XY} \cong \overline{YX}$

— **C** —

23. Look at quadrilateral *PRST*.

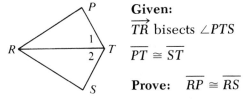

    Given:

    $\overrightarrow{TR}$ bisects $\angle PTS$

    $\overline{PT} \cong \overline{ST}$

    Prove: $\overline{RP} \cong \overline{RS}$

    a. What pair of sides are given to be congruent?

    b. Why is $\angle 1 \cong \angle 2$?

    c. What segment is a common side for $\triangle RPT$ and $\triangle RST$?

    d. What property can be used to prove $\triangle RPT \cong \triangle RST$?

    e. Why is $\overline{RP} \cong \overline{RS}$?

24. In Lesson 4–2, Construction 4 was shown to work by using properties of the diagonals of a rhombus. (See EXPLORING on page 140.) This construction can also be shown to be true by using congruent triangles. Suppose $\angle BAC$ is bisected by Construction 4 and that $\overline{BD}$ and $\overline{CD}$ are drawn as shown.

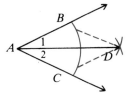

    a. Why are the following pairs of segments congruent—$\overline{AB}$ and $\overline{AC}$; $\overline{BD}$ and $\overline{CD}$; $\overline{AD}$ and $\overline{AD}$?

    b. What property can be used to prove $\triangle ABD \cong \triangle ACD$?

    c. Why is $\angle 1 \cong \angle 2$?

    d. Why is $\overrightarrow{AD}$ the bisector of $\angle BAC$?

25. A carpenter's square can be used to bisect an angle at the corner of a board:

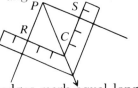

  Along the edges mark equal lengths *PS* and *PR*.

  Put the carpenter's square on the board so that $CS = CR$.

  Mark point *C* and draw $\overrightarrow{PC}$.

    a. What property can be used to prove $\triangle PRC \cong \triangle PSC$?

    b. Why is $\angle RPC \cong \angle SPC$?

    c. Why is $\overrightarrow{PC}$ the bisector of $\angle RPS$?

DID YOU KNOW THAT....

The Greek philosopher Plato (430–349 B.C.), who is perhaps best known as the author of *The Republic* and student of Socrates, is credited with introducing the idea that only straightedge and compass may be used in geometric constructions. It is said that carved above the entrance to Plato's school, The Academy, was the inscription, "Let no one ignorant of geometry enter here."

4-6

Proving Properties of Polygons

You have learned and used several geometric facts and conclusions in this book. These results were developed by a variety of methods. Some were established by measurement and observation and accepted as reasonable. Others were defined and accepted as true by definition. In Chapter 3, several properties of triangles and quadrilaterals were developed by drawing lines of symmetry and using properties of symmetry. In some instances, you reasoned from previously accepted statements to develop additional conclusions.

Congruent triangles gives you another method for developing conclusions and showing that they are true. In this lesson, you will learn how some of the properties developed earlier by other methods can be proved using congruent triangles.

Suppose you wish to prove the following property using congruent triangles:

"If a line bisects the vertex angle of an isosceles triangle, then it is the perpendicular bisector of the base."

Before you can prove a property, you must first decide what information is given and what is to be proved. A diagram is usually drawn to represent the information.

In this example, we are given an isosceles triangle with a line bisecting the vertex angle. We want to prove that the bisector of the vertex angle of an isosceles triangle is also the perpendicular bisector of its base. Notice we must prove not only that this line is perpendicular to the base but that it also bisects it.

The figure shown has been drawn to represent this information. We could prove the desired conclusion by answering a series of questions like this:

Given: △ABC is isosceles. $\overline{AB}$ is the base. $\overleftrightarrow{CD}$ is the bisector of ∠ACB.

Prove: $\overleftrightarrow{CD}$ is the perpendicular bisector of $\overline{AB}$.

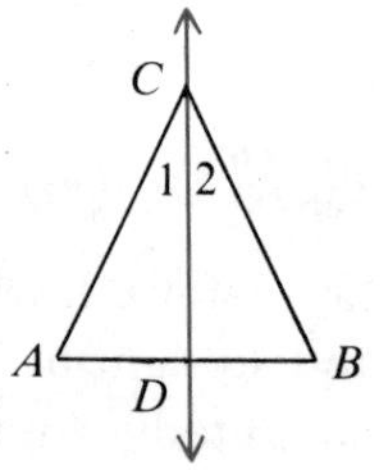

1. What pairs of angles or segments are congruent because of the given information? ($\overline{AC} \cong \overline{BC}$ because △ABC is isosceles. ∠1 ≅ ∠2 because $\overleftrightarrow{CD}$ bisects ∠ACB.)

2. Look at △ACD and △BCD. What other pairs of corresponding sides or angles of these triangles are congruent? Why? ($\overline{CD} \cong \overline{CD}$, because $\overline{CD}$ is a common side of the triangles.)

3. What property can be used to prove △ACD ≅ △BCD? (SAS)

4. Why is ∠ADC ≅ ∠BDC? (The corresponding parts of congruent triangles are congruent.)

5. Why is $\overleftrightarrow{CD}$ perpendicular to $\overline{AB}$? (∠ADC and ∠BDC are right angles since they are both congruent and supplementary.)

6. Why is $\overline{AD} \cong \overline{BD}$? (The corresponding parts of congruent triangles are congruent.)

7. Why does $\overleftrightarrow{CD}$ bisect $\overline{AB}$? (Definition of a bisector.)

8. Why is $\overleftrightarrow{CD}$ the perpendicular bisector of $\overline{AB}$? ($\overleftrightarrow{CD} \perp \overline{AB}$ and $\overleftrightarrow{CD}$ bisects $\overline{AB}$.)

EXERCISES

_ A _

For each exercise, a property or construction to be proved is stated and a diagram representing the given information is provided. Prove each property or construction by answering the series of questions provided.

1. **To Be Proved:** Each diagonal of a rhombus bisects the angles whose vertices are its endpoints.

   Given: Rhombus ABCD

   Prove: $\overline{AC}$ bisects ∠DAB and ∠DCB.

   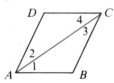

   a. Look at △CDA and △CBA. What pairs of corresponding segments are congruent because of the given information?

   b. What other pair of corresponding sides are congruent? Why?

   c. What property can be used to prove △CDA ≅ △CBA?

   d. Why is ∠1 ≅ ∠2 and ∠3 ≅ ∠4?

   e. Why does $\overline{AC}$ bisect ∠DAB and ∠DCB?

2. **To Be Proved:** If two sides of a triangle are congruent, then the angles opposite these sides are congruent.

   Given: $\overline{DF} \cong \overline{EF}$

   Prove: ∠D ≅ ∠E

   a. What pairs of angles or segments are congruent because of the given information?

   b. To help prove this property, we can construct the bisector of

   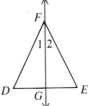

∠*DFE*, producing two smaller triangles, as shown. What pair of angles are congruent because $\overleftrightarrow{FG}$ bisects ∠*DFE*?

c. Look at △*DFG* and △*EFG*. What other pairs of corresponding sides or angles are congruent? Why?

d. What property can be used to prove △*DFG* ≅ △*EFG*?

e. Why is ∠*D* ≅ ∠*E*?

3. **To Be Proved:** Construction 8 (Perpendicular to a Line at a Point on the Line)

Given: Construction 8 has been used to construct $\overleftrightarrow{AD}$ perpendicular to line *l* at point *A*.

Prove: $\overleftrightarrow{AD} \perp l$

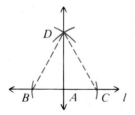

a. Look at △*ABD* and △*ACD*. Why is $\overline{AB} \cong \overline{AC}$? $\overline{BD} \cong \overline{CD}$? $\overline{DA} \cong \overline{DA}$?

b. What property can be used to prove △*ABD* ≅ △*ACD*?

c. Why is ∠*BAD* ≅ ∠*CAD*?

d. Why is $\overleftrightarrow{AD} \perp l$?

— **B** —

4. **To Be Proved:** The diagonals of a rectangle are congruent.

Given:
Rectangle *PQRS*

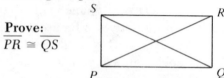

Prove:
$\overline{PR} \cong \overline{QS}$

a. Notice that $\overline{PR}$ and $\overline{QS}$ are corresponding sides of △*PRQ* and △*QSP*, which overlap. Look at △*PRQ* and △*QSP*. Why is $\overline{PS} \cong \overline{QR}$? ∠*SPQ* ≅ ∠*RQP*? $\overline{PQ} \cong \overline{QP}$?

b. What property can be used to prove △*PRQ* ≅ △*QSP*?

c. Why is $\overline{PR} \cong \overline{QS}$?

5. **To Be Proved:** Construction 7 (Perpendicular Bisector of a Segment)

Given:
Construction 7 has been used to construct $\overleftrightarrow{RS}$, the perpendicular bisector of $\overline{AB}$. *AR*, *BR*, *SB*, and *SA* have been drawn as shown.

Prove:
$\overleftrightarrow{RS}$ is the perpendicular bisector of $\overline{AB}$.

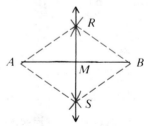

a. Look at △*RAS* and △*RBS*. Why is $\overline{RA} \cong \overline{RB}$? $\overline{AS} \cong \overline{BS}$? $\overline{SR} \cong \overline{SR}$?

b. Why is △*RAS* ≅ △*RBS*?

c. Why is ∠*ARM* ≅ ∠*BRM*?

d. Look at △*ARM* and △*BRM*. Why is $\overline{AR} \cong \overline{BR}$? $\overline{MR} \cong \overline{MR}$?

e. Why is △*ARM* ≅ △*BRM*?

f. Why is ∠*RMA* ≅ ∠*RMB*?

g. Why is $\overline{MA} \cong \overline{MB}$?

h. Why is $\overleftrightarrow{RS}$ the perpendicular bisector of $\overline{AB}$?

4-7

Tangents, Inscribed Circles, and Circumscribed Circles

In this lesson you will learn some new terms that will be used in the remainder of this chapter. You might also wish to review the vocabulary and skills (see page 82) learned in Chapter 2.

If every vertex of a polygon is on the same circle, we say that the circle is *circumscribed about the polygon*, or the polygon is *inscribed in the circle*. ⊙M shown is circumscribed about quadrilateral *ABCD*. Quadrilateral *ABCD* is inscribed in ⊙M.

A line is *tangent* to a circle if it is in the same plane as the circle and intersects it in exactly one point. The point of intersection is called the *point of tangency*.

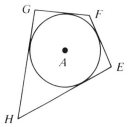

l is tangent to ⊙R at point *S*. *S* is the point of tangency.

A line tangent to two or more circles is a *common tangent* to the circles.

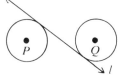

l is a common tangent to ⊙P and ⊙Q.

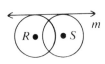

m is a common tangent to ⊙R and ⊙S.

If every side of a polygon is tangent to the same circle, we say that the polygon is *circumscribed about the circle*, or the circle is *inscribed in the polygon*. Quadrilateral *EFGH* shown is circumscribed about ⊙A. ⊙A is inscribed in quadrilateral *EFGH*.

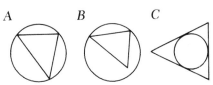

CLASS PRACTICE

Look at the four diagrams.

1. Which show(s) a circle circumscribed about a triangle?

2. Which show(s) a circle inscribed in a triangle?

A   B   C   D

Look at ⊙O. Identify each of the following.

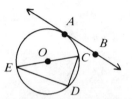

3. Tangent line
4. Point of tangency
5. Triangle inscribed in a circle
6. Three chords
7. Two radii
8. One diameter

EXERCISES

— A —

Look at ⊙P. Identify each of the following.

1. Three radii
2. One diameter
3. Three chords
4. Two central angles
5. One inscribed angle
6. One right angle
7. Triangle inscribed in a circle
8. Two tangent lines
9. Two points of tangency

Look at figures A–H. State which figures fit each description.

10. Triangle inscribed in a circle
11. Triangle circumscribed about a circle
12. Circle inscribed in a triangle
13. Circle circumscribed about a triangle

A

B

C

D

E

F
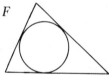

G

H

— B —

Draw a figure to fit each description.

14. Isosceles triangle inscribed in a circle
15. Obtuse triangle inscribed in a circle
16. Obtuse triangle circumscribed about a circle
17. Quadrilateral inscribed in a circle
18. Quadrilateral circumscribed about a circle
19. Line tangent to a circle
20. Two chords with a common endpoint
21. Circle with a point P outside it and all lines through P tangent to the circle (There are two of them.)

Draw a figure similar to each one shown. Draw all common tangents to the two circles in each figure.

22.   23.

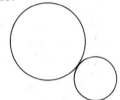

4-8

Using Perpendicular Bisectors

If arcs of equal radius (same compass opening) are drawn from two points, the point of intersection of the two arcs is *equidistant* (the same distance) from the points. In the figure shown, C is equidistant from A and B.

Suppose different radii are used to locate several points equidistant from two points A and B. Notice that the points equidistant from A and B seem to be collinear and located on the perpendicular bisector of $\overline{AB}$.

Suppose the perpendicular bisector of a segment is constructed. Look at the points marked on l, the perpendicular bisector of $\overline{CD}$. Notice that each of these points seems to be equidistant from C and D.

These examples illustrate the following relationships between a point equidistant from two points and the segment determined by these two points.

> If a point is equidistant from the endpoints of a segment, then it lies on the perpendicular bisector of the segment.
>
> If a point lies on the perpendicular bisector of a segment, then it is equidistant from the endpoints of the segment.

By definition all points of a circle are equidistant from its center. In other words, all radii of a circle are congruent.

The following EXPLORING uses the relationships stated above to develop some properties of the perpendicular bisectors of the chords of a circle.

$$\overline{PA} \cong \overline{PB} \cong \overline{PC}$$

EXPLORING

The Properties of the Perpendicular Bisectors of Chords

1. Construct a circle with any radius. Label the center O.
2. Draw any two nonparallel chords of ⊙O. Label the chords $\overline{AB}$ and $\overline{CD}$.
3. Why is $\overline{OA} \cong \overline{OB}$ and $\overline{OC} \cong \overline{OD}$?

4. Why is point O equidistant from A and B? from C and D?
5. Why is point O on the perpendicular bisector of $\overline{AB}$ and of $\overline{CD}$?
6. Construct the perpendicular bisectors of $\overline{AB}$ and $\overline{CD}$. Where do they intersect?
7. If different chords had been drawn for step 2, would your answers to the questions in steps 3–6 have been the same? Why or why not?

If your constructions were done correctly, you discovered the following conclusions:

> **The perpendicular bisector of a chord contains the center of a circle.**
>
> **The perpendicular bisectors of any two non-parallel chords intersect at the center of the circle.**

The following EXPLORING develops a surprising fact about the perpendicular bisectors of the sides of any triangle.

EXPLORING

The Intersection of the Perpendicular Bisectors of the Sides of a Triangle

1. Draw an acute triangle. Construct the perpendicular bisector of each side.
2. Draw an obtuse triangle. Construct the perpendicular bisector of each side.
3. Draw a right triangle. Construct the perpendicular bisector of each side.

If your constructions were done correctly, you discovered the following conclusion:

> **The perpendicular bisectors of the three sides of any triangle meet at a single point. This point is called the *circumcenter*.**

The conclusions from the preceding EXPLORINGs can be used to develop a method for constructing a circle circumscribed about a triangle. Construction 10 shows the steps for this construction.

Construction 10

A Circle Circumscribed About a Triangle

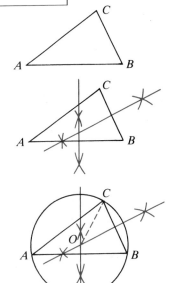

Problem

Construct a circle circumscribed about △*ABC*.

Procedure

Step 1 Construct the perpendicular bisectors of any two sides of △*ABC*. The perpendicular bisectors you constructed will intersect at a point. Label this point *O*.

Step 2 Construct a circle using *O* as the center and either *OA*, *OB*, or *OC* as the radius. You are done.

DISCUSS

1. Look at the first EXPLORING on page 161. Suppose the two chords in step 2 had been drawn parallel to each other. How would this have changed your answers in steps 3–6?

Look at Construction 10 above.

2. Why is point *O* equidistant from *A*, *B*, and *C*?
3. Suppose the perpendicular bisector of $\overline{AC}$ were also constructed. Why must it also pass through point *O*?

Draw an arc of a circle and two nonparallel chords whose endpoints are on this arc.

4. Construct the perpendicular bisectors of these two chords. Why is the point where these perpendicular bisectors intersect the center of the circle that contains the arc?

Suppose you are given three noncollinear points such as those shown.

5. Explain how to construct a circle passing through all three points. (Hint: Think of the points as the vertices of a triangle.)

The perpendicular bisectors of the three sides of any triangle meet at a single point. Describe the location of that point for each type of triangle.

6. Acute   7. Right   8. Obtuse

1. Draw two points and label them A and B. Use a compass to locate six points that are equidistant from A and B.

Look at the figure.

2. If $RC = 5$, then $RD = $? .
3. If $SD = 6$, then $SC = $? .
4. If $CM = 4$, then $DM = $? and $CD = $? .
5. What kind of triangles are $\triangle RCD$ and $\triangle SCD$?
6. Do Construction 10 using a different kind of triangle. (Example: If you used an acute triangle the first time, use either an obtuse or right triangle.)

l is the perpendicular bisector of $\overline{CD}$.

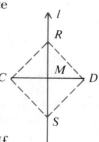

EXERCISES

— A —

Look at the diagram. $\overleftrightarrow{PQ}$ **is the perpendicular bisector of** $\overline{AB}$.

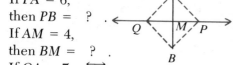

1. If $PA = 6$, then $PB = $? .
2. If $AM = 4$, then $BM = $? .
3. If $QA = 7$, then $QB = $? .
   $\overleftrightarrow{PQ}$ is the perpendicular bisector of $\overline{AB}$.
4. Suppose V is a point such that $VA = 9$ and $VB = 9$. Where is V located?
5. What kind of triangles are $\triangle APB$ and $\triangle AQB$?

Look at $\triangle BAM$. $\overleftrightarrow{MO}$ **is the perpendicular bisector of both** $\overline{CD}$ **and** $\overline{AB}$.

6. $MD = $?
7. $DB = $?
8. $CA = $?
9. $ND = $?
10. $OB = $?
11. $CD = $?
12. $AB = $?
13. What kind of triangles are $\triangle CMD$ and $\triangle AMB$?

$MC = 5$
$CN = 3$
$MB = 8$
$AO = 4$

Find the indicated information.

14. In the figure shown, l, m, and n

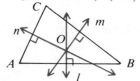

are perpendicular bisectors of the sides of $\triangle ABC$. If $OA = 6$, then $OB = $? and $OC = $? .

15. In the figure shown, l is the perpen-

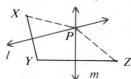

dicular bisector of $\overline{XY}$ and m is the perpendicular bisector of $\overline{YZ}$. P is on both l and m. Why is $PX = PZ$?

Perform the indicated constructions.

16. Draw a circle. Locate its center by constructing the perpendicular bisectors of any two nonparallel chords.

17. Draw an acute triangle. Circumscribe a circle about the triangle.

18. Draw an obtuse triangle. Circumscribe a circle about the triangle.

19. Draw three noncollinear points. Construct the circle that passes through all three points.

— B —

20. Look at ⊙O.

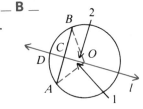

l is the perpendicular bisector of $\overline{AB}$.

a. Why is $\overline{OA} \cong \overline{OB}$? $\overline{AC} \cong \overline{BC}$? $\overline{OC} \cong \overline{OC}$?

b. Why is △ACO ≅ △BCO?

c. Why is ∠1 ≅ ∠2?

d. ∠1 and ∠2 are central angles. Identify the intercepted arc for ∠1 and for ∠2.

e. Why is m AD = m BD?

21. Look at ⊙C.

$\overleftrightarrow{CD}$ bisects ∠ACB.

m ∠ACB = 70°

AB = 10 cm,
AC = 8 cm

a. m AB = ?° b. m∠1 = ?°
c. m∠2 = ?° d. m $\widehat{AD}$ = ?°
e. m $\widehat{BD}$ = ?° f. AM = ? cm
g. BC = ? cm

22. The results from Exercise 20 indicate that l bisects ∠AOB, $\overline{AB}$, and AB. This suggests a method for constructing the bisector of any arc. Do this construction by following these steps.

a. Draw a circle.

b. Label the endpoints (A and B) of an arc of this circle.

c. Construct the bisector of the arc. (Hint: Begin by drawing $\overline{AB}$.)

— C —

23. **To Be Proved:** If a point is on the perpendicular bisector of a segment, then it is equidistant from the endpoints of the segment.

Given: A is on l.
l is the perpendicular bisector of $\overline{BC}$.

Prove: $\overline{AB} \cong \overline{AC}$

a. Look at △ADB and △ADC. What pairs of corresponding sides or angles are congruent? Why?

b. Why is △ADB ≅ △ADC?

c. Why is $\overline{AB} \cong \overline{AC}$?

24. **To Be Proved:** If a point is equidistant from the endpoints of a segment, then it is on the perpendicular bisector of the segment.

Given: $\overline{XY} \cong \overline{XZ}$

Prove: X is on the perpendicular bisector of $\overline{YZ}$.

a. What pairs of angles or segments are congruent because of the given information?

b. To help prove this property, we can draw the segment from X to W, the midpoint of $\overline{YZ}$. What pair of segments are congruent because M is the midpoint of $\overline{YZ}$?

c. Look at $\triangle YWX$ and $\triangle ZWX$. What other pairs of corresponding sides or angles are congruent? Why?

d. Why is $\triangle YWX \cong \triangle ZWX$?

e. Why is $\angle YWX \cong \angle ZWX$?

f. Why is $\overleftrightarrow{XW} \perp \overline{YZ}$?

g. Why is $\overleftrightarrow{XW}$ the perpendicular bisector of $\overline{YZ}$?

Test Yourself

Suppose you wish to prove $\triangle GHI \cong \triangle XYZ$. Identify three pairs of corresponding parts you could use when using the indicated property.

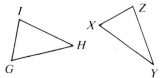

1. SSS Property   **2.** SAS Property

3. ASA Property

Draw a figure to fit each description.

4. Obtuse triangle inscribed in a circle

5. Triangle circumscribed about a circle

6. Line tangent to a circle

7. Draw an acute triangle. Construct the circle that is circumscribed about the triangle.

Look at $\odot O$. $\overleftrightarrow{OX}$ is the perpendicular bisector of $\overline{CD}$.

$OC = 8$, $CM = 5$,

$m\angle COD = 86°$

8. $CD = $?

9. $DO = $?

10. $m \overset{\frown}{CD} = $?°

11. $m \overset{\frown}{CX} = $?°

DID YOU KNOW THAT...

For over 2000 years, mathematicians searched for a method to trisect any angle using only compass and straightedge. *Some* angles *can* be trisected and the search for a general solution led to the discovery of many new mathematical concepts. However, in the nineteenth century it was proved that it is impossible to trisect *all* angles using only compass and straightedge.

4-9
Altitudes of a Triangle

The distance from a point to a line (or part of a line) is determined along the segment that is perpendicular to the line. For example, the distance from A to line l is found by measuring the length of $\overline{AE}$, since it is the only segment from A perpendicular to l.

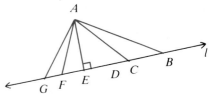

An *altitude* of a triangle is a segment from one vertex perpendicular to the line containing the opposite side, which is called the *base*. Any of its sides can be considered the base of a triangle.

The following figures show the three pairs of bases and altitudes for each of two triangles.

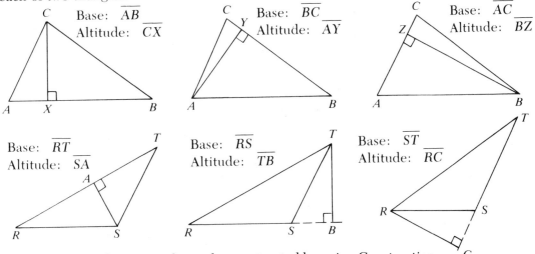

Base: $\overline{AB}$
Altitude: $\overline{CX}$

Base: $\overline{BC}$
Altitude: $\overline{AY}$

Base: $\overline{AC}$
Altitude: $\overline{BZ}$

Base: $\overline{RT}$
Altitude: $\overline{SA}$

Base: $\overline{RS}$
Altitude: $\overline{TB}$

Base: $\overline{ST}$
Altitude: $\overline{RC}$

An altitude of any triangle can be constructed by using Construction 9, the construction of a perpendicular from a point to a line. The following EXPLORING develops a surprising fact about the three altitudes of a triangle.

EXPLORING
The Intersection of the Altitudes of a Triangle

1. Draw an acute triangle. Construct the three altitudes of the triangle.
2. Draw an obtuse triangle. Construct the three altitudes of the triangle.
3. Draw a right triangle. Construct the three altitudes of the triangle.

If your constructions were done correctly, you discovered the following conclusion:

> **The three altitudes of any triangle meet at a single point. This point is called the *orthocenter*.**

Look at △*ABC*.

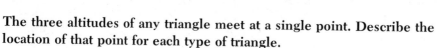

1. How many segments can be drawn from *A*?
2. How many segments from *A* will be perpendicular to $\overline{BC}$?
3. How many vertices does △*ABC* have? How many sides?
4. How many bases does △*ABC* have? How many altitudes?

The three altitudes of any triangle meet at a single point. Describe the location of that point for each type of triangle.

5. Acute   6. Right   7. Obtuse

CLASS PRACTICE

The base of each figure is indicated. Identify the segment that is the altitude to that base.

1.   Base: $\overline{AB}$

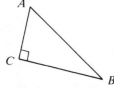

2.   Base: $\overline{XY}$

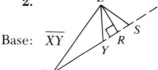

3.   Base: $\overline{ST}$

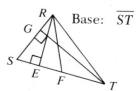

Draw a triangle similar to, but larger than, each one shown. Construct the altitude to $\overline{AB}$.

4.

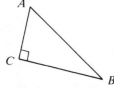

5.

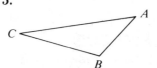

6.

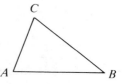

Using graph paper, draw a triangle to fit each description. The height is the length of the altitude.

7. Acute triangle with a base length of 4 and a height of 3

8. Right triangle with a base length of 6 and a height of 4
9. Obtuse triangle with a base length of 7 and a height of 4
10. Three noncongruent triangles with a base length of 8 and a height of 5

EXERCISES

— A —

For △ABC shown, identify the side opposite each vertex.

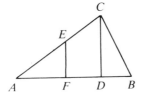

1. A
2. B
3. C

Look at the diagram.

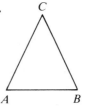

4. If $\overline{CD}$ is an altitude of △ABC, $m\angle CDA = $?°
5. What side of △ABC is the base for the altitude $\overline{CD}$?
6. Identify the base for the altitude from vertex B.
7. $\overline{EF} \perp \overline{AB}$. Why is $\overline{EF}$ not an altitude for △ABC?

For each triangle, the base is indicated. Identify the segment that is the altitude to that base.

8.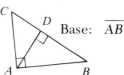
Base: $\overline{AB}$

9.
Base: $\overline{RT}$

10.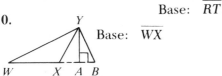
Base: $\overline{WX}$

Draw a triangle similar to, but larger than, each one shown. Construct the altitude to $\overline{AB}$.

11.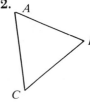

12.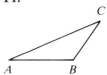

13.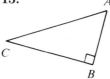

14.

15.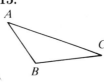

16.

— B —

Using graph paper, draw a triangle to fit each description. The height is the length of the altitude.

17. Acute triangle with a base length of 6 and height of 3
18. Right triangle with a base length of 4 and height of 3
19. Obtuse triangle with a base length of 5 and height of 4
20. Three noncongruent triangles with a base length of 6 and height of 4

Constructions and Properties of Congruent Triangles   **169**

4-10
Angle Bisectors and Medians of a Triangle

Suppose the bisector of some angle has been constructed and several points have been located on this bisector, as shown. From each of these points, a segment perpendicular to each side of the angle has been constructed. Notice that each point seems to be equidistant from the sides of the angle. This illustrates the following property of angle bisectors.

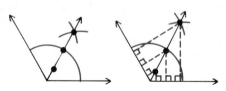

> **Each point on the bisector of an angle is equidistant from the sides of the angle.**

The following EXPLORING develops a surprising fact about the bisectors of the three angles of any triangle.

EXPLORING
The Intersection of the Angle Bisectors of a Triangle

1. Draw an acute triangle. Construct the bisector of each angle.
2. Draw an obtuse triangle. Construct the bisector of each angle.
3. Draw a right triangle. Construct the bisector of each angle.

If your constructions were done correctly, you discovered the following conclusion:

> **The angle bisectors of any triangle meet at a single point. This point is called the *incenter*.**

In △ABC shown, the bisectors of the three angles have been constructed. O is the intersection of the bisectors. $\overline{OX}$, $\overline{OY}$, and $\overline{OZ}$ have been drawn perpendicular from O to each side of the triangle. These segments represent the distance of O from the sides of the triangle.

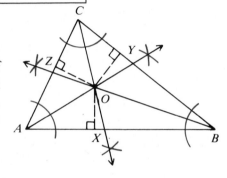

Since each point on the bisector of an angle is equidistant from the sides of the angle, O can be shown to be equidistant from the sides of $\triangle ABC$. This fact can be used to develop a method for constructing a circle inscribed in a triangle. Construction 11 shows the steps for this construction.

Construction 11

A Circle Inscribed in a Triangle

Problem
Construct a circle inscribed in $\triangle ABC$.

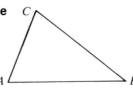

Procedure
Step 1 Construct the bisectors of any two angles of $\triangle ABC$. The angle bisectors you constructed will intersect at a point. Label this point O.

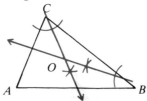

Step 2 Construct a perpendicular from O to $\overline{AB}$. Label the point of intersection X.

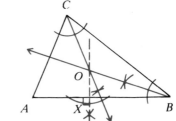

Step 3 Construct a circle using O as the center and $\overline{OX}$ as the radius. You are done.

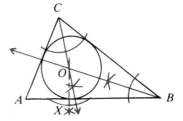

A *median* of a triangle is a segment from a vertex to the midpoint of the opposite side. Every triangle has three medians.

In $\triangle RST$ shown, $\overline{RX}$ is the median from R to X, the midpoint of $\overline{TS}$.

The following EXPLORING develops a surprising fact about the medians of any triangle.

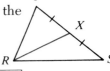

EXPLORING

The Intersection of the Medians of a Triangle

1. Draw an acute triangle. Locate the midpoint of each side and draw the three medians.

2. Draw an obtuse triangle. Locate the midpoint of each side and draw the three medians.

3. Draw a right triangle. Locate the midpoint of each side and draw three medians. If your constructions were done correctly, you discovered the following conclusion:

> **The three medians of any triangle meet at a single point. This point is called the *centroid*.**

DISCUSS

The three angle bisectors of any triangle meet at a single point. Describe the location of that point for each type of triangle.

  1. Acute   **2.** Right   **3.** Obtuse

The three medians of any triangle meet at a single point. Describe the location of that point for each type of triangle.

  4. Acute   **5.** Right   **6.** Obtuse

  7. Look at Construction 11. Suppose the bisector of $\angle A$ were also constructed. Why must it also pass through point O?

EXERCISES

_ A _

Look at the figure.
$\overrightarrow{AC}$ is the angle bisector.

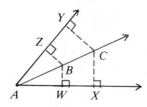

  1. If $CY = 5$, then $CX = $? .
  2. If $BW = 4$, then $BX = $? .

Draw a triangle similar to, but larger than, each one shown. (a) Construct the bisector of $\angle D$. (b) Locate the midpoint of $\overline{EF}$ and draw the median from D to $\overline{EF}$.

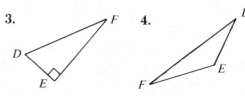

3.   **4.**

5.

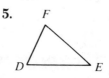

Perform the indicated constructions.
  6. Draw an acute triangle. Construct a circle inscribed in the triangle.

7. Draw an obtuse triangle. Construct a circle inscribed in the triangle.

_ B _

Refer to the conclusions from the EXPLORINGs on pages 162, 167, 170, and 171. Using these results, state the location—inside, outside, or on the triangle—of the point of intersection for (a) any acute triangle, (b) any right triangle, and (c) any obtuse triangle.

8. Angle Bisectors

9. Perpendicular Bisectors of Sides

10. Altitudes

11. Medians

_ C _

12. Look at $\triangle XYZ$. $\triangle XYZ$ is isosceles with $\overline{XY} \cong \overline{XZ}$. $\overrightarrow{XC}$ is the bisector of the vertex angle of $\triangle YXZ$.

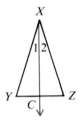

a. Look at $\triangle YCX$ and $\triangle ZCX$. What pairs of corresponding sides and angles are congruent because of the given information?

b. What property can be used to prove $\triangle YCX \cong \triangle ZCX$?

c. Why is $\angle XCY \cong \angle XCZ$?

d. Why is $\overleftrightarrow{XC} \perp \overleftrightarrow{YZ}$?

e. Why is $\overline{YC} \cong \overline{ZC}$?

f. Why is $\overleftrightarrow{XC}$ the perpendicular bisector of $\overline{YZ}$?

g. Why is $\overline{XC}$ the altitude from X to $\overline{YZ}$?

h. Why is $\overline{XC}$ the median from X to $\overline{YZ}$?

i. Suppose the bisector of one of the base angles were drawn. $\overleftrightarrow{YD}$ is the bisector of $\angle XYZ$. Do you think this angle bisector is on the same line as the perpendicular bisector of $\overline{XZ}$? as the altitude from Y to $\overline{XZ}$? as the median from Y to $\overline{XZ}$?

13. Draw an equilateral triangle and label it like the triangle in Exercise 12. Answer the questions from Exercise 12 for this triangle.

═══════ **MORE EXPLORING** ═══════
The Balance Point of a Triangle

Use a piece of cardboard.
1. Draw a triangle.
2. Draw the three medians.
3. Cut out the triangle.
4. Insert the point of a well-sharpened pencil through the point of intersection of the medians of the triangle.
5. What happens to the triangle? Does it tilt or remain level? Can you spin the triangle?
6. Why is the intersection of the medians called the *centroid* or *balance point* of the triangle?

4-11

Constructing Tangents

This lesson shows the steps for two additional constructions involving tangents and circles.

Construction 12

The Tangent to a Circle at a Point on the Circle

Problem

Construct a tangent to $\odot O$ at point A.

Procedure

Step 1 Draw circle O and select any point A on it.

Step 2 Draw $\overrightarrow{OA}$.

Step 3 Construct a line through A perpendicular to $\overrightarrow{OA}$. $\overleftrightarrow{AB}$ is tangent to $\odot O$. You are done.

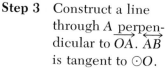

Notice in the steps for Construction 12 that $\overline{OA}$ is a radius of $\odot O$ and that the tangent line, $\overleftrightarrow{AB}$, was constructed perpendicular to $\overline{OA}$ at point A. This illustrates the following property of tangents to a circle:

> **The tangent at a point on a circle is perpendicular to the radius drawn to that point.**

Construction 13

Tangents to a Circle from a Point Outside the Circle

Problem

Construct the tangents to $\odot O$ from point A outside the circle.

Procedure

Step 1 Draw circle O and point A outside the circle.

Step 2 Draw $\overline{OA}$.

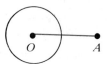

Step 3 Locate the mid-point M of $\overline{OA}$ by constructing the perpendicular bisector of $\overline{OA}$.

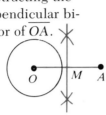

Step 4 Draw a circle with center M and radius MA.

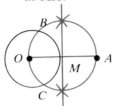

Step 5 Draw $\overleftrightarrow{AB}$ and $\overleftrightarrow{AC}$. You are done. (The dashed segments $\overline{OB}$ and $\overline{OC}$ are *not* part of the construction.)

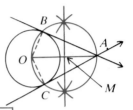

This construction illustrates the following additional properties of tangents:

> Exactly two tangents can be drawn to a circle from an outside point.
>
> The two segments tangent to a circle from an outside point are congruent.

DISCUSS

Look at Construction 13.
1. $\angle OCA$ and $\angle OBA$ are both inscribed angles of $\odot M$. Identify the intercepted arc for each angle.
2. What is the measure of $\angle OCA$? of $\angle OBA$?
3. $\overline{OB}$ and $\overline{OC}$ are radii of $\odot O$. Why are $\overleftrightarrow{AB}$ and $\overleftrightarrow{AC}$ both tangent to $\odot O$?

EXERCISES

1. Draw a circle and select any point outside the circle. Construct two lines through this point that are tangent to the circle.
2. Draw a circle and select any point on the circle. Construct the line tangent to the circle at this point.

Look at the drawing of circle D.

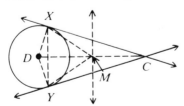

$\overleftrightarrow{CX}$ and $\overleftrightarrow{CY}$ are tangent to $\odot D$ at points X and Y.
3. $\overline{XY}$ is a ? of $\odot D$.
4. $m\angle DXC$ = ?°
5. $m\angle DYC$ = ?°
6. If $DX = 8$, then $DY =$? .
7. What kind of triangle is $\triangle XDY$?
8. If $CX = 20$, then $CY =$? .

Geometry on the Job
DRAFTER

Yolanda Kingston is a drafter for an architectural firm. Working from architects' sketches, she prepares careful drawings of planned buildings and landscapes. Her tools include compass and straightedge. She is allowed to measure with ruler and protractor, but the ability to do constructions is helpful.

EXERCISES

For each of these sketches, prepare a drawing that accurately represents the relationships of lines and angles.

1.

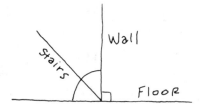

2.

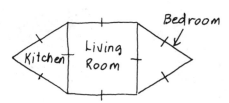

3.

ARITHMETIC REVIEW — *Multiplying Decimals*

Multiplication with decimals is like multiplication with whole numbers.

However, you must know how to locate the decimal point properly in the product.

Examples

14	1.4	1.4	0.14	0.14
× 3	× 3	× 0.3	× 0.3	× 0.03
42	4.2	0.42	0.042	0.0042

> When multiplying decimals, the number of digits to the right of the decimal point in the product is the sum of the number of digits to the right of the decimal point in both factors.

This pattern can be verified by using fractions:

$$1.4 \times 0.3 = 1\tfrac{4}{10} \times \tfrac{3}{10} = \tfrac{14}{10} \times \tfrac{3}{10} = \tfrac{42}{100} = 0.42$$

EXERCISES

Copy each product. Insert the decimal point in the proper location. Write extra zeros if necessary.

1. 3.2		**2.** 3.2		**3.** 0.32		**4.** 0.32	
× 4		× 0.4		× 0.4		× 0.04	
1 2 8		1 2 8		1 2 8		1 2 8	

5. 3.24	**6.** 0.368	**7.** 47.6	**8.** 8.2
× 0.03	× 0.6	× 1.2	× 0.65
9 7 2	2 2 0 8	5 7 1 2	5 3 3 0

Multiply.

9. 65	**10.** 4.2	**11.** 0.37	**12.** 4.5
× 0.05	× 8	× 0.8	× 0.5

13. 3.14	**14.** 6.05	**15.** 8.04	**16.** 0.596
× 16	× 0.04	× 0.9	× 2.8

17. 9.3	**18.** 2.5	**19.** 73.9	**20.** 846
× 70	× 2.5	× 0.06	× 0.007

Chapter 4 Review

Vocabulary

The following terms and symbols were introduced in this chapter. You should be able to write a brief description, draw a picture, or give an example to illustrate the meaning of each.

altitude (p. 167)

ASA Property (p. 143)

circumscribed (p. 159)

common tangent (p. 159)

construction (p. 132)

equidistant (p. 161)

included angle (side) (p. 141)

inscribed (p. 159)

median (p. 171)

point of tangency (p. 159)

SAS Property (p. 142)

SSS Property (p. 134)

tangent (p. 159)

Skills Checklist

In Chapter 4 you learned several geometric constructions; developed and reviewed several geometric properties illustrated by these constructions; and learned how to use congruent triangles to verify geometric properties.

The following list indicates the major skills, facts, and results you should have mastered in this chapter:

● Recognize and use the geometric facts illustrated by the constructions learned:

- The Triangle Inequality Property (**4-1**, pp. 132–137)
- SSS Property (**4-1**, pp. 132–137)
- SAS Property (**4-3**, pp. 141–145)
- ASA Property (**4-3**, pp. 141–145)
- If two coplanar lines are perpendicular to the same line, then the two lines are parallel. (**4-4**, pp. 146–151)
- Properties of perpendicular bisectors of segments and of non-parallel chords of circles. (**4-8**, pp. 161–166)
- The perpendicular bisectors of the sides of any triangle intersect at a point. The location of this point depends on the type of triangle. (**4-8**, pp. 161–166)
- The three altitudes of any triangle intersect at a point. The location depends on the type of triangle. (**4-9**, pp. 167–169)
- The three angle bisectors of any triangle intersect at a point inside the triangle. (**4-10**, pp. 170–173)
- The three medians of any triangle intersect at a point inside the triangle. (**4-10**, pp. 170–173)
- Each point on the bisector of an angle is equidistant from the sides of the angle. (**4-10**, pp. 170–173)

- The tangent at a point on a circle is perpendicular to the radius drawn to that point. (**4-11,** pp. 174–175)
- There are exactly two tangents to a circle from an outside point and these tangent segments are congruent. (**4-11,** pp. 174–175)
- Know how to use congruent triangles to prove pairs of angles or segments congruent and to prove properties of polygons. (**4-5—4-6,** pp. 152–158)
- Know how to do Constructions 1–13. (A complete listing of constructions appears at the back of the text.) (**4-1—4-4,** pp. 132–151; **4-8,** pp. 161–166; **4-10—4-11,** pp. 170–175)

Exercises

State whether each set of lengths can be used to construct a triangle. (4-1)

1. 5 cm, 6 cm, 9 cm
2. 5 cm, 5 cm, 5 cm
3. 5 cm, 3 cm, 9 cm
4. 8 cm, 4 cm, 5 cm
5. cm, 8 cm, 4 cm
6. 5 cm, 10 cm, 6 cm

Find the indicated information.

7. Look at **△RIP.** Complete each statement. (4-3)

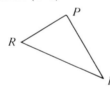

   a. ∠P is opposite side ? .
   b. ∠P is included by sides ? and ? .
   c. $\overline{PR}$ is opposite ∠ ? .
   d. $\overline{PR}$ is included by ∠ ? and ∠ ? .

Use segments y and z as needed. Construct a triangle to fit each description. (4-1)

$$\underline{}\ x$$
$$\underline{}\ y$$
$$\underline{}\ z$$

8. All sides of length y
9. Two sides of length z and one side of length y

Use each given method and the indicated sides and angles to construct a triangle congruent to △CON shown.

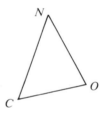

10. SSS: $\overline{CO}$, $\overline{CN}$, and $\overline{ON}$ (4-1)
11. SAS: $\overline{CO}$, ∠C, and $\overline{CN}$ (4-3)
12. ASA: $\overline{ON}$, ∠N, and ∠O (4-3)

For each exercise, copy ∠E shown. (4-2)

13. Construct an angle congruent to ∠E.
14. Construct the bisector of ∠E.

Suppose you wish to prove △DEF ≅ △MNO shown. Identify three pairs of

corresponding parts you could use when using the indicated property.

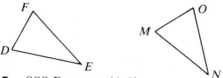

15. SSS Property (4–1)
16. SAS Property (4–3)
17. ASA Property (4–3)

Draw a segment.
18. Construct its perpendicular bisector. (4–4)

Use a diagram like the one shown.
19. Construct the line through P that is perpendicular to l. (4–4)
20. Construct the line through Q that is perpendicular to l. (4–4)

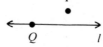

Find the indicated information.
21. Look at the figure. $\overleftrightarrow{CD}$ is the perpendicular bisector of $\overline{AB}$. (4–8)
    a. If AB = 10 cm, AD = ? cm.
    b. Does CA = CB?
    c. Is ∠DAC ≅ ∠DBC?
    d. Does CA = EA?
22. Look at ⊙D. Identify each of the following. (4–7)

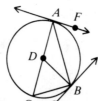

    a. All tangents
    b. All points of tangency
    c. Triangle inscribed in a circle

For each exercise copy △DEF shown.
23. Construct the altitude from D to $\overline{EF}$. (4–8)
24. Construct the circle circumscribed about △DEF. (4–9)

Find the indicated information.
25. Draw three noncollinear points. Construct the circle passing through all three points. (4–8)
26. Look at △ABC. Identify each of the following. (4–9)
    a. Side opposite point A
    b. Altitude if $\overline{BC}$ is base
    c. Altitude if $\overline{AB}$ is base

Draw a figure to fit each description. (4–7)
27. Quadrilateral inscribed in a circle
28. Triangle circumscribed about a circle
29. Line tangent to a circle
30. All common tangents to two circles like those shown

Classify each statement as true or false. (4–10)
31. The medians of any triangle intersect at a point inside the triangle.
32. A median is sometimes perpendicular to a side of a triangle.
33. The angle bisectors of any triangle intersect at a point inside the triangle.

Find the indicated information.
34. Draw a triangle similar to, but larger than, △XYZ shown. Construct the median from X to $\overline{YZ}$. (4–10)

CROSSROADS

Transversals and Angle-Measure Sums for Polygons

5-1

Angles Formed by Transversals

In the next few lessons you will learn some properties of angles formed 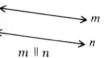 when parallel lines are intersected (crossed) by other lines.

$m \parallel n$

A *transversal* is a line that intersects two or more lines, each at a different point.

t_1 is a transversal.

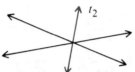

t_2 is not a transversal.

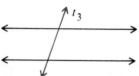

t_3 is a transversal.

Although transversals may occur for lines that are not parallel, most of the work in this chapter will be with transversals for parallel lines.

In the figure below, transversal t intersects lines a and b. Notice that eight angles are formed, four *interior angles* inside or between lines a and b and four *exterior angles* outside lines a and b.

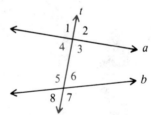

t is a transversal for lines a and b.
$\angle 3$, $\angle 4$, $\angle 5$, and $\angle 6$ are interior angles.
$\angle 1$, $\angle 2$, $\angle 7$, and $\angle 8$ are exterior angles.
$\angle 1$ and $\angle 3$, $\angle 2$ and $\angle 4$, $\angle 5$ and $\angle 7$, and
$\angle 6$ and $\angle 8$ are pairs of congruent vertical angles.

Certain *pairs* of angles determined by a transversal have special names. In the figure shown here, $\angle 1$ and $\angle 2$ are a pair of *alternate interior angles*. The word "alternate" tells you that these angles are on *opposite* sides of the transversal l. $\angle 3$ and $\angle 4$ are also a pair of alternate interior angles.

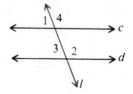

Notice that alternate interior angles have these features:
* They are both interior angles.
* They have different vertices.
* They are on opposite sides of the transversal.

In the figure shown here, $\angle 1$ and $\angle 2$ are a pair of *corresponding angles*. The word "corresponding" tells you that these angles are in corresponding positions with respect to the two lines (e and f). The following pairs of angles are also corresponding angles: $\angle 3$ and $\angle 4$, $\angle 5$ and $\angle 6$, and $\angle 7$ and $\angle 8$.

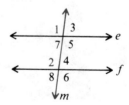

Notice that corresponding angles have these features:
- One angle is an interior angle while the other is an exterior angle.
- They have different vertices.
- They are on the same side of the transversal.

DISCUSS

1. Describe how the use of the term "parallel" in the term "parallel bars" in gymnastics is consistent with our use of the term in geometry.
2. Describe some other everyday uses of the term "parallel."

CLASS PRACTICE

Look at lines *l* and *m* crossed by line *t*. Identify each of the following.

1. Transversal
2. Four interior angles
3. Four exterior angles
4. Four pairs of vertical angles
5. Four pairs of corresponding angles
6. Two pairs of alternate interior angles
7. Two pairs of interior angles on the same side of the transversal
8. Two pairs of exterior angles on the same side of the transversal

Look at lines *n* and *p* crossed by lines *l* and *m*. Identify each of the following.

9. Two lines for which *l* is a transversal
10. Two lines for which *n* is a transversal
11. Four interior angles along transversal *p*
12. Four exterior angles along transversal *n*

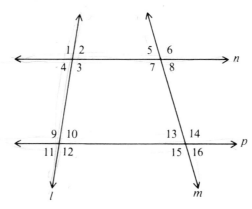

Transversals and Angle-Measure Sums for Polygons 183

— **A** —

1. Look at the figure. Identify each of the following.

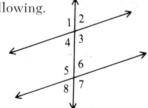

   a. Four interior angles
   b. Four exterior angles
   c. Two pairs of alternate interior angles
   d. Four pairs of corresponding angles
   e. Four pairs of vertical angles

2. Look at lines m and l cut by lines r and s. Find each of the following.

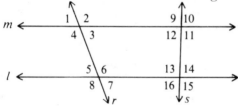

   a. Four interior angles along transversal m
   b. Four exterior angles along transversal r
   c. Two pairs of alternate interior angles along transversal s
   d. Two transversals for lines r and s
   e. Two pairs of alternate interior angles along transversal m
   f. Four pairs of corresponding angles along transversal l

   g. Two pairs of interior angles on the same side of transversal r
   h. Two pairs of exterior angles on the same side of transversal m

Look at the two lines cut by a transversal. Classify each pair of angles listed as (a) alternate interior angles, (b) corresponding angles, (c) vertical angles, (d) interior angles on the same side of the transversal, (e) adjacent supplementary angles, or (f) none of the above.

3. $\angle 2$ and $\angle 8$
4. $\angle 2$ and $\angle 6$
5. $\angle 4$ and $\angle 5$
6. $\angle 5$ and $\angle 7$
7. $\angle 6$ and $\angle 7$
8. $\angle 1$ and $\angle 3$
9. $\angle 1$ and $\angle 6$
10. $\angle 2$ and $\angle 7$

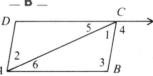

— **B** —

Look at $ABCD$. Complete each statement.

11. $\angle 1$ and $\angle 2$ are alternate interior angles determined by lines ? and ? and the transversal $\overleftrightarrow{AC}$.

12. $\angle 3$ and $\angle 4$ are alternate interior angles determined by lines $\overleftrightarrow{AB}$ and ? and the transversal ? .

13. $\angle 5$ and $\angle 6$ are alternate interior angles determined by lines ? and ? and the transversal ? .

DID YOU KNOW THAT....

In 1300 the use of Hindu-Arabic numerals (0, 1, . . . , 9) was forbidden in commercial documents and in the banks of some European cities.

5-2

Transversals and Interior Angles

When two parallel lines are cut by a transversal, each of the eight angles formed has a measure less than 180°. In the next two lessons you will learn some useful relationships among the measures of those angles.

EXPLORING

Parallel Lines and the Measures of Interior Angles

1. Use the two edges of a ruler to draw two parallel lines. Then draw any transversal *t*. Label the interior angles as shown.
2. Use a protractor to measure ∠1, ∠2, ∠3, and ∠4. Which pairs of angles are congruent? Which pairs are supplementary?
3. Repeat steps 1–2 using a different pair of parallel lines and a different position for the transversal. Do you get the same results?

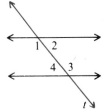

If you did the preceding EXPLORING carefully, you discovered the following conclusions:

> **If two parallel lines are cut by a transversal, then each pair of alternate interior angles are congruent.**
> **If two parallel lines are cut by a transversal, then each pair of interior angles on the same side of the transversal are supplementary.**

The above conclusions are true only when the lines cut by the transversal are parallel. This can be shown by measurement.

In the figure shown, lines *l* and *m* are *not* parallel. The pairs of alternate interior angles (∠1 and ∠3; ∠2 and ∠4) are *not* congruent and the pairs of interior angles on the same side of the transversal (∠1 and ∠4; ∠2 and ∠3) are *not* supplementary.

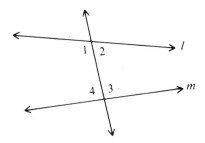

The next EXPLORING indicates two ways to show that two lines are parallel to each other.

EXPLORING

Making Lines Parallel

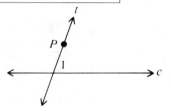

1. Draw two intersecting lines t and c. Label point P on t and $\angle 1$ as shown.

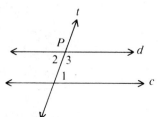

2. Using a protractor and a straightedge, draw a line d through point P so that $\angle 1 \cong \angle 2$. ($\angle 1$ and $\angle 2$ are a pair of alternate interior angles.)

3. Why is $\angle 2$ supplementary to $\angle 3$? Why is $\angle 1$ supplementary to $\angle 3$?

4. What is the relationship between the interior angles on the same side of the transversal t?

5. What seems to be the relationship between lines c and d?

6. Repeat steps 1–5 for a different pair of intersecting lines for which $\angle 1$ has a different measure. Do you get the same results?

If you did the preceding EXPLORING carefully, you discovered the following conclusions:

> **If two lines are cut by a transversal so that one pair of alternate interior angles are congruent, then the lines are parallel.**
>
> **If two lines are cut by a transversal so that the interior angles on one side of the transversal are supplementary, then the lines are parallel.**

DISCUSS

1. Explain the difference between the two conclusions from the first EXPLORING and the two from the second EXPLORING.

2. Describe two methods for proving that two lines are parallel.

3. Explain how the conclusions in the first EXPLORING could be used to show that in any parallelogram each pair of consecutive angles are supplementary and each pair of opposite angles are congruent.

Look at the parallel lines a and b cut by transversal t. Identify each of the following.

1. Angle congruent to $\angle 1$
2. Angle congruent to $\angle 4$
3. Two angles supplementary to $\angle$
4. Two angles supplementary to $\angle 3$

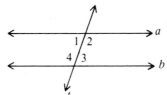

Look at parallel lines l and m cut by two transversals. Find the measure of each indicated angle.

5. $\angle 1$	6. $\angle 2$
7. $\angle 3$	8. $\angle 4$
9. $\angle 5$	10. $\angle 6$
11. $\angle 7$	12. $\angle 8$

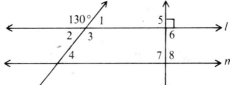

EXERCISES

— A —

Look at parallel lines a and b cut by transversal t. Identify each of the following angles.

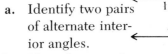

1. Angle congruent to $\angle 1$
2. Angle congruent to $\angle 4$
3. Two angles supplementary to $\angle 2$
4. Two angles supplementary to $\angle 3$

Look at parallel lines a and b cut by parallel lines c and d. Find the measure of each indicated angle.

5. $\angle 1$	6. $\angle 2$
7. $\angle 3$	8. $\angle 4$
9. $\angle 5$	10. $\angle 6$
11. $\angle 7$	12. $\angle 8$

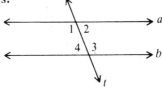

13. Look at lines l and m cut by a transversal.
    a. Identify two pairs of alternate interior angles.
    b. Identify two pairs of interior angles on the same side of the transversal.
    c. If $\angle 1 \cong \angle$? , then $l \parallel m$.
    d. If $m \angle 1 + m \angle$? $= 180°$, then $l \parallel m$.
    e. If $\angle 2 \cong \angle$? , then $l \parallel m$.

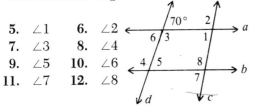

Find the measure of each angle.

14. a. $\angle M$
    b. $\angle Q$
    c. $\angle R$

    Parallelogram

15. a. $\angle 1$
    b. $\angle 2$
    c. $\angle 3$

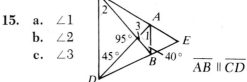

$\overline{AB} \parallel \overline{CD}$

16.
 a. ∠EFG
 b. ∠HEG
 c. ∠HGE
 d. ∠EGF

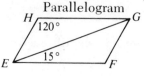
Parallelogram

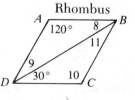
Rhombus

17.
 a. ∠8
 b. ∠9
 c. ∠10
 d. ∠11

— B —

18. Look at the figure showing lines r, s, x, and y. Identify the lines, *if any*, that must be parallel if each statement is true. 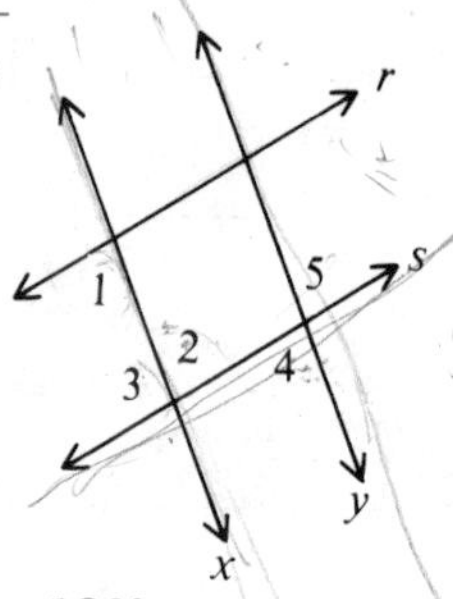
 a. ∠1 ≅ ∠2
 b. $m∠1 + m∠3 = 180°$
 c. ∠2 ≅ ∠4

d. $m∠2 + m∠3 = 180°$
e. ∠4 ≅ ∠5

19. To Be Proved: The diagonals of a parallelogram bisect each other.

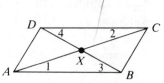

Given: ABCD is a parallelogram.

Prove: $\overline{AX} ≅ \overline{CX}$ $\overline{BX} ≅ \overline{DX}$

 a. ABCD is a parallelogram. Why is $\overline{CD} ∥ \overline{AB}$?
 b. Look at △AXB and △CXD. Why is $\overline{AB} ≅ \overline{CD}$? ∠1 ≅ ∠2? ∠3 ≅ ∠4?
 c. What property can be used to prove △AXB ≅ △CXD?
 d. Why is $\overline{AX} ≅ \overline{CX}$? $\overline{BX} ≅ \overline{DX}$?

Everyday Geometry
Lattices

A *lattice* is a structure of crossed wooden or metal strips. These strips usually form a diagonal pattern of open spaces between the strips. Fences and trellises are good examples of latticework. Lattices often illustrate several properties of parallel lines.

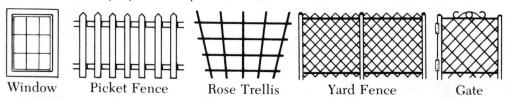

Window   Picket Fence   Rose Trellis   Yard Fence   Gate

EXERCISES

Answer these questions about the latticework in each figure above.
 1. Describe the types of quadrilaterals formed by the latticework.
 2. State properties of parallel lines illustrated by the latticework.

5-3

Transversals and Corresponding Angles

In this lesson you will learn more relationships among the measures of the angles formed when parallel lines are cut by a transversal.

EXPLORING

Parallel Lines and the Measures of Corresponding Angles

1. Use the conclusions from Lesson 5-2 and the facts that (a) vertical angles are congruent and (b) the sum of the measures of supplementary angles is 180° to find the measures of the other angles in the figure shown.

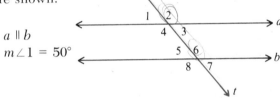

$a \parallel b$

$m\angle 1 = 50°$

2. Which pairs of angles are corresponding angles?
3. How do the measures of corresponding angles compare?

If you did the preceding EXPLORING carefully, you discovered the following conclusion:

> **If two parallel lines are cut by a transversal, each pair of corresponding angles are congruent.**

As was the case with the conclusions in Lesson 5-2, the above conclusion is true *only when the lines cut by a transversal are parallel*.

For example, in the figure shown, lines c and d are not parallel. Notice that the corresponding angles (such as $\angle 1$ and $\angle 2$) are *not* congruent.

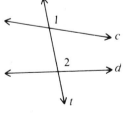

The next EXPLORING indicates another way to show that two lines are parallel to each other. Recall that the following statements are true:

- If two lines are cut by a transversal so that the alternate interior angles are congruent, then the lines are parallel.
- Vertical angles are congruent.

EXPLORING

Making Lines Parallel

1. Look at the figure shown. Why is $\angle 2 \cong \angle 3$?
2. Why is $\angle 1 \cong \angle 2$?
3. Why is $a \parallel b$?

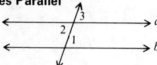

$\angle 1 \cong \angle 3$

$\angle 1$ and $\angle 3$ are corresponding angles.

If you did the preceding EXPLORING carefully, you discovered the following conclusion:

> **If two lines are cut by a transversal so that one pair of corresponding angles are congruent, then the lines are parallel.**

DISCUSS

Describe three methods for proving that two lines are parallel.

CLASS PRACTICE

Look at parallel lines l and m cut by transversal t. Identify each of the following.

1. Four pairs of corresponding angles
2. Three angles congruent to $\angle 2$
3. Three angles congruent to $\angle 5$

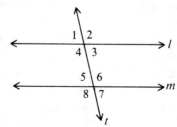

Look at the figure showing parallel lines r and s cut by two transversals. Find the measure of each indicated angle.

4. $\angle 1$ 5. $\angle 2$
6. $\angle 3$ 7. $\angle 4$
8. $\angle 5$ 9. $\angle 6$
10. $\angle 7$ 11. $\angle 8$

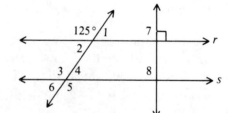

_ A _

1. Look at parallel lines *a* and *b* cut by transversal *t*. Identify each of the following.

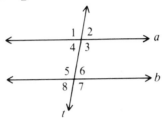

   a. Three angles congruent to ∠1
   b. Three angles supplementary to ∠1
   c. Four pairs of corresponding angles
   d. Three angles congruent to ∠2

Look at the figure with *a* ∥ *b* and *c* ∥ *d*. Find the measure of each indicated angle.

2. ∠1
3. ∠2
4. ∠3
5. ∠4
6. ∠5
7. ∠6
8. Look at lines *l* and *m* cut by a transversal.
   a. Identify two pairs of alternate interior angles.
   b. Identify two pairs of corresponding angles.
   c. Identify two pairs of interior angles on the same side of the transversal.

   d. If *m* ∠3 + *m* ∠ ? = 180°, then *l* ∥ *m*.
   e. If ∠2 ≅ ∠ ? , then *l* ∥ *m*.
   f. If ∠1 ≅ ∠ ? , then *l* ∥ *m*.

Find the measure of each indicated angle.

9. a. ∠1
   b. ∠2
   c. ∠3

   Rectangle

10. a. ∠4
    b. ∠5
    c. ∠6

    $\overline{AB}$ ∥ $\overline{CD}$

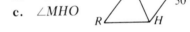

11. a. ∠MRH
    b. ∠RMH
    c. ∠MHO

    Rhombus

12. a. ∠IPH
    b. ∠IPL
    c. ∠PHI
    d. ∠LPH

    Parallelogram

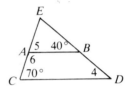

13. a. ∠1
    b. ∠2
    c. ∠3
    d. ∠4
    e. ∠5

    l ∥ *m*

14. a. ∠1
    b. ∠2
    c. ∠3
    d. ∠4

    l ∥ *m* and *r* ∥ *s*

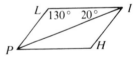

Answer questions 15–19 about parallelogram *PQRM*.

15. ∠1 and ∠3 are alternate interior angles determined by lines $\overleftrightarrow{QR}$ and $\overleftrightarrow{MP}$ and the transversal ? .

16. ∠2 and ∠4 are alternate interior angles determined by lines ? and $\overleftrightarrow{PQ}$ and the transversal ? .

17. ∠5 and ∠*MPQ* are corresponding angles determined by lines ? and ? and the transversal ? .

18. Are ∠2 and ∠3 interior angles on the same side of the transversal?

19. Are ∠3 and ∠5 alternate interior angles?

20. Look at lines *r* and *s* cut by lines *x* and *y*. Identify the lines, if any, that must be parallel if each statement is true.

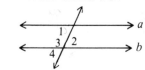

a. ∠1 ≅ ∠4
b. ∠4 ≅ ∠6
c. ∠8 ≅ ∠9
d. ∠4 ≅ ∠5
e. $m\angle 2 + m\angle 1 = 180°$

21. Look at lines *a* and *b* cut by a transversal. Suppose that $m\angle 1 = 65°$. What must be the measure of each angle in order that *a* ∥ *b*?

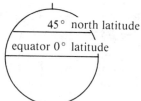

a. ∠2   b. ∠3   c. ∠4

Applications

Latitude and Longitude

The *latitude* of any point on Earth is measured in degrees north or south of the equator. Points with the same latitude form a circle around Earth. These circles are called *parallels of latitude*. Like parallel lines in a plane, these parallels of latitude never intersect.

Longitude is measured in degrees east or west of a line through Greenwich, England. Lines of longitude, called *meridians*, are half-circles from the North Pole to the South Pole. Each line of longitude is perpendicular to the equator.

Notice that unlike two lines in a plane, if two lines on a sphere are perpendicular to the same line, these two lines will intersect. In fact, any two lines of longitude will intersect at two points.

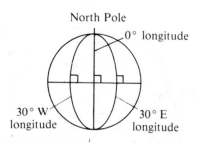

5-4
Constructing Parallel Lines

The constructions in this lesson describe three different methods for constructing the line parallel to a given line through a point not on the line. All these methods have been suggested by Exercises and EXPLORINGs from previous lessons and make use of constructions already learned.

Construction 14 uses properties of corresponding angles and is suggested by the EXPLORING on page 190.

Construction 14
(Using Corresponding Angles)

The Line Parallel to a Given Line Through a Point Not on the Line

Problem
Construct the line through P that is parallel to l.

Procedure
Step 1 Draw a line through P intersecting l.

Step 2 At vertex P, construct $\angle 2$ congruent to $\angle 1$. (See Construction 3 on page 138.) You are done.

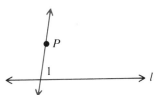

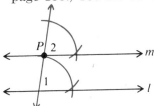

The next construction uses properties of perpendicular lines and depends on the fact that two coplanar lines perpendicular to the same line are parallel. This construction is suggested by the EXPLORING on page 148 and Exercise 12 on page 150.

Construction 15
(Using Perpendicular Lines)
The Line Parallel to a Given Line Through a Point Not on the Line

Problem
Construct the line through P that is parallel to l.

Procedure

Step 1 Construct line x through P perpendicular to l. (See Construction 9 on page 148.)

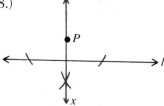

Step 2 Construct a line through P that is perpendicular to x. (See Construction 8 on page 147.) $m \parallel l$. You are done.

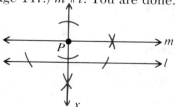

The following construction uses the facts that the opposite sides of a parallelogram are parallel and that a rhombus is a parallelogram having four congruent sides.

Construction 16

(Using a Rhombus)
The Line Parallel to a Given Line Through a Point Not on the Line

Problem

Construct the line through P that is parallel to l.

Procedure

Step 1 From P draw an arc intersecting l at A.

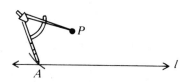

Step 2 Construct $\overline{AB}$ on l so that $\overline{AB} \cong \overline{PA}$. (See Construction 1 on page 132.) The dashed line is not part of the construction.

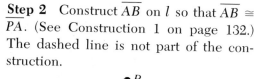

Step 3 Using the same compass setting (AB), locate point C equidistant from P and B. $(\overline{PC} \cong \overline{BC} \cong \overline{AB})$

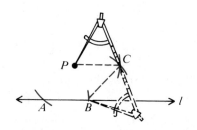

Step 4 Draw $\overleftrightarrow{PC}$. $\overleftrightarrow{PC} \parallel l$. You are done.

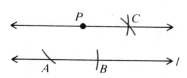

Look at Construction 14.

1. How many lines through P are parallel to l?
2. $\angle 2$ was constructed congruent to $\angle 1$. Why does this guarantee $m \parallel l$?

Look at Construction 15.

3. What property guarantees that $m \parallel l$?
4. Tell why Construction 15 may be considered a special case of Construction 14.

The figure shown is a completed copy of Construction 16. $\overline{PA}$ and $\overline{CB}$ have been drawn.

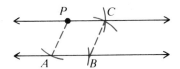

5. Why is $PABC$ a rhombus?
6. Why does this guarantee that $\overleftrightarrow{PC} \parallel l$?

EXERCISES

— A —

For each of Exercises 1–3, draw a figure like the one shown. Use the indicated Construction to construct the line through P that is parallel to l.

1. Construction 14
2. Construction 15
3. Construction 16
4. Draw a line l. Using any method presented in this lesson, construct two lines, one on each side of l, that are parallel to l.

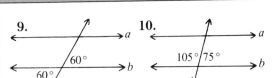

Using only the given information, can you conclude that $a \parallel b$?

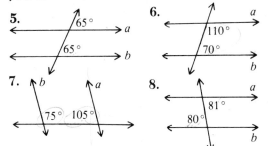

5. 65°, 65°
6. 110°, 70°
7. 75°, 105°
8. 81°, 80°

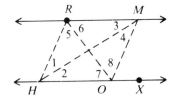

9. 60°, 60°
10. 105° / 75°

11. Look at rhombus $RHOM$. Identify each of the following.

a. Four transversals for $\overleftrightarrow{RM}$ and $\overleftrightarrow{HO}$
b. Three segments congruent to $\overline{RH}$
c. Three angles supplementary to $\angle MOH$
d. All angles congruent to $\angle 1$
e. All angles congruent to $\angle 5$

12. Look at the figure. Lines *l* and *m* are parallel.

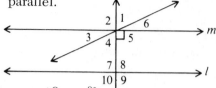

a. $m\angle 9 = $?°
b. $m\angle 7 = $?°
c. $m\angle 1 + m\angle 3 = $?°
d. If $m\angle 1 = 65°$, then $m\angle 6 = $?°
e. Identify five pairs of vertical angles.

— **B** —

13. Maple Road and Fourteen Mile Road are both perpendicular to Orchard Lake Road. Why are Maple Road and Fourteen Mile Road parallel to each other?

14. Draw a figure like the one shown. Construct a square with one vertex at *A* and one side along line *m*.

•*A*

←————————→ *m*

15. Draw a figure like the one shown. Construct a parallelogram having *A*, *B*, and *C* as three of its vertices.

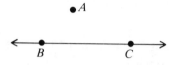

— **C** —

16. Construct a rectangle having two sides of length 5 cm and two sides of length 3 cm.

17. Another construction for parallel lines uses properties of alternate interior angles and is suggested by the EXPLORING on page 186. Draw a figure like the one shown and use this construction to construct the line through *P* that is parallel to *l*.

=== ***Test Yourself*** ===

For Exercises 1–6, look at the figure.

Lines *l* and *m* are parallel. Identify each of the following.

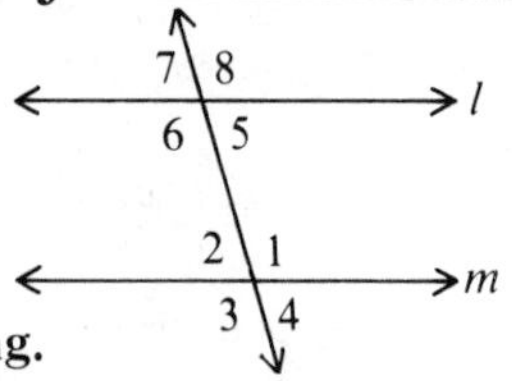

1. Two pairs of alternate interior angles
2. Two pairs of interior angles on the same side of the transversal
3. Four pairs of corresponding angles
4. All angles supplementary to $\angle 1$
5. All angles congruent to $\angle 1$

6. If $m\angle 2 = 60°$, then $m\angle 5 = $?° , $m\angle 6 = $?° , and $m\angle 7 = $?° .

Suppose that $m\angle 1 = 115°$. What must be the measure of each angle in order that *a* ∥ *b* in the figure shown?

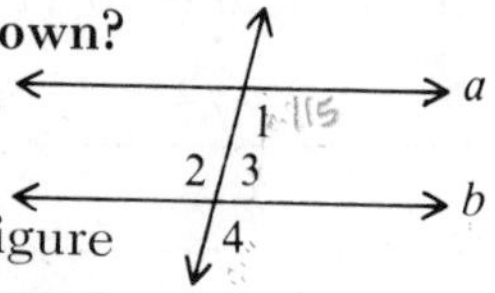

7. $\angle 2$
8. $\angle 3$
9. $\angle 4$
10. Copy the figure twice. In two ways construct through *X* the line parallel to *m*.

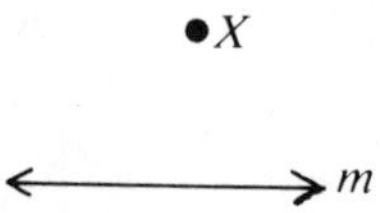

5-5

Interior-Angle Measures of a Triangle

In Chapter 3 you learned to classify triangles by their sides—scalene, isosceles, equilateral—and by their angles—obtuse, right, acute, equiangular—and developed some properties for certain types of triangles. In this lesson and the next, we will develop some additional properties of triangles, most of which are true for all triangles. The first EXPLORING develops the fact that in any triangle the sum of the measures of the interior angles is the same. In the series of pictures shown here, a model of $\triangle ABC$ is folded so that B lies on $\overline{AC}$ and so that A and C are at B.

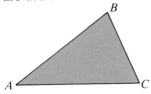
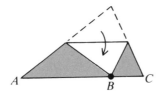
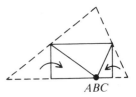

The folding suggests that $m\angle A + m\angle B + m\angle C = 180°$. The first EXPLORING shows why this is true for all triangles.

EXPLORING

The Sum of the Interior-Angle Measures of a Triangle

1. What is $m\angle 5 + m\angle 3 + m\angle 4$?
2. Why is $\angle 5 \cong \angle 1$? Why is $\angle 4 \cong \angle 2$?
3. What is $m\angle 1 + m\angle 3 + m\angle 2$?

$\angle 1$, $\angle 2$, and $\angle 3$ are the *interior angles* of $\triangle ABC$.

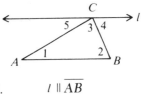

$l \parallel \overline{AB}$

If you did the preceding EXPLORING carefully, you discovered the following conclusion:

> **The sum of the interior-angle measures of any triangle is 180°.**

This fact can be used to develop more conclusions.

EXPLORING

Other Interior-Angle Relationships for Triangles

Part A

Look at equilateral triangle ABC. Recall that every
equilateral triangle is equiangular.

1. What is the sum of the interior-angle measures?
2. What is the measure of each interior angle?

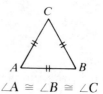

$\angle A \cong \angle B \cong \angle C$

Part B

Look at right triangle XYZ. Recall that complementary angles are two angles whose measures add up
to 90°.

1. What is $m\angle X + m\angle Y + m\angle Z$?
2. What is $m\angle Y$?   3. What is $m\angle X + m\angle Z$?

Part C

Look at $\triangle ABC$ and $\triangle DEF$. Notice that $\angle A \cong \angle D$
and $\angle C \cong \angle F$.

1. What is $m\angle B$? $m\angle E$?
2. How do the measures of $\angle B$ and $\angle E$ compare?

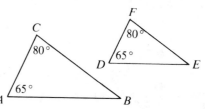

If you did the preceding EXPLORING carefully, you discovered the
following conclusions:

> The measure of each interior angle of an equilateral
> triangle is 60°.
>
> The acute angles of any right triangle are com-
> plementary.
>
> If two angles of one triangle are congruent to
> two angles of another triangle, then the third pair of
> angles are congruent.

CLASS PRACTICE

Find the measure of each indicated angle.

1. $\angle 1$

2. $\angle 2$
3. $\angle 3$

4. $\angle 4$

5. ∠5
6. ∠6

7. ∠7
8. ∠8
9. ∠9

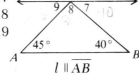

$l \parallel \overline{AB}$

10. ∠10
11. ∠11

EXERCISES

_ A _

Classify each statement as true or false. Give a reason or example to support each answer.

1. A triangle can have no obtuse angles.
2. A triangle can have exactly one obtuse angle.
3. A triangle can have two obtuse angles.
4. A triangle can have no right angles.
5. A triangle can have exactly one right angle.
6. A triangle can have two right angles.
7. A triangle can have no acute angles.
8. A triangle can have exactly one acute angle.
9. A triangle can have two acute angles.
10. It is possible to have a triangle with two 89° angles.
11. The acute angles of any right triangle are supplementary.
12. An equiangular triangle is a special kind of acute triangle.
13. It is possible to have a triangle with angles of measure 74°, 43°, and 62°.
14. At least one angle of a triangle must have a measure of at least 60°.
15. Every equilateral triangle is also equiangular.
16. If two angles of one triangle are congruent to two angles of a second triangle, then the third pair of angles are congruent.
17. It is possible for a right triangle to be equilateral.
18. It is possible for an isosceles triangle to be obtuse.

Find the measure of each indicated angle.

19. ∠1

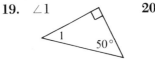

20. ∠2

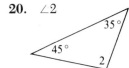

21.
 a. ∠3
 b. ∠4

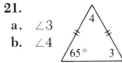

22.
 a. ∠5
 b. ∠6

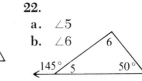

23. ∠7

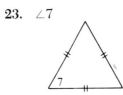

24.
 a. ∠8
 b. ∠9
 c. ∠10

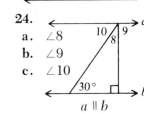

$a \parallel b$

25. a. ∠QPS   b. ∠RPS
     c. ∠RPM   d. ∠RSP

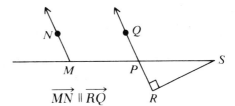

$\overrightarrow{MN} \parallel \overrightarrow{RQ}$

26. **a.** ∠DCE   **b.** ∠DCA

    c. ∠DEC

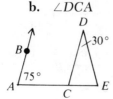

$\overrightarrow{AB} \parallel \overline{CD}$

27. **a.** ∠ONX   **b.** ∠XAB

    c. ∠BXA

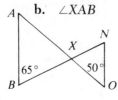

$\overline{ON} \parallel \overline{AB}$

28. **a.** ∠6

    b. ∠7

29. **a.** ∠1

    b. ∠2

    c. ∠3

    d. ∠4

    e. ∠5

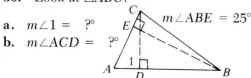

$l \parallel m$

— B —

30. Look at △ABC.

a. $m\angle 1 =$?°

b. $m\angle ACD =$?°

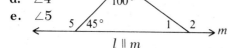

$m\angle ABE = 25°$

Find the indicated information.

31. One of the base angles of an isosceles triangle has a measure of 35°.

    a. Find the measure of the other base angle.

    b. Find the measure of the vertex angle.

32. The vertex angle of an isosceles triangle has a measure of 150°. Find the measure of each base angle.

33. One acute angle of a right triangle has a measure of 28°. Find the measure of the other acute angle.

— C —

34. Two angles of a triangle are congruent and the third angle has a measure equal to the sum of the measures of the other two. Find the measures of all three angles.

35. One acute angle of a right triangle is five times the measure of the other acute angle. Find the measure of each acute angle.

36. The measure of the largest angle of a triangle is five times the measure of the smallest angle. The measure of the third angle is three times the measure of the smallest angle. Find the measures of all three angles.

37. △PQR is isosceles. One of the base angles, ∠P, has a measure of 25° and $\overline{PQ} \cong \overline{QR}$.

    a. $m\angle R =$?°   **b.** $m\angle Q =$?°

    c. Classify △PQR by its angles.

38. Explain why the following statement is true: "Any triangle has at least two acute angles."

39. **Given:**

    ∠BAD ≅ ∠CAD

    ∠B ≅ ∠C

    Prove:

    △ABD ≅ △ACD

    a. Why is $\overline{AD} \cong \overline{AD}$?

    b. What property developed in this lesson can be used to show that ∠BDA ≅ ∠CDA?

    c. What property can be used to prove that △ABD ≅ △ACD?

5-6

Exterior-Angle Measures of a Triangle

An *exterior angle* of a triangle (or any other polygon) is formed by one side of the triangle and the extension of the adjacent side. $\angle 1$ is an exterior angle of $\triangle ABC$ shown.

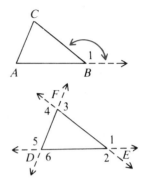

Each triangle has six exterior angles. The exterior angles of $\triangle DEF$ shown are $\angle 1$, $\angle 2$, $\angle 3$, $\angle 4$, $\angle 5$, and $\angle 6$. Notice that there is a pair of exterior angles at each vertex. Also, at each vertex the exterior angles are congruent. For example, $\angle 1 \cong \angle 2$.

Each exterior angle of a triangle has one *adjacent interior angle* and two *remote interior angles*. These terms are illustrated in the following diagrams.

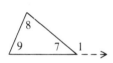

For exterior angle 1:
Adjacent Interior
Angle: $\angle 7$
Remote Interior
Angles: $\angle 8$, $\angle 9$

For exterior angle 4:
Adjacent Interior
Angle: $\angle 8$
Remote Interior
Angles: $\angle 7$, $\angle 9$

EXPLORING

Exterior-Angle Measures of a Triangle

1. For each triangle pictured, one exterior angle is shown at one vertex. Find the measure of each numbered angle.

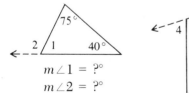

$m\angle 1 = ?°$
$m\angle 2 = ?°$

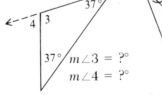

$m\angle 3 = ?°$
$m\angle 4 = ?°$

$m\angle 5 = ?°$
$m\angle 6 = ?°$

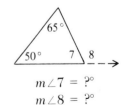

$m\angle 7 = ?°$
$m\angle 8 = ?°$

2. Compare the measure of each exterior angle shown with the measure of each of its remote interior angles. Are they the same? If not, which is greater?

3. Add the measure of each exterior angle shown to the measure of its adjacent interior angle. What is each sum? What is the relationship between each exterior angle and its adjacent interior angle?
4. Compare the measure of each exterior angle shown with the sum of the measures of its remote interior angles. Are they the same in each case?

EXPLORING
Midpoints and Parallels

X is the midpoint of $\overline{AC}$. Y is the midpoint of $\overline{BC}$.

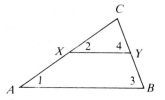

1. Measure ∠1, ∠2, ∠3, and ∠4 in the figure shown. Which pairs of angles are congruent?
2. Why is $\overline{XY} \parallel \overline{AB}$?
3. Measure $\overline{XY}$ and $\overline{AB}$ to the nearest millimeter. How do their lengths compare?
4. Repeat steps 1–3 with at least one other triangle not congruent to the one shown. Do you get the same results?

If you did the preceding EXPLORINGs carefully, you discovered the following conclusions:

> In a triangle, the measure of each exterior angle is greater than the measure of either of its remote interior angles.
> In a triangle, each exterior angle is supplementary to its adjacent interior angle.
> In a triangle, the measure of each exterior angle is equal to the sum of the measures of its two remote interior angles.

> A segment joining the midpoints of two sides of a triangle is parallel to the third side and one half its length.

CLASS PRACTICE

Look at △PQR.

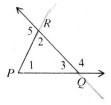

1. Identify the exterior angles shown for adjacent interior angles ∠2 and ∠3.
2. Identify the remote interior angles for ∠4.

3. Identify an angle that is supplementary to ∠2.
4. $m\angle 1 + m\angle 3 = m\angle$?   5. $m\angle 4 = m\angle$? $+ m\angle$?

Look at △XYZ.
6. $m\angle 1 =$?°
7. $m\angle 2 =$?°
8. If $AB = 4$ cm, then $YZ =$? cm.

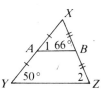

Find the measure of each indicated angle.

9. ∠1   12. ∠4   14. ∠6
10. ∠2   13. ∠5   15. ∠7
11. ∠3

EXERCISES

— A —

Look at △RST. Identify the adjacent interior angle and the two remote interior angles for each indicated exterior angle.

1. ∠1
2. ∠2
3. ∠3

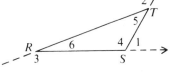

Find the indicated information.

4. Look at the triangle with 12 numbered angles. Identify each of the following.

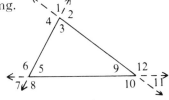

a. Three interior angles
b. Six exterior angles
c. Three angles that are neither exterior nor interior angles
d. Adjacent interior angle and two remote interior angles for ∠4

e. Two exterior angles for which ∠3 and ∠5 are the two remote interior angles
f. Six pairs of vertical angles

Draw a triangle similar to but larger than each one shown. For each triangle, draw and label an exterior angle at vertex A.

5.   6.   7.

Classify each statement as true or false.

8. Each exterior angle of a triangle is supplementary to its adjacent interior angle.
9. All exterior angles of an acute triangle are obtuse angles.
10. All exterior angles of an equiangular triangle are congruent.
11. All exterior angles of an obtuse triangle are acute angles.
12. All exterior angles of a right triangle are right angles.

Find the indicated information.

13. A, B, and C are midpoints of the sides of △RST shown.
    a. If $AB = 5$ cm, $RS = $? cm.
    b. If $RT = 14$ cm, $BC = $? cm.
    c. If $AC = 4$ cm, $ST = $? cm.
    d. $m\angle 1 = $?°
    e. $m\angle 2 = $?° f. $m\angle 3 = $?°
    g. $m\angle 4 = $?° h. $m\angle 5 = $?°

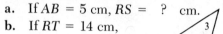

Find the measure of each indicated segment or angle.

14. a. $\angle 2$ b. $\angle 3$
    c. $\angle 4$ d. $\overline{XY}$

$RS = 6$ cm
$m\angle Z = 78°$
$m\angle 1 = 66°$

15. a. $\angle 1$
    b. $\angle 2$

16. a. $\angle 3$
    b. $\angle 4$

17. a. $\angle 5$
    b. $\angle 6$

18. a. $\angle 7$
    b. $\angle 8$

19. a. $\angle 1$
    b. $\angle 2$

20. a. $\angle 3$ Parallelogram
    b. $\angle 4$
    c. $\angle 5$

21. a. $\angle 6$
    b. $\angle 7$
    c. $\angle 8$

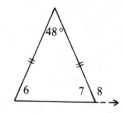

22. a. $\angle 1$
    b. $\angle 2$
    c. $\angle 3$
    d. $\angle 4$
    e. $\angle 5$

23. a. $\angle 6$
    b. $\angle 7$
    c. $\angle 8$
    d. $\angle 9$

$a \parallel b$

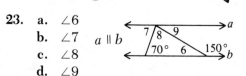

24. a. $\angle 4$
    b. $\angle 5$

    Trapezoid

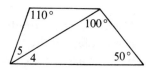

25. a. $\angle 1$
    b. $\angle 2$ $c \parallel d$
    c. $\angle 3$
    d. $\angle 4$
    e. $\angle 5$
    f. $\angle 6$

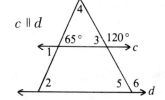

_ B _

26. In △ABC, $m\angle A = 45°$ and $m\angle B = 80°$. Find the measure of $\angle C$ and of the exterior angle at C.

27. In △PQR, $m\angle RPQ = 35°$ and the measure of the exterior angle at Q is 105°. Find the measure of $\angle PQR$ and of $\angle PRQ$.

28. An exterior angle of a triangle is three times the measure of its adjacent interior angle. Find the measure of both angles.

5-7

Sum of the Angle Measures for a Polygon

Recall that in any parallelogram, consecutive angles are supplementary. Using this fact, you can show that the sum of the interior-angle measures for the parallelogram shown is 360°.

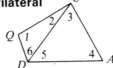

$m\angle 1 + m\angle 2 = 180°$
$m\angle 3 + m\angle 4 = 180°$
$m\angle 1 + m\angle 2 + m\angle 3 + m\angle 4 = 360°$

The above procedure can be used to show that the sum of the interior-angle measures for any parallelogram—rhombus, rectangle, or square—is 360°. The fact that the sum of the interior-angle measures of any triangle is 180° can be used to show that the sum of the interior-angle measures of *any* quadrilateral is 360°.

EXPLORING

The Sum of the Interior-Angle Measures of a Quadrilateral

1. Draw a quadrilateral that is not a parallelogram, rhombus, rectangle, or square.
2. Draw the diagonal from one vertex of the quadrilateral and label your figure like the one shown.
3. Find the sum of the interior-angle measures of the quadrilateral by using the angles of $\triangle QUD$ and $\triangle AUD$.
4. Use a protractor to measure the four interior angles of *QUAD*. Find the sum of these measures. Do you get the same results as in step 3?
5. Repeat steps 1–4 using a different quadrilateral not congruent to the first one used. Do you get the same results?

$\angle Q$, $\angle QUA$, $\angle A$, and $\angle ADQ$ are interior angles of *QUAD*.

If you did the preceding EXPLORING carefully, you discovered the following conclusion:

> **The sum of the interior-angle measures of any quadrilateral is 360°.**

A similar procedure can be used for polygons with more than four sides. For the polygons shown, all possible diagonals from one vertex have been drawn.

Pentagon   Hexagon

Notice that for each polygon the sum of the interior-angle measures is the same as the sum of the interior-angle measures of all the triangles determined by drawing all possible diagonals from one vertex. The results from this procedure are shown in the table:

Polygon	Sides	Triangles	Sum of Interior-Angle Measures
Pentagon	5	3	$3 \times 180° = 540°$
Hexagon	6	4	$4 \times 180° = 720°$

These results and that of the EXPLORING suggest the following property for the sum of the interior-angle measures of any polygon.

> **The sum of the interior-angle measures of any polygon having n sides is $(n - 2)\,180°$.**

The above conclusion can be used to find the sum of the exterior-angle measures of any polygon. One exterior angle has been drawn at each vertex of pentagon $ABCDE$ shown. At vertex A, $m\angle 1 + m\angle 2 = 180°$ and at vertex B, $m\angle 3 + m\angle 4 = 180°$.

Notice that at each vertex, the sum of one exterior angle and the adjacent interior angle is 180°. The pentagon has five vertices. Therefore, the sum of one exterior angle and the adjacent interior angle at all vertices is $5 \times 180° = 900°$.

The sum of the interior-angle measures for the pentagon is $(5-2)180°$ or $3 \times 180° = 540°$. The sum of the exterior-angle measures, one at each vertex, is $2 \times 180° = 360°$. Notice that $900° - 540° = 360°$.

The following table shows the results of a similar procedure using polygons of four and seven sides.

	Quadrilateral	Septagon
Number of vertices	4	7
Sum of an exterior angle and the interior angle at each vertex	180°	180°
Sum of an exterior angle and the interior angle at all vertices	$4(180°) = 720°$	$7(180°) = 1260°$
Sum of interior-angle measures	$2(180°) = 360°$	$5(180°) = 900°$
Sum of exterior-angle measures (one at each vertex)	$720° - 360° = 360°$	$1260° - 900° = 360°$

> **The sum of the exterior-angle measures, one at each vertex, of any polygon is 360°.**

Find the sum of the interior-angle measures of a polygon with each given number of sides.

1. 7 sides   **2.** 9 sides   **3.** 10 sides

4. Recall that in a regular polygon the interior angles are congruent to each other. Are the exterior angles congruent?

5. The measure of each interior angle of a regular polygon is 135°.
   a. Find the measure of each exterior angle.
   b. Find the number of sides.

Find the measure of each angle indicated.

6. ∠1

7. ∠2

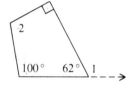

8. ∠3

EXERCISES

_ A _

Copy and complete the table.

	Number of Sides of Polygon	Sum of Interior-Angle Measures	Sum of Exterior-Angle Measures
1.	4	?	360°
2.	6	4 × 180 = 720°	?
3.	?	7 × 180 = 1260°	?
4.	16	?	?
5.	24	?	?

Find the measure of each indicated angle.

6. ∠1

Parallelogram

7. ∠2

Regular Pentagon

8. ∠3

9. ∠9

10.   **a.** ∠4   Trapezoid
      b. ∠5
      c. ∠6
      d. ∠7
      e. ∠8

11. ∠10

12. ∠2

13.   **a.** ∠3   **b.** ∠4

14. Parallelogram
     a. ∠5
     b. ∠6

15.

Parallelogram

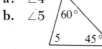

a. ∠1
b. ∠2
c. ∠3

16.

a. ∠7
b. ∠8

$\overline{BC} \parallel \overline{DE}$ △ABC and △ADE are isosceles.

17.

a. ∠4
b. ∠5

shown and measure the interior angles indicated. Is the sum of the interior-angle measures of a concave quadrilateral also 360°?

For each regular polygon pictured find the measure of (a) each interior angle and (b) each exterior angle.

25.

26.

— B —

The sum of the interior-angle measures is given for some polygons. Find the number of sides of each polygon.

18. 540°
19. 900°
20. 1440°
21. 1800°
22. 2340°
23. 3240°

24. You learned that the sum of the interior-angle measures of any *convex* quadrilateral is 360°. Draw a *concave* quadrilateral like the one

27. The measure of each interior angle of a regular polygon is 144°.

a. Find the measure of each exterior angle.

b. Find the number of sides.

Test Yourself

Look at △XYZ.

1. m∠1 = ?°
2. m∠2 = ?°
3. If XY = 10, RS = ? .

Look at the regular hexagon.

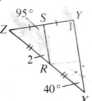

4. Find the sum of the exterior-angle measures.
5. Find the sum of the interior-angle measures.
6. m∠1 = ?°   **7.** m∠2 = ?°

Find the measure of each indicated angle.

8. ∠1   **11.** ∠4
9. ∠2   **12.** ∠5
10. ∠3

13. ∠6   **14.** ∠7

5-8

Using Diagonals to Determine the Type of Quadrilateral

In Chapter 3 you learned some properties of the diagonals of any parallelogram, rhombus, rectangle, or square. These properties are summarized in the table at the end of Chapter 3 (page 128).

The way in which the diagonals of a quadrilateral are related to each other determines the type of quadrilateral. This is demonstrated in the following EXPLORING.

EXPLORING

Diagonal Properties that Determine the Type of Quadrilateral

Draw segments to fit each description. Connect the endpoints of the segments. Identify the special type of quadrilateral—parallelogram, rectangle, rhombus, or square—formed.

1. Two noncongruent, nonperpendicular segments that bisect each other
2. Two congruent, nonperpendicular segments that bisect each other
3. Two noncongruent segments that are the perpendicular bisectors of each other
4. Two congruent segments that are the perpendicular bisectors of each other

If your drawings were done accurately, they illustrated the following properties:

> If the diagonals of a quadrilateral bisect each other, then the quadrilateral is a parallelogram.
>
> If the diagonals of a quadrilateral are congruent and bisect each other, then the quadrilateral is a rectangle.
>
> If the diagonals of a quadrilateral are the perpendicular bisectors of each other, then the quadrilateral is a rhombus.
>
> If the diagonals of a quadrilateral are congruent and are the perpendicular bisectors of each other, then the quadrilateral is a square.

_ A _

Find the measure of each indicated angle.

1. Parallelogram
   a. ∠1
   b. ∠2
   c. ∠3

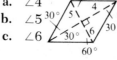

2. Rhombus
   a. ∠4
   b. ∠5
   c. ∠6

3. Rectangle
   a. ∠7
   b. ∠8
   c. ∠9

4. Square
   a. ∠10
   b. ∠11
   c. ∠12

Find the indicated information.

5. Look at parallelogram *PRST*.
   a. Is $\overline{PS} \cong \overline{TR}$?
   b. Is $\overline{PS} \perp \overline{TR}$?
   c. If *PM* = 6,
      SM = ? ,
      and *PS* = ? .

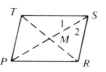

6. Look at rectangle *RECT*.
   a. Is $\overline{RC} \cong \overline{TE}$?
   b. Is $\overline{RC} \perp \overline{TE}$?
   c. If *RM* = 5,
      CM = ? ,
      and *RC* = ? .

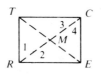

7. Look at rhombus *RHOM*.
   a. Is $\overline{RO} \cong \overline{MH}$?
   b. Is $\overline{RO} \perp \overline{MH}$?
   c. If *MX* = 6,
      HX = ? .

8. Look at square *ABCD*.
   a. Is $\overline{AC} \cong \overline{BD}$?
   b. Is $\overline{AC} \perp \overline{BD}$?
   c. If *DX* = 6,
      DB = ? .

_ B _

9. Parallelograms, rhombuses, rectangles, and squares are all special types of quadrilaterals. Identify all types of quadrilaterals that make each statement true.
   a. The diagonals of a ? bisect each other.
   b. The diagonals of a ? are congruent.
   c. The diagonals of a ? are perpendicular.
   d. The diagonals of a ? are the perpendicular bisectors of each other.
   e. The diagonals of a ? bisect the angles whose vertices are endpoints of the diagonals.
   f. The diagonals of a ? are congruent and the perpendicular bisectors of each other.

Draw a quadrilateral to fit each given description.

10. Parallelogram that is *not* a rhombus and that has diagonals of length 6 cm and 4 cm

11. Rectangle that is *not* a square and that has diagonals of length 6 cm

12. Rhombus with diagonals of length 6 cm and 4 cm

13. Square with both diagonals of length 6 cm

14. Quadrilateral with perpendicular diagonals that do not bisect each other

15. Quadrilateral with congruent diagonals that do not bisect each other

16. **To Be Proved:** If two sides of a quadrilateral are parallel and congruent, then the quadrilateral is a parallelogram.

    Given: $\overline{AB} \parallel \overline{CD}$ $\overline{AB} \cong \overline{CD}$

    Prove: $ABCD$ is a parallelogram.

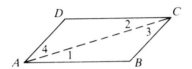

We can prove that $ABCD$ is a parallelogram by proving that both pairs of opposite sides are parallel. That is, that $\overline{AB} \parallel \overline{CD}$ and $\overline{AD} \parallel \overline{CB}$. This can be done by answering the following series of questions.

   a. Why is $\overline{AB} \parallel \overline{CD}$?
      Why is $\overline{AB} \cong \overline{CD}$?
   b. Why is $\overline{AC} \cong \overline{CA}$?
   c. Why is $\angle 1 \cong \angle 2$?
   d. What property can be used to prove that $\triangle ABC \cong \triangle CDA$?
   e. Why is $\angle 3 \cong \angle 4$?
   f. Why is $\overline{AD} \parallel \overline{CB}$?

17. **To Be Proved:** If both pairs of opposite sides of a quadrilateral are congruent, then the quadrilateral is a parallelogram.

Given: $\overline{AB} \cong \overline{CD}$ $\overline{BC} \cong \overline{DA}$

Prove: $ABCD$ is a parallelogram.

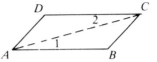

   a. Why is $\overline{AC} \cong \overline{CA}$?
   b. What property can be used to prove that $\triangle ABC \cong \triangle CDA$?
   c. Why is $\angle 1 \cong \angle 2$?
   d. Why is $\overline{AB} \parallel \overline{CD}$?
   e. How can the property proved in Exercise 16 be used to prove that $ABCD$ is a parallelogram?

18. **To Be Proved:** If the diagonals of a quadrilateral bisect each other, then the quadrilateral is a parallelogram.

Given: $\overline{AO} \cong \overline{CO}$ $\overline{BO} \cong \overline{DO}$

Prove: $ABCD$ is a parallelogram.

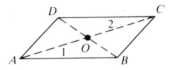

   a. Why is $\angle AOB \cong \angle COD$?
   b. What property can be used to prove that $\triangle AOB \cong \triangle COD$?
   c. Why is $\angle 1 \cong \angle 2$?
   d. Why is $\overline{AB} \parallel \overline{CD}$?
   e. Why is $\overline{AB} \cong \overline{CD}$?
   f. How can the property proved in Exercise 16 be used to prove that $ABCD$ is a parallelogram?

DID YOU KNOW THAT....

In the early 1800s, two other types of geometry were developed using the assumptions that through a point not on a line there exists either more than one or no lines parallel to the given line. These geometries are called *hyperbolic* and *elliptic*, respectively.

5-9

Mastering Properties of Triangles and Quadrilaterals

The exercises in this lesson use properties of triangles and quadrilaterals developed in the last three chapters. The Skills Checklists at the end of Chapter 3 (p. 128) and Chapter 5 (p. 217) summarize these properties.

EXERCISES

Classify each statement as true or false.

1. Every equilateral triangle is equiangular.
2. Every equilateral triangle is isosceles.
3. Every isosceles triangle is equilateral.
4. Every equiangular triangle is an acute triangle.
5. All exterior angles of an obtuse triangle are obtuse.
6. Every rhombus is a parallelogram.
7. A parallelogram may be a square.
8. A quadrilateral with four right angles must be a square.
9. The opposite angles of any parallelogram are congruent.
10. A rhombus may have four right angles.
11. Every square is a rectangle.
12. Some rhombuses are rectangles.
13. The diagonals of any rectangle are perpendicular.
14. The diagonals of any rhombus must be congruent.
15. If the diagonals of a quadrilateral are congruent and bisect each other, the quadrilateral is a rhombus.

For each type of triangle, list all the triangles shown that fit each description.

16. Scalene
17. Isosceles
18. Equilateral
19. Acute
20. Right
21. Obtuse
22. Equiangular

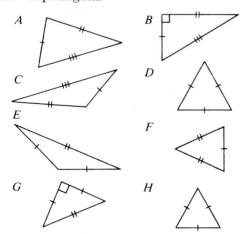

23. △ABC shown is an isosceles triangle. Identify each of the following.
    a. Legs
    b. Vertex angle
    c. Base
    d. Base angles
    e. Line of symmetry

State whether it is possible to draw a triangle to fit each description.

24. Isosceles right triangle
25. Equilateral right triangle
26. Equiangular isosceles triangle
27. Triangle with two right angles
28. Acute equiangular triangle
29. Scalene obtuse triangle
30. Equilateral obtuse triangle

State the types of quadrilateral (parallelogram, rhombus, rectangle, or square) that best fit(s) each description.

31. Parallelogram with 4 right angles
32. Rectangle with 4 congruent sides
33. Rhombus with 4 right angles
34. Parallelogram with congruent diagonals
35. Parallelogram with 4 congruent sides
36. Quadrilateral with opposite sides parallel
37. Rectangle with perpendicular diagonals
38. Rhombus with congruent diagonals
39. Parallelogram with exactly 2 lines of symmetry
40. Rectangle with exactly 4 lines of symmetry
41. *ABCD* is a parallelogram.

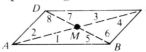

a. Is $\overline{AC} \cong \overline{BD}$?
b. Is $\overline{AC} \perp \overline{BD}$?
c. If *DM* = 4, *DB* = ? .
d. Identify all angles congruent to ∠1.
e. Identify all pairs of parallel lines.
f. If $m\angle DAB = 40°$, $m\angle ADC = $?° , and $m\angle DCB = $?° .

g. Is ∠5 ≅ ∠6?
h. Is $\overleftrightarrow{AC}$ a line of symmetry for *ABCD*?

42. *ABCD* is a rectangle.
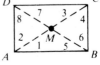
a. Is $\overline{AC} \cong \overline{BD}$?
b. Is $\overline{AC} \perp \overline{BD}$?
c. If *DM* = 4, *BM* = ? .
d. Identify all angles congruent to ∠1.
e. Identify all right angles.
f. Is ∠5 ≅ ∠6?
g. Is $\overleftrightarrow{AC}$ a line of symmetry for *ABCD*?

43. *EFGH* is a rhombus.
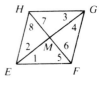
a. Is $\overline{EG} \cong \overline{HF}$?
b. Is $\overline{EG} \perp \overline{HF}$?
c. Identify all angles congruent to ∠1.
d. Identify all segments congruent to $\overline{EH}$.
e. Identify all segments congruent to $\overline{EM}$.
f. Is ∠5 ≅ ∠6?
g. If $m\angle HEF = 50°$, $m\angle EHG = $?° and $m\angle HGF = $?° .
h. Identify all isosceles triangles.
i. Is $\overleftrightarrow{EG}$ a line of symmetry for *EFGH*?

44. *WXYZ* is a square.

a. Is $\overline{WY} \cong \overline{ZX}$?
b. Is $\overline{WY} \perp \overline{ZX}$?
c. Identify all angles congruent to ∠1.
d. Identify all segments congruent to $\overline{WZ}$.
e. Identify all segments congruent to $\overline{WM}$.
f. Identify all isosceles triangles.

Geometry on the Job

Astronomer

In her work as an astronomer, Arlene Watt sometimes needs to calculate the distance to a planet or star. To do so she uses the fact that if an object is seen from a different position, its location seems to change. This change is called *parallax.* (You can observe parallax on a small scale: Close your left eye and hold up a pencil, lining it up with an object in the background. Now open your left eye and close your right eye. Notice that the pencil seems to have moved.)

Arlene knows that rays of light from very distant stars can be considered to be parallel. When a planet or nearby star is observed from two different positions, its location seems to be slightly different with respect to very distant stars. In the diagram, planet *P* is observed from positions *A* and *B* on Earth. Seen from *A*, *P* is in line with star *S.* From *B,* it is not. By using information she gets from these observations, Arlene can compare the angles in the diagram. With techniques you will learn later in this course, she can calculate the distance to *P.*

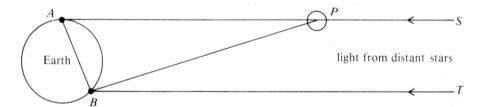

EXERCISES

1. An astronomer can measure ∠*PBT*. How does *m* ∠*PBT* compare with *m* ∠*APB*? Why?
2. Suppose ∠*ABP* and ∠*BAP* each measure 89°. What is *m* ∠*APB*?

ARITHMETIC REVIEW — *Rounding Numbers*

The following rule is used to round numbers.

> Look at the digit to the *right* of the place being rounded to.
>   If it is less than 5, round down.
>   If it is 5 or greater, round up.

Examples

	Rounded to the nearest				
Number	Hundredth	Tenth	Whole Number	Ten	Hundred
76.056	76.06	76.1	76	80	100
342.865	342.87	342.9	343	340	300
8.733	8.73	8.7	9	10	0

EXERCISES
Round each number (a) to the nearest hundredth and (b) to the nearest tenth.

1. 3.046
2. 2.872
3. 8.301
4. 0.087
5. 3.555
6. 4.993
7. 6.438
8. 0.493

Round each number (a) to the nearest hundred and (b) to the nearest ten.

9. 348
10. 63.2
11. 683
12. 1530
13. 736
14. 3865
15. 849
16. 573

Round each number to the nearest thousandth.

17. 0.0019
18. 0.4362
19. 0.2025
20. 3.0568
21. 14.3270
22. 5.5893
23. 0.0624
24. 3.1006

Round each number to the nearest whole number.

25. 9.8
26. 6.36
27. 0.6235
28. 15.09
29. 1.6203
30. 4.501
31. 4.58
32. 10.39

Chapter 5 Review

Vocabulary

The following terms were introduced in this chapter. You should be able to write a brief description, draw a picture, or give an example to illustrate the meaning of each.

Parallel Lines and Transversals
alternate interior angles (p. 182)
corresponding angles (p. 182)
exterior angles (p. 182)
interior angles (p. 182)
interior angles on the same side of the
  transversal (p. 185)
transversal (p. 182)

Angles of Polygons
adjacent interior angle (p. 201)
exterior angles (p. 201)
interior angles (p. 197)
remote interior angles (p. 201)

Skills Checklist

In Chapter 5 you learned some relationships between the measures of pairs of angles determined by parallel lines cut by a transversal; how to determine the sum of the interior-angle and exterior-angle measures of polygons; and how to construct parallel lines. In addition, you reviewed several properties of triangles and quadrilaterals.

The following list indicates the major skills, facts, and results you should have mastered in this chapter:

● Identify pairs of alternate interior angles, interior angles on the same side of the transversal, and corresponding angles determined by two lines cut by a transversal. (**5-1**, pp. 182–184)

● Recognize and use relationships between the measures of pairs of angles determined by parallel lines cut by a transversal. (**5-2—5-3**, pp. 185–192)

● Recognize and use relationships between the measures of pairs of angles that can be used to show that two lines cut by a transversal are parallel. (**5-2—5-3**, pp. 185–192)

● Know how to construct the line parallel to a given line through a point not on the line. (**5-4**, pp. 193–196)

● Recognize and use the following facts about interior- and exterior-angle measures of triangles:
  ● The sum of the interior-angle measures of any triangle is 180°. (**5-5**, pp. 197–200)
  ● Each angle of an equilateral triangle has a measure of 60°. (**5-5**, pp. 197–200)

- The acute angles of any right triangle are complementary. (**5-5**, pp. 197-200)
- The measure of each exterior angle of a triangle is equal to the sum of the measures of the two remote interior angles. (**5-6**, pp. 201-204)
- Each exterior angle of a triangle is supplementary to its adjacent interior angle. (**5-6**, pp. 201-204)
- Recognize and use the fact that a segment joining the midpoints of two sides of a triangle is parallel to the third side and one half its length. (**5-6**, pp. 201-204)
- Recognize and use the following facts about interior- and exterior-angle measures of polygons:
  - The sum of the interior-angle measures of any polygon having n sides is $(n - 2)180°$. (**5-7**, pp. 205-208)
  - The sum of the exterior-angle measures, one at each vertex, of any polygon is 360°. (**5-7**, pp. 205-208)
- Recognize and use the properties of diagonals that determine special types of quadrilaterals. (**5-8**, pp. 209-211)

Exercises

1. Look at lines a and b cut by transversal t. Identify each of the following. (**5-1**)
   a. Two pairs of alternate interior angles
   b. Four pairs of corresponding angles
   c. Two pairs of interior angles on the same side of the transversal
   d. Four pairs of vertical angles

For Exercises 2-6, look at lines c and d cut by a transversal.

2. Identify four angles supplementary to $\angle 6$. (**5-2—5-3**)

$c \parallel d$

$m\angle 6 = 55°$

Find the measure of each indicated angle. (5-2—5-3)

3. $\angle 8$ 4. $\angle 4$
5. $\angle 5$ 6. $\angle 2$

Find the indicated information.

7. Draw two figures similar to but larger than the one shown. Use two different methods to construct the line through X parallel to l. (**5-4**)

• X

8. Look at the triangle. (**5-6**)

   a. Identify the remote interior angles for $\angle 5$.
   b. $\angle 1$ and $\angle 2$ are remote interior angles for what exterior angle?

Find the measure of each indicated angle or segment.

Parallelogram

9. a. $\angle 1$
(5-6) b. $\angle MRG$
   c. $\angle 2$

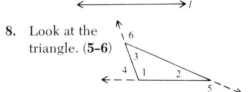

10. a. $\overline{DE}$
(5–6) b. $\angle D$
   c. $\angle 1$
   d. $\angle 2$

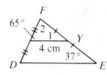

11. (5–6)
 a. $\angle 1$
 b. $\angle 2$

12. $\angle 1$
(5–5)

13. (5–5)
 a. $\angle 2$
 b. $\angle 3$

14. $\angle E$
(5–5)

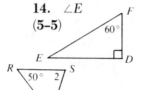

15. a. $\angle 1$
   b. $\angle 2$
   c. $\angle 3$
   d. $\angle 4$
(5–2—5–3)

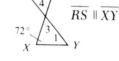

$\overline{RS} \parallel \overline{XY}$

16. a. $\angle 1$
   b. $\angle 2$
   c. $\angle 3$
   d. $\angle 4$
(5–9)

Rhombus

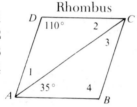

Classify each statement as true or false.

17. The sum of the measures of the interior angles of any triangle is 180°. **(5–5)**

18. Every equiangular triangle is equilateral. **(5–5)**

19. A triangle may have two acute angles. **(5–5)**

20. All exterior angles of a right triangle are right angles. **(5–6)**

21. Draw a triangle like the one shown. Draw and label an exterior angle at vertex X. **(5–6)**

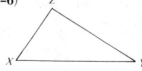

Find the measure of each indicated angle. (5–7)

22. $\angle 1$

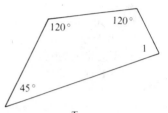

23. a. $\angle 1$
   b. $\angle 2$

Regular Pentagon

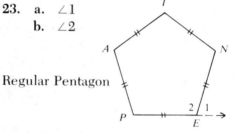

Identify all special types of quadrilaterals—parallelogram, rectangle, rhombus, or square—for which each statement is true.

24. The diagonals are congruent. **(5–8)**

25. All angles are congruent. **(5–9)**

26. The diagonals bisect each other. **(5–8)**

27. The sum of the interior-angle measures is 360°. **(5–7)**

28. The diagonals are perpendicular. **(5–8)**

29. The diagonals are the perpendicular bisectors of each other. **(5–8)**

30. The figure is symmetric. **(5–9)**

Draw a quadrilateral to fit each description. (5–8)

31. Parallelogram that is *not* a rhombus and that has diagonals of length 8 cm and 5 cm

32. Rectangle that is *not* a square and that has diagonals of length 8 cm

33. Square with both diagonals of length 8 cm

CUMULATIVE REVIEW — CHAPTERS 1-5

Classify each statement as true or false.

1. Each segment has exactly one bisector. (**1-2**)
2. Each segment has exactly one perpendicular bisector. (**3-5**)
3. Each angle has exactly one bisector. (**3-5**)
4. Supplementary angles must be adjacent. (**2-11**)
5. Every diameter is also a chord. (**2-1**)
6. Each equilateral triangle is also isosceles. (**3-6**)
7. A right triangle can be isosceles. (**3-6**)
8. Each diagonal of any rectangle bisects a pair of angles. (**3-10**)
9. The diagonals of any rhombus are congruent. (**3-9**)
10. The diagonals of any parallelogram are congruent. (**3-8**)

Draw a figure to fit each description.

11. Three collinear points (**1-1**)
12. Obtuse angle (**2-10**)
13. Cube (**1-9**)
14. Triangular prism (**1-9**)
15. Two parallel horizontal planes (**1-10**)
16. Line intersecting a vertical plane in one point (**1-10**)
17. Angle with a measure of 105° (**2-5**)
18. Two supplementary angles (**2-11**)
19. Isosceles acute triangle (**3-6**)
20. Scalene triangle (**3-6**)
21. Segment with a length of 46 mm (**3-1**)
22. Two perpendicular lines (**2-3**)
23. Triangle inscribed in a circle (**4-7**)
24. Line tangent to a circle (**4-7**)

Find the indicated information.

25. Look at the angle. Identify each of the following. (**1-4**)
    a. Vertex
    b. Sides
    c. Four different names for the angle

26. Look at the isosceles triangle. Identify each of the following. (**3-6**)
    a. Legs
    b. Base
    c. Vertex angle
    d. Base angles

27. Look at ⊙ C. Identify each of the following. (**2-9**)
    a. A diameter
    b. All radii
    c. All chords
    d. Inscribed angle
    e. Two central angles

Complete the following.

28. 100° = ? turn (**2-3**)
29. $\frac{3}{5}$ turn = ?° (**2-3**)
30. 8 cm = ? mm (**3-2**)
31. 3.7 cm = ? mm (**3-2**)
32. 190 mm = ? cm (**3-2**)
33. 5 m = ? cm (**3-2**)

Find the indicated information.

34. Count the number of faces, edges, and vertices for the rectangular prism. (**1-8**)

35. Suppose that $ABCD \cong RXTS$. Complete the following. (3–3)
   a. $\overline{BC} \cong$?   b. $\overline{SR} \cong$?
   c. $\angle C \cong \angle$?   d. $CBAD \cong$?

Suppose you wish to prove $\triangle RST \cong \triangle XYZ$. Identify three pairs of corresponding parts you could use when using the indicated property. (4–5)

36. SSS
37. SAS
38. ASA

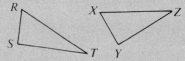

Copy or trace to make two copies of each figure. For each figure, draw (a) all the lines of symmetry and (b) all the diagonals. (3–5)

39.   40.

Perform each indicated construction.

41. Draw an obtuse angle. Construct an angle congruent to it. (4–2)
42. Draw an acute angle. Construct the bisector of the angle. (4–2)
43. Construct a triangle with sides of length x, y, and z, as shown. (4–1)

x
y
z

Use a diagram like the one shown.

•R

P

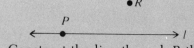 l

44. Construct the line through R that is perpendicular to l. (4–4)
45. Construct the line through P that is perpendicular to l. (4–4)
46. Construct the line through R that is parallel to l. (5–4)

Find the measure of each indicated angle, arc, or segment.

47. $m\angle CBA = 95°$
(2–6) $m\angle CBD =$?°

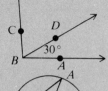

48. a. $\angle AOB$
     b. $\angle ARB$
(2–9) c. $\overset{\frown}{ARB}$

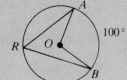

49. a. $\angle 1$
     b. $\angle 2$
(2–11) c. $\angle 3$

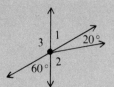

50. a. $\angle 1$ b. $\angle 2$
(5–3) c. $\angle 3$ d. $\angle 4$

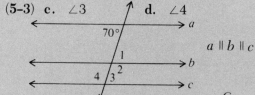

$a \parallel b \parallel c$

51. a. XY
(5–6) b. $\angle 1$
     c. $\angle 2$
     d. $\angle CAB$

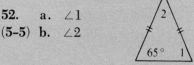

$AB = 6$ cm

52. a. $\angle 1$
(5–5) b. $\angle 2$

53. $\angle 1$
(5–7)

54. a. $\angle DAB$
(3–8) b. $\angle 1$
     c. $\angle 2$
Parallelogram

Chapter 6

AROUND THE EDGE
AND OVER THE SURFACE

Perimeter and Area

6-1

Perimeter

Suppose you wish to determine the amount of fencing needed to fence in a garden or the length of baseboard molding needed for a room. Each of these situations requires that you determine the distance around a region or object.

The distance around any region is called its *perimeter*. The word "perimeter" comes from two Greek words—*peri*, meaning "around," and *meter*, meaning "to measure." Therefore, the word "perimeter" means "to measure around."

The perimeter of the region shown is the distance from A to B to C to D and back to A. (The direction taken has no effect on the outcome.) If the lengths of the sides are as indicated, the perimeter of this quadrilateral is 39 centimeters.

For any polygon, a formula for finding the perimeter can be written.

Write a formula for the perimeter of each polygon.

Example 1:

Solution:

All sides of the square have the same length. If P is the perimeter, then

$$P = s + s + s + s, \quad \text{or}$$
$$= 4s$$

Example 2:

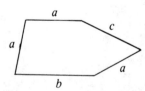

Solution:

$$P = a + a + c + a + b, \quad \text{or}$$
$$= 3a + b + c$$

DISCUSS

1. Describe some situations in which it is necessary to find the distance around some object.
2. Name five standard units of measure that can be used for perimeter.
3. The word "perimeter" contains the word "rim." In what way does this emphasize the meaning of "perimeter"?

Find the perimeter of each polygon.

1.
3 cm
7 cm

2.
3 cm
3 cm

3.

4 cm
7 cm

Find the length of each indicated side.

4. Perimeter = 32 cm
   a. $a = ?$ cm
   b. $b = ?$ cm

12 cm
b
a

5. Perimeter = 24 ft
   $x = ?$ ft

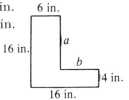
x
x

6. Perimeter = 28 cm
   $y = ?$ cm

7 cm
6 cm
y
10 cm

7. **a.** $a = ?$ in.
   b. $b = ?$ in.

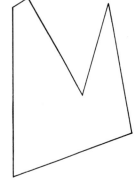
6 in.
16 in.
a
b
4 in.
16 in.

Write a formula for the perimeter of each polygon.

8.
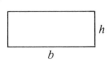
h
b

9.
x x
y

EXERCISES

— A —

For each figure, measure each side to the nearest centimeter and find its perimeter. Look for shortcuts! **2.**

1.

2.

3.

4.

5.

Find the perimeter of each figure.

6.

10

6

7.
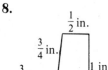
8

6

8.
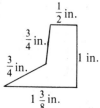
$\frac{1}{2}$ in.

$\frac{3}{4}$ in.

$\frac{3}{4}$ in.

1 in.

$1\frac{3}{8}$ in.

9.
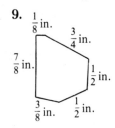
$\frac{1}{8}$ in.

$\frac{3}{4}$ in.

$\frac{7}{8}$ in.

$\frac{1}{2}$ in.

$\frac{3}{8}$ in.

$\frac{1}{2}$ in.

Find the length of each indicated side.

10. Perimeter = 10.0 cm

    $x = $? cm

3.3 cm

x

2.9 cm

1.7 cm

11. Perimeter = 96 mm

  a. $a = $? mm

  b. $b = $? mm

32 mm

b

a

12. Perimeter = 83 in.

  a. $r = $? in.

  b. $s = $? in.

15 in.

r

s

28 in.

13. Perimeter = 20 cm

  $x = $? cm

x

x

Write a formula for the perimeter of each polygon.

14.

x

15.

y

16.

a

b

17.
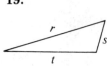
d

c

18.
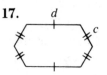
d

a

b

c

19.
r

s

t

—— **B** ——

20. Look at △ACE. (Each measurement is to the nearest 0.1 cm.)

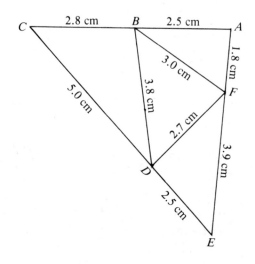

C 2.8 cm B 2.5 cm A

5.0 cm

3.8 cm

3.0 cm

2.7 cm

1.8 cm

F

D

2.5 cm

3.9 cm

E

  a. Identify five triangles.

  b. Identify six quadrilaterals.

  c. Find the perimeter of all eleven figures. Record your results in separate tables.

21. A chain-link fence is to be put up around a rectangular garden that is 18 meters long and 7 meters wide. How many meters of fencing are needed?

22. Look at the diagram of a room.

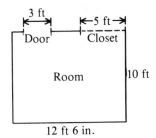

a. What is the perimeter of the room?

b. How much baseboard molding is needed for the room? (Do *not* include the door or closet.)

c. Suppose the closet is 3 feet deep. How much baseboard molding is needed for the interior of the closet?

23. How many 9-inch-long bricks are needed to make a border for this flower bed in the shape of the regular hexagon shown?

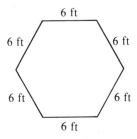

Use graph paper to draw a polygon to fit each description.

24. Square with a perimeter of 12

25. Square with a perimeter of 24

26. Rectangle that is not a square and that has a perimeter of 12

27. Three noncongruent rectangles each having a perimeter of 14

For each figure, find (a) the length of each indicated side and (b) its perimeter.

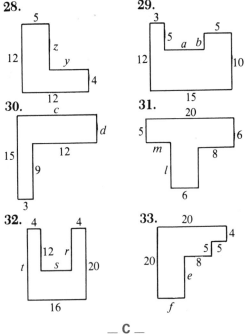

28.

29.

30.

31.

32.

33.

— C —

34. A picture (shown) that is 12 inches by 16 inches is to be framed with a $1\frac{1}{2}$-inch wide frame.

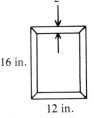

a. Find the perimeter of the picture.

b. Find the *outside* perimeter of the frame.

Use dot or graph paper to draw either a convex or concave polygon to fit each description. Each side should be either a horizontal or vertical segment.

35. 6 sides, Perimeter = 10

36. 8 sides, Perimeter = 10

37. 8 sides, Perimeter = 12

38. 12 sides, Perimeter = 12

39. 12 sides, Perimeter = 16

6-2

Circumference of a Circle

In the preceding lesson you found the perimeter of various polygons. In this lesson you will learn how to find the perimeter, which is called its *circumference*, of a circle.

EXPLORING
Measuring the Circumference

You will need three objects of different size each of which has at least one face that is shaped like a circle. Follow the directions in steps 1–3 below for each object. Record your results in a table like the one shown.

1. Find the circumference of the circle to the nearest millimeter. Some suggested methods are (a) wrap a string around the object and measure the length of the string, or (b) use a flexible tape measure, or (c) mark a point on the outer edge of the object and roll it along a meter stick for one complete turn.
2. Measure the diameter of the circle to the nearest millimeter.
3. Divide the circumference by the diameter.

Object	Circumference	Diameter	Circumference ÷ Diameter
quarter	?	?	?

4. Look at the numbers in the last column of the table. What pattern do you see?

If you did the preceding EXPLORING carefully, you discovered the following:

> **The circumference of any circle divided by the diameter is always a number a little greater than 3.** $\dfrac{C}{d} \approx 3$

Over 2000 years ago it was proved that the circumference divided by the diameter is the same number for every circle. This constant value is called *pi* (pronounced "pie") and is represented by the symbol π.

$\dfrac{C}{d} = \pi$

You know that $C \div d = \pi$. Therefore, $C = \pi d$.

> **The formula for the circumference of any circle is**
>
> $$C = \pi d$$

Mathematicians have also proved that π cannot be represented exactly by either a decimal or a fraction. Therefore approximations are used for π. The most common approximations are

$\pi \approx \frac{22}{7}$ or $3\frac{1}{7}$ $\pi \approx 3.14$ ($\approx$ is read "approximately equal to.")

Example 1:   Find the circumference of a circle with a diameter of 6 cm.

Solution:
$C = \pi d$ $C = \pi \cdot 6 = 6\pi$ cm (exact value) $C \approx 3.14(6) \approx 18.84$ cm (approximate value)

Example 2:   Find the circumference of a circle with a radius of 2 cm.

Solution:
If the radius is 2 cm, the diameter is 4 cm. $C = \pi \cdot 4 = 4\pi$ cm (exact value)
$C \approx 3.14(4) \approx 12.56$ cm (approximate value)

Example 3:   The circumference of a circle is approximately 25.12 feet. Find the diameter and the radius.

Solution:
$$C = \pi d \qquad 25.12 \approx (3.14)d \qquad d \approx \frac{25.12}{3.14} \approx 8$$

Answer: The diameter is about 8 feet and the radius is about 4 feet.

Example 4:   Find the length of arc x.

Solution:
The arc is $\frac{1}{4}$ of the circle.   The diameter is $2 \cdot 7$ or 14 inches long.
$C = \pi d \approx \frac{22}{7} \times \frac{14}{1} \approx \frac{308}{7} \approx 44$ in.

Answer: The length of the arc is about $\frac{1}{4} \times \frac{44}{1} = \frac{44}{4} = 11$ inches.

Notice that the exact circumference of any circle is expressed in terms of π. When using an approximation for π, the circumference obtained is only an approximation.

═══════════ **CLASS PRACTICE** ═══════════

Complete the following.
1. If the radius of a circle is 8 cm, its diameter is ? cm.
2. If the diameter of a circle is 10 cm, its radius is ? cm.

For a circle with each given diameter or radius, find (a) the exact circumference (leave answer in terms of π) and (b) the approximate circumference. (Use 3.14 for π.)

3. $d = 12$ cm 　　4. $d = 9$ cm 　　5. $r = 6$ cm

Find the indicated information.

6. The circumference of a circle is approximately 50.24 cm. Find the diameter and the radius. (Use 3.14 for π.)

7. Find the length of arc y. It is $\frac{1}{8}$ of the circle shown. (Use $\frac{22}{7}$ for π.)

EXERCISES

— **A** —

The radius of a circle is given. Find the diameter of the circle.　　1. 6 cm

2. 8.2 cm　　3. 10 in.　　4. x

The diameter of a circle is given. Find the radius of the circle.　　5. 6 cm

6. 8.2 cm　　7. 10 in.　　8. x

For a circle with each given diameter or radius, find (a) the exact circumference and (b) the approximate circumference.

Use 3.14 for π.

9. $d = 8$ cm　　　10. $r = 5$ cm
11. $d = 15$ in.　　12. $d = 2.5$ m
13. $d = 20$ ft　　　14. $r = 6$ cm

Use $\frac{22}{7}$ for π.

15. $d = 14$ in.　　　16. $d = 35$ cm
17. $r = 7$ in.　　　18. $d = 3\frac{1}{2}$ in.
19. $d = 49$ mm　　20. $d = 70$ m

— **B** —

21. The circumference of a circle is 21.98 cm. Find the diameter and radius. (Use 3.14 for π.)

22. Arc y is $\frac{1}{6}$ of a circle. The radius of the circle is $3\frac{1}{2}$ inches. What is the length of arc y? Use $\frac{22}{7}$ for π. (Hint: First find the circumference.)

23. Arc x is $\frac{1}{3}$ of a circle. If the circumference of the circle is 24 cm, what is the length of arc x?

— **C** —

24. The minute hand on a watch is 8 mm long. How far does the tip of the minute hand travel in one hour (one complete revolution)? (Use 3.14 for π.)

25. Look at $\overset{\frown}{AB}$. If n is the degree measure of $\overset{\frown}{AB}$, the length of $\overset{\frown}{AB}$ can be found with the following formula:

$m \overset{\frown}{AB} = n°$

Arc length $= \left(\dfrac{n}{360}\right)\pi d$

a. The diameter of the circle is 6 cm. Use the above formula to find the length of $\overset{\frown}{CD}$.

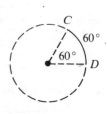

b. Explain why the formula works.

6-3

Area

Suppose you wish to determine the amount of wall-to-wall carpeting needed to cover a floor, how many cans of wall paint to buy for a certain size room, or how many bags of fertilizer to buy for a lawn. In each of these situations you must determine the amount of surface of a region.

1 cm

1 cm

1 square centimeter = 1 cm²

The amount of surface of a region is called its *area*. Using the square centimeter as the unit of area, the area of the rectangular region shown is 8 square centimeters.

A region of any shape can be used to measure area. However, since square units are the easiest to use, they are the most commonly used to measure area.

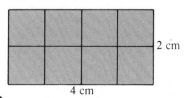

2 cm

4 cm

Area is 8 cm².

Find the area of each region. 1 square unit.

Example 1:

Solution:
It takes 5 square units to cover the region.
Area = 5 square units

Example 2:

Solution:
Each small triangular region is $\frac{1}{2}$ a square unit.
It takes $5\frac{1}{2}$ square units to cover the region.
Area = $5\frac{1}{2}$ square units

Example 3:

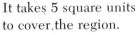

Solution:
The long triangular region is $\frac{1}{2}$ the area of a rectangular region of 3 square units. It takes $7\frac{1}{2}$ square units to cover the region. Area = $7\frac{1}{2}$ square units

The following example illustrates another method that can be used to find the area of some regions.

Example 4: Find the area of the shaded region.

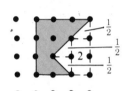

$\frac{1}{2}$

$\frac{1}{2}$

2

$\frac{1}{2}$

Solution:
Draw a rectangle around it.
Find the area of the part of the rectangular region that is *not* shaded.
$2 + \frac{1}{2} + \frac{1}{2} + \frac{1}{2} = 3\frac{1}{2}$ square units
Subtract this area from the area of the rectangular region.
Area = $9 - 3\frac{1}{2} = 5\frac{1}{2}$ square units

1. Describe some situations in which it is necessary to find the amount of surface (area) of some region.
2. Name five standard units of measure that can be used for area.

═══════════ **CLASS PRACTICE** ═══════════

Find the area of each shaded region.

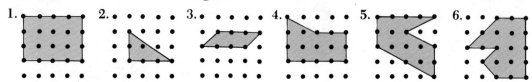

1. 2. 3. 4. 5. 6.

Use dot or graph paper to draw (a) region(s) to fit each description.
7. Rectangular region with an area of 8 and a perimeter of 12
8. Two noncongruent rectangular regions each with an area of 18
9. Triangular region with an area of 4   10. Triangular region with an area of $4\frac{1}{2}$

EXERCISES

— A —

Use dot or graph paper for all drawings. Use each small square as one unit of area. Vertices of all figures should be a point of your dot paper or a point of intersection of lines on your graph paper.

Find the area of each shaded region. It may be helpful to first draw each region on dot or graph paper.

1. 2.

3. 4.

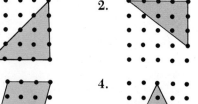

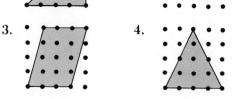

5. 6.

7. 8.

9. 10.

11. 12.

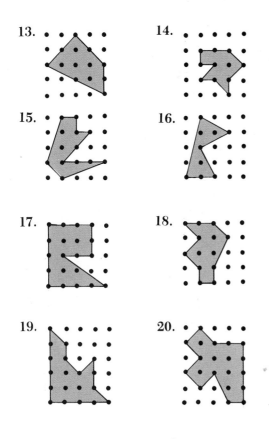

13. 14.

15. 16.

17. 18.

19. 20.

Draw a region to fit each description. An
* indicates that the region may be concave.

21. Square region with a perimeter
    of 20

22. Rectangular region with an area
    of 4

23. Rectangular region with an area of
    6 and a perimeter of 10

24. Rectangular region with an area of
    6 and a perimeter of 14

25. Rectangular region with an area of
    20 and a perimeter of 24

26. Rectangular region with an area of
    20 and a perimeter of 18

27. Rectangular region with an area of
    20 and a perimeter of 42

*28. Hexagonal region with an area of 3
*29. Hexagonal region with an area of 4
*30. Hexagonal region with an area
     of 10

— C —

Draw a triangular region having each
area.

31. 1   32. 2
33. 3   34. 4
35. 5   36. 6
37. $1\frac{1}{2}$ 38. $7\frac{1}{2}$

39. Draw two noncongruent triangular
    regions each with an area of 4.

40. a. Draw a triangular region and a
       square region having the same
       area.
    b. Which region has the smaller
       perimeter?
    c. Try another example. Is the
       answer to part b the same?

41. a. Draw a rectangular region and
       a square region having the
       same area.
    b. Which region has the smaller
       perimeter?
    c. Try another example. Is the
       answer to part b the same?

42. a. Draw a rectangular region and
       then draw a diagonal of the
       rectangle.
    b. What is the area of the rectan-
       gular region?
    c. What shape are the two parts of
       the rectangular region?
    d. Do the two parts have the same
       area?
    e. What is the area of each part?

43. Draw at least 20 noncongruent
    polygonal regions of area 4. The
    polygonal regions may be concave.

6-4

Area of a Rectangular Region

The term *height* refers to the distance between the base of a polygon and its opposite side. For a rectangular region, the term *base* may refer to any of the sides, and the height is equal to the length of either of the sides perpendicular to the base. Since the base is a segment, the term *base length* will be used to refer to its length.

If $\overline{WX}$ is the base, either ZW or YX is the height.

If $\overline{YX}$ is the base, either ZY or WX is the height.

1 square centimeter = 1 cm²

The area of the rectangular region shown is 8 square centimeters (written, 8 cm²). Notice that the area is found by multiplying the base length by the height.

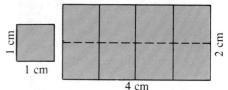

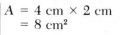

$A = 4$ cm × 2 cm
$\quad = 8$ cm²

To find the area of a rectangular region, multiply the base length by the height. (Both base length and height must be in the same units.)

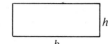

Area = base length × height

$$A = bh$$

Example 1:
Find the area of the rectangular region shown.

6 cm

8 cm

Solution:
$A = bh$
$\quad = 8 \times 6$
$\quad = 48$ cm²

Example 2:
Find the area (a) in square centimeters and (b) in square meters of a rectangular region that is 3 meters long and 50 centimeters wide.

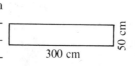

300 cm

50 cm

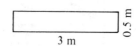

3 m

0.5 m

Solution:

a. 3 m = 3 × 100 cm = 300 cm
$\quad A = bh$
$\qquad = 300 \times 50$
$\qquad = 15,000$ cm²

b. 50 cm = $\frac{50}{100}$ m = 0.5 m
$\quad A = bh$
$\qquad = 3 \times 0.5$
$\qquad = 1.5$ m²

27. Perimeter = 26, Area = 12
28. Perimeter = 20, Area = 9
29. Perimeter = 20, Area = 16
30. Perimeter = 20, Area = 21
31. Perimeter = 20, Area = 24
32. Perimeter = 20, Area = 25

For Exercises 33 and 34 do not use any of the regions drawn for Exercises 23–32.

33. Draw three noncongruent rectangular regions having the same area but different perimeters.

34. Draw three noncongruent rectangular regions having the same perimeter but different areas.

When answering Exercises 35–38, refer to the results of Exercises 23–32.

35. Must rectangular regions with the same area have the same perimeter?

36. Must rectangular regions with the same perimeter have the same area?

37. If one rectangular region has a greater area than a second rectangular region, must it also have a greater perimeter?

38. If one rectangular region has a greater perimeter than a second rectangular region, must it also have a greater area?

39. For the two congruent square regions shown, complete the following statement: 1 square yard = ? square feet.

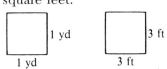

40. Two rectangular lots are for sale. The first lot is 100 feet wide and 150 feet long. The second lot is 20 feet wide and 750 feet long.

a. Find the area of each lot.

b. How do the areas compare?

c. If you were to build a house, which lot would you prefer? Why?

41. A rectangular shelf is 12 inches wide and 30 inches long. The rectangular base of a stereo turntable is 16 inches long and 14 inches wide.

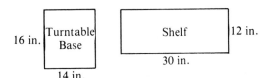

a. Find the area of the shelf and of the turntable base.

b. Which has the greater area?

c. Is it safe to place the turntable on the shelf? Why or why not?

42. Find the number of square feet of heat-proof plastic needed to cover the counter top shown. (Do not count the shaded area.)

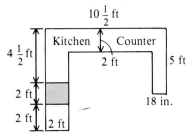

43. A football field is 100 yards long and 160 feet wide.

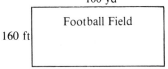

a. Find the area in square feet.

b. Find the area in square yards.

c. Is the area of a football field greater or less than 1 acre? (1 acre = 4840 yd)

44. Refer to these regulation dimensions:

Baseball Diamond: 90 ft × 90 ft
Basketball Court: 84 ft × 50 ft
Football Field: 300 ft × 160 ft

  a. About how many basketball courts would cover the same area as a baseball diamond?

  b. About how many baseball diamonds would cover the same area as a football field?

  c. About how many basketball courts would cover the same area as a football field?

Answer the following questions for each figure in Exercises 45–48.

  a. Area of rectangular region $ABCD$ is ? cm².

  b. Area of triangular region ADC is ? of the area of rectangular region $ABCD$.

  c. Area of triangular region ADC is ? cm².

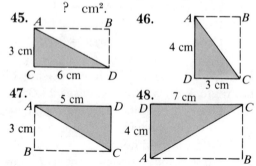

Find the area in square centimeters of each shaded triangular region.

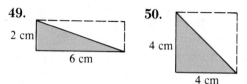

MORE EXPLORING

How Many Regions Have a Given Area?

All rectangular regions should be drawn on graph or dot paper. Use each square of the graph or dot paper as one unit of area. Both dimensions (base length and height) should be whole numbers.

1. Draw as many rectangular regions as you can that have the following areas:
     a. 1   **b.** 2   **c.** 3   **d.** 4
2. Continue this process for each whole number through 25.
3. List the whole-number areas for which only one rectangular region can be drawn.
4. List the whole-number areas for which more than one rectangular region can be drawn.
5. List the whole-number areas for which one of the rectangular regions is a square.
6. What is special about the numbers listed for step 3? for step 4? for step 5? What special names are given to these numbers?
7. Name three whole-number areas greater than 25 for which only one rectangular region can be drawn.

8. Name three whole-number areas greater than 25 for which more than one rectangular region can be drawn.
9. Name three whole-number areas greater than 25 for which one of the rectangular regions is a square.

MORE EXPLORING
Some Patterns with Squares

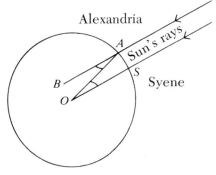

1. Find the area and perimeter of the square region shown.
2. Draw regions that result from the following changes in the figure shown. For each part, try to find all ways in which the problem can be done.
    a. Remove one square and leave the perimeter the same.
    b. Remove two squares and leave the perimeter the same.
    c. Remove three squares and leave the perimeter the same.
    d. Remove four squares and leave the perimeter the same.
    e. Remove one square and increase the perimeter by 2.
    f. Remove two squares and increase the perimeter by 4.
    g. Remove three squares and increase the perimeter by 6.
    h. Remove four squares and increase the perimeter by 8.

Applications

Eratosthenes and the Circumference of Earth

Eratosthenes was a Greek geographer who lived about 200 B.C. He made a very good estimate of the circumference of Earth based on the fact that in Syene, a town south of Alexandria, Egypt, the sun was directly overhead at noon on a certain day of the year and the assumptions that the sun's rays are parallel and that Earth is round.

When the sun was directly overhead in Syene, Eratosthenes measured the angle of the shadow of a vertical post in Alexandria (see the diagram.) From geometry he know that this angle, $\angle OAB$, was congruent to $\angle AOS$. The angle turned out to be $\frac{1}{50}$ of a circle. So he multiplied the distance from Alexandria to Syene by 50 to find the circumference of Earth. His answer was very close to modern measurements.

6-5

Mastering Perimeter and Area of a Rectangular Region

These exercises provide additional practice on the ideas of perimeter and area.

EXERCISES

_ A _

Classify each statement as true or false.

1. Rectangular regions with the same area must have the same perimeter.
2. Rectangular regions with the same perimeter must have the same area.
3. A square is a special kind of rectangle.
4. A rectangle is a special kind of square.
5. If two rectangular regions have the same area, then they are congruent.
6. Congruent figures have the same area.

Find the area of each region.

7.

8.

9. 1 ft / 6 in.

10. 2 cm / 3 cm

11. $\frac{2}{3}$ yd / $\frac{1}{3}$ yd

12. 3 ft / 3 ft

Find the indicated information.

13. Perimeter = 24 cm
    $w =$? cm
    8 cm, w

14. a. Perimeter = ? cm   5 cm
    b. Area = ? cm²
    10 cm, 5 cm

15. Area = 12 cm²
    a. $h =$? cm
    b. Perimeter = ? cm
    2 cm, h

16. a. Perimeter = ? cm   7 cm
    b. Area = ? cm²
    4 cm

_ B _

Use dot or graph paper for all drawings.

Draw a rectangular region to fit each description.

17. Area is 12 square units.
18. Area is 12 square units but the region is not congruent to the one drawn for Exercise 17.
19. One side has a length of 3 and the area is 18 square units.
20. Base length is 8 and the area is 24 square units.

21. One side has a length of 7 and the perimeter is 20.
22. One side has a length of 6 and the perimeter is 20.
23. Area is 20 square units and the perimeter is 18.
24. Area is 36 square units and the perimeter is 24.
25. Use whole-number lengths for both base length and height.
    a. Draw all rectangular regions having a perimeter of 16.
    b. For the regions drawn for part a, what is the smallest area? the largest area?
26. a. Suppose two rectangular regions have the same area. Must their base lengths be the same?

    b. Suppose two square regions have the same area. Must their base lengths be the same?

The perimeter and the length of one side of regular polygons are given. Find the number of sides in each regular polygon.

27. Perimeter = 66 cm
    Length of one side = 11 cm
28. Perimeter = 80 cm
    Length of one side = 20 cm
29. Perimeter = 45 cm
    Length of one side = 9 cm
30. Perimeter = 3 cm
    Length of one side = 5 mm
31. Perimeter = 1 m
    Length of one side = 10 cm

Test Yourself

Find the perimeter and area of each region described.
1. Rectangular region with a base length of 9 cm and a height of 5 cm
2. Square region with sides of 8 cm
3. Rectangular region with a base length of 1 yd and a height of 2 ft

Find the indicated information.
4. Area = ? square units

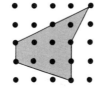

5. a. Perimeter = ? cm
   b. Area = ? cm²

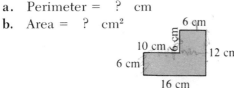

6. Perimeter = 38 cm
   x = ? cm

7. Area = 50 cm²
   h = ? cm

8. Perimeter = 30 cm
   y = ? cm

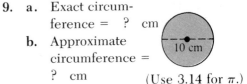

9. a. Exact circumference = ? cm
   b. Approximate circumference = ? cm
   (Use 3.14 for π.)

10. Draw a rectangular region with an area of 36 and a perimeter of 24.

6-6

Finding Heights and Altitudes

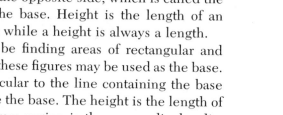

In Construction 9 in Chapter 4, you learned how to construct a perpendicular from a point to a line. Later in that chapter you used this construction to construct the three altitudes of a triangle. The three altitudes for one triangle are shown here.

Recall that an altitude of a triangle is a segment from one vertex perpendicular to a line containing the opposite side, which is called the base. Any side may be used as the base. Height is the length of an altitude. Any altitude is a segment while a height is always a length.

In this chapter you will also be finding areas of rectangular and parallelogram regions. Any side of these figures may be used as the base. An altitude is a segment perpendicular to the line containing the base from any point on the side opposite the base. The height is the length of an altitude and for any parallelogram region is the perpendicular distance between the base and its opposite side. All altitudes to a given base have the same length. This is illustrated by the following examples.

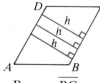
Base: $\overline{BC}$

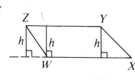
Base: $\overline{WX}$

Base: $\overline{RE}$

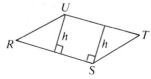
Base: $\overline{RS}$

CLASS PRACTICE

Draw a polygon similar to but larger than each one shown. Draw the altitude to $\overline{AB}$.

1.

2.

3.

4.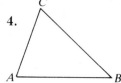

On dot or graph paper, draw a figure to fit each description.
5. Rectangular region with a base length of 8 and a height of 3
6. Parallelogram region that is not rectangular and that has a base length of 6 and a height of 3
7. Isosceles triangular region with a base length of 6 and a height of 6
8. Triangular region with a base length of 5 and a height of 4

_ A _

Draw a polygon similar to but larger than each one shown. Draw the altitude to $\overline{AB}$.

1.

2.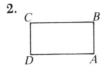

3.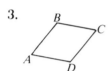

4.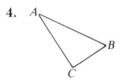

5.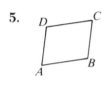

6.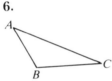

For each parallelogram, identify all segments shown that can be used to measure the height of the parallelogram. For each height identify the two corresponding bases.

7.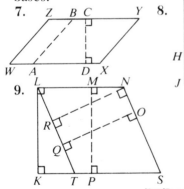

8.

9.

10. How do the lengths of the four segments labeled h in the figure shown compare? Explain your answer.

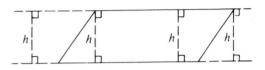

_ B _

On dot or graph paper, draw a figure or figures to fit each description.

11. Rectangular region with a base length of 6 and a height of 2

12. Square region with a height of 3

13. Parallelogram region that is not rectangular and that has a height of 2

14. Parallelogram region that is not rectangular and that has a base length of 4 and a height of 3

15. Three noncongruent parallelogram regions each of which has a base length of 5 and a height of 3

16. Triangular region with a height of 5

17. Triangular region with a base length of 5 and a height of 3

18. Right triangular region with a base length of 4 and a height of 2

19. Isosceles triangular region with a base length of 4 and a height of 3

20. Three noncongruent triangular regions each of which has a base length of 6 and a height of 4

DID YOU KNOW THAT....

In 1973 two French mathematicians used a computer to calculate the value of pi to one million decimal places.

6-7

Area of a Parallelogram Region

The following EXPLORING illustrates one useful relationship between the areas of rectangular and parallelogram regions.

EXPLORING
The Relationship Between the Areas of Parallelograms

1. On graph or dot paper, draw a nonrectangular parallelogram region. Use each small square on your paper as one unit of area.

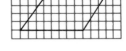

2. Draw an altitude as shown.

3. Cut along the altitude, separating the parallelogram region into two regions.

4. Move the left-hand region to the right of the other region. Fit the two regions together as shown. The newly formed region is rectangular in shape.

5. Compare the base length, height, and area of the parallelogram region with that of the rectangular region.

6. Write a formula for the area of the parallelogram region.

If you did the preceding EXPLORING carefully you discovered that the base length and height of the parallelogram region are equal to those of the rectangular region formed. In addition, the areas of the regions are equal.

The formula for the area of a parallelogram region is the same as that for the area of a rectangular region with the same base length and height.

> To find the area of a parallelogram region, multiply the base length by the height. (Both base length and height must be in the same units.)
>
>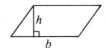
>
> Area = base length × height
>
> $A = bh$

Find the area of each parallelogram region.

Example 1:

Solution:

$A = bh$
$A = 8 \times 6$
$\quad = 48 \text{ cm}^2$

Example 2:

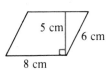

Solution:

Notice that the height is 5 cm, *not* 6 cm.

$A = bh$
$A = 8 \times 5$
$\quad = 40 \text{ cm}^2$

DISCUSS

1. For any rectangular region, the height is also the length of the sides adjacent to the base. Is this true for all parallelogram regions as well?

Explain why the area computed for each region is incorrect.

2. $A = bh$
   $\quad = 6 \cdot 1 = 6$

3. $A = bh$
   $\quad = 8 \cdot 3 = 24$

CLASS PRACTICE

Classify each statement as true or false.

1. Each rectangle is a parallelogram.
2. Each parallelogram is a rectangle.
3. Each square is a parallelogram.
4. Each parallelogram is a square.

Find the perimeter and area of each parallelogram region.

5.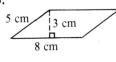

6.

7.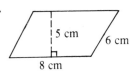

Find the indicated information.

8. Area = 60 cm²
   $h =$? cm

9. Perimeter = 36 cm
   $x =$? cm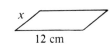

— A —

Find the area in square units of each shaded region.

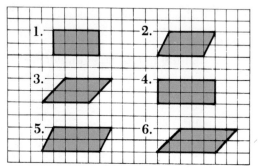

Find the perimeter and area of each parallelogram region. Write each answer with an appropriate unit of area or perimeter.

7.
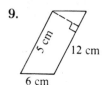

8.
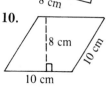

9.
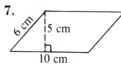

10.

Find the area of a parallelogram region with each given base length and height. Write each answer with an appropriate unit of area.

11. $b = 9$ cm, $h = 6$ cm
12. $b = 8$ ft, $h = 1\frac{1}{2}$ ft
13. $b = 3$ yd, $h = 6$ ft
14. $b = 50$ cm, $h = 4$ m

Find the indicated information.

15. Area = ? cm²
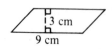

16. Area = 50 cm²
    x = ? cm
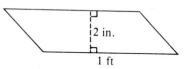

17. Area = ? in.²
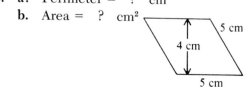

18. a. Perimeter = ? cm
    b. Area = ? cm²
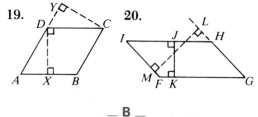

Answer the following questions for each parallelogram.

a. Identify two altitudes.
b. For each altitude, identify the two corresponding bases.

19. 20.

Draw figures to fit each description.

21. Four noncongruent parallelogram regions each of which has a base length of 6 and a height of 3

22. Three parallelogram regions that are not congruent to ABCD shown but have the same area

23. Three noncongruent rectangular regions that have the same area as the parallelogram region EFGH shown

24. In the figure shown, the unshaded region is a square. Find the combined area of the two shaded regions.

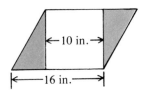

← 10 in. →

← 16 in. →

Find the area of each shaded region.

25.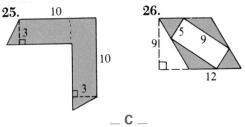

10

3

10

3

26.

5

9

9

12

27. **a.** Draw a rectangular region and a nonrectangular parallelogram region that both have a base length of 6 and a height of 2.
  b. How do their areas compare?
  c. How do their perimeters compare?
  d. Complete the following statement: If a rectangular region and a nonrectangular parallelogram region have the same base length and height, then their areas are ? and the ? has the larger perimeter.

28. Is the area of the parallelogram region shown 12 square units? Why or why not?

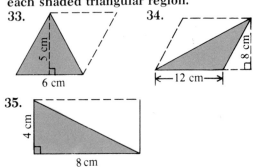

2

6

29. Which phrase best describes the area of the parallelogram region shown?

3

8

  a. 24 square inches
  b. More than 24 square inches
  c. Less than 24 square inches

Complete the following statements for each figure.

  a. Area of parallelogram region *ABCD* is ? cm².
  b. Area of triangular region *ABC* is ? of the area of the parallelogram region *ABCD*.
  c. Area of triangular region *ABC* is ? cm².

30.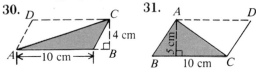

D ---- C

4 cm

A ← 10 cm → B

31. A ---- D

5 cm

B   10 cm   C

32. A ---- D

5 cm

B ← 8 cm → C

Find the area in square centimeters of each shaded triangular region.

33.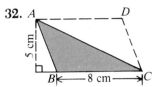

5 cm

6 cm

34.

8 cm

← 12 cm →

35.

4 cm

8 cm

6-8

Area of a Triangular Region

Earlier in this chapter you found that the area of a triangular region equals one half the area of a parallelogram or rectangular region with the same base length and height. Here are some examples:

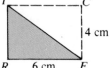

Area of $RECT$ = 24 cm²

Area of $\triangle RET$ = 12 cm²

Area of $ABCD$ = 20 cm²

Area of $\triangle ABD$ = 10 cm²

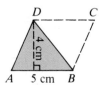

Any side of a triangle can be used as the *base*. The corresponding height is the perpendicular distance from the opposite vertex to that side. Some examples are shown below. Notice that each base is a segment and each height is a length.

Base: $\overline{RS}$
Height: TY

Base: $\overline{AB}$
Height: CX

Base: $\overline{BC}$
Height: AY

Base: $\overline{RT}$
Height: SX

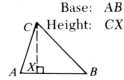 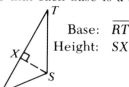

If you have not already discovered a formula for the area of a triangular region, the following will help you do so. Look at the two figures shown here. The area of the shaded triangular region is one half the area of a parallelogram or rectangular region with the same base length and height.

A = 9 cm²

6 cm
A = 9 cm²

> To find the area of a triangular region, multiply $\frac{1}{2}$ by the product of the base length and height. (Both base length and height must be in the same units.)
>
> Area = $\frac{1}{2}$ × base length × height
>
> $A = \frac{1}{2}bh$

Find the area of each triangular region.

Example 1:

Solution:

$A = \frac{1}{2}bh$

$A = \frac{1}{2} \times 8 \times 6$

$\quad = 24$ cm²

Example 2:

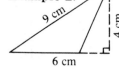

Solution:

Base length is 6 cm and height is 4 cm.

$A = \frac{1}{2}bh$

$A = \frac{1}{2} \times 6 \times 4 = 12$ cm²

Find the area of each shaded triangular region. Write each answer with an appropriate unit of area.

1.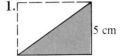
5 cm
7 cm

2.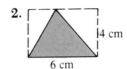
4 cm
6 cm

3.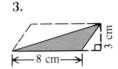
3 cm
8 cm

Find the area of a triangular region with each given base length and height. Write each answer with an appropriate unit of area.

4. $b = 10\,\text{cm}, \quad h = 4\,\text{cm}$ **5.** $b = 9\,\text{ft}, \quad h = 6\,\text{ft}$ **6.** $b = 4\,\text{cm}, \quad h = 5\,\text{mm}$

Find the length of the indicated side.

7. Area = 30 cm²

$h = \,?\,$ cm

10 cm

8. Area = 16 cm²

$x = \,?\,$ cm

8 cm
x

9. Draw some noncongruent triangles. For each triangle drawn, draw a parallelogram or rectangular region with the same base length and height. Notice that the triangular region has an area that is one half the area of its corresponding parallelogram or rectangular region.

10. Draw some noncongruent triangles. Select one side of each triangle as the base. For each base selected, draw the segment that would be used to measure the corresponding height of the triangle.

EXERCISES

_ A _

Find the area in square units of each shaded region.

1. a. b. c. d.

2. a. b. c.

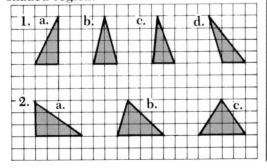

Find the area of each shaded region. Write each answer with an appropriate unit of area.

3.
4 cm
8 cm

4.
4 cm
8 cm

5.
4 cm
8 cm

6.
4 cm
8 cm

7.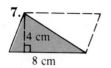
4 cm
8 cm

8.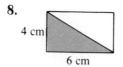
4 cm
6 cm

9.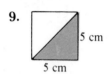
5 cm
5 cm

10.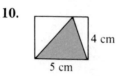
4 cm
5 cm

11.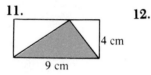
4 cm
9 cm

12.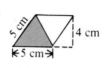
5 cm
5 cm
4 cm

Find the area of a triangular region with each given base length and height. Write each answer with an appropriate unit of area.

13. $b = 8$ cm, $h = 7$ cm
14. $b = 6$ cm, $h = 6$ cm
15. $b = 12$ ft, $h = 1\frac{1}{2}$ ft
16. $b = 6$ ft, $h = 9$ ft
17. $b = 2$ yd, $h = 9$ ft
18. $b = 50$ cm, $h = 4$ m

Find the area of each triangular region. Write each answer with an appropriate unit of area.

19.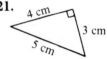
3 in.
1 ft

20.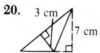
3 cm
7 cm
5 cm

21.
4 cm
3 cm
5 cm

22.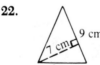
9 cm
7 cm
8 cm

Find the length of each indicated segment.

23. Area = 24 cm²
$h = $? cm
h
8 cm

24. Area = 48 cm²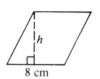
$h = $? cm
h
8 cm

Identify the following for each triangle.
a. Three altitudes
b. Corresponding base for each altitude

25.
I
X
Y
T
Z
R

26.
X
W
T
R
Y
S

_ **B** _

Draw a figure to fit each description.
27. Right triangular region with an area of 12
28. Right triangular region that has an area of 12 and that is not congruent to the region drawn for Exercise 27
29. Triangular region with the same area as a rectangular region with a base length of 4 and a height of 3
30. Right triangular region with an area of 6
31. Right triangular region with one side of length 5 and an area of 10
32. Obtuse triangular region with a base length of 4 and a height of 3
33. Acute triangular region with a base length of 4 and a height of 3
34. Obtuse triangular region with a base length of 6 and an area of 9
35. Acute triangular region with a base length of 8 and an area of 12
36. Four noncongruent triangular regions each with an area of 3

Look at the figure.

37. Find the area of the following regions.

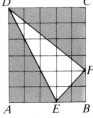

a. Rectangle *ABCD*
b. △*EAD*
c. △*DCF*
d. △*FBE*
e. Shaded region
f. △*DEF*

___ C ___

Find the area of each shaded region.

38.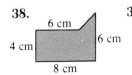

39.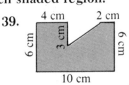

40.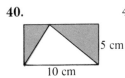

41.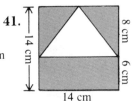

42.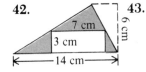

43.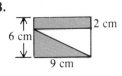

44.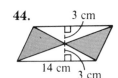

45.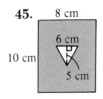

46. Four different triangles with base $\overline{XY}$ are shown.

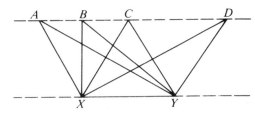

a. How does the length of the altitude from *A* to $\overline{XY}$ compare with that from *B* to $\overline{XY}$? from *C* to $\overline{XY}$? from *D* to $\overline{XY}$?
b. How do the areas of the four triangular regions compare?
c. Are the four triangles congruent?
d. If two triangular regions have the same base length and height, how do their areas compare?

═══════ **MORE EXPLORING** ═══════

Area of Regions Formed by Medians

Recall that a *median* is a segment drawn from a vertex to the midpoint of the opposite side of a triangle.

1. Look at △*DEF*. Suppose $\overline{DE}$ is the base. Find each of the following:
    a. Base length
    b. Height
    c. Area

2. Suppose the median ($\overline{FX}$) is drawn from *F* to $\overline{DE}$. Look at △*DFX* and △*EFX*. Suppose $\overline{DX}$ is the base of △*DFX* and $\overline{EX}$ is the base of △*EFX*. Find each of the following for each triangle:
    a. Base length   b. Height   c. Area

$\overline{AX}$ is a median of △*ABC*.

3. How do the areas of $\triangle DFX$ and $\triangle EFX$ compare with one another and with the area of $\triangle DEF$?
4. Write a conclusion. Complete the following statement:

> **A median of a triangle divides it into two triangular regions having   ?   areas that are   ?   the area of the original triangular region.**

 *Everyday Geometry*

Remodeling a Kitchen

Many home-improvement projects make use of perimeter and area techniques.

EXERCISES

Suppose you want to remodel a kitchen. Listed below are some of the jobs you wish to complete. For each job, indicate the following:

a. Factors that must be considered in deciding how much material (tile, paint, wallpaper, etc.) to buy.
b. How perimeter and/or area is involved in making this decision.
c. Units of measure that might be involved.
  1. Put new tile on floor.
  2. Wallpaper the walls.
  3. Paint the ceiling.
  4. Refinish the cabinets.
  5. Put new baseboard around room.
  6. Put new trim around windows.
  7. Put new heat-proof plastic on counter-tops.

DID YOU KNOW THAT....

The smallest unit of area is a *shed*, a unit used in subatomic physics.
A *shed* is 0.000000000000000000000000000000000000000000000000 cm².

6-9

Area of Other Polygonal Regions

In earlier lessons of this chapter, you found the area of rectangular, parallelogram, and triangular regions, as well as of regions made up of two or more of these shapes. Any concave or convex polygonal region can be separated into regions for which we have a formula for computing the area. The following examples illustrate this for three different regions.

Find the area of each shaded region.

Example 1:

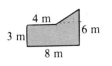

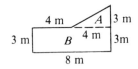

Solution:

Area of region A = 6 m²
Area of region B = 24 m²
Area of shaded region = 6 + 24
= 30 m²

Example 2:

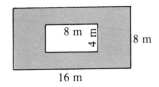

Solution:

Area of large rectangular
region = 128 m²
Area of small rectangular
region = 32 m²
Area of shaded region = 128 − 32
= 96 m²

Example 3:

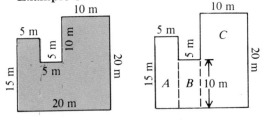

Solution:

Area of region A = 75 m²
Area of region B = 50 m²
Area of region C = 200 m²
Area of shaded region = 75 + 50 + 200
= 325 m²

CLASS PRACTICE

Draw two copies of each region. On each copy, draw dashed segments to show two different ways to separate the shaded region into regions for which you know an area formula.

1.

2.

3.

Find the area of each shaded region.

4.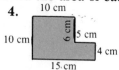

5.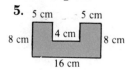

6.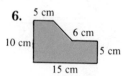

7. Look at Examples 1–3 on page 251. Find the area of each shaded region by separating the shaded region differently than shown. Can some regions be separated in more than two ways?

EXERCISES

— A —

Find the area of each shaded region. All dimensions are in centimeters.

1.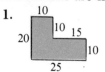

2.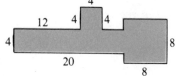

3.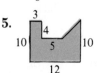

4.

5.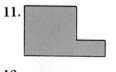

6.

7.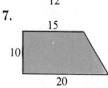

8–10. Find the perimeter of the regions in Exercises 1, 2, and 3.

Draw two copies of each region. On each copy, draw dashed segments to show two different ways to separate the shaded region into regions for which you know an area formula.

11.

12.

13.

14.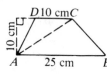

— B —

15. Look at trapezoidal region $ABCD$. Find each of the following.
    a. Base length and height for $\triangle ADC$
    b. Base length and height for $\triangle ABC$

    c. Area of $\triangle ADC$
    d. Area of $\triangle ABC$
    e. Area of region $ABCD$

16. Regular hexagonal region $ABCDEF$ has been separated into six congruent triangular regions.
    a. Find the area of each triangular region.
    b. Find the area of the regular hexagonal region.
    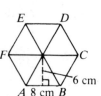

Minimizing the Perimeter of a Rectangular Region

1. Using whole-number lengths for the base length and height, draw all possible rectangular regions with an area of 36.
2. Find the perimeter of each region. Which region has the smallest perimeter?
3. Repeat steps 1 and 2 for rectangular regions of area 16, 64, and 100.
4. Write a conclusion. Complete the following statement:

> **Of all the rectangular regions with a given area, the region with the smallest perimeter is a(n)   ?**

═══════ *Test Yourself* ═══════

Find the indicated information.

1. Area = 64 cm²
   h = ? cm

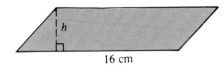
16 cm

2. Area = ? cm²
3. Perimeter = ? cm

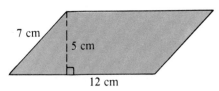
7 cm   5 cm
12 cm

4. Area = ? cm²
5. Perimeter = ? cm

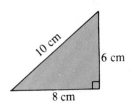
10 cm   6 cm
8 cm

6. Area = ? cm²

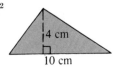
4 cm
10 cm

7. Area = 30 cm²
   x = ? cm

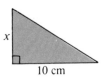
x
10 cm

8. Area = ? cm² 6 cm

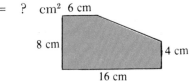
8 cm   4 cm
16 cm

Draw (a) figure(s) to fit each description.

9. Parallelogram region with a height of 3 and an area of 12
10. Two noncongruent parallelogram regions with a base length of 6 and an area of 18
11. Triangular region with a base length of 6 and an area of 12

6-10

Area of a Circular Region

The following EXPLORING develops a formula for finding the area of any circular region.

EXPLORING

The Area of a Circular Region

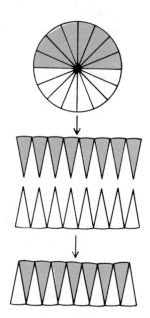

1. The figures show a circular region separated into congruent parts that have been rearranged to form a region of a different shape. How does the area of the new region compare to the area of the circular region?

2. The new region resembles what kind of quadrilateral? What is the formula for the area of this type of region?

3. How does the base length of the new region compare to the circumference of the circular region? What is the formula for the circumference of a circular region? Use this formula to write a formula relating the base length b to the radius r.

4. How does the height of the new region compare to the radius of the circular region? Write a formula relating the height h to the radius r.

If you did the preceding EXPLORING carefully, you discovered that the figure formed by rearranging the parts of the circular region looks like a parallelogram. Recall that the formula for the area of a parallelogram is $A = bh$.

The height h is about the same as the radius r of the circle. $h \approx r$

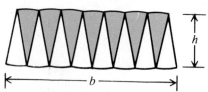

The base length b is about one half the circumference C of the circle.

$b = \frac{1}{2}C$ and

$C = \pi d = 2\pi r$ so

$b = \frac{1}{2}(2\pi r) = \pi r$

$A = b \times h$

$\quad = \pi r \times r$

$\quad = \pi r^2$

Of course, the figure formed by cutting up the circle is not really a parallelogram. However, as the circle is divided into more and more parts, the figure formed becomes more like a parallelogram.

The formula suggested by this activity, which can be proved for all circular regions, is stated below.

To find the area of a circular region, multiply π by the square of the radius.

$$A = \pi r^2, \text{ where } \pi \approx 3.14 \text{ or } \frac{22}{7},$$

and r is the radius.

Example 1:   Find the area of a circular region with radius 5 cm.

Solution:

$A = \pi r^2$ $A \approx (3.14)\,(5^2)$
$A = \pi \cdot 5^2$ $\approx (3.14)\,(25)$
$\quad = \pi \cdot 25$ ≈ 78.50 cm² (approximate value)
$\quad = 25\,\pi$ cm² (exact value)

Example 2:   The area of a circular region is approximately 28.26 in.².
             Find the radius and the diameter.

Solution:

$A = \pi r^2$ $9 \approx r^2$
$28.26 \approx 3.14 \times r^2$ $r \approx 3$
$28.26 \div 3.14 \approx r^2$

Answer: Since the radius is about 3 in., the diameter is about 6 in.

Example 3:   Find the area of the shaded region. (Use $\frac{22}{7}$ for π.)

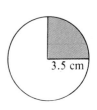

3.5 cm

Solution:
First find the area A of the circular region.
$3.5 = \frac{7}{2}$ $A = \pi r^2$ $A \approx \frac{22}{7} \times \frac{7}{2} \times \frac{7}{2}$
                            $\approx \frac{1078}{28}$
                            $\approx \frac{77}{2} \approx 38.5$ cm²

Answer: The shaded region is $\frac{1}{4}$ of the circular region. So its area is
           approximately $\frac{1}{4} \times 38\frac{1}{2} = \frac{1}{4} \times \frac{77}{2} = \frac{77}{8} = 9.625$ cm².

For a circle with each given radius or diameter, find (a) the exact area (leave answer in terms of π) and (b) the approximate area. (Use 3.14 for π.)

1. $r = 4$ cm   2. $r = 5$ cm   3. $d = 8$ cm

4. The approximate area of a circular region is 113.04 cm². Find the radius and the diameter. (Use 3.14 for π.)

EXERCISES

_ A _

The radius of a circle is given. Find the diameter.   1. 6 cm   2. 4.4 cm   3. 8 in.   4. x

The diameter of a circle is given. Find the radius.   5. 6 cm   6. 4.4 cm   7. 8 in.   8. x

For a circle with each given radius or diameter, find (a) the exact area (in terms of π) and (b) the approximate area.

Use 3.14 for π.

9. $r = 2$ cm   10. $r = 3$ cm
11. $d = 6$ cm   12. $r = 1.2$ m
13. $r = 20$ ft   14. $d = 10$ cm

Use $\frac{22}{7}$ for π.

15. $r = 7$ cm   16. $r = 14$ cm
17. $d = 14$ cm   18. $r = 28$ ft
19. $r = 3.5$ m   20. $d = 56$ ft

_ B _

Copy and complete the following table about circles. (Use 3.14 for π.)

	Radius	Diameter	Circumference	Area
21.	10 cm	?	?	?
22.	?	8 cm	?	?
23.	?	?	6.28 cm	?
24.	?	?	?	28.26 cm²

25. The area of a circular region is 25π cm². Find the radius and the diameter of the circle.

Find the area of each region. (Use 3.14 for π.)

26. 12-inch pizza (Diameter is 12 in.)
27. Watch face with a 15-mm radius
28. 8-inch pie pan (Diameter is 8 in.)

Find the area of each shaded region. (Use 3.14 for π unless otherwise indicated.)

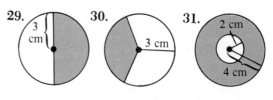

29.   30.   31.

_ C _

32. Look at the figure. If n is the degree measure of $\overset{\frown}{AB}$, the area of the shaded region can be found by using the following formula:

$$\text{Area} = \left(\frac{n}{360}\right)\pi r^2$$

a. Use the above formula to find the area of the shaded region.

b. Explain why the formula works.

6-11

Stretching Rectangular and Circular Regions

In this lesson you will investigate some additional properties of area and perimeter for rectangular and circular regions.

EXPLORING
Stretching Rectangular Regions

1. Find the perimeter and area of each rectangular region described in the table. Record your results in a table such as this:

Region	Base Length	Height	Perimeter	Area	Region	Base Length	Height	Perimeter	Area
A	3	2	?	?	E	9	2	?	?
B	6	2	?	?	F	3	6	?	?
C	3	4	?	?	G	9	6	?	?
D	6	4	?	?					

2. What happens to the perimeter of a rectangular region when both the base length and height are multiplied by 2 and by 3?

3. What happens to the area of a rectangular region when both the base length and height are multiplied by 2 and by 3?

4. Suppose both the base length and height of region A were multiplied by 4. What would happen to the perimeter? to the area?

EXPLORING
Stretching Circular Regions

1. Find the circumference and area of each circular region described in the table. Record your results in a table such as this:

Circle	Radius	Circumference	Area	Circle	Radius	Circumference	Area
A	1	2π	1π	D	4	?	?
B	2	4π	4π	E	5	?	?
C.	3	?	?				

2. Use your results to determine what happens to the circumference of a circular region when the radius is multiplied by 2, by 3, by 4, and by 5.

3. Use your results to determine what happens to the area of a circular region when the radius is multiplied by 2, by 3, by 4, and by 5.

If you did the preceding EXPLORINGs carefully, you discovered the following conclusions:

> **If both the base length and height of a rectangular region are multipled by _n_, its perimeter is multiplied by _n_ and its area is multiplied by _n²_.**

> **If the radius of a circular region is multiplied by _n_, its circumference is multiplied by _n_ and its area is multiplied by _n²_.**

EXERCISES

Classify each statement as true or false.

1. If both base length and height of a rectangular region are multiplied by 2, its area is multiplied by 2.

2. If both base length and height of a rectangular region are multiplied by 2, its perimeter is multiplied by 2.

For each exercise, assume that the base length and height of the larger rectangular region are three times the base length and height of the smaller region.

3. Area of smaller region = 20 cm²
   Area of larger region = ? cm²

4. Perimeter of smaller region = 18 cm
   Perimeter of larger region = ? cm

5. Area of larger region = 72 cm²
   Area of smaller region = ? cm²

6. Perimeter of larger region = 36 cm
   Perimeter of smaller region = ? cm

Find the indicated information.

7. By what number is the area of a circular region multiplied if its radius is multiplied by each of the following factors?
   a. 2   b. 4   c. 5

8. The area of a certain circular region is 15 cm². Find the area of a circular region whose radius is three times as great.

9. By what number is the circumference of a circular region multiplied if its radius is multipled by each of the following factors?
   a. 2   b. 4   c. 5

10. The circumference of a certain circular region is 20 cm. Find the circumference of a circular region whose radius is three times as great.

6-12

Pick's Formula

In this lesson you will learn Pick's Formula for finding the area of any concave or convex polygonal region that can be drawn on dot or graph paper. For this formula to work, every vertex of the polygon must be at one of the dots on dot paper or one of the intersections of the lines on graph paper.

Pick's Formula requires that we count the number of border points and interior points. For any polygonal region drawn on dot paper, a *border point* is any dot on a side of the polygon, and an *interior point* is any dot that is inside the region and not on any of the sides.

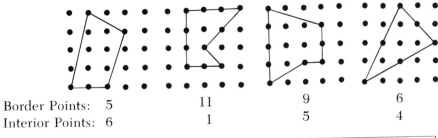

Border Points: 5   11   9   6
Interior Points: 6   1   5   4

EXPLORING

Pick's Formula

1. Find the following information for each polygonal region shown below: the number of border points, the number of interior points, and the area. Record your results in a table like the one below:

Region	Number of Border Points (b)	Number of Interior Points (i)	Area (A)

2. For each region, compare the area with the number of border and interior points. Using A to represent area, b to represent the number of border points, and i to represent the number of interior points, write a formula that can be used to find the area of each region. (Hint: Compare $\frac{1}{2}b + i$ with A.)

3. Draw two or three other regions like those shown. Use your formula to find the area of each region. Did it work? If not, revise it.

In the preceding EXPLORING you discovered Pick's Formula for finding the area of a polygonal region drawn on dot or graph paper. Suppose we put a hole into such a polygonal region (as shown). The shaded region has 16 border points and 4 interior points.

In the following EXPLORING you will learn how to modify Pick's Formula so that it can be used to find the area of a polygonal region with one hole.

EXPLORING

Pick's Formula with One Hole

1. Find the following information for each shaded region shown: the number of border points, the number of interior points, and the area. Record your results in a table like the one below.

Region	Number of Border Points (b)	Number of Interior Points (i)	Area (A)

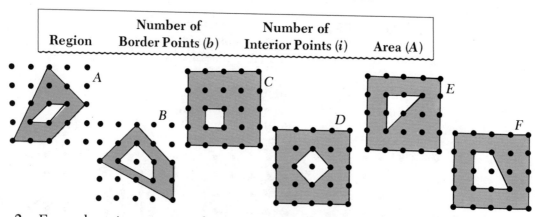

2. For each region, compare the area with the number of border and interior points. Write a formula that can be used to find the area of each region.

3. Draw two or three other regions with one hole. Use your formula to find the area of each region. Did it work? If not, revise it.

If you did the preceding EXPLORINGs carefully, you discovered the following formulas:

> **Pick's Formula:** $A = \frac{1}{2}b + i - 1$
>
> **Pick's Formula with One Hole:** $A = \frac{1}{2}b + i$

EXERCISES

Use Pick's Formula to find the area of each shaded region. Show your work.

1.

2.

3.

4.

5.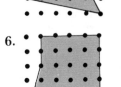

6.

Use Pick's Formula with One Hole to find the area of each shaded region. Show your work.

7.

8.

9.

10.

MORE EXPLORING
Extending Pick's Formula

1. Suppose there are two holes in a polygonal region drawn on dot or graph paper. Find a formula for the area in terms of the numbers of border and interior points.
2. Find an area formula for a polygonal region with *n* holes.

DID YOU KNOW THAT....

The use of the Greek letter π to denote the ratio of the circumference of a circle to its diameter was introduced in 1706. One earlier symbol used for this ratio was the letter "e."

6-13

Units of Area and Some Special Area Formulas

The three drawings indicate the relationship between some units of area. (The drawings are to different scales.)

1 yd (3 ft)   1 ft (12 in.)   1 m (100 cm)

1 yd (3 ft)   1 ft (12 in.)   1 m (100 cm)

1 square yard = 9 square feet			
1 square foot = 144 square inches			
1 square meter = 10,000 square centimeters			

$A = 3 \times 3$ $A = 12 \times 12$ $A = 100 \times 100$
$= 9 \text{ ft}^2$ $= 144 \text{ in.}^2$ $= 10,000 \text{ cm}^2$

Here are some examples using some of these relationships.

Example 1: $108 \text{ ft}^2 = ? \text{ yd}^2$

Solution:
$9 \text{ ft}^2 = 1 \text{ yd}^2$

To convert from a smaller unit to a larger one, divide. $108 \div 9 = 12$

There are 12 square yards in 108 square feet.

Example 2: $15 \text{ yd}^2 = ? \text{ ft}^2$

Solution:
$1 \text{ yd}^2 = 9 \text{ ft}^2$

To convert from a larger unit to a smaller one, multiply. $15 \times 9 = 135$

There are 135 square feet in 15 square yards.

The area of any parallelogram region can be found with the formula $A = bh$. However, a special formula can be developed for finding the area determined by a rhombus.

Look at rhombus $ABCD$. The diagonals are perpendicular. Suppose a segment parallel to one of the diagonals is drawn through each vertex. The figure formed, $WXYZ$, is a rectangle. The base length and height of $WXYZ$ are equal to the lengths of the diagonals of $ABCD$. Notice that the area determined by the rhombus is one half the area of the rectangular region. Therefore the area determined by rhombus $ABCD$ is 24 cm², which is one half the product of the lengths of its diagonals.

$AC = 8$ cm
$BD = 6$ cm

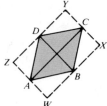

$WX = 8$ cm
$BD = 6$ cm
Area of $WXYZ = 48$ cm²

This example illustrates the following formula for finding the area determined by any rhombus:

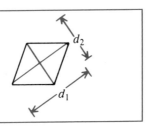

> **The area determined by a rhombus is equal to one half the product of the lengths of the diagonals.**
>
> $$A = \tfrac{1}{2}d_1d_2$$

The area of any trapezoidal region can be found by dividing the region into two triangular regions. A special formula can also be developed for finding such areas.

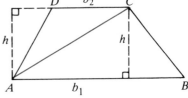

Look at trapezoid $ABCD$, which has been divided into two triangular regions by diagonal $\overline{AC}$. Notice that the heights of the two triangular regions are equal. The area of trapezoidal region $ABCD$ can be found by combining the areas of the two triangular regions:

$$\text{Area } \triangle ABC = \tfrac{1}{2}b_1h$$
$$\text{Area } \triangle ADC = \tfrac{1}{2}b_2h$$

$$\text{Area of } ABCD = \tfrac{1}{2}b_1h + \tfrac{1}{2}b_2h = \tfrac{1}{2}h(b_1 + b_2)$$

This illustrates the following formula for finding the area of any trapezoidal region:

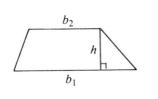

> **The area of any trapezoidal region is equal to one half the product of the height and the sum of the base lengths.**
>
> $$A = \tfrac{1}{2}h(b_1 + b_2)$$

DISCUSS

1. Explain why the following statement is incorrect:
   "There are 3 feet in 1 yard. Therefore, 1 square yard equals 3 square feet."
2. Can the formula $A = \tfrac{1}{2}d_1d_2$ be used to find the area of a square region? Why or why not?

Convert each measurement to the indicated unit.

1. $27 \text{ ft}^2 = \text{?} \quad \text{yd}^2$
2. $27 \text{ yd}^2 = \text{?} \quad \text{ft}^2$
3. $2 \text{ ft}^2 = \text{?} \quad \text{in.}^2$
4. $576 \text{ in.}^2 = \text{?} \quad \text{ft}^2$
5. $3 \text{ m}^2 = \text{?} \quad \text{cm}^2$
6. $50,000 \text{ cm}^2 = \text{?} \quad \text{m}^2$
7. One square foot is equal to 144 square inches. Using only whole-number lengths, draw three noncongruent rectangular regions each having an area of one square foot.

Use the formula $A = \frac{1}{2}d_1 d_2$ to find the area determined by each rhombus described.

8. Rhombus with diagonals of length 10 cm and 6 cm
9. Rhombus with diagonals of length 6 cm and 8 cm
10. Square with both diagonals of length 10 cm

Use the formula $A = \frac{1}{2}h(b_1 + b_2)$ to find the area of each trapezoidal region described.

11. Trapezoidal regions with height of 4 cm and bases of length 10 cm and 15 cm
12. Trapezoidal region with height of 6 cm and bases of length 5 cm and 10 cm

EXERCISES

— A —

Convert each measurement to the unit indicated.

1. $18 \text{ yd}^2 = \text{?} \text{ ft}^2$
2. $5 \text{ yd}^2 = \text{?} \text{ ft}^2$
3. $18 \text{ ft}^2 = \text{?} \text{ yd}^2$
4. $162 \text{ ft}^2 = \text{?} \text{ yd}^2$
5. $10 \text{ ft}^2 = \text{?} \text{ in.}^2$
6. $3 \text{ ft}^2 = \text{?} \text{ in.}^2$
7. $288 \text{ in.}^2 = \text{?} \text{ ft}^2$
8. $720 \text{ in.}^2 = \text{?} \text{ ft}^2$
9. $5 \text{ m}^2 = \text{?} \text{ cm}^2$
10. $20,000 \text{ cm}^2 = \text{?} \text{ m}^2$

Use the formula $A = \frac{1}{2}d_1 d_2$ to find the area determined by each rhombus. Show your work.

11.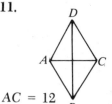

$AC = 12$
$BD = 20$

12.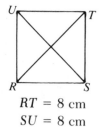

$RT = 8 \text{ cm}$
$SU = 8 \text{ cm}$

Use the formula $A = \frac{1}{2}h(b_1 + b_2)$ to find the area of each trapezoidal region. Show your work.

13.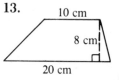

14.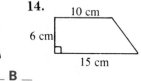

— B —

Use the formula $A = \frac{1}{2}h(b_1 + b_2)$ to find the area of each region described.

15. parallelogram: $b = 10$ cm, $h = 4$ cm
16. rectangle: $l = 6$ cm, $h = 3$ cm
17. square: $s = 4$ cm
18. Describe how the formula $A = bh$ for the area of parallelogram, rectangular, or square regions is a special case of the formula $A = \frac{1}{2}h(b_1 + b_2)$ for the area of trapezoidal regions.

6-14

Mastering Perimeter and Area

These exercises provide additional practice on perimeter and area and illustrate some additional applications of these concepts.

EXERCISES

— A —

Find the perimeter and area of each shaded region.

1.

2.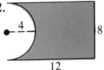

3.

4.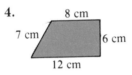

Find the area of each shaded region.

5.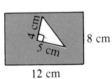

6.

— B —

Select the polygonal region that has the same area as the given region.

7.
   a.

b.
   c.

8.
   a.

b.
   c.

9.
   a.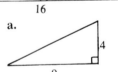

b.
   c.

10.
   a.

b.
   c.

Select the polygon that has the same perimeter as the given polygon.

11.
   a.

b. 5
   c.

12.
6

a.
3
8

b.
6
6

c.
4
5
3
7

13.
4
6

a.
3
8

b.
3
7

c.
2
10

14.
4
5

a.
2
10

b.
5
8

c.
3
6

15. A kitchen counter is shaped like the one shown. Find the number of square feet of heat-proof plastic needed to cover this surface.

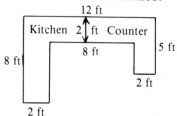

12 ft
Kitchen 2 ft Counter
8 ft
8 ft
5 ft
2 ft
2 ft

16. A ceiling is being hung in a basement shaped like the one shown. If the ceiling tiles are 12-in. × 12-in. squares, how many tiles are needed?

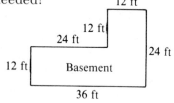

12 ft
12 ft
24 ft
24 ft
12 ft
Basement
36 ft

17. A backyard is rectangular in shape. 300 feet of fencing are needed to fence in the yard. (No fencing is put along the back of the house.) Find the width of the yard.

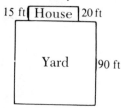

15 ft House 20 ft
Yard
90 ft

18. A new roof is to be put on the cabin shown. Find the area of the roof. (Remember to include both sides.)

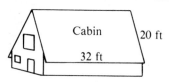

Cabin
20 ft
32 ft

— C —

19. A sketch of a house and lot is shown.

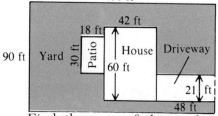

150 ft
42 ft
18 ft
90 ft
Yard
30 ft
Patio
House
Driveway
60 ft
21 ft
48 ft

a. Find the area of the yard in square feet. (Do not include the house, patio, or driveway.)

b. If one bag of fertilizer will cover 5000 square feet, how many bags are needed for the yard?

c. How many square yards of sod are needed to cover the yard?

20. Suppose that you wish to use 12-in. × 12-in. vinyl or carpet tiles to cover a kitchen floor like the one shown.

a. How many tiles are needed?

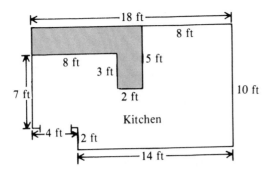

b. Vinyl tiles come in cartons of 45. How many cartons are needed?

c. Carpet tiles come in packages of 10. How many packages are needed?

21. Excessive heat loss in a building will occur when the building is not relatively airtight.

a. Look at the space under the door in your classroom. Find the length and width of the space.

b. Find the area of the space.

c. State the dimensions of two other rectangular regions that have the same area as the space.

d. If you were paying to heat a home, would you be concerned if a wall contained a hole with the same area as the space under the door in your classroom?

Each of Exercises 22–27 contains either too much or not enough information. Identify the information that is not needed or that must be provided in order to solve each problem. Solve if you can.

22. A 4-m × 3-m rectangular region has a diagonal of length 5 m. Find its area.

23. How many 2-ft × 4-ft ceiling tiles are needed to cover a ceiling that is 12 feet wide?

24. How many tiles are needed to cover a floor that is 12 feet long and 10 feet wide?

25. Area = ? cm²

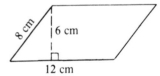

26. Perimeter = ? cm

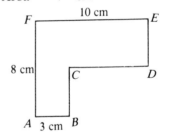

27. Area = ? cm²

DID YOU KNOW THAT....

Although some similar symbols were used as early as 300 B.C., the Hindu-Arabic numerals we use today did not become commonly used until the seventeenth century. One reason for this delay was that the abacus commonly used for calculation did not require a symbol for zero.

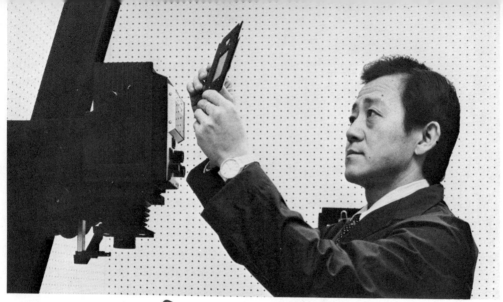

Geometry on the Job

COMMERCIAL PHOTOGRAPHER

The taking of pictures of people and other subjects is only part of the work of a commercial photographer such as Kim Lam. After taking a photograph, Kim develops the negatives and produces enlarged prints. He also makes frames to display some of his photographs. To ensure an adequate stock of photographic paper and various other supplies, he must be able to calculate perimeter and area.

EXERCISES

1. Kim plans to use 1-inch-wide molding to frame some

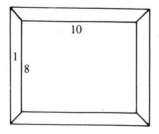

photographs. The amount of molding he needs is the outside perimeter of the frame. How much molding will he need for a photograph that is 8 by 10 inches? for one that is 16 by 20 inches?

2. Glass is sold by the square inch. How many square inches does Kim need to cover a photograph that measures 8 by 10 inches? 16 by 20 inches?

3. Kim buys photographic paper in 8 by 10 inch sheets. From each sheet, how many 5 by 7 inch prints can be made? how many $3\frac{1}{2}$ by 5 inch prints? how many $2\frac{1}{2}$ by $3\frac{1}{2}$ inch prints?

4. Kim photographs a coin with a radius of 1 cm. What is the area of the coin? If he enlarges the photograph so that the radius is 10 cm, what is the area of the image of the coin?

ALGEBRA REVIEW — *Exponents*

An *exponent* is a small, raised numeral that tells how many times a number is used as a factor.

	Written	Read
5	5^1	"Five."
5×5	5^2	"Five squared" or "five to the second power."
$5 \times 5 \times 5$	5^3	"Five cubed" or "five to the third power."
$5 \times 5 \times 5 \times 5$	5^4	"Five to the fourth power."

Examples
Find the value of each expression.

1. $4^3 = 4 \times 4 \times 4 = 64$
2. $2^5 = 2 \times 2 \times 2 \times 2 \times 2 = 32$
3. $\left(\frac{1}{2}\right)^3 = \frac{1}{2} \times \frac{1}{2} \times \frac{1}{2} = \frac{1}{8}$
4. $10^2 = 10 \times 10 = 100$

EXERCISES
Classify each statement as true or false.

1. $3^2 = 2^3$
2. $a^3 = a \times a \times a$
3. $1^3 = 3$
4. $0^3 = 0$
5. $2^2 + 3^2 = (2 + 3)^2$
6. $1^4 = 1^6$

Rewrite each product using exponents.

7. $3 \times 3 \times 3 \times 3$
8. 4×4
9. $6 \times 6 \times 6$
10. $8 \times 8 \times 8$
11. $b \times b$
12. $8 \times 8 \times 8 \times 8 \times 8$
13. $3 \times 3 \times 4 \times 4 \times 4$
14. $c \times c \times d \times d \times d$
15. $7 \times 11 \times 11 \times 2 \times 2$

Find the value of each expression.

16. 6^2
17. 8^2
18. 2^3
19. 2^4
20. 3^5
21. 10^3
22. 1^5
23. 3^2
24. 5^3
25. 15^1
26. 4^4
27. 6^3
28. 3^3
29. 9^2
30. 4^3
31. 12^2
32. 2^6
33. 3^4
34. 0.3^2
35. $\left(\frac{1}{2}\right)^4$
36. $\left(\frac{3}{4}\right)^2$
37. 3×4^2
38. 0.4^2
39. $\left(\frac{2}{3}\right)^3$
40. 1.3^2
41. $\left(\frac{3}{5}\right)^2$
42. 2×3^2
43. 5×2^3
44. 0.5^3
45. 7×4^2
46. $2^3 \times 2^2$
47. $0.2^2 \times 3^3$

Chapter 6 Review

Vocabulary

The following terms and symbols were introduced in this chapter. You should be able to write a brief description, draw a picture, or give an example to illustrate the meaning of each.

area (p. 229)
base length (p. 232)
circumference (p. 226)
height (p. 232)
perimeter (p. 222)
pi (p. 226)

Symbols

$\approx$ (approximately equal to) (p. 226)
A (area) (p. 232)
b (base length) (p. 232)

C (circumference) (p. 226)
h (height) (p. 232)
P (perimeter) (p. 222)
π (pi) (p. 226)

Skills Checklist

In Chapter 6 you learned how to find the perimeter and area of any polygonal or circular region. In addition, you were introduced to some applications of perimeter and area.

The following list indicates the major skills, facts, and results you should have mastered in this chapter:

- Find the perimeter and area of any concave or convex polygonal region. (**6-1**, pp. 222–225; **6-9**, pp. 251–253)
- Use the formulas $C = \pi d$ and $A = \pi r^2$, respectively, to find the circumference and area of any circular region. (**6-2**, pp. 226–228; **6-10**, pp. 254–256)
- Count the number of square units in the area of any concave or convex polygonal region. (**6-3**, pp. 229–231)
- Draw a rectangular, parallelogram, or triangular region to fit a description in terms of its perimeter and/or area and/or dimensions. (**6-3—6-4**, pp. 229–236; **6-6—6-8**, pp. 239–249)
- Use the formula $A = bh$ to find either the area or a missing dimension of any rectangular or parallelogram region. (**6-4**, pp. 232–236; **6-7**, pp. 242–245)
- Draw an altitude of any rectangular, parallelogram, or triangular region. (**6-6**, pp. 240–241)
- Use the formula $A = \frac{1}{2}bh$ to find either the area or a missing dimension of any triangular region. (**6-8**, pp. 246–249)
- Determine the change in the perimeter and area of a rectangular region when each dimension of the region is multiplied by the same number. (**6-11**, pp. 257–258)

- Determine the change in the circumference and area of a circular region when the radius is multiplied by some number. (**6-11**, pp. 257–258)
- Use Pick's Formula to find the area of any concave or convex polygonal region. (**6-12**, pp. 259–261)
- Convert a given area measurement to a different unit of area. (**6-13**, pp. 262–264)
- Use the formulas $A = \frac{1}{2}d_1d_2$ and $A = \frac{1}{2}h\,(b_1 + b_2)$, respectively, to find the area determined by any rhombus and by any trapezoidal region. (**6-13**, pp. 262–264)

Exercises

Find the perimeter or circumference of each region. (6-1—6-2)

1.

2.

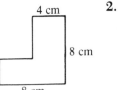

Find the indicated information. (6-1)

3. Perimeter = 28 cm
   $x =$? cm

4. Perimeter = 30 cm
   $z =$? cm

Draw a polygon similar to each one shown. Draw the altitude to $\overline{AB}$. (6-6)

5.

6.

Find the indicated information.

7. Area = ? (**6-3**)

8. Area = 18 cm² (**6-4**) $h =$? cm

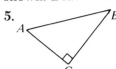

Draw (a) figure(s) to fit each description. (6-4)

9. Rectangular region with a height of 4 and an area of 24
10. Rectangular region with a height of 4 and a perimeter of 24
11. Rectangular region with an area of 24 and a perimeter of 28
12. Square region with a perimeter of 24
13. Two rectangular regions with the same area and different perimeters
14. Two rectangular regions with the same perimeter and different areas

Find the indicated information. (6-7—6-8)

15. Area = 30 cm²
    $h =$? cm

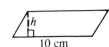

16. a. Area = ? cm²
    b. Perimeter = ? cm

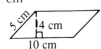

17. Area = ? cm²

18. Area = ? cm²

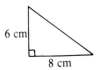

19. Area = 16 cm²
     h = ? cm

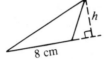

20. a. Area = ? cm²
     b. Perimeter = ? cm

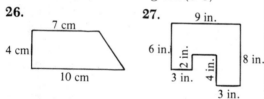

Draw (a) figure(s) to fit each description. Make parallelogram regions nonrectangular.

21. Parallelogram region with a base length of 8 and a height of 5 **(6–7)**

22. Parallelogram region with a base length of 8 and an area of 32 **(6–7)**

23. Acute triangular region with a base length of 6 and a height of 3 **(6–8)**

24. Obtuse triangular region with a base length of 6 and a height of 3 **(6–8)**

25. Three noncongruent triangular regions each with an area of 8 **(6–8)**

Find the area of each region. (6–9)

26.

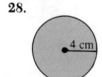

27.

Find the area of each shaded region. (6–10)

28.

29.

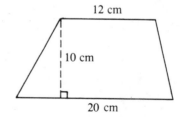

Classify each statement as true or false. (6–11)

30. If both the base length and height of a rectangular region are doubled, then the perimeter is doubled.

31. If both the base length and height of a rectangular region are doubled, then the area is doubled.

Find the indicated information. (6–11)

32. The area of a circular region is 10 square centimeters. Find the area of a circular region whose radius is four times as great.

33. The circumference of a circular region is 25 centimeters. Find the circumference of a circular region whose radius is four times as great.

Convert each measurement to the unit indicated. (6–13)

34. 45 ft² = ? yd²

35. 9 yd² = ? ft²

36. 6 ft² = ? in.²

37. 2 m² = ? cm²

Find each area. (6–13)

38. Use the formula $A = \frac{1}{2}d_1d_2$ to find the area determined by the rhombus shown. Show your work.

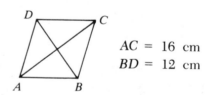

AC = 16 cm
BD = 12 cm

39. Use the formula $A = \frac{1}{2}h(b_1 + b_2)$ to find the area of the trapezoidal region shown. Show your work.

12 cm
10 cm
20 cm

INNER SPACE

Volume and Total Area

7-1

Unfolding a Prism

This chapter builds on your work in Chapter 6 on area and perimeter of two-dimensional figures and your work in Chapter 1 on interpreting drawings of three-dimensional figures. In later lessons you will find the total area and volume of prisms and other figures. In this lesson you will review how to interpret a drawing of a prism and learn how to describe the faces of a prism.

The drawing of a rectangular prism shown reviews some terms that are used when describing prisms and some other three-dimensional figures.

A *face* is a part of a plane forming a side of a three-dimensional figure.

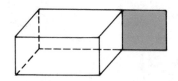

An *edge* is a segment formed by the intersection of two faces.

A *vertex* is a point formed by the intersection of at least three edges.

Refer to Lesson 1–8 for a review of other terms and definitions related to prisms that will be useful in this chapter.

Most of the work in this book will be with right prisms. Unless stated otherwise, you may assume that "prism" means "right prism."

The following series of pictures shows a rectangular prism being unfolded.

Step 1 Begin with a rectangular prism.

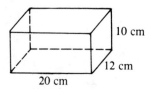

Step 2 Fold out the right face.

Step 3 Flip up the top face.

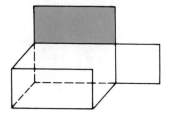

Step 4 Fold out the front face.

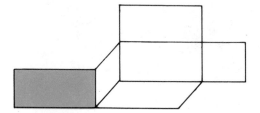

Step 5 Fold out the left face.

Step 6 Flip down the bottom face.

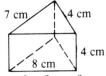

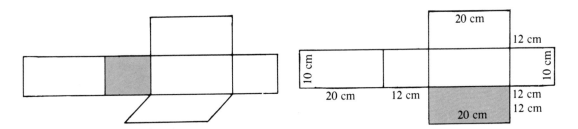

The rectangular prism shown has six faces, which can be described as follows:

Number	Shape	Size
2	Rectangular	10 cm × 12 cm
2	Rectangular	20 cm × 10 cm
2	Rectangular	20 cm × 12 cm

The following series of pictures shows a triangular prism being unfolded.

Step 1 Begin with a triangular prism.

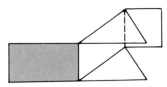

Step 2 Fold out the right face.

Step 3 Fold out the front face.

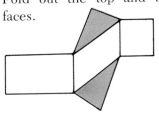

Step 4 Fold out the top and bottom faces.

Step 5 Stretch it out flat.

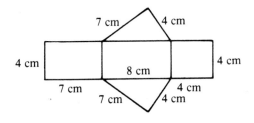

Some applications require the ability to determine the size and shape of each face of a prism, as described in the following examples.

Example 1:
For the rectangular prism shown, describe the size and shape of the faces.

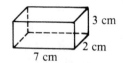
3 cm
2 cm
7 cm

Solution:
2 rectangular faces—7 cm × 3 cm
2 rectangular faces—7 cm × 2 cm
2 rectangular faces—3 cm × 2 cm

Example 2:
For the triangular prism shown, describe the size and shape of the faces.

6 cm
10 cm
4 cm   4 cm

Solution:
2 triangular faces—
    4 cm × 4 cm × 6 cm
2 rectangular faces—10 cm × 4 cm
1 rectangular face—10 cm × 6 cm

===== **CLASS PRACTICE** =====

1. The series of pictures on pages 274-275 shows one way of unfolding a rectangular prism. If the steps are done in a different order, the result is a different pattern for the prism. Draw at least two other patterns that can be folded into a rectangular prism like this one. Label the lengths of the sides of the pattern.

2. Look at the pattern for the triangular prism on page 275.
    a. How many faces are there?
    b. Describe the size and shape of the faces.
    c. Draw at least one other pattern that can be folded into a triangular prism like this one. Label the lengths of the sides of the pattern.

Describe the size and shape of the faces of each prism.

3.   4.

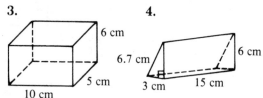

6 cm
5 cm
10 cm

6.7 cm
3 cm   15 cm
6 cm

5.   6.

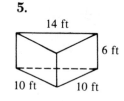

14 ft
6 ft
10 ft   10 ft

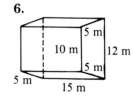

5 m
10 m   12 m
5 m
5 m   15 m

7-10. State the type of prism shown in each of Exercises 3-6.

Classify each statement as true or false.
11. Each prism has two bases.   12. All faces of a prism are rectangular.
13. The bases of a prism are congruent.

EXERCISES

_ A _

Describe the size and shape of the faces of each prism.

1.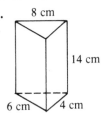
8 cm
14 cm
6 cm 4 cm

2.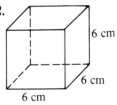
6 cm
6 cm
6 cm

3.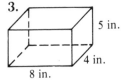
5 in.
4 in.
8 in.

4.
9 cm 8 cm
7 cm
3 cm

5.
7 cm 7 cm
10 cm
10 cm

6.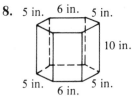
6 cm 8 cm
10 cm
4 cm 4 cm
7 cm

7.
15 m
5 m
5 m

8.
5 in. 6 in. 5 in.
10 in.
5 in. 6 in. 5 in.

9–16. State the type of prism shown in each of Exercises 1–8.

_ B _

Select the patterns that can be folded into the prism shown.

17.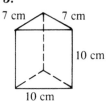
a. b. c. d. e.

18.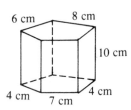
a. b. c. d. e.

Two copies of the same pattern are given for each prism shown. The bottom face is labeled *B*. For each pattern, state the number of the face that becomes the top when the pattern is folded.

19.

a.

	5	
1	*B*	3	4
	2	

b.

		5
1	2	3	4
	B	

20.

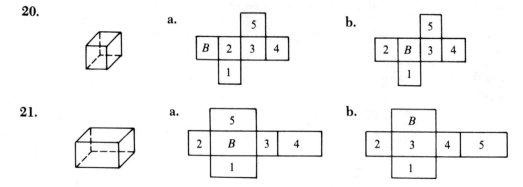

21.

Three of its faces are shown with each prism. For each prism, find the length of each labeled edge.

22.

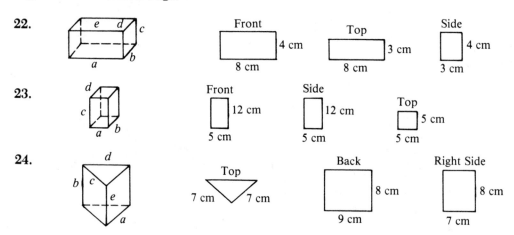

Front
4 cm
8 cm

Top
3 cm
8 cm

Side
4 cm
3 cm

23.

Front
12 cm
5 cm

Side
12 cm
5 cm

Top
5 cm
5 cm

24.

Top
7 cm   7 cm

Back
8 cm
9 cm

Right Side
8 cm
7 cm

DID YOU KNOW THAT....

In 1765 the Swiss mathematician Leonard Euler proved that the intersections of the altitudes (orthocenter), the bisectors of the angles (circumcenter), and the medians (centroid) of any triangle are collinear. It is also true that in a triangle, the midpoints of the sides, the feet of the altitudes, and the midpoints of the segments joining the circumcenter to each vertex lie on a circle. The circle containing these 9 points is called "Euler's circle" or "Feuerbach's circle," after the German mathematician Karl Wilhelm Feuerbach, who developed the properties of this circle in the early 1800s.

7-2

Total Area of a Prism

The ability to describe the size and shape of each face of a prism will help you in finding the total area of a prism. The *total area* of a three-dimensional figure is the sum of the areas of all its faces. Some examples are given:

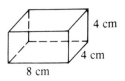

Example 1: Find the total area of this rectangular prism.

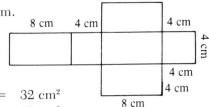

Solution:
The prism has six faces, as shown.

Number	Shape	Size	Area
2	Rectangular	4 cm × 4 cm	2 × (4 × 4) = 32 cm²
4	Rectangular	8 cm × 4 cm	4 × (8 × 4) = 128 cm²
		Total Area:	160 cm²

Example 2: Find the total area of this triangular prism.

Solution:
The prism has five faces.

Number	Shape	Size	Area
1	Rectangular	7 in. × 4 in.	1 × (7 × 4) = 28 in.²
1	Rectangular	4 in. × 4 in.	1 × (4 × 4) = 16 in.²
1	Rectangular	6 in. × 4 in.	1 × (6 × 4) = 24 in.²
2	Triangular	b = 7 in., h = 3 in.	2 × ($\frac{1}{2}$ × 7 × 3) = 21 in.²
		Total Area:	89 in.²

Example 3: Find the total area of this open-topped box.

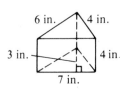

Solution:
The figure has five faces. (The top is open.)

Number	Shape	Size	Area
1	Rectangular	10 cm × 6 cm	1 × (10 × 6) = 60 cm²
2	Rectangular	10 cm × 4 cm	2 × (10 × 4) = 80 cm²
2	Rectangular	6 cm × 4 cm	2 × (6 × 4) = 48 cm²
		Total Area:	188 cm²

CLASS PRACTICE

Look at prisms *ABCDEF* and *GHIJKLMN*.
State the length of each edge.

1. $\overline{FC}$ 　　　　　2. $\overline{AB}$ 　　　　　3. $\overline{AC}$
4. $\overline{AD}$ 　　　　　5. $\overline{KG}$ 　　　　　6. $\overline{KN}$
7. $\overline{LH}$ 　　　　　8. $\overline{JI}$ 　　　　　9. $\overline{MN}$

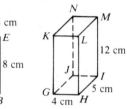

State the dimensions (length and width) of each face.

10. *ABED* 　　　　11. *ADFC* 　　　　12. *BCFE*
13. *GHIJ* 　　　　14. *GHLK* 　　　　15. *KGJN*
16. Find the total area of each prism.

EXERCISES

For Exercises 1–24, look at the prisms.

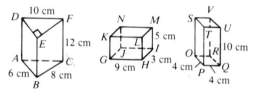

State the length of each edge.

1. $\overline{EF}$ 　　　2. $\overline{AD}$ 　　　3. $\overline{AC}$
4. $\overline{DE}$ 　　　5. $\overline{BE}$ 　　　6. $\overline{JI}$
7. $\overline{KL}$ 　　　8. $\overline{KG}$ 　　　9. $\overline{KN}$
10. $\overline{NJ}$ 　　　11. $\overline{GJ}$ 　　　12. $\overline{UV}$
13. $\overline{SV}$ 　　　14. $\overline{SO}$ 　　　15. $\overline{VR}$

State the dimensions (length and width) of each face.

16. *ABED* 　17. *ACFD* 　18. *BCFE*
19. *KGHL* 　20. *KLMN* 　21. *KGJN*
22. *SOPT* 　23. *STUV* 　24. *QRVS*

Describe the size and shape of all faces of each prism.

25.

26.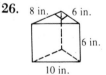

27.

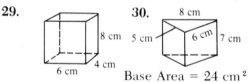

28.

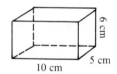

Base Area = 25 in.²

29.

8 cm
6 cm
4 cm

30.

8 cm
5 cm
6 cm
7 cm

Base Area = 24 cm²

31–36. Find the total area of each prism shown in Exercises 25–30.

Find the total area of each prism.

37.

6 in.
7 in.
6 in.
4 in.
4 in.
10 in.

Base Area = 50 in.²

38.

6 cm
10 cm
5 cm

39.

6 cm
6 cm
6 cm

40.

5 in.
4 in.
3 in.
8 in.

Lateral Area of a Prism

In Lesson 7–2 you found the total area of various prisms. Sometimes you wish to find the area of only part of the surface, as will be illustrated in this lesson.

Remember that total area means the sum of the areas of *all* faces. The *lateral area* of a prism is the sum of the areas of its faces *not including* the bases.

The rectangular prism shown has been unfolded.

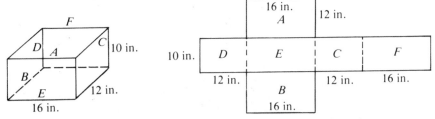

Total Area = Sum of areas of all six faces (*A–F*)
Lateral Area = Sum of areas of faces *D, E, C,* and *F*

The following series of pictures shows the relationship between the total area and lateral area for various prisms.

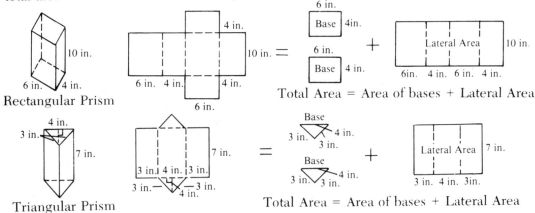

Rectangular Prism

Total Area = Area of bases + Lateral Area

Triangular Prism

Total Area = Area of bases + Lateral Area

Example: Find the lateral area of the rectangular prism above.

Lateral Faces

Solution:	Number	Shape	Size	Area
The figure has	2	Rectangular	4 in. × 10 in.	2(4 × 10) = 80 in.²
4 lateral faces.	2	Rectangular	6 in. × 10 in.	2(6 × 10) = 120 in.²
			Lateral Area:	200 in.²

Find the lateral area and the total area of each prism.

1.

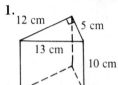

12 cm · 5 cm · 13 cm · 10 cm

2.

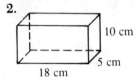

10 cm · 5 cm · 18 cm

3. Look at the "horizontal" rectangular prism. Its lateral area is 88 cm² and its total area is 136 cm². Suppose the figure were turned so it looked like the "vertical" prism beside it. Would its total area remain the same? its lateral area? Why or why not?

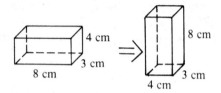

4 cm · 3 cm · 8 cm · 8 cm · 3 cm · 4 cm

EXERCISES

— A —

Find the lateral area of each prism.

1.

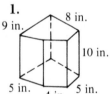

8 in. · 9 in. · 10 in. · 5 in. · 4 in. · 5 in.

2.

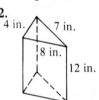

4 in. · 7 in. · 8 in. · 12 in.

Find the lateral area and the total area of each prism.

3.

8 cm · 5 cm · 2 cm

4.

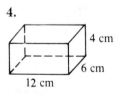

4 cm · 6 cm · 12 cm

Find the total area of each prism.

5.

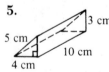

3 cm · 5 cm · 10 cm · 4 cm

6.

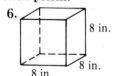

8 in. · 8 in. · 8 in.

7.

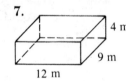

4 m · 9 m · 12 m

8.

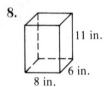

11 in. · 8 in. · 6 in.

Find the indicated information.

9. The triangular prism shown was formed by cutting in half the rectangular prism in Exercise 8. Find the total area of the triangular prism.

6 in. · 10 in. · 11 in. · 8 in.

— B —

10. Look at the figure. Find its lateral area and its total area.

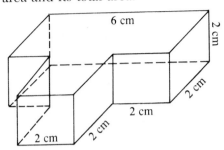

6 cm

2 cm

2 cm

2 cm

2 cm

2 cm

2 cm

Find the total area of each figure.

11.

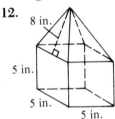

2 cm

2 cm

11 cm

8 cm

8 cm

12.

8 in.

5 in.

5 in.

5 in.

13. Find the total area of a cube that is 5 inches on each edge.

14. A cube has a total area of 294 square feet. What is the area of each face of the cube? What is the length of an edge of the cube?

15. Total area: 166 ft²
   Length: 7 ft
   Width: 4 ft
   Height: ? ft

7 ft

4 ft

16. **a.** Find the lateral area of the prism shown.

   b. Suppose the total area of the prism were 258 square feet.

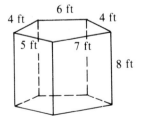

6 ft

4 ft

4 ft

5 ft

7 ft

8 ft

What would be the area of a base of the prism?

17. Shown are a regular square pyramid and a pattern for constructing it. What is the total area of the pyramid?

9 in.

8 in.   8 in.

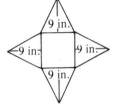

9 in.

9 in.   9 in.

9 in.

18. Suppose you are making a copper flower box in the shape of a rectangular prism with an open top. The rectangular base is 5 in. × 12 in. The height is 4 in.

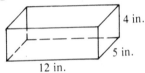

4 in.

5 in.

12 in.

   a. Ignoring waste, how many square inches of sheet copper are needed?

   b. A square piece of sheet copper 14 inches on each edge has an area of 196 square inches. Could a pattern for the flower box be cut out of this sheet? Why or why not?

19. The top and all 4 sides of a toy box are to be painted.

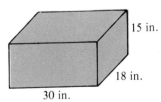

15 in.

18 in.

30 in.

   a. How many square inches of surface are to be painted?

b. To the nearest square foot, how many square feet of surface are to be painted? (1 ft² = 144 in.²)

20. A sketch of a gable roof for a house is shown.

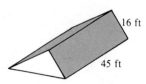

a. Find the roof area. (Include both halves.)

b. Asphalt shingles are sold by the "square," the amount needed to cover an area of 100 square feet. How many "squares" will be needed for the roof?

_ C _

21. One end of a barn is shown. (The roof is shaded.)

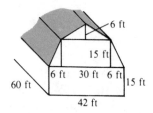

a. Find the area of one end of the barn.

b. Find the area of one side of the barn.

c. Find the combined area of both ends and both sides of the barn.

d. One gallon of paint covers 400 square feet. How many gallon cans of paint are needed to paint the barn?

22. A drawing of a swimming pool and a side view of it are shown. Find each indicated area.

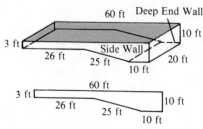

a. One side wall   **b.** Bottom

c. Wall at shallow end

d. Wall at deep end

e. Combined area of the walls of the pool (Be sure to include both sides.)

23. The walls of a room that is 13 ft × 20 ft and 10 ft high are to be painted. There are four 5-ft × $2\frac{1}{2}$-ft windows and one 6-ft × $2\frac{1}{2}$-ft door. One gallon of paint will cover 400 square feet. Find each of the following.

a. Combined area of the door and windows

b. Combined area of the walls (including the door and windows)

c. Wall area, excluding the door and windows

d. Number of gallons of paint needed

e. Area of the ceiling

24. A gallon of paint covers 400 square feet and costs $9.95. You are to paint the walls of the following room:

Length: 24 feet   Width: 18 feet
    Height: 10 feet
4 windows, each $2\frac{1}{2}$ ft × 5 ft
2 doors, each $3\frac{1}{2}$ ft × 8 ft

Find each of the following.

a. Area to be painted

b. Number of gallons of paint needed

c. Cost of the paint

7-4

Lateral Area and Total Area of a Cylinder

A *right circular cylinder* is a three-dimensional figure with two congruent parallel circular bases connected by a curved lateral surface. As in a prism, the bases of a right circular cylinder are directly above or directly opposite each other. In addition, any segment perpendicular to both bases and with one endpoint in each base is an *altitude*. The *height* is the length of an altitude. In this book we will use "cylinder" to mean "right circular cylinder."

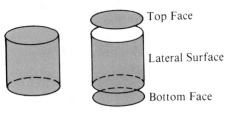

Top Face

Lateral Surface

Bottom Face

Suppose you were to remove both ends (bases) from a cylinder and slit the lateral surface along a line perpendicular to both ends. If you unrolled the lateral surface until it lay flat, it would form a rectangular region, as shown.

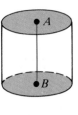

The bases are shaded. $\overline{AB}$ is an altitude.

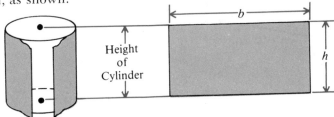

Notice that the base length of the rectangular region is equal to the circumference of the base of the cylinder and that the height of the rectangular region is equal to the height of the cylinder.

Therefore, to find the lateral area of a cylinder you must find the area of a rectangular region whose dimensions are the circumference of the base and the height of the cylinder. Since the formula for the area of a rectangular region is $A = bh$, the following is true:

> **To find the lateral area of a cylinder, multiply the circumference of the base by the height.**
>
> **Lateral Area = Circumference of base × Height**
>
> **L.A. = πdh**

Example 1:

Circumference of base of cylinder = 12 cm

Height of cylinder = 4 cm

Lateral Area of cylinder = ? cm²

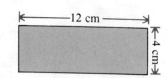

Solution:

Lateral Area = Circumference of base × Height

= 12 × 4 = 48 cm²

As for a prism, the total area of a cylinder is found by adding the area of the two bases to the lateral area.

Here are some examples that illustrate the difference between lateral area and total area and show how to find the total area of a cylinder.

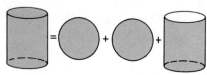

Total Area = Area of bases + Lateral Area

Example 2: For the cylinder shown, find (a) the lateral area and (b) the total area.

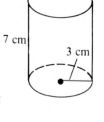

Solution:

a. Lateral Area = Circumference of base × Height

= πdh

The diameter of the base is 6 cm.

Lateral Area ≈ (3.14 × 6) × 7 ≈ 131.88 cm²

$C = \pi d \approx 3.14 \times 6$ cm

b. Total Area = Lateral Area + Area of bases

Each base is a circular region with area

$A = \pi r^2 \approx 3.14 \times 3^2 \approx 28.26$ cm²

Total Area = Area of bases + Lateral Area

≈ 28.26 cm² + 28.26 cm² + 131.88 cm²

≈ 188.40 cm²

Example 3:

Circumference of base = 22 in.

Total Area = 187 in.²

Area of each base = ? in.²

Solution:

First find the lateral area.

Lateral Area = Circumference of base × Height

= 22 × 5

= 110 in.²

Total Area = Area of bases + Lateral Area

187 in.² = Area of bases + 110 in.²

77 in.² = Area of bases

Answer: Area of each base is 77 ÷ 2 = 37.5 in.²

Find the following information for each cylinder. Use the indicated approximation for π.

a. Circumference of base
b. Lateral Area
c. Area of base
d. Total Area

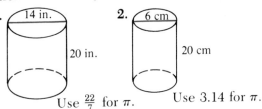

1. 14 in. 20 in. Use $\frac{22}{7}$ for π.

2. 6 cm 20 cm Use 3.14 for π.

Find the indicated information.

3. A cylinder has a lateral area of 120 cm² and the circumference of its base is 15 cm. Find the height of the cylinder.

4. A cylinder has a height of 10 cm and the circumference of its base is 16 cm. Find the lateral area of the cylinder.

EXERCISES

— A —

Find the indicated information for each cylinder. Use the indicated approximation for π.

1. Circumference
    of base = 6 cm
    Height = 3 cm
    Lateral Area =   ? cm²

    3 cm

2. Lateral Area = 38 in.²
    Height =   2 in.
    Circumference
    of base =   ? in.

    2 in.

3. Lateral Area = 132 ft²
    Circumference
    of base =   22 ft
    Height =   ? ft

    ? ft

4. Lateral Area =   ? cm²
    (Use 3.14 for π.)   2 cm

    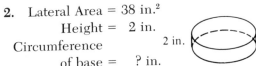

    4 cm

5. Lateral Area =   ? cm²
    (Use $\frac{22}{7}$ for π.)   7 cm

    9 cm

6. a. Lateral Area =   ? in.²
    b. Total Area =   ? in.²
    (Use $\frac{22}{7}$ for π.)

    7 in.
    8 in.

7. Total Area =   ? cm²
    (Use 3.14 for π.)

    7 cm
    4 cm

8. Total Area =   ? cm²
    (Use $\frac{22}{7}$ for π.)

    14 cm
    7 cm

— B —

9. A cylindrical tank has a height of 25 feet and a base diameter of 18 feet.
    (Use 3.14 for π.)
    a. Total Area =   ?   ft²

    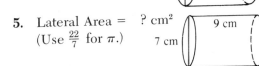

    18 ft
    25 ft

Volume and Total Area   **287**

b. If one gallon of paint covers 400 square feet, how many gallon cans are needed to paint the outside surface of the tank? (Do *not* include the bottom of the tank.)

10. A lawn roller has a base 21 inches ($1\frac{3}{4}$ feet) in diameter and is 3 feet long. How much surface is rolled in one full turn? (Use $\frac{22}{7}$ for π.)

11. A stove pipe is to be 22 inches in base circumference and 24 inches in length. Allowing $\frac{1}{2}$ inch for an overlapping seam, how many square inches of material are needed to make the pipe?

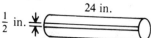

_ C _

12. Look at the prism. Find each of the following.
  a. Perimeter of base
  b. Height of prism
  c. Lateral Area of prism
  d. Perimeter of base × Height of prism

13. Look at the prism. If P is the perimeter of the base and h is the height of the prism, the lateral area (L.A.) of the prism can be found with the following formula: L.A. = Ph. Use this formula to find the lateral area of the prism.

14. a. Explain why the formula used in Exercise 13 works.
  b. Explain what the formula in Exercise 13 has in common with the procedure used to find the lateral area of a cylinder.

Test Yourself

Describe the size and shape of the faces of each prism.

1. **2.** **3.**

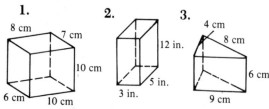

4–6. Find the lateral area of each of the prisms in Exercises 1–3.

7. Find the total area of the prism in Exercise 2.

Find the lateral area and the total area of each figure.

8. **9.** **10.**

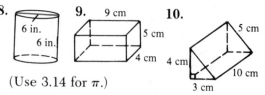

(Use 3.14 for π.)

Find the indicated information.

11. Each edge of a cube is 3 inches long. Find the total area of the cube.

12. A cylinder has a lateral area of 102 cm² and a height of 6 cm. Find the circumference of the base.

7-5

Volume of a Rectangular Prism

Suppose you wish to determine how much food a freezer will hold or the amount of storage space in a warehouse. Each of these situations requires that you determine the amount of space contained in an object.

The amount of space contained within, or occupied by, a three-dimensional figure is called its *volume.* Using the cubic centimeter as the unit of volume, the volume of the rectangular prism shown is 16 cubic centimeters.

1 cubic centimeter = 1 cm³

1 cm

1 cm   1 cm

Volume = 16 cm³

Any three-dimensional object can be used to measure volume. However, cubic units are the most commonly used. Some common units of volume are the cubic inch, cubic foot, cubic yard, cubic centimeter, and cubic meter.

A concept closely related to volume is that of capacity. *Capacity* is the measure of material, liquid, or gas that a container can hold. Some familiar units of capacity are the pint, quart, gallon, milliliter, and liter.

Units of capacity are usually associated with fluid substances and containers, such as bags, that lack rigid walls. Units of volume, on the other hand, are usually associated with rigid-walled containers and their contents. For example, we speak of the number of cubic meters of air space in a room or the number of cubic feet of space in a car's trunk.

It should be noted that the distinction between volume and capacity is often not clear-cut. An amount of liquid and the capacity of an object are sometimes described using units of volume. However, the volume or amount of space occupied is seldom described using units of capacity. This book will deal primarily with volume.

EXPLORING

The Volume of a Rectangular Prism

1. The bottom of each rectangular prism shown has been covered by a layer of cubes.

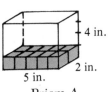

4 in.

2 in.

5 in.

Prism *A*

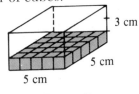

3 cm

5 cm

5 cm

Prism *B*

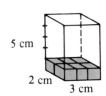

5 cm

2 cm

3 cm

Prism *C*

For each figure, find the following:
  a. Number of cubes in the bottom layer
  b. Number of layers needed to fill the prism
  c. Number of cubes needed to fill the prism
2. Without actually counting cubes, how can you find the following?
  a. Number of cubes in the bottom layer of a rectangular prism
  b. Number of cubes needed to fill a rectangular prism

By finding the number of cubes needed to fill a rectangular prism, you were actually finding its volume. Notice that the number of cubes in the bottom layer of each prism is equal to the number of square units in the area of the base.

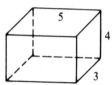

Rectangular Prism

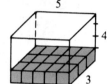

There are 15 cubes in the bottom layer.

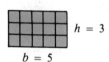

The area of the base is 15 square units.

This suggests the following conclusion:

To find the volume of a rectangular prism, multiply the area of the base by the height.

Volume = Area of base × Height

$V = Bh$

$B = lw$

Here are some examples.

Example 1:
The base area of a rectangular prism is 30 cm². The height is 6 cm. Find its volume.

Solution:
$V = Bh$
$V = 30 \times 6 = 180$ cm³

Example 2:
Find the volume of a room that is 8 meters long, 5 meters wide, and 3 meters high.

Solution:
Since the area of the base is not given, you must find it.

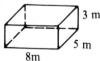

3 m
5 m
8m

Area of base = 8 × 5 = 40 m²
The height of the room is 3 m.
$V = 40 \times 3 = 120$ m³

1. Name some units of volume or capacity that could be used to measure each of the following.
   a. Gasoline   b. Freezer capacity c. Hay
   d. Sugar in a recipe e. Fresh berries f. Natural gas for a furnace
2. Name some items (other than those listed in Exercise 1) that require the measurement of volume or capacity. Name some units of volume or capacity associated with each item.

Do the following for each rectangular prism.
a. Draw a picture of a base.
b. Find the area of that base.
c. Find the volume of the prism.

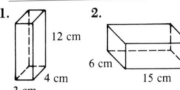

1. 12 cm, 4 cm, 3 cm

2. 6 cm, 15 cm, 3 cm

Find the indicated information for each rectangular prism where V = volume of the prism, B = area of the base, and h = height of the prism.

3. $B = 20$ cm², $h = 7$ cm, $V =$? cm³
4. $V = 180$ cm³, $h = 9$ cm, $B =$? cm²
5. $V = 125$ cm³, $B = 25$ cm², $h =$? cm

EXERCISES

_ A _

Look at the rectangular prism. Find each of the following.

1. EH   2. EA
3. HG   4. HD
5. Lateral Area
6. Area of a base
7. Total Area
8. Volume

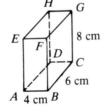

Do the following for each rectangular prism.
a. Draw a picture of a base.
b. Find the area of that base.
c. Find the volume of the prism.

9.
5 cm, 3 cm, 10 cm

10.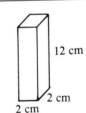
12 cm, 2 cm, 2 cm

11.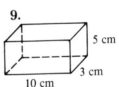
3 cm, 3 cm, 6 cm

12.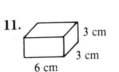
2 cm, 3 cm, 6 cm

13.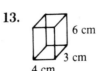
6 cm, 3 cm, 4 cm

14.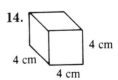
4 cm, 4 cm, 4 cm

Find the indicated information for each rectangular prism where V = volume of the prism, B = area of the base, and h = height of the prism.

15. $B = 8$ cm², $V = 32$ cm³, $h = ?$ cm
16. $h = 5$ cm, $V = 45$ cm³, $B = ?$ cm²
17. $B = 10$ cm², $h = 3$ cm, $V = ?$ cm³
18. $B = 6$ cm², $V = 36$ cm³, $h = ?$ cm
19. $h = 8$ cm, $V = 56$ cm³, $B = ?$ cm²
20. $B = 12$ cm², $h = 2.5$ cm, $V = ?$ cm³

_ B _

Find the length of an edge of a cube with each given volume.

21. 8 in.³   22. 125 in.³

Find the volume of a cube with each given total area.

23. 24 in.²   24. 216 in.²

Find the indicated information.

25. A *cord* of wood is equal in volume to a stack of wood that is 8 feet long, 4 feet wide, and 4 feet high.
    a. A cord is equivalent to how many cubic feet?
    Look at the stack of wood.
    b. Find its volume in cubic feet.
    c. Find the number of cords.

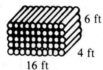
6 ft
4 ft
16 ft

26. Suppose a fan can move 3375 cubic feet of air per minute. How many minutes will it take to move all the air in a room that is 27 feet long, 25 feet wide, and 10 feet high?

27. Under normal conditions air weighs 0.0807 pounds per cubic foot. What is the weight of the air in a room that is 18 feet long, 12 feet wide, and 8 feet high?

28. A rectangular aquarium is 14 inches wide, 22 inches long, and 9 inches high.
    a. Find the volume of the aquarium in cubic inches.
    b. If the aquarium is filled to the top, how many gallons of water will it hold? (One gallon occupies 231 cubic inches of space.)

_ C _

29. A rectangular prism has a base area of 24 square centimeters and a volume of 72 cubic centimeters.
    a. What is the height of the prism?
    b. Using only whole-number lengths for the length and width, list all possible sets of dimensions for the base.

30. Suppose you are given 24 cubic-centimeter blocks. List all possible sets of dimensions for the different rectangular prisms that can be built by using all the blocks. (Two prisms are the same if their dimensions are the same *or* if one prism can be turned so that the dimensions of both prisms are the same.) Record your results in a table.

31. A concrete roadway that is 40 feet wide, 10 miles long, and 1 foot thick is being built.
    a. Find the number of cubic feet of concrete needed. (1 mile = 5280 feet)
    b. Find the number of cubic yards of concrete needed.
    c. If the concrete weighs 145 pounds per cubic foot, find the weight of the concrete needed to build the roadway.

32. One type of tropical fish requires at least 250 cubic inches of water for each inch of body length. Suppose an aquarium is shaped like the one shown and that the water level is two inches from the top.

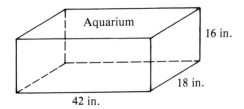

a. What is the volume of the water in cubic inches?

b. How much water is required by a 2-inch long fish of this type?

c. How many such 2-inch fish could be kept in this aquarium?

═══════ *MORE EXPLORING* ═══════
Minimizing Total Area

In this MORE EXPLORING you will learn what kind of rectangular prism has the least total area for a given volume.

1. **Find the volume and total area of each rectangular prism described.**
   a. 2 cm × 2 cm × 2 cm **b.** 4 cm × 2 cm × 1 cm **c.** 8 cm × 1 cm × 1 cm

2. **Find the volume and total area each rectangular prism described.**
   a. 4 cm × 4 cm × 4 cm   **b.** 8 cm × 4 cm × 2 cm   **c.** 8 cm × 8 cm × 1 cm
   d. 16 cm × 2 cm × 2 cm **e.** 16 cm × 4 cm × 1 cm **f.** 32 cm × 2 cm × 1 cm
   g. 64 cm × 1 cm × 1 cm

3. Look at your results from steps 1 and 2. Answer these questions for both sets of data.
   a. How do the volumes compare?
   b. How do the total areas compare?
   c. Which prism has the least total area?

4. Write a conclusion. Complete the following statement:

   > **Of all rectangular prisms with the same volume, the one with the least total area is a   ?   .**

7-6

Volume of Other Prisms

In Lesson 7-5 you learned that the volume of a rectangular prism is found by multiplying the area of the base by the height. The following EXPLORING shows that this same procedure can be used to find the volume of other prisms.

═══ EXPLORING ═══
The Volume of Other Prisms

1. Look at the triangular prism. What are the length and height of a base of the prism?
2. What is the area of a base?
3. How many cubic units does it take to cover a base?
4. How many layers of cubic units are needed to fill the prism?
5. What is the volume of the prism?
6. Can the volume of the prism be found by multiplying the area of the base by the height?
7. Look at prisms A–C. Describe or draw a picture of a base of each.

Prism A

Prism B

Prism C

8. For each prism in step 7, find each of the following: the area of the base, the height of the prism, and the volume of the prism. Record your results in a table.
9. What must be known about a prism before its volume can be found?
10. How is that information used to find the volume of a prism?

If you did the preceding EXPLORING carefully, you discovered the following conclusion:

> **To find the volume of any prism, multiply the area of the base by the height.**
>
> **Volume = Area of base × Height**
>
> **V = Bh**

Do the following for each prism.

a. Draw a picture of a base.
b. Find the area of that base.
c. Find the volume of the prism.

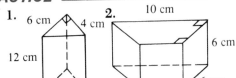

1. 6 cm 4 cm 12 cm

2. 10 cm 6 cm 6 cm 6 cm

Find the indicated information for each prism where V = volume of the prism, B = area of the base, and h = height of the prism.

3. $B = 32$ cm², $h = 4$ cm, $V = $? cm³
4. $V = 80$ cm³, $h = 5$ cm, $B = $? cm²
5. $B = 16$ cm², $V = 96$ cm³, $h = $? cm

EXERCISES

— A —

Do the following for each prism.

a. Draw a picture of a base.
b. Find the area of that base.
c. Find the volume of the prism.

1.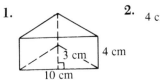
3 cm 4 cm 10 cm

2. 4 cm 4 cm 8 cm 10 cm

3.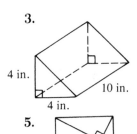
4 in. 10 in. 4 in.

4. 5 ft 3 ft 7 ft

5.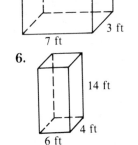
12 cm 9 cm 6 cm

6. 14 ft 4 ft 6 ft

In Exercises 7–12, find the indicated information for each prism where V = volume of the prism, B = area of the base, and h = height of the prism.

7. $B = 15$ cm², $h = 7$ cm, $V = $? cm³
8. $h = 8$ yd, $B = 12$ yd², $V = $? yd³
9. $h = 3$ ft, $V = 27$ ft³, $B = $? yd²
10. $h = 12$ in., $V = 144$ in.³, $B = $? in.²
11. $B = 45$ cm², $V = 270$ cm³, $h = $? cm
12. $V = 84$ cm³, $B = 12$ cm², $h = $? cm

— B —

13. A hexagonal prism has a base area of 18 square centimeters and a height of 14 centimeters. Find the volume of the prism.

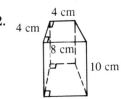
3 ft 10 ft

14. A prism has a height of 12 feet. Its base is like the figure shown. Find the volume of the prism.

15. A prism with a square base 4 feet on a side has a volume of 128 cubic feet. Find the height of the prism.

16. A rectangular prism has a base 8 centimeters long and 4 centimeters wide. Its volume is 160 cubic centimeters. Find the height of the prism.

Find the volume of each triangular prism described.

17. The height is 10 inches and the area of the base is 6 square inches.

18. The height is 10 inches and the base is a right triangular region with a base length of 10 inches and a height of 5 inches.

19. The height is 10 inches and the base is a right triangular region with a base length of 6 inches and a height of 8 inches.

_— C —_

20. A triangular prism has a base area of 18 square centimeters and a volume of 90 cubic centimeters.
    a. Find the height of the prism.
    b. Using only whole-number lengths for the base length and height of the base, list three possible sets of dimensions for the base.

21. Suppose you are given 60 cubic-centimeter blocks. Find the dimensions of all different rectangular prisms that can be built by using all the blocks. (Two prisms are the same if their dimensions are the same *or* if one prism can be turned so that the dimensions of both prisms are the same.) Record your results in a table.

22. A swimming pool is 9 feet deep at one end and 3 feet deep at the other. It is 50 yards long and 20 yards wide, as shown.

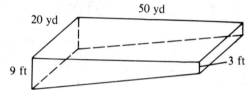

a. Find the volume of the pool in cubic feet.

b. One cubic foot is equivalent to $7\frac{1}{2}$ gallons. How many gallons of water are needed to fill the pool?

c. Find the area of the walls of the pool.

d. If one gallon of paint will cover 400 square feet, how many gallons are needed to paint the walls of the pool?

========== **MORE EXPLORING** ==========

Removing Unit Cubes to Change Total Area

The length of each side of the cube shown is 3 units.

1. Find the total area of the cube.
2. Identify one unit cube that may be removed without changing the total area. How many cubes have this property? Describe the location(s) of these cubes.

3. Identify one unit cube whose removal will increase the total area by 2. How many cubes have this property? Describe the location(s) of these cubes.

4. Identify one unit cube whose removal will increase the total area by 4. How many cubes have this property? Describe the location(s) of these cubes.

7-7

Volume of a Cylinder

A cylinder is like a prism except that its bases are congruent circular regions rather than congruent polygonal regions. We find the volume of a cylinder in the same way we find the volume of a prism—by multiplying the area of the base by the height.

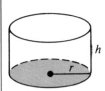

To find the volume of a cylinder, multiply the area of the base by the height.

$$\text{Volume} = \text{Area of base} \times \text{Height}$$

$$V = Bh \qquad B = \pi r^2$$

$$V = \pi r^2 h \qquad \text{(The base is a circular region.)}$$

Example 1:
Find the volume of a cylinder whose base area is 30 square inches and whose height is 4 inches.

Solution:
$$V = Bh = 30 \times 4 = 120 \text{ in.}^3$$

Example 2:
Find the volume of the cylinder shown. Use 3.14 for π.

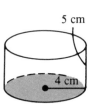

5 cm

4 cm

Solution:
$$\text{Area of base} = \pi r^2 \qquad B \approx 3.14 \times 4 \times 4$$
$$\approx 50.24 \text{ cm}^2$$
$$\text{Volume} = \text{Area of base} \times \text{Height}$$
$$V = Bh \approx 50.24 \times 5 \approx 251.2 \text{ cm}^3$$

CLASS PRACTICE

Find the following information for each cylinder. Use the indicated approximation for π.
a. Circumference of base   b. Lateral Area
c. Area of base   d. Total Area   e. Volume

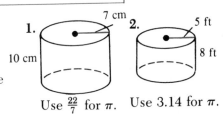

1.

7 cm

10 cm

2.

5 ft

8 ft

Use $\frac{22}{7}$ for π.   Use 3.14 for π.

Find the indicated information for each cylinder where V = volume of the cylinder, B = area of the base, h = height of the cylinder, and r = radius of the base. Use 3.14 for π.

3. $B = 32$ cm², $h = 4$ cm, $V = $? cm³
4. $r = 4$ in., $h = 5$ in., $B = $? in.², $V = $? in.³
5. $V = 75.36$ cm³, $B = 12.56$ cm², $h = $? cm

Volume and Total Area   **297**

EXERCISES

— A —

Find the volume of each cylinder described. Use 3.14 for π.

1. Height is 4 cm and radius of base is 5 cm
2. Height is 2 ft and radius of base is 3 ft
3. Height is 4 cm and diameter of base is 10 cm
4. Height is 9 in. and area of base is 45 in.²

Find the volume of each cylinder. Unless otherwise indicated, use 3.14 for π.

5. 6.

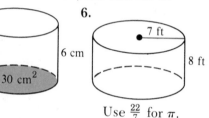

Use $\frac{22}{7}$ for π.

7. 8.

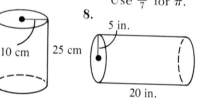

— B —

9. Can A has a radius of 2 inches and a height of 4 inches.
   Can B has a radius of 4 inches and a height of 4 inches.
   Can C has a radius of 2 inches and a height of 8 inches.
   a. Find the volume of each can.
   b. Write statements comparing their volumes.

Find the indicated information for each cylinder where V = volume of the cylinder, B = area of the base, h = height of the cylinder, and r = radius of the base. Use 3.14 for π.

10. $V = 150$ cm³, $B = 25$ cm²,
    $h = $? cm
11. $r = 6$ ft, $h = 10$ ft, $B = $? ft²,
    $V = $? ft³
12. $V = 282.6$ cm³, $B = 28.26$ cm²,
    $h = $? cm, $r = $? cm
13. $B = 30$ in.², $h = 8$ in.,
    $V = $? in.³

Find the indicated information for each figure. Use 3.14 for π.

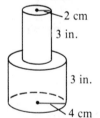

14. a. Volume of outer cylinder
    b. Volume of inner cylinder
    c. Volume of shaded cylindrical ring
15. a. Volume of top cylinder
    b. Volume of bottom cylinder
    c. Combined volume of both cylinders
16. a. Volume of each cylinder
    b. Which holds more—the largest cylinder or the two smaller ones combined?

7-8

Mastering Lateral Area, Total Area, and Volume

— A —

Find the indicated information for the rectangular prism shown.

1. Area of a base
2. Lateral Area
3. Volume
4. Total Area
5. Perimeter of a base
6. AB   7. BC
8. CD

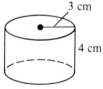

Find the indicated information for the cylinder shown.

9. Area of a base
10. Volume
11. Circumference of a base
12. Lateral Area
13. Total Area

Use 3.14 for π.

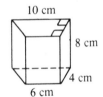

Find the indicated information for the triangular prism shown.

14. Draw a picture of a base.
15. Area of a base
16. Volume
17. Lateral Area
18. Total Area
19. Area of largest face

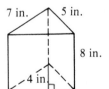

Find the indicated information for each prism.

20. Area of base = 24 ft²
    Volume = ? ft³

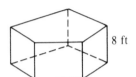

21. Volume = ? cm³

Find the indicated information.

22. A cube has one edge of length 2 inches. Find its volume.

Find the indicated information for each rectangular prism where l = length, w = width, h = height, and V = volume.

23. $l = 6$ in., $w = 4$ in., $h = 3$ in., $V = ?$ in.³
24. $l = 5$ in., $V = 60$ in.³, $w = 2$ in., $h = ?$ in.
25. $l = 6$ cm, $w = 4$ cm, $V = 120$ cm³, $h = ?$ cm.

26. The base of a prism is shown. The height of the prism is 10 inches. Find its volume.

25 in.²

— B —

27. Suppose the volume of a rectangular prism is 24 cubic inches and its height is 2 inches.
  a. Find the area of the base.
  b. Using only whole-number lengths, list three possible sets of values for the length and width of the base.

28. A rectangular prism has a volume of 16 cubic centimeters. Using only whole-number lengths, list three possible sets of dimensions (length, width, and height).

29. The volume of a cube is 125 cubic feet. Find the length of one edge.

30. How many 2-in. by 3-in. by 1-in. packages will fit into a box that is 6 in. by 9 in. by 2 in.?

31. Suppose that 12 small boxes, each the same size, will fit exactly into the box shown.
  a. What is the volume of the box shown?
  b. What is the volume of each small box?
  c. Using only whole-number lengths, list some possible sets of dimensions for the small boxes.

6 in.
6 in.
8 in.

32. Suppose box A has a volume of 30 cubic centimeters and box B has a volume of 15 cubic centimeters. Will box B necessarily fit inside box A? Why or why not?

33. A water tank 2 feet high, 8 feet wide, and 20 feet long is filled to the top.
  a. What is the volume of the tank in cubic feet?
  b. How many gallons of water does it hold? (1 ft³ holds about $7\frac{1}{2}$ gallons.)

Find the indicated information for each figure.

34. Volume = ? cm³

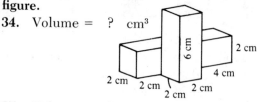

6 cm, 2 cm, 4 cm, 2 cm, 2 cm, 2 cm, 2 cm

35. Volume = ? in.³

4 in., 5 in., 8 in., 2 in., 3 in.

36. Volume = ? cm³

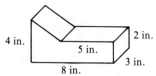

8 cm
3 cm, 1 cm, 2 cm, 1 cm
2 cm, 3 cm, 1 cm
3 cm

37. **a.** Total Area = ? ft²
  b. Volume = ? ft³

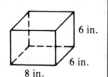

3 ft
1 ft, 2 ft
1 ft, 2 ft
1ft, 2 ft, 3 ft
6 ft

38. Prism B is formed by cutting prism A in half.
  a. Find the volume of each prism.
  b. Find the total area of each prism.

A 4 cm   B 5 cm
4 cm
8 cm   8 cm
3 cm   3 cm

39. Refer to the drawing of the house.

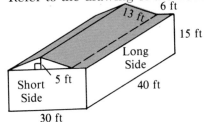

a. Area of one short side = ? ft²
b. Area of one long side = ? ft²
c. Area of all 4 sides = ? ft²
d. Area of roof (shaded) = ? ft² (Be sure to include the part of the roof *not* shown.)
e. If one gallon of paint will cover 400 ft², how many gallon cans are needed to paint all 4 sides of the house?
f. Aluminum siding is sold by the "square." One "square" is the amount needed to cover 100 ft². How many "squares" are need-ed to put aluminum siding on all 4 sides of the house?
g. Asphalt shingles are also sold by the "square." How many "squares" are needed to put a new roof on the house?

40. A room is 13 feet long, 11 feet wide, and 9 feet high. There are two windows that are each 5 ft × 2½ ft, one door that is 8 ft × 2½ ft, and a closet door that is 8 ft × 4 ft.
a. Find the combined area of the doors and windows.
b. Find the combined area of the walls (including the doors and windows).
c. A single roll of wallpaper will cover an area of 30 ft² when you allow for waste. If one roll is deducted for every two openings (doors or windows), how many rolls are needed for the walls?

Test Yourself

Do the following for each prism or cylinder.
a. Draw a picture of a base. b. Find the area of that base.
c. Find the volume of the prism or cylinder.

1.

2.

3. 4 cm

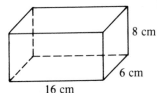

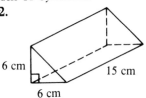

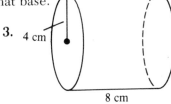

Use 3.14 for π.

Find the indicated information.

4. A cylinder has a base area of 45 cm² and a volume of 360 cm³. Find its height.
5. A prism has a height of 9 cm and a volume of 135 cm³. Find its base area.

7-9

Stretching Prisms and Cylinders

In this lesson you will explore some other properties of total area and volume for rectangular prisms and for cylinders.

EXPLORING

What Happens When Rectangular Prisms Are Stretched

1. Find the total area and volume of each cube described. Record your results in a table like this one:

Cube	Length of One Edge	Total Area	Volume
A	1 cm	6 cm²	1 cm³
B	2 cm	?	?
C	3 cm	?	?
D	4 cm	?	?
E	5 cm	?	?

2. Use your results to determine what happens to the total area of a cube when the length of each edge is multiplied by 2, by 3, by 4, and by 5.

3. Use your results to determine what happens to the volume of a cube when the length of each edge is multiplied by 2, by 3, by 4, and by 5.

4. Start with a rectangular prism that is not a cube, like the one shown.
   a. Find its total area and volume.
   b. Determine what happens to the total area and volume when the length of each edge is multiplied by 2, by 3, by 4, and by 5.

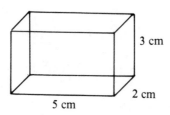

3 cm

2 cm

5 cm

What Happens When Cylinders Are Stretched

1. Find the total area and volume of each cylinder described. Record your results in a table like this one:

Cylinder	Radius of Base	Height	Total Area	Volume
A	1 cm	2 cm	6π cm^2	2π cm^3
B.	2 cm	4 cm	?	?
C	3 cm	6 cm	?	?
D	4 cm	8 cm	?	?

2. Use your results to determine what happens to the total area of a cylinder when both the radius of the base and the height are multiplied by 2, by 3, and by 4.
3. Use your results to determine what happens to the volume of a cylinder when both the radius of the base and the height are multiplied by 2, by 3, and by 4.

If you did the preceding EXPLORINGs carefully you discovered the following conclusions:

> If the length of each edge of a rectangular prism is multiplied by n, its total area is multiplied by n^2 and its volume is multiplied by n^3.

> If both the radius of the base and the height of a cylinder are multiplied by n, its total area is multiplied by n^2 and its volume is multiplied by n^3.

1. What happens to the volume of a cube if only one dimension (length, width, or height) is doubled? if only two dimensions are doubled? Support your answers with an example.
2. What happens to the volume of a cube if only one dimension is multiplied by 3? if only two dimensions are multiplied by 3? Support your answers with an example.

3. Would your answers to Ex. 1 and 2 be the same for rectangular prisms that are not cubes? Support your answer with an example.
4. What happens to the volume of a cylinder if only the radius of the base is doubled? if only the height of the cylinder is doubled? Support your answers with an example.
5. What happens to the volume of a cylinder if only the radius of the base is multiplied by 3? if only the height of the cylinder is multiplied by 3? Support your answers with an example.

EXERCISES

Classify each statement as true or false.
1. If all dimensions of a rectangular prism are doubled, the volume is also doubled.
2. If all dimensions of a rectangular prism are doubled, the total area is multiplied by four.
3. If both the radius of the base and the height of a cylinder are doubled, the volume of the cylinder is multiplied by eight.

Assume that all dimensions of the larger rectangular prism are three times those of the smaller rectangular prism.
4. Total Area of smaller prism = 94 cm²
   Total Area of larger prism =   ?   cm²
5. Total Area of larger prism = 342 cm²
   Total Area of smaller prism = ? cm²
6. Volume of smaller prism = 60 cm³
   Volume of larger prism =   ?   cm³
7. Volume of larger prism = 324 cm³
   Volume of smaller prism =   ?   cm³

Find the indicated information.
8. Look at the prism.
   a. Find the total area.
   b. Find the volume.

4 cm
8 cm   3 cm

Suppose all dimensions of the prism are doubled.
   c. Find the new total area.
   d. Find the new volume.
9. The volume of a rectangular prism is 10 cubic inches and its total area is 34 square inches. Suppose all dimensions are multiplied by 4.
   a. Find the new volume.
   b. Find the new total area.
10. By what number is the total area of a cylinder multiplied if both the radius of the base and the height of the cylinder are multiplied by each of the following?
    a. 2   b. 3   c. 5
11. The total area of a cylinder is 20 square inches. Find the total area of a cylinder whose base radius and height are four times as great.
12. By what number is the volume of a cylinder multiplied if both the radius of the base and the height of the cylinder are multiplied by each of the following?
    a. 2   b. 3   c. 5
13. The volume of a cylinder is 10 cubic inches. Find the volume of a cylinder whose base radius and height are four times as great.

How Much Does it Contain?

The volumes and capacities of containers fall within certain limits. For example, the trunk of an automobile would not have a capacity as small as 1 cubic inch or as large as 100 cubic feet.

Several items are listed below. Consult catalogues, newspaper advertisements, brochures, and similar materials to determine the normal range of volumes or capacities available for each item listed. Determine some common standard volumes or capacities available for each item.

1. Freezer
2. Hot water heater
3. Wheelbarrow
4. Vacuum bottle
5. Pressure cooker
6. Camping cooler
7. Garbage bag
8. Soft drink can
9. Soup can
10. Paint can
11. Automobile engine displacement
12. Motorcycle engine displacement

=========== *Applications* ===========

The Square/Cube Law

Recall that if the dimensions of an object are multiplied by n, its volume is multiplied by n^3 and its total area is multiplied by n^2. The mass or weight of an object is dependent on its volume. The fact that mass or weight increases faster than area when the dimensions of an object increase has important consequences.

Shown are the leg bones of two animals that have similar shapes but different sizes. The dimensions of the larger bone are 2 times the corresponding dimensions of the smaller bone. Since weight is dependent on volume, the larger animal weighs 8 times as much as the smaller one. However, the strength of any structural material, such as bone, is dependent on its cross-sectional area. Therefore, the leg bone of the larger animal is only 4 times as strong.

As a result, if the dimensions of an object are increased indefinitely without making some modification in its structure, at some point it will collapse under its own weight. Engineers and designers must make use of this principle. Even though a small model of an airplane or building may work well, a larger one with the same proportions may not be strong enough.

7-10

Area and Volume of Regular Pyramids and of Cones

In this lesson you will learn how to find the lateral area and the total area of any regular pyramid and the volume of any regular pyramid or cone.

A *regular pyramid* is a three-dimensional figure formed by joining the vertices of a regular polygon to a point (vertex) that is not in the same plane as the base and that lies directly above the center of the base.

The *height* of a pyramid is the perpendicular distance from the vertex to the base.

Pyramids, like prisms, are named by the shape of the base. Shown are a regular square pyramid and a regular triangular pyramid.

Look at the regular pyramids. Notice that all the lateral faces (all faces except the base) in each pyramid are triangular.

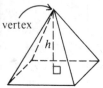

Regular Square Pyramid

Regular Triangular Pyramid

Regular Triangular Pyramid

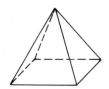

Regular Square Pyramid

Regular Hexagonal Pyramid

Since the vertex of a regular pyramid lies directly above the center of the base, all lateral faces of a regular pyramid are shaped like congruent isosceles triangles. As a result, both the lateral area and the total area of a regular pyramid can be found easily.

One new term, "slant height," is useful when discussing the lateral area of a regular pyramid. The *slant height* of a regular pyramid is the length of the altitude of one of the lateral faces. This is illustrated by the drawing.

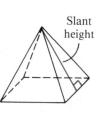

Slant height

Example 1: Find the lateral area and the total area of this regular square pyramid.

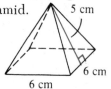

5 cm

6 cm

6 cm

Solution:

Area of one lateral face $= \frac{1}{2} \times 6 \times 5$

$= 15 \text{ cm}^2$

Lateral Area $= 4 \times 15 = 60 \text{ cm}^2$

Area of base $= 6 \times 6 = 36 \text{ cm}^2$

Total Area $= 60 + 36 = 96 \text{ cm}^2$

A *right circular cone* is somewhat like a regular pyramid except that its base is a circular region. The height and vertex of a cone are defined in a manner similar to the height and vertex of a regular pyramid. In this book we will use the word "cone" to mean "right circular cone."

vertex h = height

Right Circular Cone

Shown below are (left) a square pyramid and rectangular prism with the same base area and height, and (right) a cone and cylinder with the same base area and height.

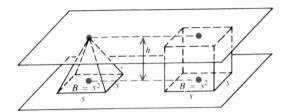 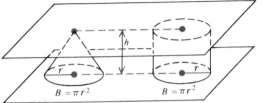

Suppose models for the figures shown were filled with either a liquid or some material such as sand or sawdust. You would find that the prism holds three times as much as the pyramid and that the cylinder holds three times as much as the cone. This suggests that the volume of the pyramid is $\frac{1}{3}$ the volume of the prism and that the volume of the cone is $\frac{1}{3}$ the volume of the cylinder.

The volume of a regular pyramid or a cone is given by the following formula.

$$\text{Volume} = \tfrac{1}{3} \times \text{Area of base} \times \text{Height}$$

$$V = \tfrac{1}{3}Bh$$

Here are some examples using this formula.

Example 2:
Find the volume of this square pyramid.

6 cm
5 cm
5 cm

Solution:
Area of base = $5 \times 5 = 25$ cm²
$V = \frac{1}{3}Bh$
$V = \frac{1}{3} \times \frac{25}{1} \times \frac{6}{1} = \frac{150}{3} = 50$ cm³

Example 3:
Find the volume of this cone. (Use 3.14 for π.)

3 cm
6 cm

Solution:
Area of base $\approx 3.14 \times 3 \times 3 \approx 28.26$ cm²
$V = \frac{1}{3}Bh$
$V \approx \frac{1}{3} \times \frac{28.26}{1} \times \frac{6}{1} \approx \frac{169.56}{3} \approx 56.52$ cm³

Although the work in this lesson is limited to regular pyramids and right circular cones, the formula on the preceding page does work for all pyramids and cones.

DISCUSS

Look at Example 1 on page 306. In finding the lateral area of the pyramid, why was the area of one lateral face multiplied by four?

CLASS PRACTICE

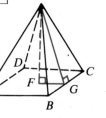

Look at the regular square pyramid.

$AB = 12$ cm,
$EF = 8$ cm,
$EG = 10$ cm

Identify each of the following.
1. Vertex of the pyramid
2. Altitude of the pyramid
3. Slant height
4. One lateral edge
5. All segments congruent to $\overline{AE}$
6. Four isosceles triangles

Find each of the following.
7. Area of $\triangle EBC$
8. Lateral Area
9. Area of base
10. Volume

Look at the cone. Find each of the following. (Use 3.14 for π.)
11. Height
12. Area of base
13. Volume

10 cm

4 cm

EXERCISES

— A —

Look at the regular square pyramid.
Classify each statement as true or false.
1. $\overline{AC}$ is an altitude of the pyramid.
2. If $WX = 10$ cm, then $BC = 5$ cm.
3. A is the vertex of the pyramid.
4. $\triangle AWX$ is equilateral.
5. $\triangle AWX \cong \triangle AXY$
6. $\overline{AW} \cong \overline{AX}$

7. The pyramid has four lateral faces.
8. The base of the pyramid is a square.

Find the volume of each figure described. Use 3.14 for π.
9. Cylinder: $r = 4$ in., $h = 8$ in.
10. Cone: $r = 4$ in., $h = 8$ in.
11. Prism: $B = 18$ cm², $h = 12$ cm
12. Regular pyramid: $B = 18$ cm², $h = 12$ cm
13. Cube: Each edge is 5 in. long.

14. Regular square pyramid: h = 5 in., base is a 5-in. × 5-in. square

15. Regular pyramid: B = 24 cm², h = 8 cm

16. Cone: B = 24 cm², h = 8 cm

Find the volume of each figure. Use 3.14 for π.

17.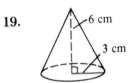

18.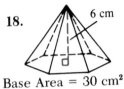

Base Area = 30 cm²

19.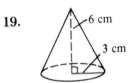

20.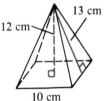

21. Look at the regular square pyramid in Exercise 20.
    a. Find its lateral area.
    b. Find its total area.

22. Find each of the following for the regular square pyramid shown.
    a. Lateral Area
    b. Area of base
    c. Total Area
    d. Volume

    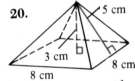

— B —

Draw a figure to fit each description.

23. Regular triangular pyramid
24. Regular square pyramid
25. Right circular cone

Find the indicated information.

26. A cone has a volume of 225 cubic centimeters. What is the volume of a cylinder with the same base area and height?

27. A prism holds 432 cubic inches. How much would a regular pyramid with the same base area and height hold?

28. A regular pyramid and a cone have the same height and their bases have the same area. How do their volumes compare?

29. A cone has a base area of 25 square centimeters and a volume of 100 cubic centimeters. Find its height.

— C —

30. Find each of the following for the regular square pyramid shown.

    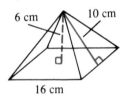

    a. Perimeter of base
    b. Slant height
    c. Lateral Area
    d. $\frac{1}{2}$ × Perimeter of base × Slant height

31. If P is the perimeter of the base and s is the slant height of a pyramid, the lateral area (L.A.) of the regular pyramid can be found with the following formula: L.A. = $\frac{1}{2}Ps$.
    Use this formula to find the lateral area of the pyramid shown.

    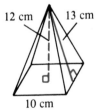

32. Explain why the formula used in Exercise 31 works.

7-11

Total Area and Volume of a Sphere

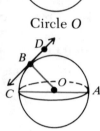

Circle O

Recall from Lesson 2–1 that a circle is the set of all points in a plane that are the same distance from some point called the center. Similarly, a *sphere* is the set of all points in space that are the same distance from some point called the *center*. Most of the terms used to describe circles are also used for spheres. Some of these terms are illustrated by the diagram shown here.

Sphere O

$\overline{OA}$, $\overline{OB}$, and $\overline{OC}$ are *radii*.

$\overline{AC}$ is a *diameter*.

$\overleftrightarrow{BD}$ is a *tangent*.

The following formulas can be used to find the total area and volume of any sphere:

> **The total area and volume of a sphere with radius r are given by the following formulas.**
>
> $$\text{T.A.} = 4\pi r^2 \qquad V = \tfrac{4}{3}\pi r^3$$

Here are some examples using these formulas.

Example 1: A sphere has a radius of 5 cm. Find (a) the exact total area and volume, and (b) the approximate total area and volume. (Use 3.14 for π.)

Solution:

(a) $\text{T.A.} = 4\pi r^2$
$= 4\pi(5)^2$
$= 4\pi(5 \times 5)$
$= 100\pi \text{ cm}^2$

$V = \tfrac{4}{3}\pi r^3$
$= \tfrac{4}{3}\pi(5)^3$
$= \tfrac{4}{3}\pi(5 \times 5 \times 5)$
$= \tfrac{500}{3}\pi \text{ cm}^3$,
or $166.\overline{6}\pi \text{ cm}^3$

(b) $\text{T.A.} = 100\pi$
$\text{T.A.} \approx 100(3.14)$
$\approx 314 \text{ cm}^2$

$V = \tfrac{500}{3}\pi$
$V \approx \dfrac{500(3.14)}{3}$
$\approx 523.33 \text{ cm}^3$
(nearest hundredth)

Example 2: The total area of a sphere is 64π cm². Find its radius and diameter.

Solution:

$\text{T.A.} = 4\pi r^2$
$64\pi = 4\pi r^2$

$r^2 = \dfrac{64\pi}{4\pi} = 16$
$r = 4$

Answer: radius = 4 cm
diameter = 8 cm

For Exercises 1–6, look at the sphere.
Identify each of the following.

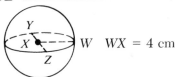

W   WX = 4 cm

1. All radii   2. All diameters

Find the indicated information. (Use 3.14 for π.)

3. XY   4. XZ   5. Total Area   6. Volume

Find the indicated information.

7. The volume of a sphere is $36\pi\,\text{cm}^3$. Find its radius and diameter.

EXERCISES

Find the indicated information.

1. If a radius of a sphere is 6 cm, how long is each diameter?
2. If a diameter of a sphere is 10 cm, how long is each radius?

Find the value of r^3 for each value of r.

3. 2   4. 3   5. 4   6. 6

For a sphere with each given radius or diameter, find (a) the exact total area and (b) the exact volume.

7. $r = 2$ cm   8. $d = 6$ cm

For a sphere with each given radius or diameter, find (a) the approximate total area and (b) the approximate volume. (Use 3.14 for π.)

9. $r = 2$ cm   10. $d = 6$ cm

Copy and complete the following table about spheres.

	r	d	Exact Total Area	Exact Volume
11.	7 cm	?	?	?
12.	?	12 cm	?	?

	r	d	Exact Total Area	Exact Volume
13.	?	?	324π	?
14.	?	?	?	$\frac{256}{3}\pi$

Find the indicated information.

15. The approximate total area of a sphere is 1256 cm². Find the radius and the diameter of the sphere. (Use 3.14 for π.)

10 cm

16. A hemisphere is one half of a sphere. Find the exact total area and volume of the hemisphere shown.

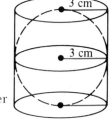

In the diagram shown, the sphere fits inside the cylinder. Find the indicated information.

17. Exact total area of the sphere
18. Height of the cylinder
19. Exact lateral area of the cylinder

3 cm

3 cm

7-12

Equivalent Volumes and Applications

This lesson presents the relationship between some commonly used units of volume and introduces metric units of capacity. The exercises in this lesson also show some applications of some ideas presented earlier.

The two drawings indicate the relationship between some commonly used customary units of volume. (The drawings are to different scales.)

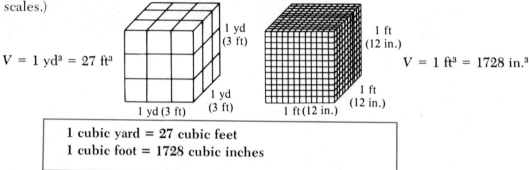

$V = 1 \text{ yd}^3 = 27 \text{ ft}^3$

1 yd (3 ft)

1 yd (3 ft)

1 yd (3 ft)

$V = 1 \text{ ft}^3 = 1728 \text{ in.}^3$

1 ft (12 in.)

1 ft (12 in.)

1 ft (12 in.)

> 1 cubic yard = 27 cubic feet
> 1 cubic foot = 1728 cubic inches

Here are some examples using some of these relationships.

Example 1: $15 \text{ yd}^3 = $? ft^3

Solution:

$1 \text{ yd}^3 = 27 \text{ ft}^3$

To convert from a larger unit to a smaller one, multiply. $15 \times 27 = 405$

There are 405 cubic feet in 15 cubic yards.

Example 2: A front sidewalk is 60 feet long, 3 feet wide, and 4 inches thick. How many cubic yards of concrete are needed for the sidewalk?

Solution:

The sidewalk is in the shape of a rectangular prism. First find the volume in cubic feet:

$V = Bh = (60 \times 3) \times \frac{1}{3}$ $4 \text{ in.} = \frac{1}{3} \text{ ft}$

$= 180 \times \frac{1}{3} = 60 \text{ ft}^3$

Now convert 60 cubic feet to cubic yards. $27 \text{ ft}^3 = 1 \text{ yd}^3$

To convert from a smaller unit to a larger one, divide. $60 \div 27 = 2\frac{2}{9}$

So $2\frac{2}{9}$ cubic yards of concrete are needed. (In actual practice, th. would be rounded up to the nearest half or full cubic yard. You order either $2\frac{1}{2}$ or 3 cubic yards of concrete for the sidewalk.)

Two commonly used metric units of capacity are the liter (L) and the milliliter (mL). The cube shown represents a capacity of 1 liter. One liter is equivalent to a volume of 1000 cubic centimeters (cm³). Notice that each small cube is $\frac{1}{1000}$ of a liter. Therefore, one milliliter of capacity is equivalent to one cubic centimeter of volume.

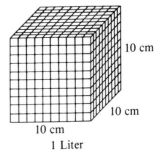

10 cm
10 cm
10 cm
1 Liter

> **Metric Units of Volume and Capacity**
> 1 liter = 1000 cubic centimeters (1L = 1000 cm³)
> 1 liter = 1000 milliliters (1L = 1000 mL)
> 1 milliliter = 1 cubic centimeter (1 mL = 1 cm³)

DISCUSS

1. Describe some other situations or industries in which metric units of volume or capacity are currently being used or will likely be used in the near future.
2. Joe helped his father find how much soil is needed to cover their yard with two inches of topsoil. The yard measures 15 yards by 25 yards. Joe multiplied 15 × 25 × 2 and said they would need 750 cubic yards. What mistake did Joe make? How many cubic yards of topsoil do they actually need?

CLASS PRACTICE

Convert each measure to the indicated unit

1. 4 yd³ = ? ft³
2. 7 yd³ = ? ft³
3. 54 ft³ = ? yd³
4. 135 ft³ = ? yd³
5. 5 L = ? mL
6. 3 L = ? cm³
7. 4000 mL = ? L
8. 100 mL = ? cm³

Find the indicated information.

9. State the dimensions (length, width, and height) of three different rectangular prisms having a capacity of one liter.
10. Using only whole-number lengths, draw pictures of three different rectangular prisms having a volume of one cubic yard.

_ A _

Convert each volume measure to cubic feet.

1. 2 yd³
2. 5 yd³
3. 10 yd³
4. 3 yd³

Convert each volume measure to cubic yards.

5. 81 ft³
6. 162 ft³
7. 540 ft³
8. 144 ft³

Convert each measure to the indicated unit.

9. 3 L = ? mL
10. 500 mL = ? L
11. 300 mL = ? cm³
12. 1.5 L = ? mL
13. 2000 mL = ? L
14. 750 cm³ = ? mL
15. 2 L = ? cm³
16. 1500 cm³ = ? L
17. 750 mL = ? L

_ B _

18. A new driveway is being built. The concrete is to be 4 inches ($\frac{1}{3}$ ft) thick. The driveway is 54 feet long and 9 feet wide.
    a. Find the number of cubic feet of concrete needed.
    b. Find the number of cubic yards of concrete needed.

19. The engine displacement of a motorcycle is usually given in cubic centimeters. What part of a liter is each of the following?
    a. 150 cm³
    b. 200 cm³
    c. 750 cm³

20. The displacement of most American-built automobile engines is now given in liters instead of cubic inches. If one liter is about 60 cubic inches, give the approximate displacement in cubic inches for the following engines.
    a. 3.8 L
    b. 4.2 L
    c. 6.6 L
    d. 2.5 L
    e. 5.1 L
    f. 1.6 L

21. Suppose you wish to cover the garden shown with 3 inches ($\frac{1}{4}$ ft) of topsoil.

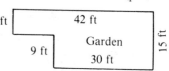

    a. Find the number of cubic feet of topsoil needed.
    b. Find the number of cubic yards of topsoil needed.

_ C _

22. The pit for the foundation and basement of a house is shaped like the figure shown.

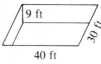

    a. Find the number of cubic feet of soil to be removed.
    b. Find the number of cubic yards of soil to be removed.
    c. Suppose a dump truck has a capacity of 6 cubic yards. How many truckloads of soil must be removed?

23. A prism-shaped container that is 11 inches high holds 1 gallon of liquid. (1 gallon = 231 cubic inches)

a. Find the area of the base.

b. Suppose the base is rectangular. State one possible set of values for the length and width of the base.

c. Suppose the base is triangular. State one possible set of values for the base length and height of the base.

24. Refer to the swimming pool shown.

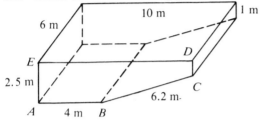

a. Find the area of face *ABCDE*.

b. Find the volume of the pool. (Think of the pool as a right prism lying on its side with *ABCDE* as the base.)

c. What is the capacity of the pool in liters?
(1 cubic meter = 1000 liters)

25. One health standard requires that 200 cubic feet of air space be available for each person in a room.

a. Find the volume of your classroom in cubic feet.

b. Find the maximum number of students this health standard would permit in your classroom.

c. Would you like to have that many students in your classroom? Why or why not?

Everyday Geometry

Swimming Pool Capacity

People who maintain a large container such as a swimming pool or water tank often need to know the capacity of the container. For example, a homeowner must know how many gallons or liters of water a backyard swimming pool will hold to determine how much water conditioner to use.

To find the capacity of a large container, first find its volume in cubic feet or cubic meters. Then use the fact that a cubic foot is about 7.5 gallons or that a cubic meter is 1000 liters.

EXERCISES

1. A rectangular pool is 6 meters wide, 15 meters long, and 1.5 meters deep. Find its volume in cubic meters and its capacity in liters.

2. A pool in the shape of a trapezoidal prism is 25 feet wide and 40 feet long. The water is 3 feet deep at one end and 8 feet deep at the other. Find its volume in cubic feet and its capacity in gallons.

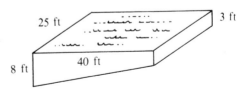

7-13

Customary Units of Capacity

With a few exceptions, such as the liter and milliliter, the only units of volume and capacity used so far in this chapter have been cubic units. This lesson introduces some other units of capacity.

The customary system of measurement has one set of units for measuring fluid capacity and another set for dry capacity. Fluid measure is often used in the kitchen. Dry cooking ingredients such as flour and spices are also measured with fluid capacity units. The following table gives the relationships among some commonly used units of fluid measure.

Customary Units of Liquid Measure

3 teaspoons (tsp) = 1 tablespoon

2 tablespoons (Tbsp) = 1 fluid ounce

16 fluid ounces (fl oz) = 1 pint

2 cups = 1 pint

2 pints (pt) = 1 quart

4 quarts (qt) = 1 gallon (gal)

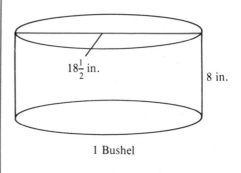

$18\frac{1}{2}$ in. 8 in.

1 Bushel

At one time items such as corn, wheat, and coal were sold by the bushel. A bushel had the size and shape shown in the figure. Today, though, the bushel is defined as a weight, since it is easier to weigh goods than to fill a bushel container several times. It is still common, however, to buy fruits and vegetables by units of dry measure. For example, you may buy a bushel of apples or a quart of strawberries. The following table gives the relationships among some commonly used units of dry measure.

Customary Units of Dry Measure

2 pints = 1 quart

8 quarts = 1 peck (pk)

4 pecks = 1 bushel (bu)

When these measures were standardized, the dry quart was defined as $\frac{1}{32}$ of a bushel. The liquid quart was defined as $\frac{1}{4}$ of a gallon. Since a bushel is not exactly equivalent to 8 gallons, the volumes of a liquid quart and a dry quart are different. A fluid quart is about $\frac{6}{7}$ of a dry quart.

══════════════════ **CLASS PRACTICE** ══════════════════

Shown is a linear scale from the wrapper of a quarter-pound stick of oleomargarine. Look at this scale and the table of liquid measures on page 316. Convert each measure to the indicated unit.

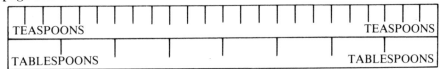

4 TABLESPOONS-¼ CUP 5⅓ TABLESPOONS-½ CUP 8 TABLESPOONS-½ CUP

1. 1 tablespoon = ? teaspoons
2. 1 cup = ? fluid ounces
3. 1 cup = ? tablespoons
4. $\frac{1}{4}$ cup = ? tablespoons
5. 1 cup = ? teaspoons
6. 1 quart = ? fluid ounces
7. 1 gallon = ? cups
8. 1 gallon = ? pints

Look at the table of dry measures on page 316. Convert each measure to the indicated unit.

9. 1 bushel = ? quarts
10. 6 pints = ? quarts
11. $\frac{1}{2}$ bushel = ? pecks
12. 3 quarts = ? pints
13. Describe some situations in which customary units of liquid and dry measure are used.

EXERCISES

— A —

Convert each measure to the indicated unit.

1. 9 teaspoons = ? tablespoons
2. 5 tablespoons = ? teaspoons
3. 1 pint = ? tablespoons
4. 1 pint = ? teaspoons
5. 48 fluid ounces = ? pints
6. 2 quarts = ? fluid ounces
7. $1\frac{1}{2}$ cups = ? tablespoons
8. 1 quart = ? half-pints
9. 16 cups = ? pints
10. 16 cups = ? quarts
11. 6 pints = ? quarts
12. 6 pints = ? fluid ounces
13. 48 tablespoons = ? cups
14. 48 tablespoons = ? pints
15. $2\frac{1}{2}$ gallons = ? quarts
16. $2\frac{1}{2}$ gallons = ? pints
17. 2 bushels = ? quarts
18. 96 quarts = ? bushels
19. 2 bushels = ? pints

20. 8 quarts = ? bushels
21. $\frac{1}{2}$ peck = ? quarts
22. $\frac{1}{2}$ peck = ? pints

— B —
Find the indicated information.

23. Which holds more, a can of fruit drink labeled 46 fl oz or a bottle of carbonated drink labeled 1 qt? how much more?

24. Suppose a horse is fed 2 quarts of oats each day. At this rate, how long will a bushel of oats last?

25. In most states a legal bushel of potatoes weighs 60 pounds.
   a. How many ten-pound bags of potatoes are there in one bushel?
   b. Suppose a family uses 15 pounds of potatoes per week. How many pounds is this per year? how many bushels?

26. Strawberries are usually sold by the quart. One crate of strawberries contains 16 quarts.
   a. 2 crates = ? quarts
   b. 1 crate = ? bushels

27. To mix an orchard spray you need 2 cups of powdered concentrate for every 6 gallons of water. Three gallons will spray one small tree. Suppose you have six small fruit trees to spray.
   a. How many gallons are needed?
   b. How many cups of powdered concentrate are needed?

28. Suppose you can 9 quarts of corn. For each quart, you add 1 teaspoon salt and 2 cups of boiling water.
   a. How many teaspoons of salt are needed? how many table-spoons?
   b. How many cups of boiling water are needed? how many pints? how many quarts?

29. A recipe for 3 dozen cookies calls for $1\frac{1}{2}$ cups melted chocolate and 2 teaspoons vanilla. Suppose you make 9 dozen cookies.
   a. How many cups of melted chocolate are needed?
   b. How many teaspoons of vanilla are needed? how many table-spoons?

— C —

30. How many 6-ounce servings are there in a half-gallon of punch?

31. Some service stations now sell gasoline by the liter instead of by the gallon. (1 gal ≈ 3.8 L)
   a. Which would cost more, a gallon or a liter?
   b. Based on current prices, what would a liter of gasoline probably cost?

32. Suppose you wish to spray the strawberry patch shown with a liquid fertilizer. To mix the spray you need 4 tablespoons of powdered concentrate per gallon of water. One gallon will cover 10 square feet. Find the following information.
   a. Area of the straw-berry patch
   b. Number of table-spoons of con-centrate needed
   c. Number of cups of concentrate needed

Strawberry Patch — 12 ft — 15 ft

33. Suppose you can 20 quarts of peaches, adding $1\frac{1}{2}$ cups of syrup to each quart. Five cups of syrup can be made from a recipe that requires

2 cups of sugar per quart of water.

a. How many cups of syrup are needed?

b. To make the syrup, how many cups of sugar are needed?

c. To make the syrup, how many quarts of water are needed? how many pints? how many gallons?

34. Suppose you wish to spray the front lawn shown. To mix the insect spray you need 4 fluid ounces ($\frac{1}{2}$ cup) of concentrate for every 15 gallons of water. Fifteen gallons will cover 500 square feet. Find the following information.

a. Area of the front lawn

b. Number of gallons of spray needed

c. Number of fluid ounces of concentrate needed

d. Number of cups of concentrate needed

MORE EXPLORING
The Relationship Between Volume and Total Area

1. Copy and complete a table like this one for each rectangular prism described.

Dimensions of Prism	Volume	Total Area	Dimensions of Prism	Volume	Total Area
8 cm × 2 cm × 4 cm	?	?	12 cm × 2 cm × 2 cm	?	?
7 cm × 3 cm × 3 cm	?	?	5 cm × 3 cm × 4 cm	?	?
4 cm × 4 cm × 4 cm	?	?	10 cm × 2 cm × 3 cm	?	?
4 cm × 4 cm × 3 cm	?	?	9 cm × 2 cm × 3 cm	?	?
5 cm × 4 cm × 4 cm	?	?			

2. Look at your results. Classify the following statements as true or false.

a. Rectangular prisms with equal volumes have equal total areas.

b. Rectangular prisms with equal total areas have equal volumes.

c. If one rectangular prism has a greater volume than a second rectangular prism, it also has a greater total area.

d. If one rectangular prism has a greater total area than a second rectangular prism, it also has a greater volume.

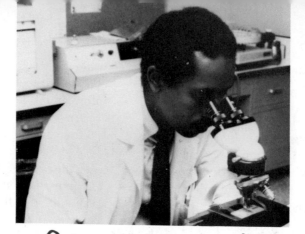

Geometry on the Job

MEDICAL LABORATORY TECHNICIAN

In his job as a medical laboratory technician, Leon Roosevelt performs chemical tests on blood and other substances. He also examines blood samples under a microscope to look for abnormal cells. The ability to make very accurate measurements of area, volume, and capacity is helpful in his work.

To separate the components of a mixture, Leon sometimes uses a technique called **chromatography**. He puts a small sample of the mixture on a rectangular piece of filter paper which is cut to fit the lateral area of a test tube. The paper is then placed in the test tube, which contains a small amount of liquid. As the liquid soaks into the paper, the different components of the mixture move upward at different rates.

EXERCISES
Use 3.14 for π.
Assuming that the test tube is a cylinder, find the dimensions of the piece of filter paper for test tubes with the following inside measurements.

1. $d = 16$ mm, $h = 125$ mm
2. $d = 20$ mm, $h = 150$ mm
3. $d = 25$ mm, $h = 200$ mm
4. $d = 22$ mm, $h = 175$ mm

5–8. One cubic centimeter is equivalent to 1000 cubic millimeters. Find the volume of each test tube in Exercises 1–4 in (a) cubic millimeters and (b) cubic centimeters.

9–12. One cubic centimeter is equivalent to one milliliter. Find the capacity of each test tube in Exercises 1–4 in milliliters.

Use the indicated scale to read the capacity of the liquid in each of these graduated cylinders. Each scale is in milliliters.

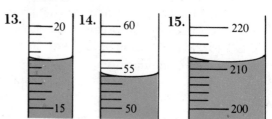

13. 20 / 15

14. 60 / 55 / 50

15. 220 / 210 / 200

ALGEBRA REVIEW — *Parentheses*

> In numerical expressions, parentheses ( ) are used to indicate (a) which operation to do first and (b) multiplication.

Examples
1. $(2 + 5) \times 4 = 7 \times 4 = 28$
2. $2 + (5 \times 4) = 2 + 20 = 22$
3. $(8 - 3) \times 2 = 5 \times 2 = 10$
4. $3(4) = 3 \times 4 = 12$

Sometimes other grouping symbols, such as brackets [ ], are used together with parentheses.

Examples
5. $[3 \times (2 + 4)] + 5 = [3 \times 6] + 5 = 18 + 5 = 23$
6. $20 - [8 \div (5 - 3)] = 20 - [8 \div 2] = 20 - 4 = 16$

EXERCISES
Find the value of each expression.

1. $7 + (3 \times 2)$
2. $(7 + 3) \times 2$
3. $(8 + 3) + 6$
4. $8 + (3 + 6)$
5. $5(3 + 2)$
6. $3(6 - 4)$
7. $(8 \times 4) + 2$
8. $8 \times (4 + 2)$
9. $9 - (2 \times 3)$
10. $(9 - 2) \times 3$
11. $11 - (5 + 2)$
12. $(11 - 5) + 2$
13. $16 \div (8 \times 2)$
14. $(16 \div 8) \times 2$
15. $(6 \times 3) \times 2$
16. $6 \times (3 \times 2)$
17. $64 \div (8 \div 4)$
18. $(64 \div 8) \div 4$
19. $12 - (7 - 2)$
20. $(12 - 7) - 2$
21. $(8 - 3) \times (5 + 1)$
22. $5[(1 + 4) \times 2]$
23. $15 - [4 \times (12 \div 4)]$

Copy each statement. Write parentheses and +, −, ×, or ÷ to make it true. (Some exercises have more than one solution.)

24. 12   6   2 = 0
25. 12   6   2 = 1
26. 12   6   2 = 3
27. 12   6   2 = 4
28. 12   6   2 = 8
29. 12   6   2 = 9

Chapter 7 Review

Vocabulary

The following terms were introduced in this chapter. You should be able to write a brief description, draw a picture, or give an example to illustrate the meaning of each.

capacity (p. 289)

lateral area (p. 281)

regular pyramid (p. 306)

right circular cone (p. 306)

right circular cylinder (p. 285)

slant height (p. 306)

sphere (p. 310)

total area (p. 279)

volume (p. 289)

Symbols

B (area of the base) (p. 290)

V (volume) (p. 290)

Skills Checklist

In Chapter 7 you learned how to find the total area and the lateral area of any right prism, right circular cylinder, or regular pyramid; the volume of any right prism, right circular cylinder, regular pyramid, right circular cone, or sphere; and the total area of any sphere. In addition, you learned some commonly used units of capacity and volume.

The following list indicates the major skills, facts, and results you should have mastered in this chapter:

- Recognize patterns that can be folded into a given prism. (**7–1**, pp. 274–278)
- Describe the size and shape of the faces of any given prism. (**7–1**, pp. 274–278)
- Find the total area or lateral area of any right prism or right circular cylinder. (**7–2—7–4**, pp. 279–288)
- Use the formula $V = Bh$ to find either the volume or a missing dimension of any right prism or right circular cylinder. (**7–5—7–7**, pp. 289–298)
- Determine what happens to the total area and volume of a rectangular prism or right circular cylinder when each dimension is multiplied by the same number. (**7–9**, pp. **302–305**)
- Find the total area or lateral area of any regular pyramid. (**7–10**, pp. 306–309)
- Use the formula $V = \frac{1}{3}Bh$ to find the volume of any regular pyramid or right circular cone. (**7–10**, pp. 306–309)
- Use the formulas T.A. $= 4\pi r^2$ and $V = \frac{4}{3}\pi r^3$, respectively, to find the total area or volume of any sphere. (**7–11**, pp. 310–311)
- Rewrite a given volume or capacity as an equivalent measure with another unit. (**7–12** and **7–13**, pp. 312–319)

Exercises

Describe the size and shape of the faces of each prism. (7–1)

1.

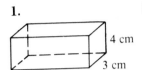

10 cm

4 cm

3 cm

2.

4 cm   3 cm

5 cm

5 cm

Find the indicated information.

3–4. Find the lateral area and the total area of the prisms in Exercises 1–2. (**7–2, 7–3**)

5. Find the lateral area of the prism shown. (**7–3**)

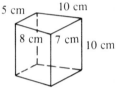

5 cm   10 cm

8 cm   7 cm   10 cm

6. Look at the cylinder shown. Find the following information. Use 3.14 for π. (**7–4**)
 a. Circumference of a base
 b. Lateral Area
 c. Area of a base
 d. Total Area

5 cm

10 cm

7. Do the following for the prism shown. (**7–2, 7–3**)

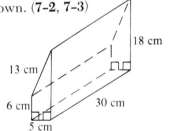

18 cm

13 cm

6 cm   30 cm

5 cm

 a. Find the lateral ara.
 b. Draw a picture of a base.
 c. Find the area of a base.
 d. Find the total area of the prism.

8. Select the patterns that can be folded into the prism shown. (**7–1**)

a.

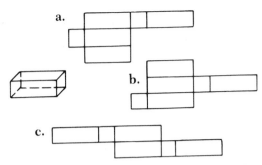

b.

c.

9. A cube has a total area of 216 cm². (**7–2**)
 a. Find the area of each face.
 b. Find the length of each edge.

10. A cylinder has a lateral area of 144 cm². The circumference of its base is 18 cm. Find its height. (**7–4**)

Do the following for each prism or cylinder. (7–6, 7–7)
 a. Draw a picture of a base.
 b. Find the area of a base.
 c. Find the volume of the prism or cylinder.

11.

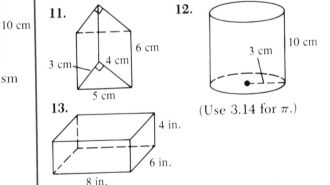

6 cm

3 cm   4 cm

5 cm

12.

10 cm

3 cm

13.

4 in.

6 in.

8 in.

(Use 3.14 for π.)

Find the volume of each prism described.

14. Each edge of a cube is 7 inches long. (**7–5**)

15. A rectangular prism has a base that is 4 cm by 6 cm and a height of 7 cm. (**7–5**)

16. A pentagonal prism has a base area of 33 in.² and a height of 8 in. (**7–6**)

Find each indicated measure.

17. The volume of a rectangular prism is 40 cubic feet. Using only whole-number lengths, give three different sets of possible dimensions for the prism. (**7–5**)

18. Find the (whole-number) dimensions of a rectangular prism that has a volume of 8 cubic inches and a total area of 34 square inches. (**7–5**)

19. A cube has a volume of 27 cm³. Find the length of one edge. (**7–5**)

20. A cylinder has a volume of 180 cm³ and a height of 12 cm. Find its base area. (**7–7**)

Find the volume of each figure. (7–10)

21.

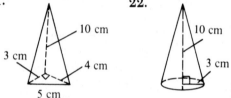

10 cm

3 cm

4 cm

5 cm

22.

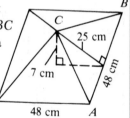

10 cm

3 cm

23. Look at the pyramid. Find the following information. (**7–10**)
    a. Slant height
    b. Area of △ABC
    c. Lateral Area
    d. Total Area
    e. Height
    f. Volume

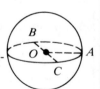

B

C

25 cm

7 cm

48 cm

48 cm   A

Find the indicated information.

24. Look at the sphere. Find the indicated information. (**7–11**)
    a. All segments congruent to $\overline{OA}$
    b. Exact total area
    c. Exact volume

B

O   A

C

OA = 6 cm

25. A regular square pyramid has a base that is 6 inches on each side and a height of 9 inches. Find its volume. (**7–10**)

26. A regular pyramid has a volume of 80 cm³ and a base area of 40 cm². Find its height. (**7–10**)

27. The volume of a cylinder is 600 cm³. Find the volume of a cone that has the same base area and height as the cylinder. (**7–10**)

28. The volume of a rectangular prism is 12 in.³ and its total area is 40 in.² Suppose all dimensions of the prism are multiplied by three. (**7–9**)
    a. Find the new volume.
    b. Find the new total area.

29. The volume of a cylinder is 77 in.³ Find the volume of a cylinder whose radius and height are two times as great. (**7–9**)

30. The total area of a cylinder is 25 cm². Find the total area of a cylinder whose radius and height are two times as great. (**7–9**)

Convert each measure to the indicated unit.

31. 1 L = ? cm³ (**7–12**)
32. 3000 mL = ? L (**7–12**)
33. 1 cup = ? Tbsp (**7–13**)
34. 8 cups = ? pt (**7–13**)
35. 8 cups = ? qt (**7–13**)
36. 1 Tbsp = ? tsp (**7–13**)
37. 32 fl oz = ? pt (**7–13**)
38. 500 cm³ = ? mL (**7–12**)
39. 1 yd³ = ? ft³ (**7–12**)
40. 108 ft³ = ? yd³ (**7–12**)
41. 6 qt = ? pt (**7–13**)
42. 3 gal = ? qt (**7–13**)

SQUARING OFF

Square Roots and the Pythagorean Theorem

8-1

Squares and Square Roots

A square region with sides of length 5 has an area of 25 square units because $5 \times 5 = 25$. The symbol 5^2 stands for 5×5 and is read "five squared" or "the *square of 5*."

5
Area = ?
$5^2 =$
$5 \times 5 = 25$
Area =
25 sq. units

What is the length of a side of a square region whose area is 16 square units? The answer is 4, since $4^2 = 16$. 4 is the *square root* of 16.

The *square root* of a number is the number which multiplied by itself (squared) gives that number as a product. The symbol $\sqrt{}$ is read "the square root of" and is called a *radical sign*. Here are examples.

x
Area =
16 sq. units
$x = ?$
$x = 4$
($4^2 = 4 \times 4$
= 16)

$$\sqrt{9} = 3 \quad \text{because} \quad 3^2 = 3 \times 3 = 9 \qquad \sqrt{16} = 4 \quad \text{because} \quad 4^2 = 4 \times 4$$
$$\sqrt{81} = 9 \quad \text{because} \quad 9^2 = 9 \times 9 \qquad\qquad\qquad\qquad = 16$$
$$= 81$$

The tables list some squares and square roots with which you should be familiar.

Number	Square	Number	Square	Number	Square Root	Number	Square Root
1	1	7	49	1	1	49	7
2	4	8	64	4	2	64	8
3	9	9	81	9	3	81	9
4	16	10	100	16	4	100	10
5	25	11	121	25	5	121	11
6	36	12	144	36	6	144	12

What is the length of a side of a square region whose area is 15 square units? The answer is $\sqrt{15}$, the positive number which when squared is 15. Notice that $\sqrt{15}$ is not a whole number. The square root of 15 is between 3 and 4 ($\sqrt{9} = 3$ and $\sqrt{16} = 4$). It is approximately equal to 3.87.

x
Area =
15 sq. units
$x = ?$
$x = \sqrt{15}$
$(\sqrt{15})^2$
$= \sqrt{15} \cdot \sqrt{15}$
$= 15$

If a number can be written as the product of two equal factors it is called a *perfect square*. For example, 25 is a perfect square because $5 \times 5 = 25$. Since $5 \times 5 = 25$, $\sqrt{25} = 5$. The square root of a whole number that is a perfect square is a whole number. The five least whole numbers that are perfect squares are 1, 4, 9, 16, and 25.

Find the value of each expression.
1. Square of 4   2. 4 squared   3. Square root of 4   4. 4^2 5. $\sqrt{100}$

Use the fact that $69^2 = 4761$ to complete each statement.
6. $\sqrt{4761} = $?   7. $6.9^2 = $?   8. $0.69^2 = $?

Complete each statement by identifying the two consecutive whole numbers that the square root is between.
9. $\sqrt{19}$ is between ? and ? .
10. $\sqrt{63}$ is between ? and ? .
11. $\sqrt{48}$ is between ? and ? .
12. $\sqrt{80}$ is between ? and ? .

EXERCISES

The area of each square is given. Find the length of a side of the square.

1.
Area = 9 cm²

2.
Area = 36 cm²

3.
Area = 21 cm²

Classify each statement as true or false.
4. If $32^2 = 1024$, then $\sqrt{1024} = 32$.
5. If $32^2 = 1024$, then $3.2^2 = 10.24$.
6. If a whole number is a perfect square, its square root is a whole number.

Find the indicated information.
7. Identify the first ten whole numbers that are perfect squares.
8. State whether each number is a perfect square.
   a. 2   b. 4   c. 8   d. 10
   e. 25   f. 36   g. 40   h. 49

Find the value of each expression.
9. Square of 10   10. Square of 9
11. Square root of 100

12. Square root of 81
13. 15 squared   14. 9 squared
15. 11^2 16. 20^2 17. 8^2
18. 10^2 19. $\sqrt{64}$ 20. $\sqrt{16}$
21. $\sqrt{49}$ 22. $\sqrt{400}$

Find the indicated information.
23. Use the fact that $48^2 = 2304$ to complete each statement.
   a. $\sqrt{2304} = $?   b. $4.8^2 = $?
   c. $0.48^2 = $?
24. Complete each statement by identifying the two consecutive whole numbers that the square root is between.
   a. $\sqrt{21}$ is between ? and ? .
   b. $\sqrt{30}$ is between ? and ? .
   c. $\sqrt{33}$ is between ? and ? .
   d. $\sqrt{69}$ is between ? and ? .
25. State the dimensions of the square patio that can be built with 196 one-foot square concrete patio stones.
26. A square flower bed has an area of 64 square feet. What are the dimensions of the square?

Everyday Geometry
Indoor Lighting

Illumination refers to the amount of light that falls on a unit area, such as 1 cm². Illumination depends on both the intensity of the source of light (watts) and the distance from the source.

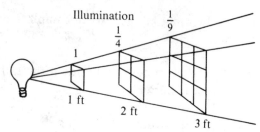

Distance from Source

The diagram shows the effect of distance on illumination. Light rays spread out as they travel away from a bulb. The same amount of light that passes through 1 ft² at 1 ft from the bulb passes through 4 ft² at 2 ft and 9 ft² at 3 ft. So, compared to the illumination at 1 ft, the illumination is $\frac{1}{4}$ as bright at 2 ft and $\frac{1}{9}$ as bright at 3 ft.

EXERCISES

1. Suppose your desk lamp, with one bulb, is 2 ft above your desk and the ceiling is 6 ft above your desk.

To give the same illumination, how many bulbs of the same wattage would you need in a ceiling fixture to give the same illumination as your desk lamp?

2. Suppose your desk lamp, with one bulb, is 0.5 m above your desk. If the ceiling is 2 m above your desk, how many bulbs of the same wattage would you need in a ceiling fixture?

8-2

Approximating and Simplifying Square Roots

In Lesson 8–1, you learned the following facts:
- Some whole numbers are perfect squares and their square root is a whole number. (Example: 36 is a perfect square and $\sqrt{36} = 6$.)
- The square root of some whole numbers is *not* a whole number. (Example: $\sqrt{30}$ is between 5 and 6.)

It is often helpful to *simplify* square root expressions. If the number under the radical has at least one perfect-square factor other than one, the expression can be simplified as shown in the examples below. To do so, we make use of the following fact:

> **For any positive numbers a and b, it is true that**
> $$\sqrt{a} \cdot \sqrt{b} = \sqrt{a \cdot b}$$

Some examples are shown:

$$\sqrt{4} \cdot \sqrt{9} = \sqrt{4 \cdot 9} = \sqrt{36} = 6 \qquad \sqrt{3} \cdot \sqrt{2} = \sqrt{3 \cdot 2} = \sqrt{6}$$

$$\sqrt{3} \cdot \sqrt{7} = \sqrt{3 \cdot 7} = \sqrt{21}$$

The following examples show how to simplify a square root expression.

Example 1: Simplify each expression.   **a.** $\sqrt{8}$ **b.** $\sqrt{80}$

Solutions:

a. $\sqrt{8} = \sqrt{4 \cdot 2}$ (Write 8 as the product of a perfect square and another number.)

$\qquad = \sqrt{4} \cdot \sqrt{2}$ $(\sqrt{a \cdot b} = \sqrt{a} \cdot \sqrt{b})$

$\qquad = 2\sqrt{2}$ $(\sqrt{4} = 2)$

b. $\sqrt{80} = \sqrt{16 \cdot 5} = \sqrt{16} \cdot \sqrt{5} = 4\sqrt{5}$

Shown below are some square root expressions that have been simplified and some that have not. Notice that for those that have not been simplified, the number under the radical sign has at least one whole-number perfect-square factor other than one.

These square root expressions have been simplified.

$$\sqrt{15} \qquad \sqrt{21} \qquad 5\sqrt{3} \qquad \sqrt{6} \qquad 4\sqrt{2} \qquad \sqrt{11}$$

These square root expressions have *not* been simplified.

$$\sqrt{20} \qquad \sqrt{16} \qquad \sqrt{45} \qquad 5\sqrt{8} \qquad \sqrt{200} \qquad 3\sqrt{20}$$

As indicated earlier, some whole numbers, such as 12 and 27, do not have a whole-number square root. For example, $\sqrt{12}$ is between 3 and 4 and $\sqrt{27}$ is between 5 and 6. To find approximations for $\sqrt{12}$ and $\sqrt{27}$, you can use a table like the one on page 475, which gives the squares and square roots of the whole numbers from 1 through 150.

Most of the entries in the square-root column of the table are approximations. If you look up $\sqrt{12}$ in the table, you find 3.464. However, $3.464^2 = 11.999296$, which is very close to, but not equal to, 12. The only whole numbers whose square roots are *not* approximations are whole numbers that are perfect squares.

The following example shows how an approximation for the square root of some whole numbers that are greater than 150 and that are not perfect squares can be found.

Example 2: Find the value of $\sqrt{180}$.

Solution:

$$180 = \sqrt{36 \cdot 5} = \sqrt{36} \cdot \sqrt{5} = 6\sqrt{5} \qquad (\sqrt{a \cdot b} = \sqrt{a} \cdot \sqrt{b})$$
$$\approx 6(2.236) \quad (\sqrt{36} = 6)$$
$$\approx 13.416 \quad (\sqrt{5} \approx 2.236 \quad \text{See table on page 475.})$$

CLASS PRACTICE

For each number identify all whole-number perfect-square factors other than one.

1. 10   2. 64   3. 18   4. 7   5. 32   6. 8

State whether the expression has been simplified.

7. $\sqrt{10}$ 8. $\sqrt{64}$ 9. $\sqrt{18}$ 10. $\sqrt{7}$ 11. $\sqrt{32}$ 12. $\sqrt{8}$

13. Simplify all expressions in Exercises 7–12 that have not been simplified.
14. In which column of the table is every number a perfect square?

Find the value of each of the following.

15. $72^2 = \ ?$ 16. $7.2^2 = \ ?$ 17. $\sqrt{441} = \ ?$ $\sqrt{23} \approx \ ?$
19. $\sqrt{2916} = \ ?$ 20. $\sqrt{62} \approx \ ?$ 21. $\sqrt{93} \approx \ ?$ $\sqrt{14{,}400} = \ ?$

EXERCISES

_ A _

Use the table on page 475 when needed. State whether the number is a perfect square.

1. 200   2. 225   3. 250
4. 400   5. 576   6. 625

State whether the expression has been simplified.

7. $\sqrt{14}$ 8. $\sqrt{18}$ 9. $\sqrt{24}$
10. $\sqrt{30}$ 11. $3\sqrt{12}$ 12. $9\sqrt{10}$

Simplify each expression.

13. $\sqrt{20}$ 14. $\sqrt{27}$ 15. $\sqrt{32}$
16. $\sqrt{49}$ 17. $\sqrt{75}$ 18. $\sqrt{300}$

Find the value of each expression.

19. $\sqrt{25}$ 20. $\sqrt{67}$
21. $\sqrt{86}$ 22. $\sqrt{99}$
23. $\sqrt{121}$ 24. $\sqrt{400}$
25. $\sqrt{625}$ 26. $\sqrt{2500}$
27. 68^2 28. 6.8^2

29. 25^2 **30.** $\sqrt{25^2}$

31. 54^2 **32.** $\sqrt{1936}$

33. $\sqrt{19.36}$ **34.** 32 squared

35. Square of 68 **36.** Square root of 68

Locate each square root expression between two consecutive whole numbers.

37. $\sqrt{37}$ is between ? and ? .

38. $\sqrt{43}$ is between ? and ? .

39. $\sqrt{72}$ is between ? and ? .

40. $\sqrt{160}$ is between ? and ? .

Find the indicated information.

41. Use the fact that $77^2 = 5929$ to complete each statement.

   a. $\sqrt{5929} = $?   **b.** $\sqrt{59.29} = $?

   c. $7.7^2 = $?   **d.** $0.77^2 = $?

42. Find the value of each expression.

   a. $\sqrt{9}$ **b.** $\sqrt{16}$

   c. $\sqrt{9} + \sqrt{16}$ **d.** $\sqrt{9 + 16}$

— **B** —

Complete each statement.

43. $\sqrt{480} = \sqrt{16} \cdot \sqrt{30} = 4\sqrt{30} \approx 4(?) \approx ?$

44. $\sqrt{252} = \sqrt{36} \cdot \sqrt{7} = 6\sqrt{7} \approx 6(?) \approx ?$

Classify each statement as true or false.

45. $\sqrt{3} + \sqrt{5} = \sqrt{8}$ **46.** $\sqrt{\frac{4}{9}} = \sqrt{\frac{2}{3}}$

47. $\sqrt{4} \cdot \sqrt{9} = \sqrt{36}$ **48.** $\sqrt{8} = 2\sqrt{4}$

49. $\sqrt{72} = 6\sqrt{12}$

Find the indicated information.

50. Give an example to show that $\sqrt{a + b}$ is not necessarily equal to $\sqrt{a} + \sqrt{b}$.

8-3

The Pythagorean Theorem

In this lesson you will investigate the relationship among the sides of any right triangle. The terms illustrated below are used in describing right triangles.

   The *hypotenuse* of a right triangle is the side that is opposite the right angle. It is always the longest side of the triangle.

   The *legs* of a right triangle are the sides that form the right angle. They are the shorter sides of the triangle.

hypotenuse: $\overline{BC}$

legs: $\overline{CA}$ and $\overline{BA}$

Which Lengths Form Right Triangles

1. Using the lengths given in the first three columns of the table below, construct triangles having sides of length a, b, and c. (See Construction 2, on page 133.) Note that c is the length of the longest side for each triangle.

2. Copy and complete the table.

| Triangle | Length of Sides | | | a^2 | b^2 | c^2 | $a^2 + b^2$ |
	a	b	c				
A	2 cm	3 cm	4 cm	?	?	?	?
B	3 cm	4 cm	5 cm	?	?	?	?
C	4 cm	4 cm	6 cm	?	?	?	?
D	6 cm	8 cm	10 cm	?	?	?	?
E	5 cm	12 cm	13 cm	?	?	?	?
F	6 cm	9 cm	12 cm	?	?	?	?
G	9 cm	12 cm	15 cm	?	?	?	?

3. Four of the triangles that you constructed in step 1 are right triangles. Which sets of lengths form the sides of right triangles?

4. Look at your completed table. For each triangle, compare the numbers in the last two columns. What seems to be true for the right triangles that is not true for the other triangles?

The results of the preceding EXPLORING indicate a way to determine whether a triangle is a right triangle.

> If the lengths a, b, and c, where c is the longest of the three sides of a triangle, are related by the formula $a^2 + b^2 = c^2$, then the triangle is a right triangle.

Here are some examples showing how this statement is used.

Example 1: Which of the triangles shown are right triangles?

Solution:

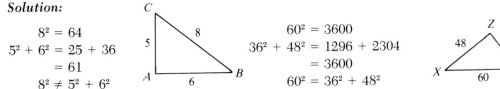

$8^2 = 64$

$5^2 + 6^2 = 25 + 36$

$\quad = 61$

$8^2 \neq 5^2 + 6^2$

$60^2 = 3600$

$36^2 + 48^2 = 1296 + 2304$

$\quad = 3600$

$60^2 = 36^2 + 48^2$

$\triangle ABC$ is *not* a right triangle. $\triangle XYZ$ is a right triangle.

The statement developed in the previous EXPLORING also works in reverse and states a property true for all right triangles. That is, if a triangle is a right triangle, then the square of the length of the hypotenuse is equal to the sum of the squares of the lengths of the legs. This property of all right triangles is called the *Pythagorean Theorem*.

The Pythagorean Theorem is probably the most famous theorem in mathematics and has been known for over 2500 years. A *theorem* is a statement that can be proved mathematically from previously accepted or proven assumptions, definitions, or theorems. Many proofs have been developed for this theorem, including one by James A. Garfield, twentieth president of the United States.

The figure shown further illustrates the meaning of the Pythagorean Theorem. A square has been drawn on each side of the triangle. Notice that the area of the square region on the hypotenuse is equal to the sum of the areas of the square regions on the legs.

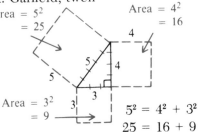

Area $= 5^2$
$= 25$

Area $= 4^2$
$= 16$

Area $= 3^2$
$= 9$

$5^2 = 4^2 + 3^2$

$25 = 16 + 9$

Pythagorean Theorem

For any right triangle, the square of the length of the hypotenuse is equal to the sum of the squares of the lengths of the legs.

$c^2 = a^2 + b^2$

The Pythagorean Theorem can be used to find the length of any side of a right triangle when the lengths of the two other sides are known. Some examples are given on the next page.

Example 2: Find the missing length.

$a = 9$
$b = 12$
$c = \ ?$

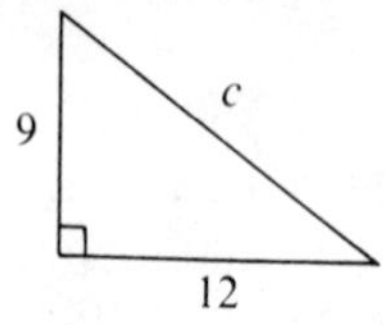

Solution:

$$c^2 = a^2 + b^2 \qquad c = \sqrt{225}$$
$$= 9^2 + 12^2 \qquad = 15$$
$$= 81 + 144$$
$$= 225$$

Example 3: Find the missing length.

$a = \ ?$
$b = 12$
$c = 13$

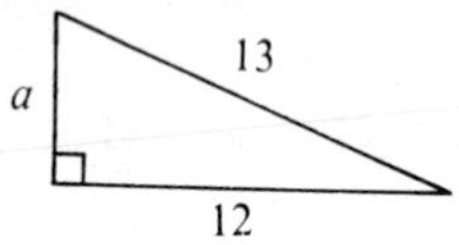

Solution:

$$a^2 + b^2 = c^2 \qquad a = \sqrt{25}$$
$$a^2 + 12^2 = 13^2 \qquad = 5$$
$$a^2 + 144 = 169$$

$$a^2 = 169 - 144$$
$$= 25$$

Example 4: Find the missing length.

$a = 4$
$b = \ ?$
$c = 8$

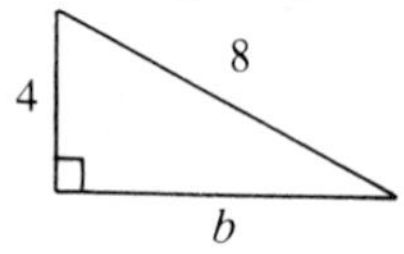

Solution:

$$a^2 + b^2 = c^2 \qquad b = \sqrt{48}$$
$$4^2 + b^2 = 8^2 \qquad = \sqrt{16} \cdot \sqrt{3}$$
$$16 + b^2 = 64 \qquad = 4\sqrt{3}$$
$$b^2 = 64 - 16$$
$$= 48$$

CLASS PRACTICE

For each set of numbers, show that $a^2 + b^2 = c^2$.

	a	b	c
1.	4	3	5
2.	8	6	10

	a	b	c
3.	15	20	25
4.	10	24	26

State whether each equation is correct.

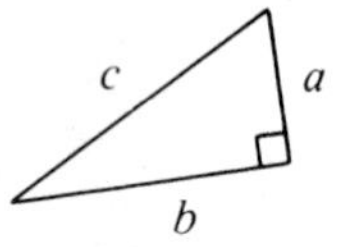

5. $a^2 + b^2 = c^2$

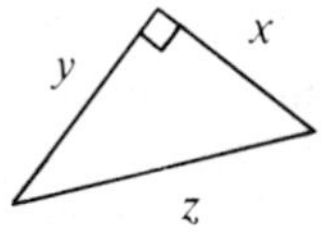

6. $z^2 = x^2 + y^2$

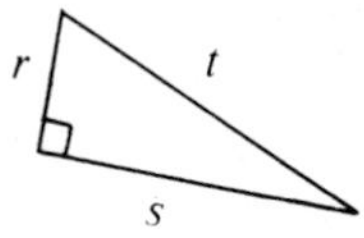

7. $s^2 + t^2 = r^2$

Determine whether each set of lengths can form a right triangle.

8. 5 cm, 9 cm, 7 cm

9. 5 cm, 12 cm, 13 cm

10. 10 cm, 6 cm, 8 cm

Use the Pythagorean Theorem to find the missing length in each right triangle.

11.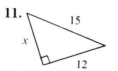

12.

_ A _

Identify the hypotenuse and legs of each right triangle.

1.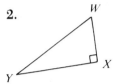

2.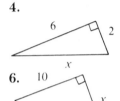

For each right triangle write an equation that can be used to find the missing length.

3.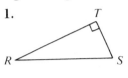

4.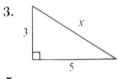

5.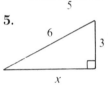

6.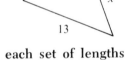

Determine whether each set of lengths can form a right triangle.

7. 3 cm, 4 cm, 5 cm
8. 6 in., 8 in., 10 in.
9. 5·ft, 6 ft, 7 ft
10. 4 cm, 4 cm, 16 cm
11. 8 ft, 5 ft, 6 ft
12. 3 cm, 7 cm, 6 cm

Use the table of squares and square roots on page 475 to find the value of each expression.

13. $\sqrt{59}$
14. $\sqrt{72}$
15. 15^2
16. 87^2
17. 8.7^2
18. 0.72^2
19. $\sqrt{841}$
20. $\sqrt{1156}$

Simplify each expression.

21. $\sqrt{12}$
22. $\sqrt{18}$

23. $\sqrt{45}$
24. $\sqrt{98}$

Find the missing length in each right triangle.

25.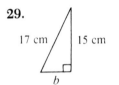

26.

27.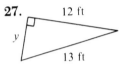

28.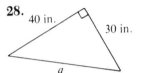

29.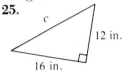

30.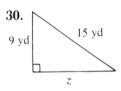

_ B _

The lengths of two sides of a right triangle are given. c stands for the length of the hypotenuse. Find the third length. Simplify any square root expressions in your answers.

31. $a = 4$, $b = 2$, $c = $?
32. $a = 10$, $b = 20$, $c = $?
33. $a = 6$, $c = 12$, $b = $?
34. $b = 1$, $c = 2$, $a = $?

Solve. Simplify any square root expressions in your answers.

35. How many meters of cable are needed to reach from point A, 15 meters high on a pole, to a point B on the ground 8 meters from the base of the pole?

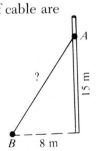

36. For the equilateral triangle shown, find h, the height.

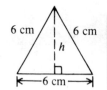

6 cm   6 cm h 6 cm

37. For the triangle shown, find x.

6 45° x 45° x

38. Softball and baseball diamonds are both in the shape of a square—60 ft × 60 ft and 90 ft × 90 ft, respectively. To the nearest foot, find the distance from home plate to second base for each field. Use the table of squares and square roots on page 475.

— **C** —

39. Find the following information for parallelogram $ABCD$ shown.

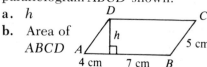

a. h
b. Area of $ABCD$

D   C h A 5 cm   4 cm 7 cm B

40. Find the following information for trapezoid $WXYZ$ shown.
a. WP b. Area of $XYZP$

c. Area of $\triangle WXP$
d. Area of $WXYZ$
e. Perimeter of $WXYZ$

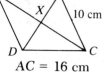

X 4 cm Y   10 cm 8 cm   W P Z

41. Recall that the diagonals of a rhombus are the perpendicular bisectors of each other. Find the following information for rhombus $ABCD$ shown.
a. AX
b. BX
c. Area of $\triangle AXB$
d. Area of $ABCD$

A 10 cm B   X 10 cm   D C $AC = 16$ cm

42. How high up on a building will a 12-foot ladder reach if its base is set 4 feet from the building? Express the answer in three ways.

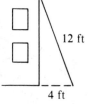

12 ft   4 ft

a. As a simplified square root expression
b. To the nearest tenth of a foot (See table on page 475.)
c. To the nearest foot (See table on page 475.)

══ MORE EXPLORING ══
Proving the Pythagorean Theorem

This activity is based upon one of the earliest known geometric proofs of the Pythagorean Theorem.

1. Each design at right has been formed using four congruent right triangles like the one shown above. Why are the largest squares in each design congruent?

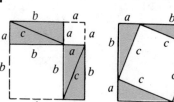

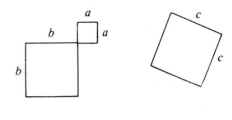

2. If the four shaded triangles are removed from each design, the regions shown at right are formed. Why are the areas of these regions equal? Why is $a^2 + b^2 = c^2$?

3. Suppose you used a different-size right triangle to form the designs in step 1. Would you get the same results?

Applications

Egyptian Rope Stretchers and the Pythagorean Theorem

The people of ancient Egypt were skilled surveyors and builders. The annual flooding of the Nile River made it necessary for them to re-survey their land every year. The great temples and pyramids still standing are evidence of their building skill.

It is known that the Egyptians knew as early as 2000 B.C. that $3^2 + 4^2 = 5^2$. Historical lore indicates that Egyptian *harpenodoptai*, or rope stretchers, used a rope with equally-spaced knots to form 3-4-5 triangles containing a right angle. However, proof has *not* been found to verify Egyptian use of 3-4-5 triangles to form right angles for construction and surveying.

Tradition credits the first proof of the statement that "the square on the hypotenuse of the right-angled triangle is equal to the squares on the sides containing the right angle" to Pythagoras, a Greek mathematician of about 500 B.C. Despite this tradition, this result was probably known prior to the time of Pythagoras.

Regardless of its origin, the Pythagorean Theorem is probably the best known and most useful theorem of mathematics. It has been proved by several methods. One book, *The Pythagorean Proposition* by E. S. Loomis, contains 370 proofs of this theorem, including one proof credited to a former U.S. President, James Garfield.

8-4

Using Products of Square Roots

In Lesson 8–2 you learned how to simplify square root expressions as shown by the following examples.

$$\sqrt{20} = \sqrt{4} \cdot \sqrt{5} = 2\sqrt{5} \qquad \sqrt{96} = \sqrt{16} \cdot \sqrt{6} = 4\sqrt{6} \qquad \sqrt{63} = \sqrt{9} \cdot \sqrt{7} = 3\sqrt{7}$$

Recall that such expressions have been simplified when the number under the radical sign has no whole-number perfect-square factors other than 1. We used the following property to simplify these expressions:

$$\sqrt{a} \cdot \sqrt{b} = \sqrt{ab}$$

The following examples show how this property can be used to find the product of any two square root expressions.

Example 1: Find the product.

a. $\sqrt{3} \cdot \sqrt{2}$
b. $\sqrt{3} \cdot \sqrt{3}$
c. $\sqrt{6} \cdot \sqrt{5}$
d. $\sqrt{3} \cdot 2\sqrt{5}$

Solution:

a. $\sqrt{3} \cdot \sqrt{2} = \sqrt{3 \cdot 2} = \sqrt{6}$
b. $\sqrt{3} \cdot \sqrt{3} = \sqrt{3 \cdot 3} = \sqrt{9} = 3$
c. $\sqrt{6} \cdot \sqrt{5} = \sqrt{6 \cdot 5} = \sqrt{30}$
d. $\sqrt{3} \cdot 2\sqrt{5} = 2 \cdot \sqrt{3} \cdot \sqrt{5} = 2\sqrt{3 \cdot 5}$
$= 2\sqrt{15}$

In some cases, your answer will have to be simplified. Here are some examples.

Example 2: Simplify each product.　　a. $\sqrt{3} \cdot \sqrt{6}$　　b. $3\sqrt{5} \cdot 2\sqrt{5}$　　c. $(3\sqrt{2})^2$
　　d. $3(\sqrt{2})^2$

Solution:

a. $\sqrt{3} \cdot \sqrt{6} = \sqrt{18}$
$= \sqrt{9 \cdot 2}$
$= \sqrt{9} \cdot \sqrt{2}$
$= 3\sqrt{2}$

b. $3\sqrt{5} \cdot 2\sqrt{5} = 3 \cdot 2 \cdot \sqrt{5} \cdot \sqrt{5}$
$= 6\sqrt{25}$
$= 6 \cdot 5$
$= 30$

c. $(3\sqrt{2})^2 = 3\sqrt{2} \cdot 3\sqrt{2}$
$= 9\sqrt{4}$
$= 9 \cdot 2$
$= 18$

d. $3(\sqrt{2})^2 = 3 \cdot \sqrt{2} \cdot \sqrt{2}$
$= 3\sqrt{4}$
$= 3 \cdot 2$
$= 6$

CLASS PRACTICE

Simplify each product.　　1. $\sqrt{3} \cdot \sqrt{7}$　　2. $\sqrt{5} \cdot \sqrt{8}$　　3. $6\sqrt{16}$
　　4. $(\sqrt{6})^2$　　5. $(4\sqrt{3})^2$　　6. $4(\sqrt{3})^2$

EXERCISES

_ A _

Classify each statement as true or false.

1. $\sqrt{3} + \sqrt{2} = \sqrt{5}$
2. $\sqrt{3} \cdot \sqrt{2} = \sqrt{6}$
3. $(3\sqrt{5})^2 = 3(\sqrt{5})^2$
4. $3\sqrt{8}$ has been simplified.

Simplify each product.

5. $\sqrt{6} \cdot \sqrt{7}$
6. $\sqrt{7} \cdot \sqrt{5}$
7. $\sqrt{5} \cdot \sqrt{4}$
8. $\sqrt{3} \cdot \sqrt{8}$
9. $3\sqrt{3} \cdot \sqrt{2}$
10. $5\sqrt{6} \cdot \sqrt{2}$
11. $5\sqrt{4}$
12. $8\sqrt{9}$
13. $(\sqrt{5})^2$
14. $(\sqrt{3})^2$
15. $(4\sqrt{2})^2$
16. $4(\sqrt{2})^2$
17. $(6\sqrt{3})^2$
18. $6(\sqrt{3})^2$
19. $(3\sqrt{5})^2$
20. $(7\sqrt{3})^2$

Determine whether each set of lengths can form a right triangle.

21. $\sqrt{3}, \sqrt{5}, \sqrt{8}$
22. $\sqrt{9}, 5, 4$
23. $\sqrt{3}, \sqrt{9}, \sqrt{4}$
24. $\sqrt{2}, 5, \sqrt{23}$

Find the missing length in each right triangle. Simplify your answers.

25.
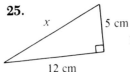

26.
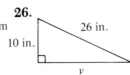

27.
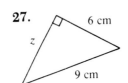

28.
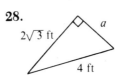

29.
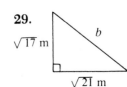

30.
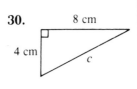

_ B _

Solve. Simplify any square root expressions in your answers.

31. The diagonal of a square is 10 cm long. Find the length of a side of the square.

32. The length of a side of a square is 10 cm. Find the length of its diagonal.

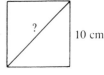

33. Write an equation that can be used to find x in the triangle shown.

34. Find the following information for rectangle $ABCD$ shown.
    a. x
    b. Area of $\triangle ABC$
    c. Area of $ABCD$

35. Find the following information for $\triangle ABC$ shown.
    a. x
    b. Area of $\triangle ABC$

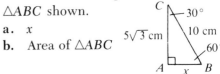

36. Find the following information for $\triangle DEF$ shown.
    a. x
    b. Area of $\triangle DEF$

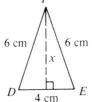

Square Roots and the Pythagorean Theorem   339

37. Find the following information for rhombus *RHOM* shown.

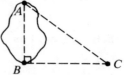

a. *RX*
b. *MX*
c. *RM*
d. Area of △*RXM*

$RO = 4\sqrt{3}$ cm
$MH = 4$ cm

38. Stakes are placed at points *A* and *B* on opposite sides of a small pond. Another stake is placed at point *C* so that ∠*B* is a right angle. If *BC* = 128 m and *AC* = 160 m, how long is the pond? (Find *AB*.)

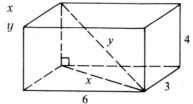

39. Find the following information for the rectangular prism shown.

a. *x*
b. *y*

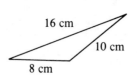

═══════ **MORE EXPLORING** ═══════

Heron's Formula

It is possible to find the area of any triangular region knowing only the lengths of its sides. The formula used for this purpose was developed in the first century A.D. by Heron of Alexandria, a Greek mathematician.

> *Heron's Formula*
> **The area of any triangular region with sides of length $a, b,$ and c can be found by using the formula**
>
> $$A = \sqrt{s(s-a)(s-b)(s-c)} \quad \text{where } s = \tfrac{1}{2}(a + b + c)$$

Example: Find the area of the triangular region shown.

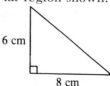

6 cm

8 cm

Solution:

$s = \tfrac{1}{2}(6 + 8 + 10)$

$A = \sqrt{12(12-6)(12-8)(12-10)}$

$A = \sqrt{12(6)(4)(2)}$

$A = \sqrt{576}$

$= 24$ cm²

1. Use Heron's Formula to find the area of each triangular region.

a.

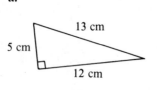

13 cm
5 cm
12 cm

b.

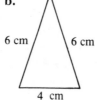

6 cm   6 cm

4 cm

c.

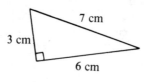

7 cm
3 cm
6 cm

d.

16 cm
10 cm
8 cm

Look at △ABC.

2. **a.** Use the Pythagorean Theorem to find x.
   b. Use the formula $A = \frac{1}{2}bh$ to find the area of △ABC.
3. The following special formula can be used to find the area of an equilateral triangular region:

$$A = \frac{e^2}{4}\sqrt{3} \quad \text{where } e \text{ is the length of one edge}$$

Use this formula to find the area of △ABC.

4. Use Heron's Formula to find the area of △ABC.

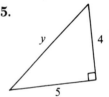

Test Yourself

Use the table on page 475 to find the value of each expression.

1. $\sqrt{61}$ 2. $\sqrt{1024}$
3. 83^2 4. Square of 18
5. 18 squared   6. Square root of 18

Simplify each expression.

7. $\sqrt{32}$ 8. $\sqrt{63}$ 9. $\sqrt{250}$

Determine whether each set of lengths can form a right triangle.

10. 10 cm, 6 cm, 8 cm
11. 5 in., $\sqrt{11}$ in., 6 in.
12. 4 cm, 5 cm, 6 cm
13. 3 ft, 3 ft, $3\sqrt{2}$ ft

Find the missing length in each right triangle. Simplify your answers.

14.   15.

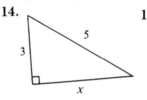

16.

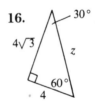

DID YOU KNOW THAT....

Perhaps the greatest achievement of the Pythagoreans, the group founded by Pythagoras about 532 B.C., was the discovery of the *irrational numbers* (such as the square roots of numbers that are not perfect squares). This discovery upset the Pythagoreans since it contradicted their assumptions that everything depends on the whole numbers and that the lengths of all segments could be expressed by ratios of whole numbers. Legend states that one Pythagorean was drowned because he related this discovery to persons outside the group.

8-5

Using Quotients of Square Roots

The following facts will be helpful in simplifying square root expressions in which the denominator or divisor contains a square root.

Multiplying any number by 1 does not change its value.

$$3 \cdot 1 = 3 \qquad \tfrac{3}{4} \cdot 1 = \tfrac{3}{4} \qquad 1 \cdot \sqrt{5} = \sqrt{5} \qquad \tfrac{3}{4} = \tfrac{3}{4} \cdot 1 = \tfrac{3}{4} \cdot \tfrac{5}{5} = \tfrac{15}{20}$$

Every division problem can be written as a fraction, and vice versa.

$$3 \div 4 = \frac{3}{4} \qquad \sqrt{2} \div 3 = \frac{\sqrt{2}}{3} \qquad 3 \div \sqrt{2} = \frac{3}{\sqrt{2}} \qquad \frac{5}{\sqrt{7}} = 5 \div \sqrt{7} \qquad \frac{2\sqrt{5}}{\sqrt{7}} = (2\sqrt{5}) \div \sqrt{7}$$

Example 1: Simplify each expression.   **a.** $\dfrac{\sqrt{3}}{\sqrt{2}}$ **b.** $6 \div \sqrt{3}$

Solution:

a. $\dfrac{\sqrt{3}}{\sqrt{2}} = \dfrac{\sqrt{3}}{\sqrt{2}} \cdot \dfrac{\sqrt{2}}{\sqrt{2}}$ $\left(\dfrac{\sqrt{2}}{\sqrt{2}} = 1 \right)$

$\qquad = \dfrac{\sqrt{3} \cdot \sqrt{2}}{\sqrt{2} \cdot \sqrt{2}}$ (Multiplication of fractions)

$\qquad = \dfrac{\sqrt{6}}{2}$ $(\sqrt{a} \cdot \sqrt{b} = \sqrt{ab}$ and $\sqrt{2} \cdot \sqrt{2} = 2)$

b. $6 \div \sqrt{3} = \dfrac{6}{\sqrt{3}}$ $\left(a \div b = \dfrac{a}{b} \right)$

$\qquad = \dfrac{6}{\sqrt{3}} \cdot \dfrac{\sqrt{3}}{\sqrt{3}}$ $\left(\dfrac{\sqrt{3}}{\sqrt{3}} = 1 \right)$

$\qquad = \dfrac{6\sqrt{3}}{3} = 2\sqrt{3}$ (Why?)

A square root expression is said to be in *simplest radical form* if there are no perfect-square factors other than 1 under a radical sign and there is no radical sign in the denominator.

These square root expressions are in simplest radical form.

$$\frac{\sqrt{3}}{4} \qquad \sqrt{6} \qquad \frac{3\sqrt{5}}{4} \qquad \frac{\sqrt{6}}{7}$$

These square root expressions are *not* in simplest radical form.

$$\frac{\sqrt{3}}{\sqrt{5}} \qquad \frac{5}{\sqrt{2}} \qquad \frac{6\sqrt{5}}{3} \qquad \frac{\sqrt{12}}{5}$$

CLASS PRACTICE
---

1. Why does multiplying $\dfrac{\sqrt{3}}{\sqrt{2}}$ by $\dfrac{\sqrt{2}}{\sqrt{2}}$ not change the value of $\dfrac{\sqrt{3}}{\sqrt{2}}$?

2. What name for one should be used in simplifying each expression?

   a. $\dfrac{\sqrt{5}}{\sqrt{6}}$ **b.** $\dfrac{\sqrt{8}}{\sqrt{2}}$ **c.** $\dfrac{2\sqrt{7}}{\sqrt{3}}$ **d.** $\dfrac{\sqrt{13}}{\sqrt{5}}$

3. Express each expression in Exercise 2 in simplest radical form.

EXERCISES

— A —

State whether each expression is in simplest radical form.

1. $\sqrt{10}$ 2. $\sqrt{27}$ 3. $\dfrac{\sqrt{7}}{\sqrt{2}}$ 4. $\dfrac{6}{\sqrt{5}}$

5. $\dfrac{\sqrt{5}}{3}$ 6. $\dfrac{\sqrt{6}}{3}$ 7. $\dfrac{6\sqrt{2}}{5}$ 8. $\dfrac{8\sqrt{3}}{4}$

Express in simplest radical form.

9. $\dfrac{8}{\sqrt{3}}$ 10. $\dfrac{\sqrt{5}}{\sqrt{3}}$ 11. $\dfrac{\sqrt{6}}{\sqrt{2}}$

12. $\dfrac{\sqrt{7}}{\sqrt{5}}$ 13. $\dfrac{3\sqrt{2}}{\sqrt{4}}$ 14. $\dfrac{5\sqrt{3}}{7}$

15. $\dfrac{12\sqrt{5}}{3}$ 16. $8 \div \sqrt{5}$

— B —

Solve. Express answers in simplest radical form.

17. Find the following information for △ABC shown.
    a. CD
    b. AC

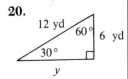

18. Find the length of the diagonal of a 10-in. by 20-in. rectangle.

Find the missing length in each triangle.

19.

20.

Find the indicated information.

21. Write an equation that can be used to find x in the triangle shown.

22. Find the following information for the rectangular prism shown.
    a. BC   b. AB

— C —

23. A person travels 3 miles north, 3 miles east, 4 miles north, and then 2 miles east.
    a. Draw the path on graph paper.
    b. Draw a segment from the starting point to the finish point.
    c. Use the Pythagorean Theorem to find the person's distance from the starting point.

24. Find the following information for the regular square pyramid shown.
    a. XY
    b. BC
    c. Slant height
    d. Area of △VBC
    e. Lateral Area
    f. Area of the base
    g. Total Area
    h. Volume

DID YOU KNOW THAT....

The symbol "$\sqrt{}$" for square root was introduced in Germany about the fifteenth century. The radical sign as we use it today—$\sqrt{}$—is attributed to the French mathematician René Descartes, who introduced it in 1637.

8-6

Some Special Right Triangles

Shown here are two special types of right triangle. In this lesson we will use the Pythagorean Theorem to demonstrate some special relationships among the sides of each triangle.

45–45–90 Triangle (Isosceles Right Triangle)

Consider the equilateral triangle ABC shown. The bisector of $\angle C$ has been drawn. Recall that the bisector of any angle of any equilateral triangle is also the perpendicular bisector of the side opposite that angle. In $\triangle ABC$, $\overline{CD}$ is the perpendicular bisector of $\overline{AB}$.

30–60–90 Triangle

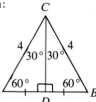

Each of the two triangles formed by $\overline{CD}$ is a *30-60-90 triangle*. Any 30-60-90 triangle can be thought of as half an equilateral triangle.

How long are the sides of $\triangle ADC$? $AD = 2$ since $\overline{CD}$ bisects $\overline{AB}$. The length of $\overline{CD}$ can be found by using the Pythagorean Theorem, as shown:

$$CD^2 + 2^2 = 4^2 \qquad CD = \sqrt{12}$$
$$CD^2 + 4 = 16 \qquad\quad = \sqrt{4}\cdot\sqrt{3}$$
$$CD^2 = 12 \qquad\qquad = 2\sqrt{3}$$

$$AB = 4$$

The preceding discussion illustrates the following statements true for any 30-60-90 triangle. (You may wish to follow the same procedure with a different-size equilateral triangle to see if you get similar results.)

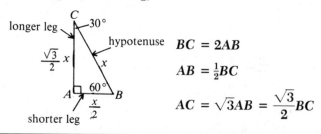

In every 30-60-90 triangle,
- the hypotenuse is twice as long as the side opposite the 30° angle (the shorter leg),
- the side opposite the 30° angle (shorter leg) is one half as long as the hypotenuse, and
- the side opposite the 60° angle (longer leg) is $\sqrt{3}$ times as long as the side opposite the 30° angle (shorter leg).

$$BC = 2AB$$
$$AB = \tfrac{1}{2}BC$$
$$AC = \sqrt{3}AB = \frac{\sqrt{3}}{2}BC$$

Some examples using these conclusions appear on the next page.

Example 1: Find x and y.

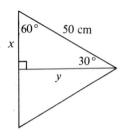

Solution:

$x = 25$ cm   (In a 30-60-90 triangle, the shorter leg is $\frac{1}{2}$ the length of the hypotenuse.)

$y = 25\sqrt{3}$ cm   (In a 30-60-90 triangle, the longer leg is $\sqrt{3}$ times the length of the shorter leg.)

Example 2: Find a and b.

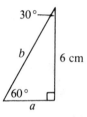

Solution:

$6 = \sqrt{3} \cdot a$ so $a = \dfrac{6}{\sqrt{3}}$

$a = \dfrac{6}{\sqrt{3}} = \dfrac{6}{\sqrt{3}} \cdot \dfrac{\sqrt{3}}{\sqrt{3}} = \dfrac{6\sqrt{3}}{3} = 2\sqrt{3}$ cm

$b = 2 \cdot (2\sqrt{3}) = 4\sqrt{3}$ cm

Consider the square shown. A diagonal $\overline{AC}$ has been drawn. Recall that any diagonal of a square bisects the angles whose vertices are its endpoints. In the square shown, $\overline{AC}$ bisects $\angle DAB$ and $\angle DCB$.

Each of the two triangles formed by $\overline{AC}$ is a *45-45-90 triangle*. Any 45-45-90 triangle can be thought of as half a square.

How long are the sides of $\triangle ABC$? $AB = BC = 4$, because they are also sides of the square. The length of $\overline{AC}$ can be found by using the Pythagorean Theorem, as shown below:

$$AC^2 = 4^2 + 4^2 \qquad AC = \sqrt{32}$$
$$= 16 + 16 \qquad\quad = \sqrt{16} \cdot \sqrt{2}$$
$$= 32 \qquad\qquad\quad = 4\sqrt{2}$$

The preceding discussion illustrates the following statements true for any 45-45-90 triangle. (You may wish to follow the same procedure with a different-size square to see if you get similar results.)

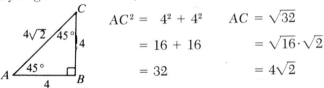

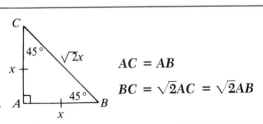

In every 45-45-90 triangle,
- both legs are the same length, and
- the hypotenuse is $\sqrt{2}$ times as long as each leg.

$AC = AB$

$BC = \sqrt{2}AC = \sqrt{2}AB$

Here are some examples using the conclusions on the previous page.

Example 3: Find c.

Solution:

$c = 3\sqrt{2}$ cm   (In a 45-45-90 triangle, the hypotenuse is $\sqrt{2}$ times as long as each leg.)

Example 4: Find d, the length of each leg.

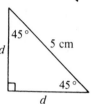

Solution:

$5 = \sqrt{2} \cdot d$ so $d = \dfrac{5}{\sqrt{2}}$ cm

$d = \dfrac{5}{\sqrt{2}} = \dfrac{5}{\sqrt{2}} \cdot \dfrac{\sqrt{2}}{\sqrt{2}} = \dfrac{\sqrt{2}}{2}$ cm

All of the above examples for both the 45-45-90 and the 30-60-90 triangle can be solved with the Pythagorean Theorem. However, the conclusions developed in this lesson provide some shortcuts.

CLASS PRACTICE

1. Look at Examples 3 and 4 above. Work these problems using the Pythagorean Theorem.

Look at △ABC. Complete each statement.

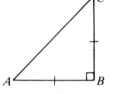

2. $m\angle A = $?°   3. $m\angle C = $?°
4. If $AB = 6$ cm, $BC = $? cm, and $AC = $? cm.
5. If $AC = 16$ cm, $AB = $? cm, and $BC = $? cm.

Look at △DEF. Find the indicated information.

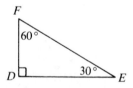

6. Identify the shorter leg, the longer leg, and the hypotenuse.
7. If $EF = 10$ in., $FD = $? in., and $DE = $? in.
8. If $FD = 8$ in., $EF = $? in., and $DE = $? in.

EXERCISES

— A —

Identify each of the following for each triangle.
a. Shorter leg   b. Longer leg
c. Hypotenuse

1. 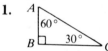   2.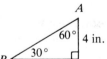

Find each indicated measure. Express all lengths in simplest radical form.
3. a. AB 4. a. YZ
   b. BC b. XY

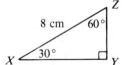

5. a. *RX*
    b. *m∠R*
    c. *m∠RTS*
    d. *m∠RTX*

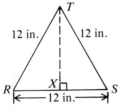

6. a. *AC*
    b. *BC*

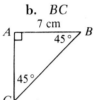

7. a. *NO*
    b. *NM*

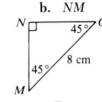

8. a. *DE*
    b. *DF*
    c. *m∠D*
    d. *m∠F*

_ B _

Find the indicated information for each figure.

9. a. Length of a side
    b. Area of the square region

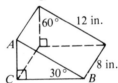

10. a. *MX*
    b. Area of *PGRM*

Parallelogram

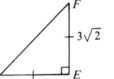

11. a. *m∠1*
    b. *m∠2*
    c. *TR*   d. *RE*
    e. Area of *RECT*

Rectangle

12. a. *BD*
    b. *CD*
    c. *AC*

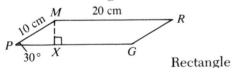

_ C _

In each exercise, *ABCD* is a parallelogram region. Find the indicated information.

13. a. *AX*
    b. *DX*
    c. Area of *ABCD*
    d. Perimeter of *ABCD*

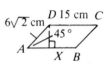

14. a. *DX*
    b. *AX*
    c. Area of *ABCD*
    d. Perimeter of *ABCD*

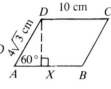

Find the indicated information for each figure.

15. a. *AB*   b. *AC*
    c. Area of △*ABC*
    d. Volume of the prism

Triangular Prism

16. a. *m* $\overparen{XWY}$
    b. *m∠Z*
    c. *m∠X*
    d. *m∠Y*
    e. *XZ*
    f. *YZ*
    g. Area of △*XYZ*   *m* $\overparen{XZ}$ = 60°
    h. Radius of ⊙*C*   *m* $\overparen{YZ}$ = 120°
    i. Area of ⊙*C*   *XY* = 14 cm

17. a. *AD*
    b. *DC*
    c. *BC*
    d. Area of △*ABC*

Geometry on the Job

HIGHWAY ENGINEER

Ping Woo is a highway engineer. When designing a highway, she makes sure that hills are not too steep and curves are not too sharp. On a curve, a road has to be *banked*, that is, sloped toward the inside of the curve, to help cars stay on the road.

Sometimes she must measure the difference in height between two locations. To do so she uses an instrument called a transit, which contains a telescope and a leveling mechanism. When the elevation in question is less than the maximum height to which she can adjust her transit, she sights through the horizontal telescope of the transit at a

measuring stick and then (see the figure) subtracts the height *CD* from *AB* to find *DE*.

EXERCISES

1. If the horizontal distance XZ between two towns is 10 miles (52,800 feet) and the difference in elevation, YZ, is 3000 feet, how long is the road (XY)?

2. If the horizontal distance between two towns is 5.0 km and the length of the road is 5.1 km, what is the difference in elevation of the towns?

3. A road is 10 m wide. On a curve it is banked so that the difference in height is 40 cm. What is the horizontal distance at that point?

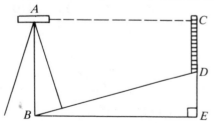

ALGEBRA REVIEW — *Order of Operations*

Suppose you are asked to find the value of $3 + 2 \times 4$.

$$3 + 2 \times 4 = (3 + 2) \times 4 = 5 \times 4 = 20, \quad \text{but}$$

$$3 + 2 \times 4 = 3 + (2 \times 4) = 3 + 8 = 11 \text{ also.}$$

To avoid confusion, mathematicians have agreed to use the following rule to find the value of an expression *when no parentheses or brackets are given*.

Order of Operations
First multiply and divide in order from left to right.
Then add and subtract in order from left to right.

Examples

1. $5 + 3 \times 2 = 5 + (3 \times 2)$
$\qquad\qquad = 5 + 6 = 11$

2. $9 + 3 - 2 = (9 + 3) - 2$
$\qquad\qquad = 12 - 2 = 10$

3. $4 \times 5 \div 2 = (4 \times 5) \div 2$
$\qquad\qquad = 20 \div 2 = 10$

4. $8 \div 4 \times 2 = (8 \div 4) \times 2$
$\qquad\qquad = 2 \times 2 = 4$

5. $10 - 6 - 2 = (10 - 6) - 2$
$\qquad\qquad = 4 - 2 = 2$

6. $10 - 4 \times 2 = 10 - (4 \times 2)$
$\qquad\qquad = 10 - 8 = 2$

7. $6 \times 3 - 4 \times 2 = (6 \times 3) - (4 \times 2)$
$\qquad\qquad\quad = 18 - 8 = 10$

8. $8 - 2 + 3 = (8 - 2) + 3$
$\qquad\qquad = 6 + 3 = 9$

EXERCISES
Find the value of each expression.

1. $19 - 7 + 2$

2. $16 \div 2 \times 4$

3. $13 - 8 - 2$

4. $6 \times 4 \div 3$

5. $6 + 4 \times 3$

6. $4 \times 5 + 6$

7. $16 - 6 \times 2$

8. $10 + 4 \times 0$

9. $18 \div 2 + 4$

10. $3 \times 2 \div 2$

11. $20 + 4 \div 2$

12. $5 \times 2 + 3$

13. $6 + 7 \times 2 + 8$

14. $16 \div 4 \times 2 - 3$

15. $6 \times 7 - 4 \div 2$

16. $7 \times 3 + 4 \times 2$

17. $5 - 2 + 4 \times 3$

18. $32 + 3 \times 4 \div 4$

Chapter 8 Review

Vocabulary

The following terms and symbols were introduced in this chapter. You should be able to write a brief description, draw a picture, or give an example to illustrate the meaning of each.

45-45-90 triangle (p. 345)
hypotenuse (p. 331)
leg (of a right triangle)(p. 331)
number squared (p. 326)
perfect square (p. 326)
Pythagorean Theorem (p. 332)
radical sign (p. 326)
simplest radical form (p. 342)
simplify (a square root expression) (p. 328)

square of a number (p. 326)
square root (p. 326)
30-60-90 triangle (p. 344)

Symbols

n^2 (number squared, or square of a number) (p. 326)

$\sqrt{}$ (positive square root of a number) (p. 326)

Skills Checklist

In Chapter 8 you learned how to use a table to find squares and approximate or exact square roots for positive numbers; how to simplify square root expressions; and how to determine whether three given numbers can be the lengths of the sides of a right triangle. In addition, you learned how to use the Pythagorean Theorem to find the length of any side of a right triangle when given the lengths of the other two sides and how to use some special relationships among the sides of a 30-60-90 or 45-45-90 triangle.

The following list indicates the major skills, facts, and results you should have mastered in this chapter.

● Find the square of any positive integer and the square root of any perfect square. (**8-1**, pp. 326–327)
● Find the exact or approximate square root of a whole number with the aid of a table. (**8-2**, pp. 328–331)
● Determine whether a square root expression is in simplest radical form. (**8-2**, pp. 328–331; **8-4—8-5**, pp. 338–343)
● Express a square root expression in simplest radical form. (**8-2**, pp. 329–330; **8-4—8-5**; pp. 338–343)
● Determine whether three given numbers can be the lengths of the sides of a right triangle. (**8-3**, pp. 331–337)
● Use the Pythagorean Theorem to find the length of any side of a right triangle if the lengths of the other two sides are known: (**8-3**, pp. 331–337)

- For any right triangle, the square of the length of the hypotenuse is equal to the sum of the squares of the lengths of the legs.
- Find the lengths of two sides of either a 30-60-90 triangle or a 45-45-90 triangle given the length of the third side. (8-6, pp. 344-347)

Exercises

Find the value of each expression. (8-1)

1. $\sqrt{16}$ 2. $\sqrt{0.16}$
3. $\sqrt{81}$ 4. $\sqrt{121}$
5. $\sqrt{15^2}$ 6. 9^2
7. $\sqrt{16} + \sqrt{49}$ 8. 10 squared
9. 6 squared 10. Square of 6
11. Square of 7 12. Square root of 64

Find the indicated information.

13. Name five numbers that are perfect squares. (8-1)

Use the table of squares and square roots on page 475 to find the value of each expression. (8-2)

14. $\sqrt{38}$ 15. $\sqrt{73}$
16. $\sqrt{54}$ 17. $\sqrt{324}$
18. $\sqrt{39.69}$ 19. $\sqrt{4356}$
20. 34^2 21. 7.7^2
22. Square of 34 23. 34 squared
24. Square root of 34
25. Square root of 69

Use the table of squares and square roots on page 475 to complete each statement. (8-2)

26. $\sqrt{175} = \sqrt{25} \cdot \sqrt{7} = 5\sqrt{7} \approx$
    $5(\ ?\ ) \approx\ ?$.
27. $\sqrt{117} = \sqrt{9} \cdot \sqrt{13} = 3\sqrt{13} \approx$
    $3(\ ?\ ) \approx\ ?$

Find the indicated information.

28. Use the fact that $41^2 = 1681$ to complete each statement. (8-2)
    a. $\sqrt{1681} =\ ?$ b. $\sqrt{16.81} =\ ?$
    c. $4.1^2 =\ ?$ d. $0.41^2 =\ ?$

Locate each square root between two consecutive whole numbers. (8-2)

29. $\sqrt{19}$ is between ? and ? .
30. $\sqrt{52}$ is between ? and ? .
31. $\sqrt{71}$ is between ? and ? .
32. $\sqrt{95}$ is between ? and ? .

State whether each expression is in simplest radical form. (8-2)

33. $\sqrt{15}$ 34. $3\sqrt{2}$
35. $\sqrt{27}$ 36. $\sqrt{49}$
37. $\sqrt{60}$ 38. $4\sqrt{8}$

Express in simplest radical form. (8-2)

39. $\sqrt{40}$ 40. $\sqrt{48}$
41. $\sqrt{63}$ 42. $3\sqrt{12}$

Identify the hypotenuse and legs of each triangle. (8-3)

43. 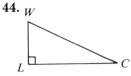 44.

Write an equation that can be used to find the missing length in each triangle. (8-3)

45. 46.

Express in simplest radical form. (8-4)

47. $\sqrt{6} \cdot \sqrt{6}$ 48. $\sqrt{5} \cdot \sqrt{10}$
49. $\sqrt{9} \cdot \sqrt{25}$ 50. $3\sqrt{2} \cdot 5\sqrt{3}$
51. $(\sqrt{7})^2$ 52. $(4\sqrt{3})^2$
53. $(3\sqrt{6})^2$ 54. $3(\sqrt{6})^2$

Determine whether each set of lengths can form a right triangle. (8–3)

55. 6 cm, 7 cm, 8 cm
56. 3 in., 4 in., 5 in.
57. 2 cm, 3 cm, $\sqrt{13}$ cm
58. 4 ft, $2\sqrt{5}$ ft, 6 ft

Find the missing length in each triangle. Express your answers in simplest radical form. (8–3)

59.
60.

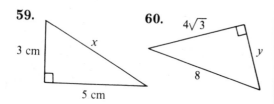

Find each indicated length. Express your answers in simplest radical form. (8–6)

61. a. XY
    b. YZ

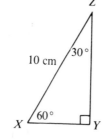

62. a. AC
    b. BC

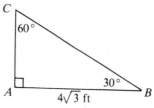

63. a. EF
    b. DF

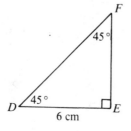

64. a. RT
    b. RS

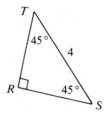

State whether each expression is in simplest radical form. (8–5)

65. $\dfrac{\sqrt{3}}{5}$
    66. $\dfrac{6}{\sqrt{5}}$

67. $\dfrac{3\sqrt{2}}{5}$
    68. $\dfrac{8\sqrt{5}}{4}$

Express in simplest radical form. (8–5)

69. $\dfrac{7}{\sqrt{5}}$
    70. $\dfrac{4}{\sqrt{3}}$

71. $\dfrac{\sqrt{7}}{\sqrt{2}}$
    72. $\dfrac{6\sqrt{3}}{2}$

73. $\dfrac{3\sqrt{5}}{\sqrt{2}}$
    74. $5 \div \sqrt{2}$

Find the indicated information for each figure. (8–6)

75. a. DX
    b. Area of $ABCD$
    c. Perimeter of $ABCD$

Parallelogram

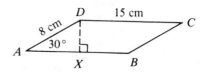

76. a. DX
    b. AX
    c. Area of $DCBX$
    d. Area of $\triangle AXD$
    e. Area of $ADCB$

Trapezoid

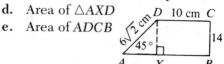

ENLARGEMENTS AND REDUCTIONS

Ratios and Similar Polygons

9-1

Ratios

In this chapter, ratios and proportions will be used to describe some properties of similar polygons. Ratios are also used to describe everyday situations. For example, comparisons of measures and rates are expressed by ratios. A *ratio* is a comparison of two numbers by division.

The following statements use ratios to describe familiar situations:

The student/teacher ratio at Central High School is 25 to 1.

The baseball team has won 6 out of 10 games.

In my first-hour class, there are 5 girls for every 2 boys.

The cost of the soap is 2 bars for 89¢.

The candidate won the election by a 3 to 2 margin.

Ratios may be written in several ways. The ratio of a to b can be written as either $a{:}b$ or $\frac{a}{b}$. This is illustrated by the following examples.

Example 1:

a. Find the ratio of squares to triangles.

b. Find the ratio of triangles to squares.

Solutions:

a. 3 to 4 or 3:4 or $\frac{3}{4}$

b. 4 to 3 or 4:3 or $\frac{4}{3}$

Example 2: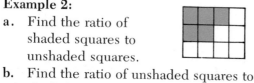

a. Find the ratio of shaded squares to unshaded squares.

b. Find the ratio of unshaded squares to shaded squares.

c. Find the ratio of shaded squares to all squares.

Solutions:

a. 5 to 7 or 5:7 or $\frac{5}{7}$

b. 7 to 5 or 7:5 or $\frac{7}{5}$

c. 5 to 12 or 5:12 or $\frac{5}{12}$

CLASS PRACTICE

Look at the picture of squares and triangles.

1. For 4 squares, there are ? triangles.
2. The ratio of squares to triangles is ? to ? .
3. The ratio of triangles to squares is ? to ? .

Make a drawing to match each ratio described.

4. 5 of 12 parts are shaded.
5. The ratio of shaded parts to all parts is 5:12.

Find the following ratios.

A basketball team played 21 games and won 13.

6. Games won to games played
7. Games played to games won
8. Games lost to games played
9. Games played to games lost
10. Games won to games lost
11. Games lost to games won

EXERCISES

— A —

Look at the picture.

1. For three triangles, there are ? circles.
2. The ratio of triangles to circles is ? to ? .
3. For four circles, there are ? triangles.
4. The ratio of circles to triangles is ? to ? .

Look at the picture.
Express each ratio as a fraction.

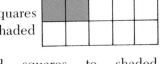

5. Shaded squares to unshaded squares
6. Unshaded squares to shaded squares
7. Shaded squares to all squares

Look at the picture of circles.

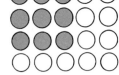

8. Shaded circles to all circles
9. All circles to shaded circles
10. Unshaded circles to all circles
11. Unshaded circles to shaded circles

Make a drawing to match each ratio described.

12. The ratio of triangles to squares is 3 to 7.
13. 3 out of 10 parts are shaded.
14. The ratio of shaded parts to all parts is 7 to 12.

Find each indicated ratio.

15. A room is 10 feet wide and 13 feet long. Find the ratio of its length to its width.

Find the following ratios.

16. A geometry class has 17 girls and 13 boys.
    a. Girls to boys   b. Boys to girls
    c. Girls to all   d. Boys to all
       students   students
    e. All students to boys

17. A batter has 3 hits in 5 times at bat. Find the ratio of hits to times at bat.

— B —

18. Find the indicated ratios for rectangular regions A and B shown.
    a. Base length of B to base length of A
    b. Height of B to height of A
    c. Area of B to area of A

3 m

2 m │ A │

6 m

4 m │ B │

Given $a = 4$ and $b = 5$, find the value of each ratio.

19. $\dfrac{b}{a}$ 20. $\dfrac{a}{a + b}$ 21. $\dfrac{b - a}{a + b}$

Use the given figures to find each ratio.

22. $\dfrac{RS}{ST}$

23. $\dfrac{ST}{RS}$

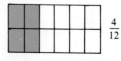

24. $\dfrac{RS}{RT}$

25. $\dfrac{AX}{XB}$

26. $\dfrac{XB}{AX}$ 27. $\dfrac{AX}{AB}$ 28. $\dfrac{BC}{XY}$

29. $\dfrac{AY}{AC}$ 30. $\dfrac{AY}{YC}$

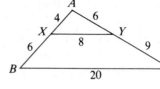

9-2

Equivalent Ratios and Simplest Form

Comparisons of two quantities or measures can be expressed by more than one ratio. The diagrams below indicate that $\dfrac{4}{12}$, $\dfrac{2}{6}$, and $\dfrac{1}{3}$ are different ways of expressing the same comparison.

Ratio of triangles to circles:

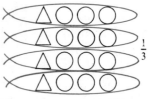

For 4 triangles, there are 12 circles.

For every 2 triangles, there are 6 circles.

For every triangle, there are 3 circles.

Ratio of shaded parts to all parts:

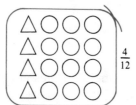

4 out of 12 parts are shaded.

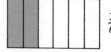

2 out of 6 parts are shaded.

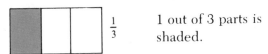 1 out of 3 parts is shaded. $\frac{1}{3}$

Since $\frac{4}{12}$, $\frac{2}{6}$, and $\frac{1}{3}$ express the same comparison, $\frac{4}{12} = \frac{2}{6} = \frac{1}{3}$.

For this reason we say that $\frac{4}{12}$, $\frac{2}{6}$, and $\frac{1}{3}$ are *equivalent ratios*. Equivalent ratios are expressed by equivalent fractions. We say that the ratio $\frac{1}{3}$ is in *simplest form* because it is expressed by a fraction written in simplest form. Recall that to write an equivalent fraction, you multiply or divide both the numerator and the denominator by the same number. A fraction is said to be in simplest form when the numerator and denominator have no common factors other than one.

The following examples show how ratios are used to make comparisons and how to find equivalent ratios.

Example 1: Draw a diagram to show that each pair of ratios are equivalent.

Solutions:

a. $\frac{2}{3}$, $\frac{4}{6}$

b. $\frac{1}{2}$, $\frac{3}{6}$

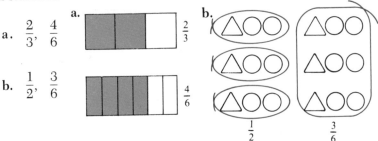

In Examples 2 and 3 below, notice that multiplying or dividing both terms of a ratio by the same number does not change the value of the ratio.

Example 2: Express each ratio in simplest form.

a. $\frac{8}{10}$

b. $\frac{18}{24}$

Solutions:

a. $\frac{8}{10} = \frac{8 \div 2}{10 \div 2} = \frac{4}{5}$

b. $\frac{18}{24} = \frac{18 \div 6}{24 \div 6} = \frac{3}{4}$

Example 3: Write two ratios equivalent to each given ratio.

a. $\dfrac{3}{7}$

b. $\dfrac{2}{5}$

Possible Solutions:

a. $\dfrac{3}{7} = \dfrac{3 \cdot 2}{7 \cdot 2} = \dfrac{6}{14}$ $\dfrac{3}{7} = \dfrac{3 \cdot 5}{7 \cdot 5} = \dfrac{15}{35}$

b. $\dfrac{2}{5} = \dfrac{2 \cdot 2}{5 \cdot 2} = \dfrac{4}{10}$ $\dfrac{2}{5} = \dfrac{2 \cdot 4}{5 \cdot 4} = \dfrac{8}{20}$

In Examples 4 and 5 below, notice that the order in which the parts of the ratio are written is important.

Example 4: Find the ratio of 30 centimeters to 45 centimeters.

Solution:

$$\dfrac{30}{45} = \dfrac{2}{3}$$

Example 5: Find the ratio of 45 centimeters to 30 centimeters.

Solution:

$$\dfrac{45}{30} = \dfrac{3}{2}$$

In Examples 6 and 7 below, notice that when measurements are compared, they must be expressed with the same unit.

Example 6: Find the ratio of 3 centimeters to 15 millimeters.

Solution:

3 cm = 30 mm   so $\dfrac{30}{15} = \dfrac{2}{1}$

or

15 mm = 1.5 cm   so $\dfrac{3}{1.5} = \dfrac{2}{1}$

Example 7: Find the ratio of 1 dime to 1 dollar.

Solution:

1 dime = 10 cents   and $\dfrac{10}{100} = \dfrac{1}{10}$
1 dollar = 100 cents

Notice that whenever you are asked to find a ratio, the answer should be expressed in simplest form.

Look at Examples 6 and 7 above. Ratios are usually used to make comparisons between *like* quantities such as two lengths. In this case you must express both quantities with the same unit before writing the ratio. However, ratios may also be used to express comparisons between *unlike* quantities, such as a distance and a time. For example, ratios may be used to express a *rate*, such as the average speed when a car travels 110 miles in 2 hours. This rate can be expressed as 110:2 or $\dfrac{110}{2}$, which in simplest form is 55:1, or 55 miles per hour.

1. Suppose you wished to find the ratio of 4 in. to 1 ft.
   a. What incorrect impression does the ratio 4:1 give about these lengths?
   b. What is the ratio of 4 in. to 1 ft in simplest form?
2. Describe some situations in which ratios are used to express rates.

_____ **CLASS PRACTICE** _____

1. Draw a diagram to show that the ratios $\frac{2}{3}$ and $\frac{4}{6}$ are equivalent.

2. Write three ratios equivalent to: (a) $\frac{4}{5}$, (b) 3 to 2, and (c) 12:16.

Express each ratio in simplest form.

3. $\frac{8}{36}$

4. 24:36

5. 45:60

6. 16 to 20

7. 20 cm to 50 cm

8. 8 mm to 2 cm

Reaction distance is the distance a vehicle travels from the time the driver realizes it is necessary to stop until the brakes are applied. The information given compares travel speed with average reaction distance.

Write a ratio in simplest form to compare reaction distances for the following speeds.

Speed	Reaction Distance
20 mi/h	22 ft
30 mi/h	33 ft
40 mi/h	44 ft
50 mi/h	55 ft
60 mi/h	66 ft

9. 60 mi/h to 20 mi/h
10. 50 mi/h to 40 mi/h
11. 20 mi/h to 40 mi/h
12. 30 mi/h to 60 mi/h

EXERCISES

Draw a diagram to show that each pair of ratios are equivalent.

1. $\frac{1}{2}, \frac{4}{8}$

2. $\frac{3}{4}, \frac{6}{8}$

Use multiplication or division to show that each pair of ratios are equivalent.

Example: $\frac{6}{8}, \frac{18}{24}$ $\frac{6}{8} = \frac{6 \cdot 3}{8 \cdot 3} = \frac{18}{24}$

or $\frac{18}{24} = \frac{18 \div 3}{24 \div 3} = \frac{6}{8}$

3. $\frac{3}{12}, \frac{15}{60}$

4. $\frac{20}{30}, \frac{2}{3}$

5. $\frac{4}{5}, \frac{24}{30}$

6. $\frac{12}{9}, \frac{24}{18}$

Write two ratios equivalent to each given ratio.

7. $\dfrac{3}{5}$ 8. $\dfrac{9}{5}$ 9. $\dfrac{14}{20}$ 10. $\dfrac{20}{35}$

11. 2:8

12. 8:24

13. 6 to 7

14. 3 to 8

Express each ratio in simplest form.

15. $\dfrac{9}{27}$ 16. $\dfrac{18}{30}$

17. $\dfrac{15}{45}$ 18. $\dfrac{24}{60}$

19. 8:20   20. 9:36
21. 24:32   22. 28:24
23. 6 to 18   24. 7 to 4
25. 10 to 15   26. 15 to 10
27. 16 to 20   28. 25 to 50
29. 36 to 12   30. 100 to 70
31. 4 inches to 10 inches
32. 1 dime to 1 quarter
33. 2 feet to 6 inches
34. 15 minutes to 1 hour
35. 6 centimeters to 50 millimeters
36. 30 centimeters to 20 centimeters
37. 7 ounces to 1 pound
38. 3 nickels to 2 quarters
39. There are 20 boys and 10 girls in one class. Find these ratios.
   a. boys to girls b. girls to boys
   c. boys to all students
40. Classify each statement as true or false.

   There are 16 boys and 8 girls in one class.
   a. The class contains twice as many boys as girls.
   b. The class contains one half as many girls as boys.
   c. One third of the class are boys.

d. The ratio of all students in the class to girls is 1:3.
e. In the class there are two boys for every girl.

Express each ratio in simplest form.

For Exercises 41–52, look at the two pairs of figures shown.

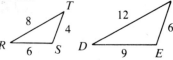

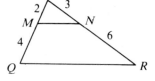

41. $\dfrac{DE}{RS}$

42. $\dfrac{FD}{TR}$

43. $\dfrac{PM}{MQ}$

44. $\dfrac{PR}{PN}$

45. TS:FE   46. PQ:PM
47. PM:PQ   48. RS:DE
49. TR to FD   50. FE to TS
51. PN to NR   52. PN to PR
53. Measure of a right angle to the measure of a straight angle
54. Length of the side of a square to the perimeter of the square
55. EF:XY   if $EF = \frac{2}{3}\cdot XY$
56. AB:RS   if $RS = 3\cdot AB$

Find the indicated information.
57. The table compares automobile speed with average stopping distance. Compare the stopping distances for the following speeds. Write ratios in simplest form.
   a. 20 mi/h to 40 mi/h
   b. 40 mi/h to 60 mi/h
   c. 30 mi/h to 60 mi/h
   d. If speed doubles, what happens to stopping distance?

Speed	Stopping Distance
20 mi/h	54 ft
30 mi/h	121 ft
40 mi/h	215 ft
50 mi/h	336 ft
60 mi/h	484 ft

9-3

Proportions

When ratios are used in problem solving, it is often necessary to use more than one ratio. A statement that two ratios are equivalent is called a *proportion*. Some proportions are given here.

$$\frac{3}{4} = \frac{6}{8}$$
$$3{:}2 = 9{:}6$$
$$\frac{x}{15} = \frac{2}{5}$$

The first proportion listed is read "3 is to 4 as 6 is to 8" or "the ratio of 3 to 4 is equivalent to the ratio of 6 to 8." How should the other proportions be read?

The first two proportions above are true because the ratios are equivalent. However, the third proportion is neither true nor false. Whether it is true or false depends on the value substituted for x. What value of x will make it a true proportion?

When using proportions in problem solving, proportions like the third one above are usually involved. Your job is to find values that will make the statement a true proportion.

The following terms and property are used to describe and solve such problems.

1st term   3rd term
$\downarrow$ $\downarrow$
$$\frac{a}{b} = \frac{c}{d}$$
$\uparrow$ $\uparrow$
2nd term   4th term

2nd term   4th term
$\downarrow$ $\downarrow$
$$a{:}b = c{:}d$$
$\uparrow$ $\uparrow$
1st term   3rd term

Means
$\downarrow$ $\downarrow$
$$a{:}b = c{:}d$$
$\uparrow$ $\uparrow$
Extremes

In a *true proportion*, the product of the means equals the product of the extremes.

If $\dfrac{a}{b} = \dfrac{c}{d}$, then $ad = bc$.   If $a{:}b = c{:}d$, then $ad = bc$.

Example 1:
Determine whether each proportion is true.

a. $\dfrac{3}{4} \overset{?}{=} \dfrac{15}{20}$

b. $\dfrac{8}{12} \overset{?}{=} \dfrac{6}{9}$

c. $\dfrac{5}{7} \overset{?}{=} \dfrac{7}{10}$

Solutions:

a. True, because $3 \cdot 20 = 4 \cdot 15$

b. True, because $8 \cdot 9 = 6 \cdot 12$

c. False, because $5 \cdot 10 \neq 7 \cdot 7$

Example 2:
Solve each proportion (that is, find the value of the unknown term).

a. $\dfrac{4}{x} = \dfrac{12}{60}$

b. $\dfrac{n}{6} = \dfrac{7}{42}$

c. $\dfrac{3}{5} = \dfrac{5}{x}$

Solutions:

a. $12 \cdot x = 4 \cdot 60$
$12x = 240$ $x = \frac{240}{12} = 20$

b. $42 \cdot n = 6 \cdot 7$
$42n = 42$ $n = \frac{42}{42} = 1$

c. $3 \cdot x = 5 \cdot 5$
$3x = 25$ $x = \frac{25}{3} = 8\frac{1}{3}$

1. Given the proportion $\frac{x}{2} = \frac{5}{7}$, identify each of the following.

a. first term   b. second term   c. third term

d. fourth term   e. means   f. extremes

Use each set of numbers to write a true proportion.

2. 4, 7, 12, 21   3. 4, 20, 16, 5

Determine whether each proportion is true.

4. $\frac{3}{7} \stackrel{?}{=} \frac{9}{21}$ 5. $\frac{9}{15} \stackrel{?}{=} \frac{12}{20}$ 6. $\frac{4}{9} \stackrel{?}{=} \frac{6}{11}$

Solve each proportion.

7. $\frac{6}{16} = \frac{9}{x}$ 8. $3{:}x = 12{:}16$ 9. $\frac{3}{5} = \frac{c}{8}$

EXERCISES

— A —

Determine if each proportion is true.

1. $\frac{2}{5} \stackrel{?}{=} \frac{4}{10}$ 2. $\frac{2}{3} \stackrel{?}{=} \frac{6}{12}$

3. $\frac{6}{3} \stackrel{?}{=} \frac{10}{5}$ 4. $\frac{7}{2} \stackrel{?}{=} \frac{28}{8}$

5. $\frac{6}{8} \stackrel{?}{=} \frac{9}{12}$ 6. $\frac{3}{2} \stackrel{?}{=} \frac{10}{7}$

7. $\frac{3}{4} \stackrel{?}{=} \frac{10}{14}$ 8. $1{:}4 \stackrel{?}{=} 7{:}28$

9. $5{:}6 \stackrel{?}{=} 7{:}8$ 10. $\frac{1}{4} \stackrel{?}{=} \frac{1\frac{1}{4}}{5}$

11. $\frac{2}{3} \stackrel{?}{=} \frac{5}{7\frac{1}{2}}$ 12. $\frac{3}{5} \stackrel{?}{=} \frac{x}{10}$

Solve each proportion.

13. $\frac{3}{2} = \frac{x}{4}$ 14. $\frac{a}{12} = \frac{3}{4}$

15. $\frac{4}{y} = \frac{2}{5}$ 16. $\frac{1}{2} = \frac{c}{9}$

17. $\frac{x}{10} = \frac{3}{4}$ 18. $x{:}2 = 5{:}3$

19. $9{:}x = 6{:}4$ 20. $4{:}7 = 8{:}y$

21. $\frac{1\frac{1}{2}}{15} = \frac{n}{60}$ 22. $\frac{1}{2\frac{1}{2}} = \frac{4}{x}$

— B —

Use each set of numbers to write a true proportion.

23. 2, 4, 8, 16   24. 3, 5, 1, 15

25. 2, 8, 12, 3   26. 5, 18, 6, 15

Solve.

27. The numbers 2, 3, and 6 are the first three terms (listed in order) of a proportion. Find the fourth term.

Using the numbers 3, 4, 12, and 16, write a true proportion to fit each description.

28. Means are 4 and 12.

29. 4 is the first term.

30. 16 is the first term and 3 is the fourth term.

31. 12 is the second term.

9-4

Using Proportions in Problem Solving

In this lesson you will use proportions in problem solving.

Example:
At 30 miles per hour, a car is traveling 44 feet per second. How many feet per second does a car travel at 45 mi/h?

Solution:
Here are two proportions that can be used to solve the problem:

$$\frac{30}{44} = \frac{45}{x} \qquad \frac{30}{45} = \frac{44}{x}$$

Suppose we use the first proportion:

$30x = 44 \cdot 45$ Product of means =

$ = 1980$ Product of extremes

$x = 66 \text{ ft/s}$ Divide both sides of the equation by 30.

CLASS PRACTICE

1. Look at the example. Use the second proportion to solve the problem. Why would either proportion work?

Do the following for each problem.
   a. Write two different proportions that can be used to solve the problem.
   b. Use one of these proportions to solve the problem.

2. A lawn crabgrass killer calls for 1 pint of liquid concentrate to make enough spray to cover an area of 2000 square feet. How many pints will be needed to make enough spray to cover 7000 square feet?

3. To mix a household cleaner, you use $\frac{1}{2}$ cup of concentrate per gallon of water. How many cups of concentrate should be mixed with 5 gallons of water?

4. Directions for a rose fertilizer state to use 3 cups of fertilizer for every 100 square feet. How much fertilizer should be used for a rose bed with an area of 175 square feet?

___ A ___

Indicate which proportion could *not* be used to solve the problem.

1. A car can travel 111 miles on 6 gallons of gas. How far can it travel on 10 gallons of gas?

    a. $\dfrac{111}{6} = \dfrac{d}{10}$ b. $\dfrac{6}{10} = \dfrac{111}{d}$

    c. $\dfrac{10}{111} = \dfrac{6}{d}$

2. On a certain map, 1 inch represents 48 miles. What length on the map represents a distance of 168 miles?

    a. $\dfrac{1}{48} = \dfrac{d}{168}$ b. $\dfrac{d}{48} = \dfrac{1}{168}$

    c. $\dfrac{1}{d} = \dfrac{48}{168}$

3. A recipe for cookies calls for $\frac{3}{4}$ cup sugar and 2 cups of raisins. Suppose 3 cups of sugar are used. How many cups of raisins are needed?

    a. $\dfrac{\frac{3}{4}}{2} = \dfrac{3}{c}$ b. $\dfrac{3}{\frac{3}{4}} = \dfrac{c}{2}$ c. $\dfrac{2}{3} = \dfrac{\frac{3}{4}}{c}$

4. An orchard spray calls for 2 cups of powdered concentrate for each 6 gallons of water. How many cups of concentrate are needed to make 9 gallons of spray?

    a. $\dfrac{2}{9} = \dfrac{6}{c}$ b. $\dfrac{2}{6} = \dfrac{c}{9}$ c. $\dfrac{6}{9} = \dfrac{2}{c}$

5. Picture postcards sell at 3 for 59¢. How much will 9 postcards cost?

    a. $\dfrac{3}{59} = \dfrac{9}{c}$ b. $\dfrac{9}{59} = \dfrac{c}{3}$ c. $\dfrac{9}{3} = \dfrac{c}{59}$

___ B ___

Use a proportion to solve each problem.

6. A car travels 232 miles on 8 gallons of gas. How far can it travel on 10 gallons of gas?

7. A car travels 56 kilometers on 7 liters of gas. How many liters of gas are needed to travel 280 kilometers?

8. Boat speeds are often measured in knots instead of miles per hour. (20 knots = 23 mi/h) A speedboat travels 90 mi/h. What is this speed in knots?

9. At 30 mi/h a car is traveling 44 feet per second.

    a. How many feet per second does a race car travel at 195 mi/h?

    b. How many miles per hour is 110 feet per second?

10. A rate of 50 mi/h is equivalent to about 80 km/h.

    a. 40 mi/h = ? km/h

    b. 60 km/h = ? mi/h

11. On a certain map, 2 centimeters represents 150 kilometers. What distance is represented by 7 centimeters?

12. A 3-pound roast requires 105 minutes to cook. How long should a 5-pound roast be cooked?

13. A chowder recipe for 6 people calls for 2 cups of diced potatoes. How many cups of potatoes are needed to use this recipe for 21 people?

14. A casserole recipe for 8 people calls for $\frac{1}{2}$ cup cracker crumbs. How many cups of cracker crumbs are needed to use this recipe for 20 people?

15. When canned, a bushel of tomatoes will yield about 16 quarts. How many bushels of tomatoes are needed to produce 40 quarts of canned tomatoes?

16. A canning guide indicates that 628 quarts of fruits and vegetables is a one-year supply for a family of four. How much is needed by a family of six for one year?

17. A candidate won an election by a 3 to 2 margin. Her opponent received 1110 votes. How many votes did the winner receive?

18. Three concert tickets cost $37.50. How much will 5 tickets cost?

19. A printer wants to reduce an 8-in. × 10-in. photograph to a size that is 6 inches wide. How high will the reduced photograph be?

20. To mix a mosquito spray, you need 8 fluid ounces of liquid concentrate for 3 gallons of water. How many gallons of water must be added to 28 fluid ounces of concentrate?

— C —

21. To mix a yard insect spray, you need $\frac{1}{4}$ cup (2 fl oz) of liquid concentrate to make an amount that will cover an area of 500 square feet. Suppose you wish to spray a 75-ft × 90-ft rectangular yard. Find the following information.
   a. Area of yard = ? ft²
   b. Write a proportion for finding the number of cups of concentrate needed.
   c. Number of cups of concentrate needed = ?
   d. Write a proportion for finding the number of fluid ounces of concentrate needed.
   e. Number of fluid ounces of concentrate needed = ?

22. To use a concentrated liquid household cleaner you mix 1 part cleaner with 8 parts water. One quart of concentrate will make a solution that will clean an area of 250 square feet. Suppose you wish to clean the floor in a 30-foot by 25-foot room. Find the following information.
   a. Find the ratio of concentrate to water.
   b. Area of floor
   c. Quarts of concentrate needed
   d. Quarts of water needed
   e. Gallons of water needed

Test Yourself

1. Draw a diagram to show that the ratios $\frac{2}{3}$ and $\frac{8}{12}$

Express each ratio in simplest form.

2. 24:40
3. 32 to 48
4. $\frac{18}{15}$
5. 4 inches to 1 foot

Find the indicated information.

6. Use the numbers 9, 12, 20, and 15 to write a true proportion.

Solve each proportion.

7. $\frac{2}{5} = \frac{5}{y}$
8. $5:6 = x:24$
9. $\frac{3}{c} = \frac{15}{35}$

Find the indicated information.

10. Use a proportion to solve the following problem:

Directions for an insecticide call for 3 tablespoons of liquid concentrate per gallon of water. How much concentrate should be added to $3\frac{1}{2}$ gallons of water?

9-5

Similar Figures

There are many everyday situations in which objects are the same shape but not necessarily the same size. For example, an enlargement is made of a photograph or a scale model is made of a plane. Figures that are the same shape but not necessarily the same size are called *similar* figures. In the remaining lessons in this chapter, we will develop properties of similar figures and indicate some familiar applications of similarity.

When used to describe similar geometric figures, the phrase "same shape" means not only that they are the same kind of figure (example: rectangle) but also that *each is an enlargement or reduction of the other*. Look at the figures in black. They are *not* similar, because neither is an enlargement or reduction of the other. However, each figure in color is an enlargement or reduction of the original figure (in black) and therefore is similar to it.

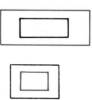

Example 1:   Which figures are similar?

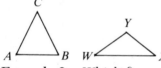

Solution:
$\triangle ABC$ and $\triangle RST$ are similar.
$\triangle WXY$ is not similar to $\triangle ABC$ or to $\triangle RST$.

Example 2:   Which figures are similar?

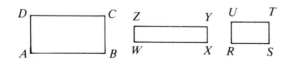

Solution:
$ABCD$ and $RSTU$ are similar.
$WXYZ$ is not similar to $ABCD$ or to $RSTU$.

The two triangles shown are similar. Segments and angles that have the same position in both figures are called *corresponding parts*. In the triangles shown, $\overline{AB}$ and $\overline{PQ}$ are corresponding segments and $\angle C$ and $\angle R$ are corresponding angles. Can you identify the other pairs of corresponding angles and corresponding segments?

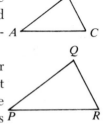

As was done for congruent figures earlier (see Lesson 3–3), similar figures are identified by listing their vertices in corresponding order, that is, corresponding vertices are named in the same order and position. The *similarity statement* below can be used to identify the two triangles shown above.

$$\triangle ABC \sim \triangle PQR \quad (\text{``}\sim\text{''} \text{ is read ``is similar to.''})$$

Can you write other similarity statements for the triangles?

Given a similarity statement such as $GOES \sim HATI$, you can name corresponding parts without referring to a figure. $\overline{GO}$ corresponds to $\overline{HA}$ and $\angle E$ corresponds to $\angle T$ because these letters are in corresponding positions in the similarity statement.

DISCUSS

Tell whether each pair of figures are similar.

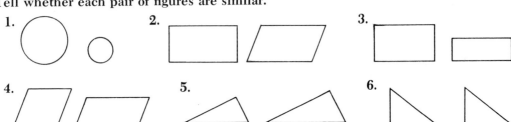

1.   2.   3.

4.   5.   6.

Refer to the figures in Exercises 1–6.

7. Look at Exercise 1. Can figures with no segments or angles be similar?

8. In Exercise 2 each figure is *both* a quadrilateral and a parallelogram. Why are they not similar?

9. In Exercise 3 both figures are rectangles. Why are they not similar?

10. In Exercise 4 both figures are parallelograms. Why are they not similar?

11. Look at Exercise 5. What appears to be true about the size of corresponding angles for a pair of similar polygons?

12. Look at Exercise 6. Are congruent figures also similar?

Find the indicated information.

13. A color slide and its image on a screen represent a pair of similar objects. Describe some other pairs of similar objects.

CLASS PRACTICE

Each pair of figures shown are similar. Identify the corresponding part for each indicated segment or angle.

1. $\overline{ST}$ 2. $\overline{XY}$ 5. $\overline{HI}$ 6. $\overline{SP}$

3. $\angle O$ 4. $\angle X$ 7. $\angle D$ 8. $\angle P$

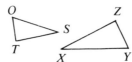

Look at the pairs of similar figures for problems 1–8 on page 367.
Complete each similarity statement.

9. $\triangle XYZ \sim \triangle$?   10. $\triangle STO \sim \triangle$?   11. $\triangle ZYX \sim \triangle$?

Find the indicated information. Assume that $\triangle PTO \sim \triangle RIB$.

12. $\angle O$ corresponds to $\angle$? .   13. $\overline{OT}$ corresponds to ? .

14. $\overline{IR}$ corresponds to ? .   15. $\angle BIR$ corresponds to $\angle$? .

EXERCISES

— A —

Classify each statement as true or false.

1. Similar figures must be the same size.

2. Congruent figures are necessarily similar.

3. If $\triangle ABC \sim \triangle WXY$, $\overline{BC}$ corresponds to $\overline{WX}$.

4. If "$\triangle ABC \sim \triangle WXY$" is true, then "$\triangle CAB \sim \triangle YWX$" is also true.

5. Two polygons with the same number of sides must be similar.

6. Any two triangles are similar.

7. Any two rectangles are similar.

8. Any two squares are similar.

Select the figure that appears to be similar to the given figure.

9.   a.   b.   c.

10. 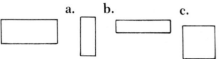   a.   b.   c.

11.   a.   b.   c.

Complete each similarity statement.

12.

a. $BEAST \sim$?   b. $CDFGH \sim$?
c. $AEBTS \sim$?   d. $GFDCH \sim$?

13.

a. $\triangle ABC \sim \triangle$?   b. $\triangle BCA \sim \triangle$?
c. $\triangle ACB \sim \triangle$?

14.

a. $WXYZ \sim$?   b. $YZWX \sim$?
c. $ZYXW \sim$?

15.

a. $TOPS \sim$?   b. $AERD \sim$?
c. $POTS \sim$?   d. $EADR \sim$?

Find the indicated information.

16. Look at the similar figures in Exercise 12.

a. Identify five pairs of corresponding angles.

b. Identify five pairs of corresponding segments.

17. Assume that $\triangle RST \sim \triangle ABC$.

    a. Identify three pairs of corresponding angles.

    b. Identify three pairs of corresponding segments.

18. **a.** Write a similarity statement for the two similar triangles shown.

    b. Identify three pairs of corresponding angles.

    c. Identify three pairs of corresponding segments.

a. Identify three pairs of corresponding angles.

b. Identify three pairs of corresponding sides.

c. Write two other similarity statements for the two triangles.

19. $\triangle ABC \sim$ **20.** $\triangle AMN \sim$
    $\triangle XYC$ $\triangle ART$

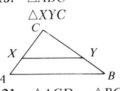

21. $\triangle ACD \sim \triangle BCD$

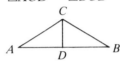

Draw and label a pair of figures to fit each description.

22. $\triangle ART \sim \triangle PLG$

23. Rectangle $ABCD \sim$ rectangle $WXYZ$

24. $\triangle ABC \sim \triangle ABD$

— **B** —

Do the following for each indicated pair of similar triangles.

Everyday Geometry
Unit Prices

The *unit price* of a package is the price per unit of measure, or the ratio of the price of a package to the number of units in the package. The unit of measure may be an ounce, a quart, a gram, a milliliter, or any other unit of volume, weight, or capacity. When you compare packages, the package with the lower unit price is less expensive.

EXERCISES

1. Suppose you are buying crackers. Brand *A* is an 11-oz package for 99¢. Brand *B* is a 16-oz package for $1.68. What is the unit price of brand *A*? What is the unit price of brand *B*? Which is less expensive?

2. Which is less expensive—a 16-oz can of tomatoes for 49¢ or a 28-oz can for 87¢?

3. Which is less expensive—an 18-oz jar of peanut butter for $2.39 or a 40-oz jar for $4.99?

4. State factors other than cost that must be considered in determining the best buy for any particular item.

9-6

Properties of Similar Polygons

The two pairs of similar figures shown illustrate two important properties of similar polygons.

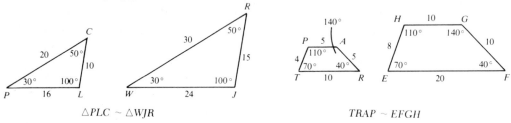

$\triangle PLC \sim \triangle WJR$ $TRAP \sim EFGH$

For each pair of polygons, notice that the measures of corresponding angles are equal. In addition, the ratios of the lengths of corresponding sides are equivalent, that is, the lengths of corresponding sides are *proportional*.

For the pair of similar triangles shown, the ratios of the lengths of corresponding sides are as follows:

$$\frac{PL}{WJ} = \frac{16}{24} = \frac{2}{3} \qquad \frac{LC}{JR} = \frac{10}{15} = \frac{2}{3} \qquad \frac{CP}{RW} = \frac{20}{30} = \frac{2}{3}$$

We say that the *constant of similarity* of $\triangle PLC$ to $\triangle WJR$ is $\frac{2}{3}$ or that the constant of similarity of $\triangle WJR$ to $\triangle PLC$ is $\frac{3}{2}$. The statement "the constant of similarity of $\triangle PLC$ to $\triangle WJR$ is $\frac{2}{3}$" may be interpreted in two ways: (1) Each side of $\triangle PLC$ is $\frac{2}{3}$ as long as the corresponding side of $\triangle WJR$. (2) The ratio of the length of each side of $\triangle PLC$ to the length of the corresponding side of $\triangle WJR$ is 2:3.

The constant of similarity is the ratio of the lengths of any pair of corresponding sides. Notice also that the value of the constant of similarity depends on the order in which the similar figures are compared with each other.

Properties of Similar Polygons

Corresponding angles are congruent.
The lengths of corresponding sides are proportional.

Some examples using these two properties are given on the next page.

370   **Chapter 9**

Example 1: Assume that $\triangle RST \sim \triangle DEF$. Find the following information.

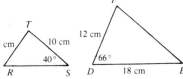

    a. Constant of similarity of $\triangle RST$ to $\triangle DEF$
    b. Constant of similarity of $\triangle DEF$ to $\triangle RST$
    c. $RS = \; ? \; \cdot DE$ **d.** $RS = \; ? \;$ cm
    e. $m\angle E = \; ?°$ **f.** $m\angle R = \; ?°$

Solution:

a. The constant of similarity of $\triangle RST$ to $\triangle DEF$ is $\frac{2}{3}$, since $\dfrac{RT}{DF} = \dfrac{8}{12} = \dfrac{2}{3}$.

b. The constant of similarity of $\triangle DEF$ to $\triangle RST$ is $\frac{3}{2}$, since $\dfrac{DF}{RT} = \dfrac{12}{8} = \dfrac{3}{2}$.

c. $RS = \frac{2}{3} \cdot DE$, since the constant of similarity of $\triangle RST$ to $\triangle DEF$ is $\frac{2}{3}$.

d. Two methods of solution are shown:

Using the Constant of Similarity

$RS = \frac{2}{3} \cdot DE$

$RS = \frac{2}{3} \cdot 18 = \frac{36}{3} = 12$ cm

Using Proportions

$\dfrac{RS}{DE} = \dfrac{RT}{DF}$ $12 \cdot RS = 8 \cdot 18 = 144$

$\dfrac{RS}{18} = \dfrac{8}{12}$ $RS = 12$ cm

e. $m\angle E = 40°$, since $\angle E$ corresponds to $\angle S$.
f. $m\angle R = 66°$, since $\angle R$ corresponds to $\angle D$.

Example 2: Two triangles are similar. The smaller triangle has sides of length 4 cm, 7 cm, and 9 cm. The longest side of the larger triangle is 18 cm. Find the lengths of the remaining two sides of the larger triangle.

Solution:
Two methods of solution are shown:

Using the Constant of Similarity
The constant of similarity of the larger triangle to the smaller triangle is 2, since the ratio of the lengths of their longest sides is $\dfrac{18}{9} = \dfrac{2}{1}$. The remaining two sides of the larger triangle have lengths of $2 \cdot 7 = 14$ cm and $2 \cdot 4 = 8$ cm.

Using Proportions
Let x and y represent the lengths of the two sides whose lengths are not known.

$\dfrac{18}{9} = \dfrac{x}{7}$ $9x = 126$ $\dfrac{18}{9} = \dfrac{y}{4}$ $9y = 72$

           $x = \frac{126}{9} = 14$ cm $y = \frac{72}{9} = 8$ cm

Assume that two polygons are similar.

1. What can you conclude about the measures of any pair of corresponding angles?

2. What can you conclude about the lengths of any pair of corresponding sides?

Assume that △ABC ~ △XYZ, as shown.

3. $\dfrac{AB}{XY} = $?

4. $AB = $? $\cdot XY$

5. $\dfrac{BC}{YZ} = $?

6. $BC = $? $\cdot YZ$

7. $BC = $? cm

8. $\dfrac{AC}{XZ} = $?

9. $\dfrac{XZ}{AC} = $?

10. $XZ = $? $\cdot AC$

11. $XZ = $? cm

12. $m\angle C = $?°

13. What is the constant of similarity of △ABC to △XYZ?

14. What is the constant of similarity of △XYZ to △ABC?

Assume that WXYZ ~ EFGH and WX = 4·EF.

15. $\dfrac{WX}{EF} = $?

16. If $EF = 3$ cm, $WX = $? cm.

17. $\dfrac{XY}{FG} = $?

18. $\dfrac{FG}{XY} = $?

19. $FG = $? $\cdot XY$

20. If $XY = 20$ cm, $FG = $? cm.

21. $\angle G \cong \angle$?

22. If $m\angle H = 30°$, $m\angle Z = $?°

23. Which figure is larger?

24. What is the constant of similarity of WXYZ to EFGH?

EXERCISES

_ A _

Find the indicated measures for each pair of similar figures.

1. a. a b. $m\angle 1$

2. a. c b. d c. e d. $m\angle 2$

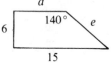

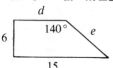

3. f

4. a. x b. y
   c. $m\angle 3$ d. $m\angle 4$

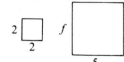

Find the indicated information.

5. Assume that $\triangle ABC \sim \triangle RST$.

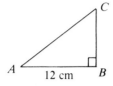
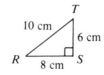

a. $\dfrac{AB}{RS} = ?$ b. $\dfrac{BC}{ST} = ?$

c. $AB = ? \cdot RS$ d. $BC = ?$ cm

e. $AC = ?$ cm

f. If $m\angle T = 59°$, $m\angle C = ?°$.

6. Assume that $\triangle PLC \sim \triangle ART$.

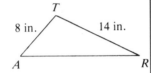

a. $\dfrac{PC}{AT} = ?$ b. $PC = ? \cdot AT$

c. $\dfrac{LC}{RT} = ?$ d. $LC = ? \cdot RT$

e. $LC = ?$ in.   f. $\dfrac{PL}{AR} = ?$

g. $PL = ? \cdot AR$ h. $AR = ?$ in.

i. If $m\angle A = 49°$, $m\angle P = ?°$.

j. What is the constant of similarity of $\triangle PLC$ to $\triangle ART$?

— B —

7. Assume that $\triangle ABC \sim \triangle ADE$.

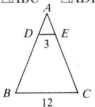

a. What is the constant of similarity of $\triangle ABC$ to $\triangle ADE$?

b. If $AD = 4$, $AB = ?$.

c. If $m\angle ADE = 68°$, $m\angle ABC = ?°$.

8. Assume that $\triangle NOP \sim \triangle MOQ$.

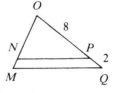

a. $OQ = ?$

b. What is the constant of similarity of $\triangle NOP$ to $\triangle MOQ$?

c. If $NP = 12$, $MQ = ?$

d. If $m\angle M = 65°$, $m\angle ONP = ?°$.

9. Assume that $\triangle ABC \sim \triangle PQR$ and $AB = 3 \cdot PQ$.

a. $BA = ? \cdot QP$ b. $PQ = ? \cdot AB$

c. $\dfrac{AB}{PQ} = ?$ d. $\dfrac{PQ}{AB} = ?$

e. If $PQ = 6$ cm, $AB = ?$ cm.

f. If $AB = 15$ cm, $PQ = ?$ cm.

g. $CA = ? \cdot RP$ h. $\dfrac{CA}{RP} = ?$

i. If $m\angle P = 45°$, $m\angle A = ?°$.

j. What is the constant of similarity of $\triangle ABC$ to $\triangle PQR$?

10. Assume that $\triangle WLC \sim \triangle XYZ$ and $LC = \frac{2}{3} \cdot YZ$.

a. $\dfrac{LC}{YZ} = ?$ b. $\dfrac{YZ}{LC} = ?$

c. $YZ = ? \cdot LC$

d. If $YZ = 12$ cm, $LC = ?$ cm.

e. If $LC = 30$ cm, $YZ = ?$ cm.

f. $WL = ? \cdot XY$ g. $\dfrac{WL}{XY} = ?$

h. If $m\angle Y = 30°$, $m\angle L = ?°$.

i. What is the constant of similarity of $\triangle WLC$ to $\triangle XYZ$?

Find the constant of similarity of the first figure to the second.

11. $\triangle ABC \sim \triangle PQR$, $AB = 5$, and $PQ = 10$

12. $\triangle ACE \sim \triangle MOT$, $AC = 6$, and $MO = 2$

13. $ABCD \sim JKLM$, $KL = 5$, and $BC = 2$

Find the indicated measures.

14. The lengths of the sides of the smaller of two similar triangles are 3 cm, 4 cm, and 5 cm. The shortest side of the larger triangle is 9 cm. Find the length of the remaining sides of the larger triangle.

15. The smaller of two similar rectangles has dimensions of 6 ft and 8 ft. If the ratio of a pair of corresponding sides is 2 to 5, find the dimensions of the larger rectangle.

16. A rectangular photo is 5 inches by 7 inches. It is enlarged so that the longer dimension is 21 inches. What is the shorter dimension of the enlargement?

17. Find the indicated information for the two similar rectangular regions shown.

a. $\dfrac{AB}{EF} = \,$?   b. $\dfrac{BC}{FG} = \,$?

c. $\dfrac{\text{Perimeter of } ABCD}{\text{Perimeter of } EFGH} = \,$?

d. $\dfrac{\text{Area of } ABCD}{\text{Area of } EFGH} = \,$?

Draw and label a pair of figures to fit each description. If the figures described cannot be drawn, write "impossible."

18. Two rectangles that are similar

19. Two rectangles that are not similar

20. Two squares that are not similar

21. Two isosceles triangles that are similar

22. Two isosceles triangles that are *not* similar

23. Two parallelograms that are not similar

24. Two regular polygons that are similar

25. Two regular polygons that are not similar

26. Are similar polygons necessarily congruent?

27. Are congruent polygons necessarily similar?

DID YOU KNOW THAT....

The notation $a{:}b = c{:}d$ for equality of ratios was not generally accepted until the 19th century in Europe and the 20th century in the United States. Earlier notations included $a.b{::}c.d$, introduced in 1648 by the English cleric William Oughtred, and $a{:}b{::}c{:}d$, proposed by the English astronomer Vincent Wing in 1649. Gottfried Leibnitz, the German mathematician, strongly supported the use of $a{:}b = c{:}d$, objecting to the special symbol for equality used in the other notations.

9-7

Drawing Similar Figures— Grid Method

As stated earlier, similar figures may be thought of as enlargements or reductions of each other. In this lesson you will draw some enlargements and reductions.

In the first six lessons of this chapter you developed the following properties of similar polygons:

Corresponding angles are congruent.

The lengths of corresponding sides are proportional.

These properties can be used to develop methods for drawing enlargements or reductions of a given figure. In this lesson you will learn the *grid method* of making enlargements and reductions.

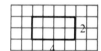

Example 1: Make a 3-to-2 enlargement of the rectangle shown.

Solution:

The ratio of the length of each side of the new rectangle to the length of the corresponding side of the original rectangle is 3 to 2. Therefore the length of each side of the enlargement is $\frac{3}{2} = 1.5$ times the length of the corresponding given side. So the new dimensions are:

$$4 \times \frac{3}{2} = \frac{12}{2} = 6 \qquad 2 \times \frac{3}{2} = \frac{6}{2} = 3$$

Example 2: Make a 1:2 reduction of the figure shown.

Solution:

Each side of the reduction is $\frac{1}{2}$ the length of the corresponding side in the given figure.

In each example, look at the ratio indicating the amount of reduction or enlargement. Each ratio is the constant of similarity of the enlargement or reduction to the original figure.

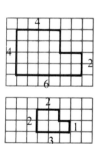

CLASS PRACTICE

State the dimensions of each enlargement or reduction of each given figure.

1. 5:2 enlargement

2. 3:1 enlargement

3. 2:3 reduction

4. 1:4 reduction

Using graph paper with $\frac{1}{2}$-cm squares, draw the indicated enlargement or reduction of each figure.

5. 3:4 reduction   **6.** 3:2 enlargement   **7.** 2:3 reduction

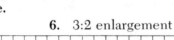

EXERCISES

For each pair of figures, state whether the second figure is an enlargement or a reduction of the first figure. If so, find the constant of similarity.

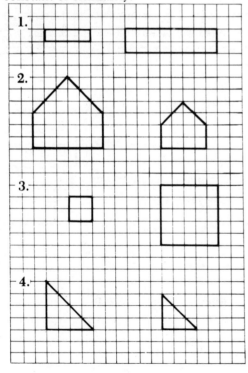

State the dimensions of each indicated enlargement or reduction of each given figure.

5. 2-to-1 enlargement

6. 1-to-2 reduction

7. 7-to-2 enlargement

8. 3:2 enlargement

9. 1:3 reduction

10. 5:2 enlargement

Using graph paper with $\frac{1}{2}$-cm squares, draw the indicated enlargement or reduction of each figure.

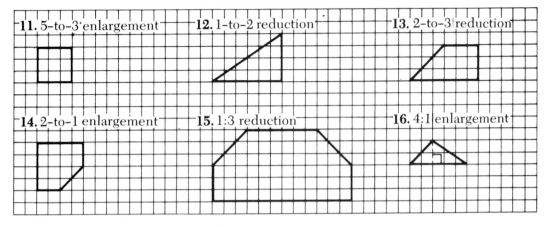

11. 5-to-3 enlargement **12.** 1-to-2 reduction **13.** 2-to-3 reduction

14. 2-to-1 enlargement **15.** 1:3 reduction **16.** 4:1 enlargement

Applications

The Golden Ratio

One special rectangle, the *golden rectangle*, has fascinated mathematicians and visual artists for centuries. Such a rectangle was thought by the ancient Greeks to be most pleasing to the eye.

A *golden rectangle* is one whose length and width satisfy the equation $\dfrac{l}{w} = \dfrac{l + w}{l}$. The ratio $\dfrac{l}{w}$ is called the *golden ratio* and has a value of about 1.6.

The golden ratio was known as early as the fifth century B.C. Several famous works of architecture and art, including the Greek Parthenon and some of Leonardo da Vinci's paintings, appear to be framed in the golden rectangle. Present-day architects and artists have also used the golden ratio in their designs.

A golden rectangle can be constructed as follows:
Given square *ABCD*, locate the midpoint *M* of $\overline{AB}$.
Draw an arc with *M* as center and *MC* as radius, intersecting $\overleftrightarrow{AB}$ at *E*.
Construct a perpendicular to $\overleftrightarrow{AB}$ at *E*.
Extend $\overline{DC}$ to meet the perpendicular at *F*.
AEFD is a golden rectangle. *BEFC* is also a golden rectangle.

Step 1

Step 2

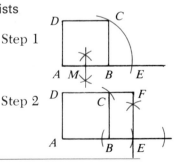

9-8

Drawing Similar Figures—Point Method

In this lesson you will use the *point method* to draw similar figures.

Example 1:
Make a 2:1 enlargement of $\triangle ABC$. (The constant of similarity is 2.)

Solution:
Locate a point P anywhere near the figure. Measure the distance from P to any vertex of the figure, say A. Multiply $\underrightarrow{PA}$ by 2. Locate the point X on $\overrightarrow{PA}$ so that $PX = 2 \cdot PA$. Follow the same procedure for the other two vertices.
$PY = 2 \cdot PB$ and $PZ = 2 \cdot PC$.
Draw the sides of the enlargement, $\triangle XYZ$.

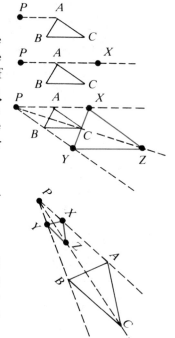

Example 2:
Make a 1:3 reduction of $\triangle ABC$. (The constant of similarity is $\frac{1}{3}$.)

Solution:
The completed figure ($\triangle XYZ$) is shown. The procedure is like that for Example 1. $PX = \frac{1}{3} \cdot PA$, $PY = \frac{1}{3} \cdot PB$, and $PZ = \frac{1}{3} \cdot PC$.

When the point method is used, point P may be located anywhere, as illustrated by the drawings below. The point P may even be located in the interior of a figure, as illustrated by the drawing at the right. The two drawings at the left show alternate solutions for Example 1.

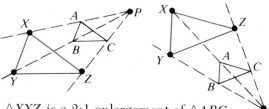

$\triangle XYZ$ is a 2:1 enlargement of $\triangle ABC$.
$PX = 2 \cdot PA$, $PY = 2 \cdot PB$, $PZ = 2 \cdot PC$

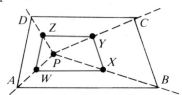

$WXYZ$ is a 1:2 reduction of $ABCD$.
$PW = \frac{1}{2} \cdot PA$, $PX = \frac{1}{2} \cdot PB$,
$PY = \frac{1}{2} \cdot PC$, $PZ = \frac{1}{2} \cdot PD$

Use the point method to make the indicated enlargement or reduction.
Trace each figure twice. If point P is provided, trace it also. If not, choose
any location for point P.

1. 2-to-1 enlargement
2. 1-to-2 reduction

3. 5:2 enlargement
4. 2:3 reduction

EXERCISES

Trace each figure and point P. Use the
point method to make the indicated enlargement or reduction.

1. 2-to-1 enlargement

4. 2-to-3 reduction

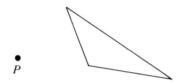

2. 3-to-1 enlargement

3. 1-to-2 reduction

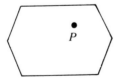

Trace each figure twice. Use the point
method to make the indicated enlargement or reduction. Choose any location
for point P.

5. 3:2 enlargement
6. 1:2 reduction

7. 5:2 enlargement
8. 3:4 reduction

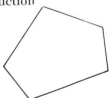

9. 1:2 reduction
10. 5:2 enlargement

11. 2:3 reduction
12. 4:3 enlargement

13. 3:1 enlargement
14. 1:2 reduction

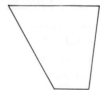

15. 2:3 reduction
16. 7:2 enlargement

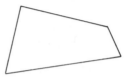

Test Yourself

The triangles shown are similar.

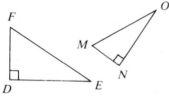

1. Identify three pairs of corresponding angles.

2. Write two different similarity statements.

Assume that △XYZ ~ △ABC, as shown.

3. $\dfrac{XY}{AB} =$?

4. $XY =$? $\cdot AB$

5. $\dfrac{YZ}{BC} =$?

6. $YZ =$? $\cdot BC$

7. $YZ =$? cm   **8.** $AC =$? cm

9. If $m\angle A = 39°$, then $m\angle X =$?° .

10. What is the constant of similarity of △XYZ to △ABC?

11. Trace the quadrilateral shown. Use the point method to make a 3:2 enlargement.

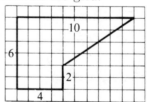

12. Using graph paper with $\frac{1}{2}$-cm squares, use the grid method to draw a 1:2 reduction of the figure shown on the grid.

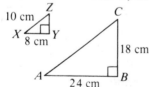

9-9
Constructing Similar Triangles

In Chapter 4 you learned three methods—SSS, SAS, and ASA—for constructing a triangle congruent to a given triangle. In this lesson you will learn three methods for constructing a triangle *similar* to a given triangle.

Construction 17
A Triangle Similar to a Given Triangle—Three Sides (SSS~)

Problem
Construct a triangle similar to $\triangle ABC$ with a constant of similarity of $\frac{1}{2}$ (a 1:2 reduction).

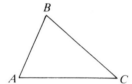

Procedure

Step 1. Bisect $\overline{AB}$, $\overline{BC}$, and $\overline{CA}$. (See Construction 7 on page 146.)

Step 2. Draw a line. Construct $\overline{PR} \cong \overline{AZ}$. (See Construction 1 on page 132.)

Step 3. From P, draw an arc with radius AX. From R, draw an arc with radius CY. The intersection of the arcs is the third vertex, Q.
Draw $\overline{PQ}$ and $\overline{RQ}$. $\triangle PQR \sim \triangle ABC$

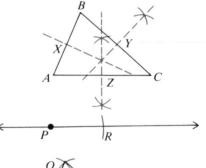

Construction 18
A Triangle Similar to a Given Triangle—Two Sides and the Included Angle (SAS~)

Problem
Construct a triangle similar to $\triangle ABC$ with a constant of similarity of 2 (a 2:1 enlargement).

Procedure

Step 1. Draw a line. Construct $PR = 2 \cdot AC$. (See Construction 1 on page 132.)

Step 2. At P, construct an angle congruent to $\angle A$. (See Construction 3 on page 138.)

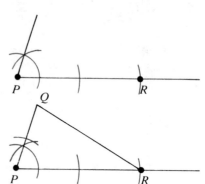

Step 3. Construct $PQ = 2 \cdot AB$. Draw QR.
$\triangle PQR \sim \triangle ABC$

Construction 19

A Triangle Similar to a Given Triangle—Two Angles and the Included Side (ASA~)

Problem

Construct a triangle similar to $\triangle ABC$ with a constant of similarity of 3:2 (a 3:2 enlargement).

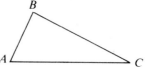

Procedure

Step 1. Bisect $\overline{AC}$.

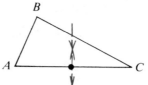

Step 2. Draw a line. Construct $PR = \frac{3}{2} \cdot AC$.

Step 3. At P, construct an angle congruent to $\angle A$. At R, construct an angle congruent to $\angle C$. The intersection of the sides of these angles is the third vertex, Q. $\triangle PQR \sim \triangle ABC$

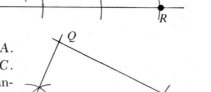

DISCUSS

1. Look at Construction 17. In Step 2 suppose you constructed $\overline{QR} \cong \overline{CY}$ or $\overline{PQ} \cong \overline{AX}$. Describe how this would change the rest of the construction and the result.

2. Look at Construction 18. In Steps 1 and 3 suppose you used a different pair of sides, such as $\overline{AB}$ and $\overline{BC}$. Describe how this would change the rest of the construction and the result.

3. Look at Construction 19. In Step 1 suppose you bisected $\overline{BC}$ or $\overline{AB}$. Describe how this would change the rest of the construction and the result.

CLASS PRACTICE

1. Construct an angle congruent to the given angle.

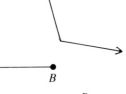

Look at $\overline{AB}$. Construct a segment of each given length.
2. AB 3. $3AB$ 4. $\frac{1}{2}AB$ 5. $\frac{3}{2}AB$

Construct a triangle similar to $\triangle ABC$ by using each indicated method and constant of similarity.
6. SSS~; 2   7. SAS~; 2   8. ASA~; $\frac{3}{2}$

EXERCISES

_ A _

Construct a triangle congruent to each given triangle.
1.
2.

Construct a triangle similar to $\triangle ABC$ by using each indicated method and constant of similarity.

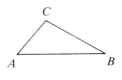

3. SSS~; 2   4. SSS~; $\frac{1}{2}$
5. SAS~; $\frac{1}{2}$ 6. SAS~; $\frac{3}{2}$
7. SAS~; 1   8. ASA~; 2
9. ASA~; $\frac{5}{2}$ 10. ASA~; 1

Use any method to construct each indicated figure.
11. Construct a triangle similar to $\triangle XYZ$ with 3 as the constant of similarity.

_ B _

Construct a square similar to QUAD by using each indicated constant of similarity.
12. 2   13. $\frac{3}{2}$

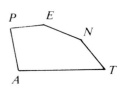

14. Construct a quadrilateral similar to WXYZ with 2 as the constant of similarity.

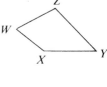

15. Construct a quadrilateral congruent to ABCD.

16. Construct a pentagon similar, but not congruent, to PENTA with a constant of similarity of 3.

9-10

SSS, SAS, *and* AA *Properties of Similar Triangles*

Triangles can be proved to be similar by demonstrating that they satisfy the definition of similar triangles. However, it is sometimes time-consuming or difficult to show that all corresponding angles are congruent and that all lengths of corresponding sides are proportional. As was the case earlier with congruent triangles, some shortcut methods can be developed for determining that a pair of triangles are similar.

In the preceding three lessons you learned two methods for drawing a polygon similar to a given polygon and three methods for constructing a triangle similar to a given triangle. These drawings and constructions illustrate some methods for showing that triangles are similar.

Construction 17 (page 381) illustrates the following property, which can be used to make or show triangles to be similar.

Side/Side/Side Property (SSS~)

If the lengths of the corresponding sides of two triangles are proportional, the triangles are similar.

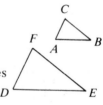

Look at the two triangles. Applying this property to these triangles means that if $\dfrac{AB}{DE} = \dfrac{BC}{EF} = \dfrac{CA}{FD}$, then $\triangle ABC \sim \triangle DEF$.

Construction 18 (page 381) illustrates the following property, which also can be used to make or show triangles to be similar.

Side/Angle/Side Property (SAS~)

If the lengths of two pairs of corresponding sides of two triangles are proportional and the corresponding included angles are congruent, the triangles are similar.

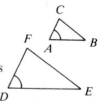

Look at the two triangles. Applying this property to these triangles means that if $\dfrac{AB}{DE} = \dfrac{AC}{DF}$ and $\angle A \cong \angle D$, then $\triangle ABC \sim \triangle DEF$.

Construction 19 (page 382) illustrates a third property (ASA~) for showing that triangles are similar. However, the angles alone will determine the shape (but not the size) of a triangle. Therefore there is a simpler property related to Construction 19 that can be used to make or show triangles to be similar. This property is developed in the following EXPLORING.

EXPLORING
The AA Property

In the two triangles shown, $\angle C \cong \angle F$ and $\angle B \cong \angle E$.

1. Measure $\overline{FE}$, $\overline{CB}$, $\overline{DE}$, $\overline{AB}$, $\overline{DF}$, and $\overline{AC}$ to the nearest millimeter.

2. Find $\dfrac{FE}{CB}$, $\dfrac{DE}{AB}$, and $\dfrac{DE}{AC}$. How do the ratios compare?

3. Why is $\angle A \cong \angle D$?

4. Why is $\triangle ABC \sim \triangle DEF$?

Now try another example.

5. Draw $\overline{AB}$ 4 cm long and $\overline{DE}$ 6 cm long.

6. Draw or construct congruent angles at A and D and another pair of congruent angles at B and E.

7. Measure $\overline{AC}$, $\overline{DF}$, $\overline{BC}$, and $\overline{EF}$ to the nearest millimeter.

8. Find $\dfrac{AC}{DF}$ and $\dfrac{BC}{EF}$. How do these ratios compare with $\dfrac{AB}{DE}$?

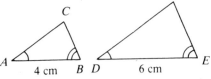

9. Why is $\angle C \cong \angle F$?

10. Why is $\triangle ABC \sim \triangle DEF$?

If you did the preceding EXPLORING carefully, you discovered the following property, which can be used to make or show triangles to be similar.

Angle/Angle Property (AA)

If two angles of one triangle are congruent to two angles of another triangle, the triangles are similar.

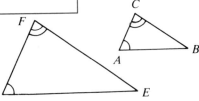

Look at the triangles. Applying this property to these triangles means that if $\angle A \cong \angle D$ and $\angle F \cong \angle C$, then $\triangle ABC \sim \triangle DEF$.

Showing that polygons with more than three sides are similar is not quite as easy as it is for triangles.

For example, the two rectangles shown are *not* similar, even though the corresponding angles are congruent, because the lengths of the corresponding sides are not proportional $\left(\dfrac{AD}{WZ} = \dfrac{2}{4} = \dfrac{1}{2}\right.$ and $\dfrac{AB}{WX} = \dfrac{4}{6} = \dfrac{2}{3}\Big)$.

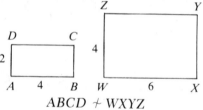

$ABCD \nsim WXYZ$

In a like manner, two polygons with more than three sides may have the lengths of corresponding sides proportional and yet not be similar.

For example, the parallelograms shown are *not* similar even though the lengths of corresponding sides are proportional because the corresponding angles are not congruent ($\angle A \ncong \angle E$).

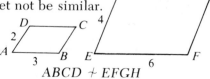

$ABCD \nsim EFGH$

Therefore, the properties—SSS~, SAS~, and AA—stated at the beginning of this lesson are true for triangles *only*. You would need more information to make or show that polygons with more than three sides are similar.

CLASS PRACTICE

Determine whether each pair of triangles are similar. If so, state the property that can be used to prove them similar.

1.

2.

3.

4.
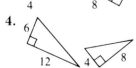

5.
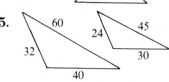

6.

Find the indicated information for $\triangle ABC$ and $\triangle DEC$.

7. $m\angle 1$
8. $m\angle B$
9. $m\angle E$
10. $\triangle ABC \sim \triangle$?
11. x
12. y

Suppose you wish to prove that $\triangle ABC \sim \triangle MNO$ (see page 387). Complete each statement.

13. To use the SSS~ Property, you must show that $\dfrac{AB}{MN} = \dfrac{?}{?} = \dfrac{?}{?}$.

14. To use the SAS~ Property, you *could* show that $\dfrac{MN}{?} = \dfrac{?}{BC}$ and $\angle N \cong \angle$? .

15. To use the AA Property, you *could* show that $\angle A \cong \angle$? and $\angle C \cong \angle$? .

16. Suppose you know that $\angle P \cong \angle G$ and you wish to prove that $\triangle PQR \sim \triangle GHI$ by using the SAS~ Property. What else must be shown to be true?

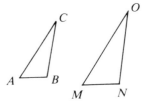

EXERCISES

— A —

Determine whether each pair of triangles are similar. If so, state the property that can be used to prove them similar.

1.

2.

3.

4.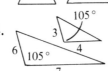

5. **6.**

7.

8.

Determine whether each pair of parallelograms are similar.

9.

10.

11.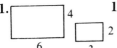

12.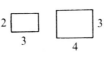

Find the indicated information.

13. **a.** $\triangle AXY \sim \triangle$?
  b. $\dfrac{AX}{AB} = \dfrac{AY}{?} = \dfrac{XY}{?}$

14. **a.** $\triangle RAB \sim \triangle$?
  b. $\dfrac{RA}{RS} = \dfrac{?}{ST} = \dfrac{RB}{?}$

15. **a.** $\triangle PQR \sim \triangle$? **b.** $m\angle A =$?°
  c. $m\angle R =$?°

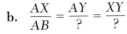

16. **a.** $m\angle T =$?° **b.** $m\angle M =$?°
  c. $\triangle RST \sim \triangle$? **d.** $x =$?
  e. $y =$?

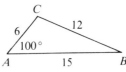

17. Assume that $\triangle DEF \sim \triangle ABC$.
  a. What is the constant of similarity of $\triangle DEF$ to $\triangle ABC$?
  b. $m\angle D =$?°
  c. $FD =$? cm
  d. $AB =$? cm

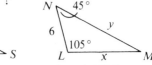

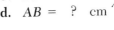

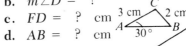

18. Assume that $WXYZ \sim QUAD$.

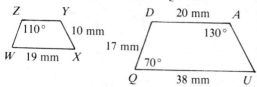

a. What is the constant of similarity of $WXYZ$ to $QUAD$?
b. $ZY = $? mm   c. $AU = $? mm
d. $ZW = $? mm   e. $m\angle D = $?°
f. $m\angle Y = $?°   g. $m\angle W = $?°

Look at $\triangle RST$ and $\triangle MNO$. Complete each statement.

19. Suppose $\dfrac{RT}{MO} = \dfrac{TS}{ON} = \dfrac{SR}{NM}$. Then $\triangle RST \sim \triangle MNO$ by the ? Property.

20. Suppose $\dfrac{RS}{MN} = \dfrac{RT}{MO}$ and $\angle R \cong \angle M$. Then $\triangle RST \sim \triangle MNO$ by the ? Property.

21. Suppose $\angle R \cong \angle M$ and $\angle T \cong \angle O$. Then $\triangle RST \sim \triangle MNO$ by the ? Property.

22. Suppose $\angle N \cong \angle S$ and $\dfrac{ON}{TS} = \dfrac{NM}{SR}$. Then $\triangle RST \sim \triangle MNO$ by the ? Property.

23. Suppose $\angle O \cong \angle T$ and $\angle N \cong \angle S$. Then $\triangle RST \sim \triangle MNO$ by the ? Property.

24. Suppose $\dfrac{NO}{ST} = \dfrac{OM}{TR} = \dfrac{MN}{RS}$. Then $\triangle RST \sim \triangle MNO$ by the ? Property.

Suppose you wish to prove $\triangle GHI \sim \triangle DEF$.

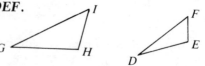

25. To use the SSS~ Property, you must show that $\dfrac{HI}{?} = \dfrac{?}{DF} = \dfrac{?}{?}$.

26. To use the SAS~ Property, you could show that $\dfrac{GH}{?} = \dfrac{?}{DF}$ and $\angle G \cong $? .

27. To use the AA Property, you could show that $\angle G \cong \angle$? and $\angle I \cong \angle$? .

28. Suppose you know that $\angle Q \cong \angle Y$ and you wish to prove that $\triangle PQR \sim \triangle XYZ$ by using the SAS~ Property. What else must be shown to be true?

29. Suppose you know that $\angle R \cong \angle Z$ and you wish to prove that $\triangle PQR \sim \triangle XYZ$ by using the AA Property. What else must be shown to be true?

— **B** —

30. Look at the triangular regions. $\triangle GHI \sim \triangle MNO$.

a. $\dfrac{GH}{MN} = $?
b. $\dfrac{HI}{NO} = $?
c. $\dfrac{IG}{OM} = $?
d. $\dfrac{IX}{OY} = $?
e. $\dfrac{\text{Perimeter of } \triangle GHI}{\text{Perimeter of } \triangle MNO} = $?
f. $\dfrac{\text{Area of } \triangle GHI}{\text{Area of } \triangle MNO} = $?
g. What is the constant of similarity of $\triangle GHI$ to $\triangle MNO$?

Geometry on the Job

SURVEYOR

In order to determine exact locations for buildings and roads, surveyors like Earl James make very precise measurements of distances and angles. To measure angles they use an instrument called a *theodolite*.

To find distances that cannot be measured directly, Earl will often use similar triangles. For example, suppose he needs to know the distance across a river. He decides to use a tree on the far side of the river as point *T*. One stake is driven into the ground at point *S* and another at point *A* so that ∠*TSA* is a right angle. Then he places a stake at point *B* so that ∠*SAB* is also a right angle. Finally, another stake is driven at point *C*, where $\overline{SA}$ and $\overline{TB}$ intersect.

EXERCISES

1. Why are triangles *STC* and *ABC* similar?

2. Suppose *SC* = 200 feet and *AC* = 50 feet. What is the constant of similarity? $\left(\dfrac{AC}{SC}\right)$

3. If *SC* = 200 feet, *AC* = 50 feet, and *AB* = 40 feet, how long is $\overline{ST}$?

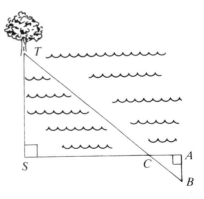

ALGEBRA REVIEW — *Evaluating Algebraic Expressions*

A *variable* is any symbol (usually a letter) that may be replaced by a number in an algebraic expression. Given a value for the variable(s) in any expression, you can find the value of the expression.

Examples

Find the value of each expression if $x = 2$ and $y = 3$.

1. $2x + 5 = 2(2) + 5 = 4 + 5 = 9$ ("$2x$" means "2 times x")
2. $9 - xy = 9 - (2)(3) = 9 - 6 = 3$ ("xy" means "x times y")
3. $3 + 5x = 3 + (5)(2) = 3 + 10 = 13$
4. $3(2y + 1) = 3[2(3) + 1] = 3(6 + 1) = 3(7) = 21$

Notice that when evaluating an algebraic expression, we follow the usual rule on order of operations.

EXERCISES

Find the value of each expression if $x = 3$ and $y = 4$.

1. $5x$
2. xy
3. $3(x - 1)$
4. $6(y + 5)$
5. $7 + 2x$
6. $3y - 2$
7. $4x + 5$
8. $x + 5y$

Find the value of each expression if $a = 2$ and $b = 5$.

9. $6a$
10. ab
11. $3b$
12. $a + 2b$
13. $4(b - 3)$
14. $4b - 3$
15. $3 + 4b$
16. $2a + 3b$

Find the value of each expression for the given values of the variable(s).

17. $2l + 2w$; $l = 3$ and $w = 4$
18. $2(l + w)$; $l = 3$ and $w = 4$
19. bh; $b = 5$ and $h = 3$
20. $\frac{1}{2}bh$; $b = 8$ and $h = 4$
21. rt; $r = 50$ and $t = 3$
22. $\frac{1}{3}Bh$; $B = 6$ and $h = 9$
23. $(n - 2)180$; $n = 5$
24. $\frac{E}{R}$; $E = 220$ and $R = 5$
25. lwh; $l = 2\frac{1}{2}$, $w = 4$, and $h = 5$
26. prt; $p = 750$, $r = 0.04$, and $t = 2$
27. $a^2 + b^2$; $a = 5$ and $b = 12$
28. $\left(\dfrac{b_1 + b_2}{2}\right)h$; $b_1 = 12$, $b_2 = 18$, and $h = 6$
29. $\pi r^2 h$; $\pi = 3.14$, $r = 3$, and $h = 7$
30. $\pi r^2 h$; $\pi = \frac{22}{7}$, $r = 3$, and $h = 7$
31. πdh; $\pi = 3.14$, $d = 7$, and $h = 2$
32. πdh; $\pi = \frac{22}{7}$, $d = 7$, and $h = 2$

Chapter 9 Review

Vocabulary

The following terms and symbols were introduced in this chapter. You should be able to write a brief description, draw a picture, or give an example to illustrate the meaning of each.

AA Property (p. 385)
constant of similarity (p. 370)
equivalent ratios (p. 357)
extremes (p. 361)
means (p. 361)
proportion (p. 361)
proportional (p. 370)
ratio (p. 354)
SAS~ Property (p. 384)

SSS~ Property (p. 384)
similar (p. 366)
similarity statement (p. 366)

Symbols

$a{:}b$, or $\dfrac{a}{b}$ (ratio of a to b) (p. 354)

~ (similar to) (p. 366)

Skills Checklist

In Chapter 9 you learned how to write ratios, how to solve proportions, to recognize some properties of similar figures, and how to draw or construct a figure similar to a given figure. In addition, you were introduced to some applications of ratio and proportion in problem solving.

The following list indicates the major skills, facts, and results you should have mastered in this chapter:

- Write a ratio equivalent to a given ratio. (**9-2**, pp. 356–360)
  Express a ratio in simplest form. (**9-2**, pp. 356–360)
- Recognize and use the fact that in a true proportion the product of the means is equal to the product of the extremes in order to solve proportions. (**9-3**, pp. 361–362)
- Use proportions in problem solving. (**9-4**, pp. 363–365)
- Identify corresponding parts and write an appropriate similarity statement for any two similar figures. (**9-5**, pp. 366–369)
- Use properties of similar polygons to solve problems: (**9-6**, pp. 370–374)
  - Corresponding angles of similar polygons are congruent.
  - The lengths of corresponding sides of similar polygons are proportional.
- Draw a reduction or enlargement of a given figure by using either
- the grid or point method. (**9-7—9-8**, pp. 375–380)
- Construct a triangle similar to a given triangle with a given constant

of similarity using the SSS~, SAS~, or ASA~ method. (9-9, pp. 381–383)

- Use the SSS~, SAS~, and AA Properties to determine whether a given pair of triangles are similar: (9-10, pp. 384–388)
  - (SSS~) If the lengths of the corresponding sides of two triangles are proportional, the triangles are similar.
  - (SAS~) If the lengths of two pairs of corresponding sides of two triangles are proportional and the corresponding included angles are congruent, the triangles are similar.
  - (AA) If two angles of one triangle are congruent to two angles of another triangle, the triangles are similar.

Exercises

Use the given figures to find each ratio. (9-1)

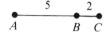

1. $\dfrac{AB}{BC}$ 2. $\dfrac{BC}{AC}$

3. Shaded squares to unshaded squares

4. Unshaded squares to shaded squares

5. Shaded squares to all squares

Write two ratios equivalent to each given ratio. (9-2)

6. $\dfrac{3}{7}$ 7. 12:16 8. 6 to 4

Express each ratio in simplest form. (9-2)

9. 10 to 18
10. 25:10
11. 2 cm to 25 mm
12. 4 in. to 2 ft
13. $\dfrac{18}{24}$
14. 9:27
15. 36 to 12
16. 2 dimes to 5 nickels
17. $RS{:}AB$ if $RS = \frac{4}{5} \cdot AB$
18. $XY{:}CD$ if $CD = 3 \cdot XY$

Determine whether each proportion is true. (9-3)

19. $\dfrac{3}{4} \stackrel{?}{=} \dfrac{6}{9}$ 20. $\dfrac{6}{18} \stackrel{?}{=} \dfrac{9}{27}$ 21. $\dfrac{10}{15} \stackrel{?}{=} \dfrac{12}{18}$

Find the indicated information. (9-3)

22. Given the proportion $\frac{4}{5} = \frac{x}{9}$, identify each of the following.
    a. first term b. second term
    c. third term d. fourth term
    e. means f. extremes

Use each set of numbers to write a true proportion. (9-3)

23. 4, 5, 12, 15 24. 6, 9, 12, 8

Solve each proportion. (9-3)

25. $3{:}y = 4{:}24$ 26. $\dfrac{a}{6} = \dfrac{4}{3}$

27. $\dfrac{3}{4} = \dfrac{5}{x}$ 28. $\dfrac{6}{y} = \dfrac{4}{3}$

Find the indicated information. (9-3)

29. a. Write a true proportion in which the means are 6 and 4.
    b. Write a true proportion in which 5 is the fourth term.

Write a proportion that can be used to solve each problem. (9-4)

30. A car travels 168 miles on 6 gallons of gas. How far can it travel on 8 gallons of gas?

31. On a certain map, 2 cm represents a distance of 130 km. What distance is represented by 5 cm?

32. A cookie recipe for 30 cookies calls for $\frac{1}{2}$ cup sugar. How much sugar is needed to use this recipe to make 75 cookies?

Find the indicated information.

33. Refer to the similar triangles shown. (9-5)

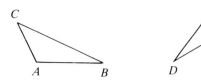

    a. $\triangle ABC \sim \triangle$? .
    b. $\overline{AC}$ corresponds to ? .
    c. $\angle B$ corresponds to $\angle$? .

34. Assume that $WXYZ \sim QUAD$. (9-5)
    a. Identify four pairs of corresponding angles.
    b. Identify four pairs of corresponding sides.

Find the indicated measures for each pair of similar triangles. (9-6)

35. **a.** x
    b. y
    c. $m\angle 1$

36. **a.** a
    b. b
    c. $m\angle 2$
    d. $m\angle 3$

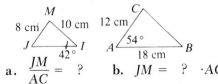

Find the indicated information.

37. Assume that $\triangle XYZ \sim \triangle ABC$ and $XY = \frac{1}{2} \cdot AB$. (9-6)
    a. $\angle C \cong \angle$? **b.** $AB =$? $\cdot XY$
    c. $YZ =$? $\cdot BC$
    d. If $m\angle Y = 60°$, $m\angle B =$?° .
    e. If $XY = 20$ cm, $AB =$? cm.

    f. If $BC = 30$ cm, $YZ \neq$? cm.
    g. Which triangle is larger?
    h. What is the constant of similarity of $\triangle XYZ$ to $\triangle ABC$?

38. Assume that $\triangle XYZ \sim \triangle ABC$. (9-6)

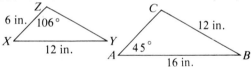

    a. $YZ =$? in. **b.** $AC =$? in.
    c. $m\angle X =$?° **d.** $m\angle C =$?°
    e. What is the constant of similarity of $\triangle XYZ$ to $\triangle ABC$?

39. Assume that $\triangle PLC \sim \triangle WXY$ and $PL = \frac{1}{3} \cdot WX$. (9-6)
    a. $LP =$? $\cdot XW$ **b.** $WX =$? $\cdot PL$
    c. $\dfrac{PL}{WX} =$? **d.** $\dfrac{WX}{PL} =$?
    e. If $WX = 6$ cm, $PL =$? cm.
    f. If $PL = 30$ cm, $WX =$? cm.
    g. If $m\angle Y = 30°$, $m\angle C =$?° .
    h. What is the constant of similarity of $\triangle PLC$ to $\triangle WXY$?

40. Assume that $\triangle JIM \sim \triangle ABC$. (9-6)

    a. $\dfrac{JM}{AC} =$? **b.** $JM =$? $\cdot AC$
    c. $\dfrac{JI}{AB} =$? **d.** $\dfrac{CB}{MI} =$?
    e. $JI =$? cm **f.** $BC =$? cm
    g. $m\angle J =$?° **h.** $m\angle B =$?°
    i. What is the constant of similarity of $\triangle JIM$ to $\triangle ABC$?

Find the constant of similarity of the first figure to the second. (9-6)

41. $\triangle RST \sim \triangle GHI$, $RS = 20$ cm, $GH = 5$ cm

42. $MATH \sim PQRS$, $QR = 30$ cm, $AT = 10$ cm

Use the grid method to draw the indicated reduction or enlargement on graph paper with squares of one-half centimeter length. (9–7)

43. 1:3 reduction

44. 3:1 enlargement

Trace each figure. Use the point method to draw the indicated reduction or enlargement. (9–8)

45. 1:2 reduction

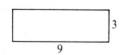

46. 5:2 enlargement

47. 2:1 enlargement

Determine whether each pair of polygons are similar. (9–10)

48.

49.

50.

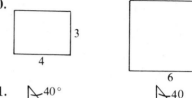

51.

Construct a triangle similar to △SCA by using the indicated method and constant of similarity. (9–9)

52. SSS~; 2
53. SAS~; 1
54. ASA~; $\frac{1}{2}$
55. SAS~; $\frac{3}{2}$

Look at △XYZ and △LMN. Complete each statement. (9–10)

56. Suppose $\frac{XY}{LM} = \frac{YZ}{MN}$ and $\angle Y \cong \angle M$. Then △XYZ ~ △LMN by the ? Property.

57. Suppose $\frac{ML}{YX} = \frac{LN}{XZ} = \frac{NM}{ZY}$. Then △XYZ ~ △LMN by the ? Property.

58. Suppose $\angle Z \cong \angle N$ and $\angle Y \cong \angle M$. Then △XYZ ~ △LMN by the ? Property.

59. Suppose you know that $\angle R \cong \angle D$ and wish to prove △RST ~ △DEF by using the SAS~ Property. What else must be shown to be true? (9–10)

OFF ON A TANGENT

Applications of Similar Polygons and Trigonometry

10-1

Proportional Segments

Two segments are said to be *divided proportionally* when the ratios of corresponding lengths are equivalent. For example, $\overline{AC}$ and $\overline{DF}$ shown below are divided proportionally by B and E, respectively, because the following are equivalent ratios:

$$\frac{AB}{BC} = \frac{DF}{EF} = \frac{2}{3} \qquad \frac{AB}{AC} = \frac{DE}{DF} = \frac{2}{5} \qquad \frac{BC}{AC} = \frac{EF}{DF} = \frac{3}{5}$$

In $\triangle ABC$ shown, $\overline{XY}$ is parallel to $\overline{BC}$. Since $\overline{XY} \parallel \overline{BC}$, $\angle 1 \cong \angle 2$ and $\angle 3 \cong \angle 4$, because when parallel lines are cut by a transversal, each pair of corresponding angles are congruent. Therefore $\triangle AXY \sim \triangle ABC$ by the AA Property. Since the ratios of the lengths of corresponding sides of similar triangles are equivalent,

$$\frac{AX}{AB} = \frac{AY}{AC} = \frac{XY}{BC}$$

All three ratios are equivalent to $\frac{1}{3}$. A comparison of other ratios indicates that the following are also equivalent ratios:

$$\frac{AX}{XB} = \frac{AY}{YC} = \frac{1}{2} \qquad \frac{XB}{AB} = \frac{YC}{AC} = \frac{2}{3}$$

Since the ratios of corresponding lengths for $\overline{AB}$ and $\overline{AC}$ in $\triangle ABC$ above are equivalent, we can conclude that $\overline{AB}$ and $\overline{AC}$ are divided proportionally by X and Y, respectively. This example illustrates the following conclusion, which is true for any triangle:

If a segment is parallel to one side of a triangle and intersects the other two sides, the following statements are true.

The triangle formed is similar to the original triangle.

The sides of the original triangle are divided proportionally.

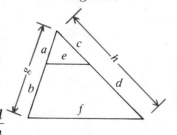

$$\frac{a}{g} = \frac{c}{h} = \frac{e}{f} \qquad \frac{a}{b} = \frac{c}{d} \qquad \frac{b}{g} = \frac{d}{h}$$

Example 1: Find each indicated measure. **a.** AR **b.** RS

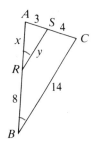

Solution:
Since $\angle ARS \cong \angle ABC$, $\overline{RS}$ and $\overline{BC}$ are parallel, because if two lines are cut by a transversal so that a pair of corresponding angles are congruent, the lines are parallel.

a. $\overline{AB}$ and $\overline{AC}$ are divided proportionally.

$$\frac{x}{8} = \frac{3}{4}$$

$$4x = 24$$

$$x = 6 \quad \textbf{\textit{Answer:}} \quad 6$$

b. $\triangle ARS \sim \triangle ABC$ so

$$\frac{3}{7} = \frac{y}{14}$$

$$7y = 42$$

$$y = 6 \quad \textbf{\textit{Answer:}} \quad 6$$

Look at the figure. Using $\triangle AEF$ and $\triangle ABF$ and the previous conclusion, the following are equivalent ratios:

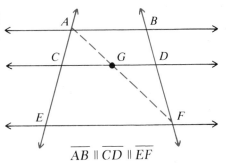

$$\frac{AC}{CE} = \frac{AG}{GF} \quad \text{and} \quad \frac{AG}{GF} = \frac{BD}{DF}$$

Therefore,

$$\frac{AC}{CE} = \frac{BD}{DF}$$

$\overline{AB} \parallel \overline{CD} \parallel \overline{EF}$

This example illustrates the following conclusion:

If three or more parallel lines intersect two transversals, the segments cut off on the transversals are divided proportionally.

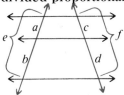

$$\frac{a}{b} = \frac{c}{d} \qquad \frac{a}{e} = \frac{c}{f} \qquad \frac{b}{e} = \frac{d}{f}$$

Example 2: Find x.

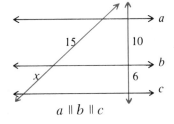

$a \parallel b \parallel c$

Solution:
$a \parallel b \parallel c$ so

$$\frac{15}{x} = \frac{10}{6}$$

$$10x = 90$$

$$x = 9$$

Find the missing measure in each proportion.

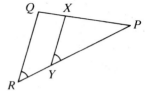

1. $\dfrac{PX}{XQ} = \dfrac{PY}{?}$

2. $\dfrac{PX}{PQ} = \dfrac{PY}{?}$

3. $\dfrac{XQ}{PQ} = \dfrac{YR}{?}$

4. $\dfrac{XY}{QR} = \dfrac{PX}{?}$

5. $\dfrac{PY}{PR} = \dfrac{XY}{?}$

6. $\dfrac{PX}{XY} = \dfrac{PQ}{?}$

Find the value of each ratio.

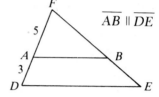

$\overline{AB} \parallel \overline{DE}$

7. $\dfrac{FA}{AD}$

8. $\dfrac{FB}{BE}$

9. $\dfrac{FA}{FD}$

10. $\dfrac{AB}{DE}$

11. $\dfrac{FB}{FE}$

12. $\dfrac{BE}{FB}$

Find the value of each ratio.

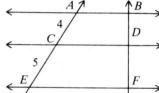

$\overline{AB} \parallel \overline{CD} \parallel \overline{EF}$

13. $\dfrac{AC}{CE}$

14. $\dfrac{BD}{DF}$

15. $\dfrac{AC}{AE}$

16. $\dfrac{BD}{BF}$

17. $\dfrac{CE}{AE}$

18. $\dfrac{DF}{BF}$

Find each indicated length.

19. x

20. y

21. c

22. d

$a \parallel b \parallel c$

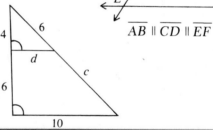

Find the missing measure in each proportion.

1. $\dfrac{RA}{AS} = \dfrac{RB}{?}$

2. $\dfrac{RA}{RS} = \dfrac{?}{RT}$

3. $\dfrac{AB}{ST} = \dfrac{RA}{?}$

4. $\dfrac{AS}{RS} = \dfrac{?}{RT}$

5. $\dfrac{RB}{RT} = \dfrac{AB}{?}$

6. $\dfrac{RA}{AB} = \dfrac{RS}{?}$

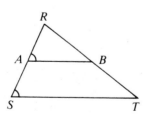

Find the value of each ratio.

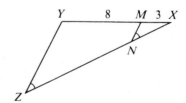

7. $\dfrac{XM}{MY}$

8. $\dfrac{XN}{NZ}$

9. $\dfrac{XM}{XY}$

10. $\dfrac{XN}{XZ}$

11. $\dfrac{MN}{YZ}$

12. $\dfrac{NZ}{XZ}$

Find the value of each ratio.

13. $\dfrac{BD}{DF}$ 14. $\dfrac{AC}{CE}$

15. $\dfrac{BD}{BF}$ 16. $\dfrac{AC}{AE}$

17. $\dfrac{DF}{BF}$ 18. $\dfrac{CE}{AE}$

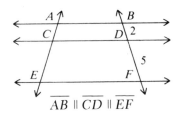

$\overline{AB} \parallel \overline{CD} \parallel \overline{EF}$

Find each indicated measure.

19. a. c 20. a. x
    b. d b. y

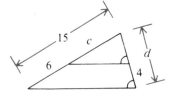

21. x 22. x

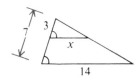

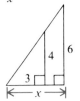

23. a. x c. $m\angle 1$
    b. y d. $m\angle 2$

$\overline{DE} \parallel \overline{BC}$

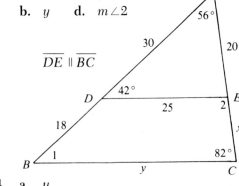

24. a. y
    b. CD

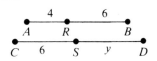

$\overline{AB}$ and $\overline{CD}$ are divided proportionally by points R and S, respectively.

25. a. x 26. y
    b. y

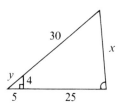

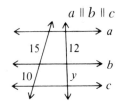

DID YOU KNOW THAT....

At rest, all warm-blooded animals lose the same amount of heat per unit area of skin. Therefore, their required food supply is proportional to their total area, *not* their volume or weight. As a result, each day a small animal must eat an amount of food equal to as much as one half or more of its weight.

10-2

Dividing a Segment into Congruent Parts

The conclusions from the previous lesson can be used to develop the following construction, which will enable you to divide any segment into any given number of congruent parts.

The statement below is a special case of one of those conclusions:

> If three or more parallel lines intersect two transversals and cut off congruent segments on one transversal, the parallel lines cut off congruent segments on the other transversal.

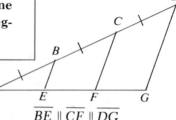

For example, in the figure shown, $AB = BC = CD$. Therefore, we can conclude that $AE = EF = FG$.

$$\overleftrightarrow{BE} \parallel \overleftrightarrow{CF} \parallel \overleftrightarrow{DG}$$

Construction 20

Dividing a Segment into Three or More Congruent Parts

Problem
Divide $\overline{AB}$ into three congruent parts.

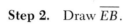

Procedure

Step 1. Draw a ray with endpoint A. Use a compass to mark off three congruent segments on this ray.
$$AC = CD = DE$$

Step 2. Draw $\overline{EB}$.

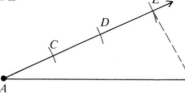

Step 3. Construct lines through C and D that are parallel to $\overline{BE}$. (See Constructions 14–16 on pages 193–194.)
$(\overleftrightarrow{CX} \parallel \overleftrightarrow{DY} \parallel \overleftrightarrow{BE}.)$
Then $AX = XY = YB$.

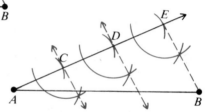

Construction 20 has an important application in constructing similar triangles. In Lesson 9–9, the constants of similarity were limited to numbers such as $\frac{1}{2}$, 1, $\frac{3}{2}$, 2, $\frac{5}{2}$, and 3. Construction 20 allows the use of a wider variety. In the problem used to demonstrate Construction 20, $\overline{AB}$ was divided into three congruent parts. After this has been done, you can construct segments having such lengths as $\frac{2}{3} \cdot AB$, $\frac{4}{3} \cdot AB$, and $\frac{5}{3} \cdot AB$. For five congruent parts, segments with lengths such as $\frac{2}{5} \cdot AB$, $\frac{3}{5} \cdot AB$, and $\frac{4}{5} \cdot AB$ can be constructed.

DISCUSS

Look at Construction 20.
1. Why is $AX = XY = YB$?
2. Would the steps of the construction be different if the size of $\angle A$ were different? if the length of $\overline{AB}$ were different? if $\overline{AC}$ were a different length?
3. How would you change the construction to divide $\overline{AB}$ into five congruent parts? into six congruent parts?
4. Suppose the problem had been to divide $\overline{AB}$ into two or four congruent parts. What other construction could have been used instead?
5. Which conclusion from Lesson 10–1 is the conclusion on page 400 a special case of?

CLASS PRACTICE

1. Draw a figure like the one shown. Construct a line through P that is parallel to $\overline{AB}$.
2. Draw a segment at least 8 cm long. Label it $\overline{CD}$. Use Construction 20 to divide it into four congruent parts.

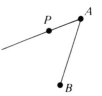

Using $\overline{CD}$ in Exercise 2, construct a segment of each indicated length.
3. $\frac{3}{4} \cdot CD$ 4. $\frac{5}{4} \cdot CD$

EXERCISES

Draw a segment at least 8 cm long. Label it $\overline{XY}$. Use Construction 20 to divide it into the indicated number of congruent parts.
1. 2   2. 3   3. 4   4. 5

Draw a segment at least 8 cm long. Label it $\overline{CD}$. Construct a segment of each indicated length.
5. $\frac{2}{3} \cdot CD$ 6. $\frac{5}{3} \cdot CD$

Construct a triangle similar to △ABC shown using the indicated method and constant of similarity.

7. SSS; $\frac{3}{2}$

8. ASA; $\frac{1}{3}$

9. ASA; $\frac{2}{3}$

10. SAS; 1

11. Construct a triangle similar to △RST using $\frac{4}{3}$ as the constant of similarity.

12. Construct a triangle similar to △RST above using $\frac{2}{3}$ as the constant of similarity.

13. $\overline{AB}$ has been drawn on a sheet of lined notebook paper. (See drawing.) Why is $\overline{AB}$ divided into five congruent parts?

===== Applications =====

Musical Harmony

When a guitar string is plucked, it vibrates. The vibrating string makes air particles vibrate. The air particles carry the vibration to your ear, so you hear a sound. Pythagoras, the Greek mathematician who stated the Pythagorean theorem more than 2500 years ago, found a relationship between the length of a string and the pitch of a musical note.

If you pluck a guitar string, it vibrates as shown in the top picture, producing a certain note. If you divide the string into two congruent segments with your finger and pluck the string, it vibrates as shown in the second picture. This note is the octave above the first note. If the string is divided into three congruent segments, the note is the fifth above the octave. Pythagoras found that, in general, notes that sound pleasing together are the result of dividing a string into a whole number of congruent segments.

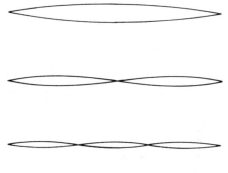

10-3

Area and Perimeter of Similar Polygonal Regions

In the following **EXPLORING** you will investigate the relationship among these three ratios for similar figures: lengths of corresponding sides, perimeters, and areas.

EXPLORING
Area and Perimeter Ratios of Similar Figures

1. $\triangle GHI \sim \triangle RST$ shown. The constant of similarity of $\triangle GHI$ to $\triangle RST$ is 2. Find the following information.

   a. Area of $\triangle GHI$ **b.** Area of $\triangle RST$

   c. $\dfrac{\text{Area of } \triangle GHI}{\text{Area of } \triangle RST}$ **d.** Perimeter of $\triangle GHI$

   e. Perimeter of $\triangle RST$ **f.** $\dfrac{\text{Perimeter of } \triangle GHI}{\text{Perimeter of } \triangle RST}$

2. Compare the ratio of the areas and the ratio of the perimeters with the constant of similarity.

3. Shown below are two more pairs of similar polygonal regions. For each pair of similar regions, compare the ratio of the areas and the ratio of the perimeters with the constant of similarity.

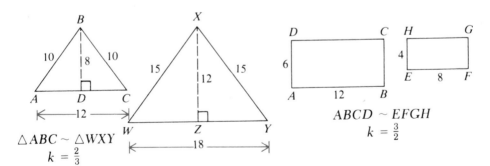

$\triangle ABC \sim \triangle WXY$
$k = \frac{2}{3}$

$ABCD \sim EFGH$
$k = \frac{3}{2}$

If you did the preceding **EXPLORING** carefully, you discovered the following conclusion, which is stated here in two different ways:

> If two polygonal regions are similar and the ratio of the lengths of a pair of corresponding sides is $a{:}b$, then the following statements are true:
>
> > The ralio of their perimeters is $a{:}b$.
> >
> > The ratio of their areas is $a^2{:}b^2$.

> If region $X \sim$ region Y and $k =$ the constant of similarity of region X to region Y, then the following statements are true:
>
> > Perimeter of region $X = k \cdot$ Perimeter of region Y
> >
> > Area of region $X = k^2 \cdot$ Area of region Y

In summary, these conclusions state that when you multiply each side of any polygonal region by some number k, you multiply its perimeter by k and its area by k^2. Although we will limit our work in this book to polygons, these conclusions apply to some similar two-dimensional figures that are not polygons.

In this book, when given information such as $\triangle ABC \sim \triangle WXY$ with $k = \frac{1}{2}$, it is assumed that we are comparing the first region to the second. (The constant of similarity of $\triangle ABC$ to $\triangle WXY$ is $\frac{1}{2}$.) Therefore, if $\triangle ABC \sim \triangle WXY$, then $k = \dfrac{AB}{WX} = \dfrac{BC}{XY} = \dfrac{AC}{WY}$.

CLASS PRACTICE

Each exercise concerns two similar regions. Find the indicated information. k is the ratio of the lengths of corresponding sides, or the constant of similarity.

1. $k = 3{:}7$; ratio of perimeters = ? ; ratio of areas = ?
2. $k =$? ; ratio of perimeters = 3:5; ratio of areas = ?
3. $k =$? ; ratio of perimeters = ? ; ratio of areas = 25:64

Find the following information for WXYZ and ABCD shown.

4. WX:AB

5. k

6. $\dfrac{\text{Perimeter of } WXYZ}{\text{Perimeter of } ABCD}$

7. Perimeter of $WXYZ =$? $\cdot$ Perimeter of $ABCD$

8. $\dfrac{\text{Area of } WXYZ}{\text{Area of } ABCD}$

9. Area of $WXYZ =$? $\cdot$ Area of $ABCD$

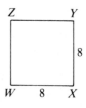

— A —

Each exercise concerns two similar regions. Copy and complete the table.

	Constant of Similarity	Ratio of Perimeters	Ratio of Areas
1.	1:2	?	?
2.	?	3:4	?
3.	?	?	4:25

Find the indicated information.

4. Find the following information for $\triangle ABC$ and $\triangle MNO$ shown.
   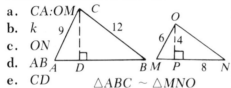
   $\triangle ABC \sim \triangle MNO$
   a. $CA:OM$
   b. k
   c. ON
   d. AB
   e. CD
   f. Perimeter of $\triangle ABC$
   g. Perimeter of $\triangle MNO$
   h. Area of $\triangle MNO$
   i. Area of $\triangle ABC$

5. Find the following information for $PQRS$ and $ABCD$ shown.
   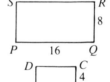
   $PQRS \sim ABCD$
   a. $RQ:CB$
   b. k
   c. AB
   d. Perimeter of $PQRS$
   e. Perimeter of $ABCD$
   f. $\dfrac{\text{Perimeter of } PQRS}{\text{Perimeter of } ABCD}$
   g. Area of $PQRS$ h. Area of $ABCD$
   i. $\dfrac{\text{Area of } PQRS}{\text{Area of } ABCD}$

6. Find the following information for the figure shown.
   a. $AD:AB$ b. $DE:BC$ c. k

d. $\dfrac{\text{Perimeter of } \triangle ADE}{\text{Perimeter of } \triangle ABC}$

e. $\dfrac{\text{Area of } \triangle ADE}{\text{Area of } \triangle ABC}$

$\triangle ADE \sim \triangle ABC$

— B —

7. Suppose the length of each side of a triangle is multiplied by four. By what number is each of the following multiplied?
   a. Perimeter   b. Area

8. The lengths of two corresponding sides of similar regions are 4 and 9.
   a. Find the ratio of perimeters.
   b. Find the ratio of areas.

9. Area of $\triangle MNO = 18$ in.²
   $\triangle MNO \sim \triangle ABC$ with $k = 3$
   Find the area of $\triangle ABC$.

10. Rectangular region $STOP \sim$ rectangular region $ABCD$. Area of $STOP = \frac{4}{9} \cdot$ Area of $ABCD$. Find the constant of similarity of $STOP$ to $ABCD$.

11. Find the following information for $\triangle RST \sim \triangle XYZ$ with $k = \frac{3}{4}$.
    a. $RS:XY$
    b. If $XY = 12$ cm, $RS = $? cm.
    c. $\dfrac{\text{Perimeter of } \triangle RST}{\text{Perimeter of } \triangle XYZ}$
    d. Perimeter of $\triangle RST = $? $\cdot$ Perimeter of $\triangle XYZ$
    e. If the perimeter of $\triangle XYZ$ is 32 cm, what is the perimeter of $\triangle RST$?
    f. $\dfrac{\text{Area of } \triangle RST}{\text{Area of } \triangle XYZ}$
    g. Area of $\triangle RST = $? $\cdot$ Area of $\triangle XYZ$
    h. If the area of $\triangle XYZ$ is 48 cm², what is the area of $\triangle RST$?

10-4

Total Area and Volume
of Similar Prisms

As was the case with polygonal regions, prisms are said to be similar when the corresponding angles are congruent and the lengths of corresponding edges are proportional.

In the following EXPLORING you will investigate the relationship among these three ratios for similar prisms: lengths of corresponding edges, total areas, and volumes.

EXPLORING

Total Area and Volume Ratios of Similar Prisms

1. Prism $A \sim$ prism B shown. The constant of similarity of prism A to prism B is 2. Find the following information.
   a. Total Area of prism A
   b. Total Area of prism B
   c. $\dfrac{\text{Total Area of prism } A}{\text{Total Area of prism } B}$
   d. Volume of prism A
   e. Volume of prism B
   f. $\dfrac{\text{Volume of prism } A}{\text{Volume of prism } B}$

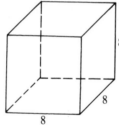

Prism A

Prism B

2. Compare the ratio of the total areas and the ratio of the volumes with the constant of similarity. Recall that the constant of similarity is equivalent to the ratio of the lengths of corresponding edges.
3. Shown below are two more pairs of similar prisms. In each case, k represents the constant of similarity of the first prism to the second.

   For each pair of similar prisms, compare the ratio of the total areas and the ratio of the volumes with the constant of similarity.

Prism $C \sim$ Prism D
$k = \frac{1}{3}$

Prism C

Prism D

Prism $E \sim$ Prism F
$k = \frac{3}{2}$

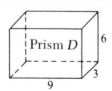

Prism E

Prism F

If you did the preceding EXPLORING carefully, you discovered the following conclusion, which is stated here in two different ways:

> If two prisms are similar and the ratio of the lengths of a pair of corresponding edges is $a{:}b$, then the following statements are true:
>
> The ratio of their total areas is $a^2{:}b^2$.
>
> The ratio of their volumes is $a^3{:}b^3$.

> If prism $X \sim$ prism Y and k = the constant of similarity of prism X to prism Y, then the following statements are true:
>
> Total Area of prism $X = k^2 \cdot$ Total Area of prism Y
>
> Volume of prism $X = k^3 \cdot$ Volume of prism Y

In summary, these conclusions state that when you multiply the length of each edge of a prism by some number k, you multiply its total area by k^2 and its volume by k^3. Although we will limit our work in this book to prisms, these conclusions apply to some similar three-dimensional figures that are not prisms.

CLASS PRACTICE

Find the value of each expression.

1. 1^2
2. 1^3
3. 2^2
4. 2^3
5. 3^2
6. 3^3
7. $\left(\frac{1}{2}\right)^2$
8. $\left(\frac{1}{2}\right)^3$
9. $\left(\frac{1}{3}\right)^2$
10. $\left(\frac{1}{3}\right)^3$
11. $\left(\frac{1}{4}\right)^2$
12. $\left(\frac{1}{4}\right)^3$
13. $\left(\frac{2}{3}\right)^3$
14. $\left(\frac{4}{3}\right)^3$
15. $\left(\frac{2}{5}\right)^2$
16. $\left(\frac{2}{5}\right)^3$

Each exercise concerns two similar prisms. Copy and complete the table.

	Ratio of Lengths of Corresponding Edges (Constant of Similarity)	Ratio of Total Areas	Ratio of Volumes
17.	3:5	?	?
18.	?	1:16	?
19.	?	?	64:27

Look at the similar prisms. Find the following information.

20. *GH:AB*   21. *HI:BC*
22. *IJ:CD*   23. *k*
24. Total Area of prism *X*
25. Total Area of prism *Y*
26. $\dfrac{\text{Total Area of prism }X}{\text{Total Area of prism }Y}$
27. Total Area of prism *X* = ? · Total Area of prism *Y*
28. Volume of prism *X*
29. Volume of prism *Y*
30. $\dfrac{\text{Volume of prism }X}{\text{Volume of prism }Y}$
31. Volume of prism *X* = ? · Volume of prism *Y*

Prism *X*: 6 cm, 3 cm, 3 cm (*G*, *H*, *I*, *J*)
Prism *Y*: 8 cm, 4 cm, 4 cm (*A*, *B*, *C*, *D*)

Prism *X* ~ Prism *Y*

EXERCISES

— A —

Each exercise concerns two similar prisms. Copy and complete the table.

	Constant of Similarity	Ratio of Total Areas	Ratio of Volumes
1.	2:3	?	?
2.	?	9:16	?
3.	?	?	8:125
4.	4:1	?	?

5. Find the following information for the similar prisms shown.

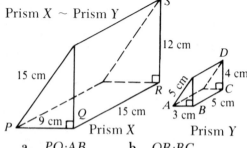

Prism *X* ~ Prism *Y*

Prism *X*: 15 cm, 12 cm, 15 cm, 9 cm (*P*, *Q*, *R*, *S*)
Prism *Y*: 4 cm, 5 cm, 3 cm, 5 cm (*A*, *B*, *C*, *D*)

a. *PQ:AB*   b. *QR:BC*
c. *RS:CD*   d. *k*
e. Total Area of prism *X*

f. Total Area of prism *Y*
g. $\dfrac{\text{Total Area of prism }X}{\text{Total Area of prism }Y}$
h. Volume of prism *X*
i. Volume of prism *Y*
j. $\dfrac{\text{Volume of prism }X}{\text{Volume of prism }Y}$

For Exercises 6–12, *k* = constant of similarity of the first prism to the second prism.

6. prism *M* ~ prism *N*   *k* = 4
   Total Area of *M* = 32 cm²
   Total Area of *N* = ?   cm²
7. prism *P* ~ prism *Q*
   Total Area of *P* = 40 cm²
   Total Area of *Q* = 10 cm²
   k = ?
8. prism *A* ~ prism *B*   *k* = 3
   Volume of *A* = 4 cm³
   Volume of *B* = ?   cm³
9. prism *C* ~ prism *D*   *k* = 2
   Volume of *D* = 24 cm³
   Volume of *C* = ?   cm³

10. prism $X \sim$ prism Y
Volume of $X = 5$ cm³
Volume of $Y = 40$ cm³
$k = $?

11. prism $E \sim$ prism F
Volume of $E = 32$ cm³
Volume of $F = 4$ cm³
$k = $?

12. A prism is similar to a second prism with a volume of 10 cubic centimeters and with $k = 5$. Find the volume of the second prism.

____ B ____

For Exercises 13–16, suppose two prisms are similar with a constant of similarity of $\frac{2}{5}$.

13. The longest edge of the larger prism is 15 cm long. Find the length of the longest edge of the smaller prism.

14. The base area of the smaller prism is 4 cm². Find the base area of the larger prism.

15. The total area of the larger prism is 350 cm². Find the total area of the smaller prism.

16. The volume of the smaller prism is 24 cm³. Find the volume of the larger prism.

Look at prism A.

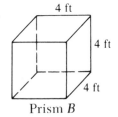

Prism A

9 cm
2 cm
3 cm

17. Find the total area of prism A.

18. Find the total area of a prism similar to prism A for each given value of k.
a. 1   b. $\frac{1}{3}$ c. 2

19. Find the volume of prism A.

20. Find the volume of a prism similar to prism A for each given value of k.
a. 1   b. 2   c. 3
d. $\frac{1}{3}$ e. $\frac{2}{3}$ f. $\frac{4}{3}$

Look at prism B.

Prism B

4 ft
4 ft
4 ft

21. Find the total area of prism B.

22. Find the total area of a prism similar to prism B for each given value of k.
a. 1   b. 2
c. $\frac{1}{2}$ d. $\frac{1}{4}$

23. Find the volume of prism B.

24. Find the volume of a prism similar to prism B for each given value of k.
a. 1   b. 2   c. 3
d. $\frac{1}{2}$ e. $\frac{1}{4}$ f. $\frac{3}{2}$

DID YOU KNOW THAT....

The introduction of the symbols used in geometry for "similar" ($\sim$) and "congruent" ($\cong$) is credited to the German mathematician Gottfried Leibnitz (1646–1760).

10-5

Scale Drawings

One application of similar figures is the making of scale drawings. The similar figures—enlargements and reductions—you drew and constructed previously are examples of *scale drawings*. Scale drawings are used to draw plans or pictures of objects that are either too large or too small to draw actual size on a sheet of paper.

The relationship between the size of a scale drawing and the actual size of the object being represented is indicated by the *scale*. The scale may be expressed in several ways, such as $\frac{1}{36}$, 1:8, or $\frac{1}{4}$ in. = 1 ft, or by means of a picture like a ruler, as is often used on road maps.

A scale such as "$\frac{1}{36}$" means that for every unit of length on the scale drawing, there are 36 units of length on the actual object. For example, a length of 1 cm on the drawing would represent 36 cm on the actual object. Notice that such a scale is the ratio of lengths on the scale drawing to corresponding lengths on the actual object. Therefore, it is also equivalent to the constant of similarity of the scale drawing to the actual object. Scales such as "1:8" have the same meaning.

A scale such as "$\frac{1}{4}$ in. = 1 ft" means that every $\frac{1}{4}$ inch on the drawing represents a length of 1 foot on the actual object. Such scales do *not* directly express the ratio of lengths on the scale drawing to corresponding lengths on the actual object. For the scale "$\frac{1}{4}$ in. = 1 ft," this ratio is 1:48.

CLASS PRACTICE

Suppose a scale drawing has a scale of 1:4. Find the actual distance represented by each length on the drawing.

1. 2 cm
2. 2.5 cm
3. 6 cm
4. 0.5 cm

Suppose a scale drawing has a scale of $\frac{1}{8}$ in. = 6 ft. Find the actual distance represented by each length on the drawing.

5. $\frac{1}{4}$ in.
6. $\frac{1}{2}$ in.
7. $\frac{5}{8}$ in.
8. 2 in.

Look at the scale drawing of a house. Using the given scale, find the following actual distances.

9. Width of bedroom 1
10. Width of bedroom 2
11. Length and width of patio
12. Length and width of living room
13. Length and width of garage

Find the indicated information.

14. A scale on a certain road map is "one inch to 1.6 miles, or 1:101,376." What part of the scale more directly expresses how actual distances are related to lengths on the map?

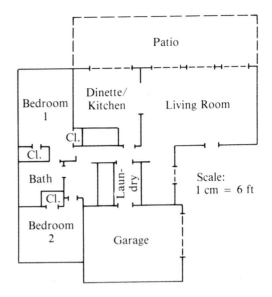

Scale: 1 cm = 6 ft

EXERCISES

— A —

Suppose a scale drawing has a scale of $\frac{1}{2}$ in. = 8 ft. Find the actual distance represented by each length on the drawing.

1. 1 in.
2. 3 in.
3. $4\frac{1}{2}$ in.
4. $\frac{1}{4}$ in.

Suppose a scale drawing has a scale of $\frac{1}{16}$ in. = 1 in. Find the actual distance represented by each length on the drawing.

5. $\frac{1}{2}$ in.
6. 1 in.
7. 2 in.
8. $\frac{1}{4}$ in.

On a certain map, a distance of 50 miles is represented by $2\frac{1}{2}$ inches. Find the number of miles represented by each length on the map.

9. 5 in.
10. 2 in.
11. 1 in.
12. 10 in.

— B —

13. On a scale drawing of a room, the dimensions are $2\frac{1}{2}$ in. by $2\frac{1}{4}$ in. Suppose the scale is $\frac{1}{4}$ in. = 2 ft. Find the following information.
    a. The actual dimensions of the room.
    b. The actual area of the room in square feet.

Regulation minimum sizes for various athletic fields are given. Using the indicated scale, make a scale drawing of each.

14. Baseball diamond: 90 ft by 90 ft; Scale: $\frac{1}{4}$ in. = 10 ft
15. Basketball court: 84 ft × 50 ft; Scale: 1 cm = 10 ft
16. Football field: 100 yd × 160 ft; Scale: $\frac{1}{2}$ in. = 40 ft
17. Football field: 100 yd × 160 ft; Scale: 1 cm = 40 ft

Make each indicated scale drawing.

18. Measure in centimeters the dimensions of the cover of this textbook. Choose an appropriate scale and make a scale drawing of the cover.

_ C _

19. Choose an appropriate scale and make a scale drawing of your classroom.

Each figure shown is a scale drawing labeled with the distances being represented. Measure the dimensions of each scale drawing and find an appropriate scale for each. Use metric units for Exercises 20 and 21 and customary units for Exercises 22 and 23.

20.

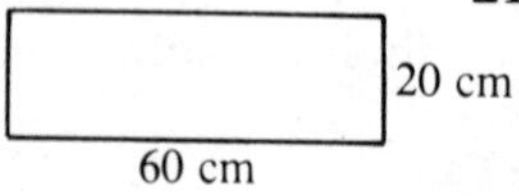

60 cm

21.

10 m
35 m

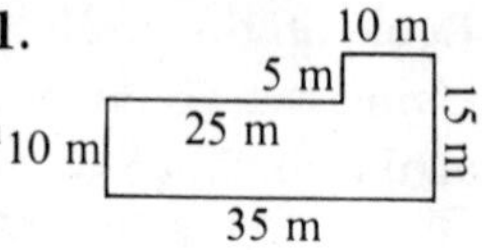

20 cm
10 m
25 m
5 m
10 m
15 m

22.

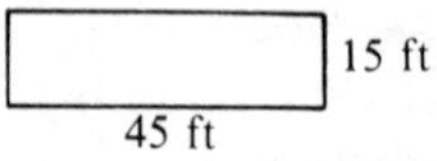

45 ft

15 ft

23.

15 ft

9 ft

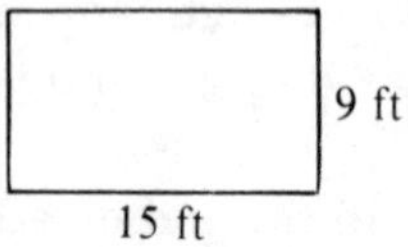

24. Suppose the length and width of a room are doubled. Compared to the original room, the new room will require how many times as much of each of the following?
  a. Baseboard   b. Carpeting
  c. Ceiling paint   d. Wall paint

Test Yourself

Find each indicated measure.

1. x
2. y

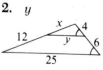

12
x
4
y
6
25

3. x

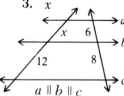

x 6
12   8
$a \parallel b \parallel c$
a
b
c

4. YD

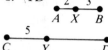

2   3
A X B
5
C Y D

Find the indicated information.

5. Draw a segment at least 8 cm long. Label it $\overline{AB}$. Construct a segment whose length is $\frac{4}{5} \cdot AB$.

6. $\triangle GHI \sim \triangle ABC$ $k = \frac{2}{3}$
  a. $\dfrac{\text{Perimeter of } \triangle GHI}{\text{Perimeter of } \triangle ABC} = $?
  b. $\dfrac{\text{Area of } \triangle GHI}{\text{Area of } \triangle ABC} = $?

7. prism $X \sim$ prism Y $k = \frac{1}{2}$
  Volume of prism Y = 160 cm³
  Volume of prism X = ? cm³

8. prism $A \sim$ prism B $k = 3$
  Total Area of prism A = 30 cm²
  Total Area of prism B = ? cm²

9. Use a scale of $\frac{1}{4}$ in. = 2 ft to make a scale drawing of a 20-ft by 12-ft rectangle.

10-6

Trigonometric Ratios

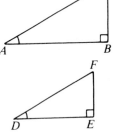

Trigonometry is based on properties of similar right triangles. The word "trigonometry" comes from two Greek words meaning "triangle measure." Using trigonometry, lengths that cannot be measured directly can be found through calculation.

Any two right triangles with a pair of congruent corresponding acute angles are similar because of the AA Property. For the two right triangles shown, $\angle A \cong \angle D$. Since $\angle B$ and $\angle E$ are also congruent, $\triangle ABC \sim \triangle DEF$ because of the AA Property. In similar triangles, the lengths of corresponding sides are proportional. Therefore these are equivalent ratios:

$$\frac{AB}{AC} = \frac{DE}{DF} \qquad \frac{BC}{AC} = \frac{EF}{DF} \qquad \frac{BC}{AB} = \frac{EF}{DE}$$

The lengths of corresponding sides in similar right triangles are proportional. Further, these ratios depend only on the size of the acute angle selected—*not* on the length of the sides of the triangles. Having chosen an acute angle, the legs of a right triangle may be identified as the *leg adjacent to the angle* and the *leg opposite the angle*, as shown.

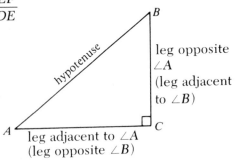

leg opposite ∠A
(leg adjacent to ∠B)

leg adjacent to ∠A
(leg opposite ∠B)

Three of the ratios of the lengths of the sides in any right triangle have been given special names.

If ∠A is an acute angle in a right triangle, then

$$\text{sine (sin) } A = \frac{\text{length of leg opposite } \angle A}{\text{length of hypotenuse}} \qquad \text{cosine (cos) } A = \frac{\text{length of leg adjacent to } \angle A}{\text{length of hypotenuse}}$$

$$\text{tangent (tan) } A = \frac{\text{length of leg opposite } \angle A}{\text{length of leg adjacent to } \angle A}$$

Example:
For the right triangle shown, find the decimal value of each ratio to the nearest thousandth.
a. sin R, cos R, tan R
b. sin T, cos T, tan T

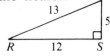

Solution:

a. $\sin R = \dfrac{ST}{RT} = \dfrac{5}{13} \approx 0.385$

$\cos R = \dfrac{RS}{RT} = \dfrac{12}{13} \approx 0.923$

$\tan R = \dfrac{ST}{RS} = \dfrac{5}{12} \approx 0.417$

b. $\sin T = \dfrac{RS}{RT} = \dfrac{12}{13} \approx 0.923$ $\cos T = \dfrac{ST}{RT} = \dfrac{5}{13} \approx 0.385$ $\tan T = \dfrac{RS}{ST} = \dfrac{12}{5} = 2.400$

CLASS PRACTICE

Look at △ABC. Identify each of the following.

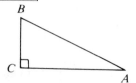

1. Hypotenuse
2. Leg opposite ∠A
3. Leg adjacent to ∠A
4. Leg opposite ∠B
5. Leg adjacent to ∠B

Look at △DEF. Find each trigonometric ratio and express it (a) in simplest fraction form and (b) to the nearest thousandth.

6. sin F
7. cos F
8. tan F
9. sin D
10. cos D
11. tan D

Look at your results for Exercises 6–11.

12. **a.** Why is sin D = cos F?   **b.** Why is cos D = sin F?
13. What does "sin D" represent—a number, an angle, or an angle multiplied by a number?

EXERCISES

_ A _

Classify each statement as true or false.

1. The longest side of any right triangle is the hypotenuse.
2. The leg opposite an acute angle of a right triangle cannot be as long as the hypotenuse.
3. The leg adjacent to an acute angle of a right triangle cannot be as long as the hypotenuse.
4. The leg opposite an acute angle of a right triangle can be longer than the leg adjacent to that same angle.
5. The leg adjacent to an acute angle of a right triangle can be longer than the leg opposite that same angle.
6. The leg opposite an acute angle of a right triangle can be congruent to the leg adjacent to that same angle.

Find the indicated information.

7. Look at △XYZ. Identify each of the following.

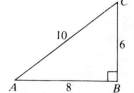

   a. Hypotenuse
   b. Leg opposite ∠X
   c. Leg adjacent to ∠X
   d. Leg opposite ∠Y
   e. Leg adjacent to ∠Y

8. Look at △ABC. Find each trigonometric ratio and express it in simplest fraction form.
   a. sin A
   b. cos A
   c. tan A
   d. sin C
   e. cos C
   f. tan C

9. Look at $\triangle RST$. Find the decimal value of each trigonometric ratio to the nearest thousandth.

a. sin R
b. cos R
c. tan R
d. sin S
e. cos S
f. tan S

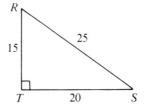

Find the following information for each 45-45-90 triangle shown. Express each trigonometric ratio in simplest radical form.

a. Length of hypotenuse b. tan 45°
c. sin 45° d. cos 45°

10.

11.

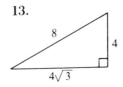

Find the following information for each 30-60-90 triangle shown. Express each trigonometric ratio in simplest radical form.

a. sin 30° b. cos 30° c. tan 30°
d. sin 60° e. cos 60° f. tan 60°

12.

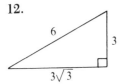

13.

— B —

14. Look at your results for Exercises 10-11. Would your answers to parts b-d be the same for any 45-45-90 triangle? Why or why not?

15. Look at your results for Exercises 12-13. Would your answers be the same for any 30-60-90 triangle? Why or why not?

16. Look at the 30-60-90 right triangle. Classify each statement as true or false.

a. sin 30° = cos 60°
b. cos 30° = sin 60°
c. tan 30° = tan 60°

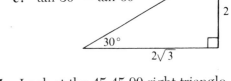

17. Look at the 45-45-90 right triangle. Does sin 45° = cos 45°?

18. Look at $\triangle ABC$. Classify each statement as true or false.

a. sin A = cos C
b. cos A = sin C
c. tan A = tan C

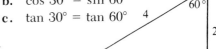

— C —

Explain why each statement is true.

19. It is impossible for the sine of an angle to be greater than 1.

20. It is impossible for the cosine of an angle to be greater than 1.

21. It is possible for the tangent of an angle to be greater than 1.

22. It is possible for the tangent of an angle to be less than 1.

23. sin 20° = cos 70°
24. cos 20° = sin 70°
25. If $m\angle A = 45°$, then tan A = 1.
26. If tan A < 1, then $m\angle A < 45°$.
27. If tan A > 1, then $m\angle A > 45°$.

10-7

Using a Table of Trigonometric Ratios

The value of the ratios used to compute sines, cosines, and tangents is determined solely by the measure of the acute angle, not by the lengths of the sides. For certain angle measures the value of these ratios can be computed easily. For example, in Exercise 12 of the previous lesson you found the following information:

$$\sin 30° = \frac{3}{6} = \frac{1}{2} \qquad \cos 30° = \frac{3\sqrt{3}}{6} = \frac{\sqrt{3}}{2}$$

$$\tan 30° = \frac{3}{3\sqrt{3}} = \frac{3}{3\sqrt{3}} \cdot \frac{\sqrt{3}}{\sqrt{3}} = \frac{3\sqrt{3}}{9} = \frac{\sqrt{3}}{3}$$

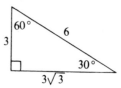

By using a decimal approximation to the nearest thousandth for $\sqrt{3}$, we obtain the following results:

$$\sin 30° = \frac{1}{2} = 0.500 \qquad \cos 30° = \frac{\sqrt{3}}{2} \approx \frac{1.732}{2}, \text{ or } 0.866$$

$$\tan 30° = \frac{\sqrt{3}}{3} \approx \frac{1.732}{3}, \text{ or } 0.577$$

In the same way we can find numerical values for sin 45°, cos 45°, tan 45°, sin 60°, cos 60°, and tan 60°.

EXPLORING

Decimal Approximations for Trigonometric Ratios

1. Draw three noncongruent right triangles that contain a 40° angle.
2. Measure the sides of each triangle to the nearest millimeter.
3. For each triangle, find each ratio and express it in simplest fraction form:
   a. sin 40°   b. cos 40°   c. tan 40°
4. Find a decimal approximation to the nearest thousandth for each ratio in step 3.
5. Look at your results in step 4. Which results are the same?

If done accurately, your results should indicate that the value of a trigonometric ratio depends solely on the measure of the acute angle, not on the lengths of the sides of the triangle. This is true because of the properties of similar triangles.

Look at the triangles with a 25° angle. The two triangles are similar because of the AA Property. Therefore, the value of sin 25° (as well as cos 25° or tan 25°) will be the same for both triangles because the ratios of the lengths of corresponding sides of similar triangles are equivalent.

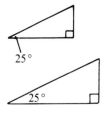

The value of the sine, cosine, and tangent ratios for a 35° angle could be found by drawing a triangle such as the one shown (any right triangle with a 35° angle would do) and finding the decimal approximation for each ratio to the nearest thousandth.

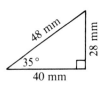

Approximate values for the trigonometric ratios of any acute angle may be found in this way. However, the values are not easy to compute. Fortunately, there is an easier way to find the desired ratios: these results are provided in a table. (See page 476.) The following examples illustrate the use of this table.

Example 1: Find each value.
 a. cos 43°
 b. tan 57°

Solution:
Using the appropriate columns,
 a. cos 43° = 0.731
 b. tan 57° = 1.540

Example 2: Find $m\angle A$.
 a. sin A = 0.156
 b. cos A = 0.358

Solution:
Using the appropriate columns,
 a. $m\angle A$ = 9°
 b. $m\angle A$ = 69°

Example 3: In $\triangle XYZ$, find each measure. a. $m\angle X$ b. XY

Solution:
a. The length of the leg opposite $\angle X$ and the length of the leg adjacent to $\angle X$ are known. Therefore the tangent ratio will be used.

$$\tan X = \frac{3}{4} = 0.750$$

Using the tangent column, we find:
tan 36° = 0.727
tan X = 0.750 difference: 0.023
tan 37° = 0.754 difference: 0.004

Since 0.750 is closer to 0.754, $m\angle X \approx$ 37° to the nearest degree.

b. By the Pythagorean Theorem,

$$XY^2 = 3^2 + 4^2 = 9 + 16 = 25$$

$$XY = \sqrt{25} = 5$$

Example 4: Find $m\angle A$.

Solution:
The length of the leg adjacent to $\angle A$ and the length of the hypotenuse are known. Therefore the cosine ratio will be used.

$$\cos A = \frac{8}{10} = 0.800$$

Using the cosine column in the table, we find that 0.800 is closest to 0.799. So $m\angle A \approx 37°$.

Notice that the ratio used in each example above depends on which lengths are known.

CLASS PRACTICE

Use the table on page 476 as needed. Find the value of each.

1. $\sin 8°$
2. $\sin 63°$
3. $\cos 17°$
4. $\cos 27°$
5. $\tan 32°$
6. $\tan 73°$

For each exercise, find $m\angle A$ to the nearest degree.

7. $\sin A = 0.788$
8. $\sin A = 0.450$
9. $\cos A = \frac{1}{2}$
10. $\cos A = 0.670$
11. $\tan A = 0.510$
12. $\tan A = 2$

In each right triangle, find $m\angle A$ to the nearest degree.

13.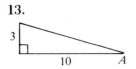

14.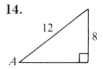

In each right triangle, find the indicated length. Write answers in simplest radical form.

15.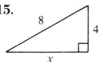

16.

EXERCISES

1. Define the following trigonometric ratios in terms of opposite leg, adjacent leg, and hypotenuse.
   a. sine
   b. cosine
   c. tangent

In Exercises 2–7, state the trigonometric ratio—sine, cosine, or tangent—you would use to find $m\angle A$.

2.

3.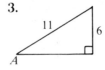

4.

5.

6.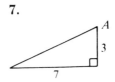

7.

Use the table of trigonometric ratios on page 476 as needed.

Find the value of each.

8.	sin 5°	**9.**	sin 32°
10.	sin 41°	**11.**	sin 87°
12.	cos 14°	**13.**	cos 26°
14.	cos 58°	**15.**	cos 71°
16.	tan 1°	**17.**	tan 13°
18.	tan 67°	**19.**	tan 77°

Locate the measure of each angle between two consecutive whole numbers.

20. If sin A = 0.300,
 m∠A is between ?° and ?° .
21. If cos A = 0.750,
 m∠A is between ?° and ?° .
22. If tan A = 1.300,
 m∠A is between ?° and ?° .

For each exercise, find m∠A to the nearest degree.

23.	sin A = 0.866	**24.**	sin A = 0.656
25.	sin A = 0.750	**26.**	sin A = $\frac{9}{10}$
27.	cos A = 0.485	**28.**	cos A = 0.974
29.	cos A = 0.750	**30.**	cos A = $\frac{2}{5}$
31.	tan A = 0.700	**32.**	tan A = 0.270
33.	tan A = 2.5	**34.**	tan A = 3

Find the indicated information.

35. Does tan 60° = 2·tan 30°?
36. Does cos 50° = cos 35° + cos 15°?
37. Complete the following statements.
 a. cos 22° = sin ?°
 b. sin 55° = cos ?°
38. Which is greater, cos 70° or tan 20°?

39. Refer to the numbered angles in the figure shown.

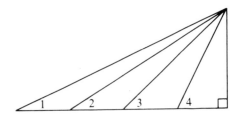

a. Which angle has the greatest sine?
b. Which has the greatest cosine?
c. Which has the greatest tangent?

In each right triangle, find the indicated length.

40.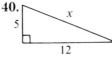
41.

42.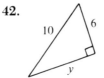
43.

In each right triangle, find the measure of ∠A to the nearest degree.

44.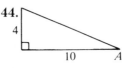
45.

46.
47.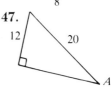

48.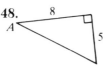
49.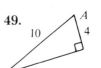

10-8

Using Trigonometric Ratios to Find a Missing Length or Angle Measure

In the preceding lesson you learned how to find the measure of an acute angle of a right triangle when the lengths of two sides are known. In this lesson you will learn how to find the lengths of the other two sides of a right triangle when you know the measure of one acute angle and the length of one side. The measure of the other acute angle can also be found by using the fact that the sum of the measures of the three angles of any triangle is 180°. Some examples are given below.

Example: Find each length to the nearest whole number.
  a. x b. y

Solution:

a. For the 28° angle, x and 9 are the lengths of the opposite leg and adjacent leg, respectively. Therefore the tangent ratio will be used.

$$\tan 28° = \frac{x}{9}$$
$$\frac{0.532}{1} \approx \frac{x}{9}$$
$$1 \cdot x \approx 9 \cdot 0.532 \approx 4.788$$
$$x \approx 5$$

b. For the 28° angle, 9 and y are the lengths of the adjacent leg and the hypotenuse, respectively. Therefore the cosine ratio will be used.

$$\cos 28° = \frac{9}{y}$$
$$\frac{0.883}{1} \approx \frac{9}{y}$$
$$(0.883)y \approx 9 \cdot 1 = 9$$
$$y \approx 9 \div 0.883 \approx 10.19$$
$$y \approx 10$$

Notice that the ratio used in each example depends on which lengths are known and which length you wish to find.

CLASS PRACTICE

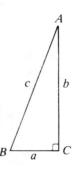

State the trigonometric ratio—sine, cosine, or tangent—you would use to solve each problem.

	Given:	Find:		Given:	Find:		Given:	Find:
1.	a, b	$m\angle A$	3.	b, c	$m\angle B$	5.	a, $m\angle A$	c
2.	a, c	$m\angle B$	4.	b, $m\angle A$	c	6.	a, $m\angle B$	b

Find the indicated measures in each triangle to the nearest whole number.

7. $m\angle D$
8. $m\angle F$

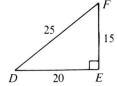

9. r
10. t

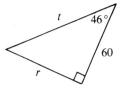

EXERCISES

State the trigonometric ratio—sine, cosine, or tangent—you would use to solve each problem.

Given:	Find:
1. d, f	$m\angle F$
2. e, f	$m\angle D$
3. e, f	$m\angle F$
4. e, d	$m\angle D$
5. f, $m\angle F$	e
6. f, $m\angle D$	e
7. d, $m\angle F$	f
8. f, $m\angle F$	d
9. d, $m\angle D$	e

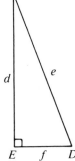

Select the equation that can be used to solve each problem.

10. a. $\sin A = \dfrac{8}{11}$

b. $\sin A = \dfrac{11}{8}$

c. $\cos A = \dfrac{8}{11}$

d. $\cos A = \dfrac{11}{8}$

$m\angle A = ?°$

11. a. $\tan A = \dfrac{3}{7}$

b. $\tan A = \dfrac{7}{3}$

c. $\sin A = \dfrac{3}{7}$

d. $\cos A = \dfrac{3}{7}$

$m\angle A = ?°$

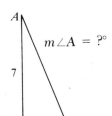

12. a. $\cos A = \dfrac{6}{13}$

b. $\cos A = \dfrac{13}{6}$

c. $\sin A = \dfrac{6}{13}$

d. $\sin A = \dfrac{13}{6}$

$m\angle A = ?°$

13. a. $\sin 35° = \dfrac{x}{10}$

b. $\cos 35° = \dfrac{x}{10}$

c. $\sin 35° = \dfrac{10}{x}$

d. $\cos 35° = \dfrac{10}{x}$

$x = ?$

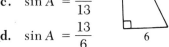

14. a. $\sin 40° = \dfrac{a}{12}$

b. $\cos 40° = \dfrac{a}{12}$

c. $\sin 40° = \dfrac{12}{a}$

d. $\cos 40° = \dfrac{12}{a}$

$a = ?$

Find x to the nearest whole number.

15.

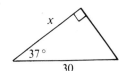

16.

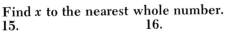

17.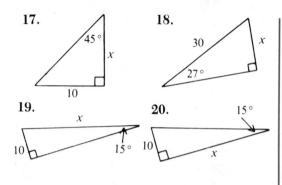

45°

x

10

18.

30

x

27°

19.

x

10

15°

20.

15°

10

x

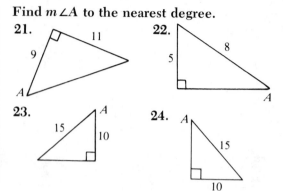

Find $m \angle A$ to the nearest degree.

21.

11

9

A

22.

8

5

A

23.

A

15

10

24. A

15

10

Everyday Geometry

Planting a Shade Tree

A tree that shades a house blocks the sun's light and heat, so the house stays cooler in summer. But in winter, when people in cool climates want more heat, even a leafless tree blocks some of the sun's energy.

Trigonometry can be used to predict how close to a house a tree can be planted without casting a shadow on the house in winter. Because Earth is tilted with respect to the sun, the altitude (angle) of the sun at noon varies throughout the year; it is lowest on December 21.

If $\angle A$ is the altitude of the sun at noon on December 21,

$$\tan A = \frac{\text{maximum height of tree}}{\text{minimum distance from house}}$$

EXERCISES

1. Suppose you live in Denver and want to plant a tree 50 feet from the house. What is the maximum height that the tree may attain?

2. Suppose you live in Minneapolis and want to plant a tree that will grow to be no more than 30 feet tall. How close to the house can you plant it?

Latitude (°N)	Cities Near This Latitude	Altitude of Sun at Noon on December 21
40	Denver; Philadelphia	24°
45	Minneapolis; Toronto	19°
50	Vancouver; Winnipeg	14°

10-9

Applying Trigonometric Ratios

These exercises provide additional practice with trigonometric ratios and present some applications of these ideas. The following terms will be used in some of the problems:

If a person looks *from A to B*, $\angle A$ is the *angle of elevation*. If a person looks *from B to A*, $\angle B$ is the *angle of depression*.

Angle of elevation and angle of depression are both determined by the line of sight and a horizontal ray. Notice that since $\angle A$ and $\angle B$ are alternate interior angles determined by parallel lines, they are congruent.

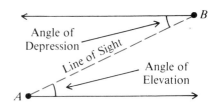

EXERCISES

— A —

1. What trigonometric ratio would you use to find the measure of $\angle A$ if the lengths of each indicated pair of sides were known?
   a. x and y
   b. x and z
   c. y and z

2. Find a decimal approximation to the nearest thousandth for each trigonometric ratio.
   a. $\sin R$
   b. $\cos R$
   c. $\tan R$
   d. $\sin T$
   e. $\cos T$
   f. $\tan T$

3. Use the table of trigonometric ratios on page 476 to find the value of each.
   a. $\cos 32°$ b. $\tan 81°$
   c. $\sin 69°$ d. $\cos 21°$

e. $m\angle A$ if $\sin A = 0.799$
f. $m\angle A$ if $\tan A = 0.445$

Look at the figure.

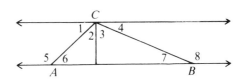

4. Name the angle of elevation for each indicated line of sight.
   a. from A to C b. from B to C

5. Name the angle of depression for each indicated line of sight.
   a. from C to A b. from C to B

Find the indicated measures for each right triangle.

6. a. MN
   b. NP

7. a. *XY*
   b. *YZ*

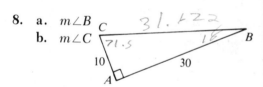

8. a. *m∠B*
   b. *m∠C*

31.422

71.5

9. a. *m∠D*
   b. *m∠F*

10. a. *x*
   b. *y*

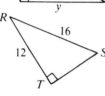

11. a. *m∠R*
   b. *m∠S*

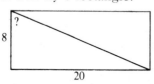

— **B** —

12. Find the measure of the angle formed by a diagonal and the shorter side of a 20-by-8 rectangle.

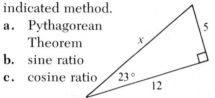

13. Look at the triangle. Find *x* by each indicated method.
   a. Pythagorean Theorem
   b. sine ratio
   c. cosine ratio

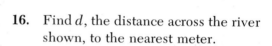

14. From the top of a tower, the angle of depression to a rock on the ground

is 52°. The rock is 126 feet from the foot of the tower. How tall is the tower? Find the answer to the nearest foot.

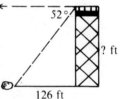

15. Look at the diagram. The shadow of a tree is 15 m long. Find the height *h* of the tree to the nearest meter.

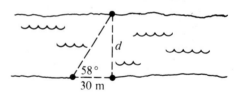

16. Find *d*, the distance across the river shown, to the nearest meter.

17. How far above the ground is the kite shown?

18. For safety, a ladder placed against a wall should make an angle of about 75° with the ground. To the nearest foot, how far from the bottom of a wall should a 16-foot ladder be?

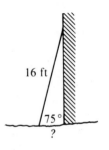

19. $\triangle ABC$ is isosceles and $m\angle ACB = 40°$. Find the height h.

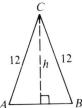

20. $RHOM$ is a rhombus and $m\angle MRH = 58°$. Find the indicated measures. (Hint: For parts b and d, use $\triangle MRX$.)

a. $m\angle MRX$
b. MX
c. MH
d. RX
e. RO

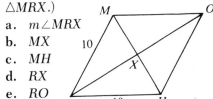
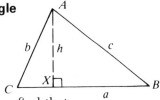

═══════════ **MORE EXPLORING** ═══════════

Another Formula for the Area of a Triangle

Look at $\triangle ABC$. The lengths of its sides are a, b, and c. h is the height. Area of $\triangle ABC = \frac{1}{2}ah$. Now look at $\triangle ACX$. In $\triangle ACX$, $\sin C = \dfrac{h}{b}$, so $h = b \cdot \sin C$.

Substituting this value of h into the area formula, we find that:

$$\text{Area of } \triangle ABC = \tfrac{1}{2}ab \cdot \sin C$$

Notice that in $\triangle ABC$, $\angle C$ is the included angle for sides a and b. This example illustrates the following method for finding the area of a triangular region if the lengths of two sides and the measure of their included angle are known:

> The area of a triangle is equal to one half the product of any two sides and the sine of their included angle.

Example:
Find the area of $\triangle ABC$.

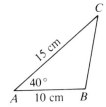

Solution:
Area $= \frac{1}{2}(15)(10)(\sin 40°)$
$= \frac{1}{2}(150)(0.643)$
$= 75(0.643) = 48.225$

To the nearest square centimeter, the area is 48 cm².

Use the above formula to find the area of each triangle.

1.

2.

3.

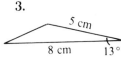

Geometry on the Job

FORESTER

As a forester, Sue Ellen Ames supervises the growing, protection, and use of trees and she works to prevent fires, floods, erosion, and tree diseases. When trees are to be harvested, she chooses which trees should be cut. A knowledge of trigonometry is helpful in determining how much lumber will be produced by each tree. After the harvesting of mature trees, she supervises the planting of new trees in their place.

EXERCISES

To estimate the length of a usable log from a tree, Sue

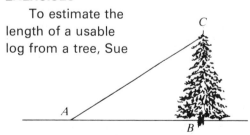

Ellen stands 100 feet from the tree and sights to the highest point of the tree that is usable for lumber.

1. If $m\angle A = 46°$, what is BC?
2. If $m\angle A = 28°$, what is BC?
3. If $m\angle A = 35°$, what is BC?
    Find the distance AC using two different methods. Do the answers agree?

Lumber is measured in board feet. One board foot is equivalent to a piece of wood 1 foot square and 1 inch thick. (1 cubic foot = 12 board feet)

4. If a log has a length of 100 feet and an average diameter of 2 feet, what is its volume in cubic feet? How many board feet of lumber does it contain?
5. If a log has a length of 60 feet and an average diameter of 1 foot, how many board feet of lumber does it contain?

ARITHMETIC REVIEW — *Percent*

Percent means "out of 100" or "for each 100." % is the symbol for percent. "$n\%$" means the ratio of n to 100 or $\dfrac{n}{100}$.

Examples
Write each percent as a ratio in simplest form.

1. $20\% = \dfrac{20}{100} = \dfrac{1}{5}$ **2.** $50\% = \dfrac{50}{100} = \dfrac{1}{2}$ **3.** $32\% = \dfrac{32}{100} = \dfrac{8}{25}$

Write each ratio as a percent.

4. $\dfrac{3}{10} = \dfrac{30}{100} = 30\%$ **5.** 3 out of $5 = \dfrac{3}{5} = \dfrac{60}{100} = 60\%$

6. $\dfrac{3}{8} = \;?\; \%$ Two methods of solution are given:

Using proportions:

$$\frac{3}{8} = \frac{x}{100}$$

$$8x = 300$$

$$x = \frac{300}{8}$$

$$= 37\tfrac{1}{2}$$

Answer: $37\tfrac{1}{2}\%$, or 37.5%

Using division:

$$\frac{3}{8} = 3 \div 8$$

$$
\begin{array}{r}
0.375 \\
8\overline{)3.000} \\
\underline{2\,4} \\
60 \\
\underline{56} \\
40 \\
\underline{40} \\
0
\end{array}
$$

Answer: 37.5%

EXERCISES
Write each percent as a ratio in simplest form.

1. 1%   **2.** 5%   **3.** 10%   **4.** 12%
5. 15%   **6.** 25%   **7.** 28%   **8.** 39%
9. 49%   **10.** 65%   **11.** 75%   **12.** 85%

Write each ratio as a percent.

13. 3:100   **14.** 6:100   **15.** $\dfrac{18}{100}$ **16.** $\dfrac{1}{5}$ **17.** $\dfrac{7}{10}$ **18.** $\dfrac{18}{25}$

19. $\dfrac{1}{20}$ **20.** 4 to 5   **21.** 9:10   **22.** $\dfrac{9}{50}$ **23.** 8:25   **24.** 24:40

25. $\dfrac{1}{8}$ **26.** $\dfrac{5}{8}$ **27.** $\dfrac{1}{3}$ **28.** $\dfrac{5}{6}$ **29.** 6:4   **30.** 8 to 3

Chapter 10 Review

Vocabulary

The following terms and abbreviations were introduced in this chapter. You should be able to write a brief definition, draw a picture, or give an example to illustrate the meaning of each.

adjacent leg (p. 412)
cosine (p. 412)
divided proportionally (segment) (p. 396)
opposite leg (p. 412)
scale (p. 409)
scale drawing (p. 409)
sine (p. 412)

tangent (p. 412)
trigonometric ratio (p. 412)

Symbols
k(constant of similarity) (p. 404)
cos (cosine) (p. 412)
sin (sine) (p. 412)
tan (tangent) (p. 412)

Skills Checklist

In Chapter 10 you learned some relationships between the perimeters and areas of any two similar figures and between the total areas and volumes of any two similar three-dimensional figures, how to find and use trigonometric ratios to solve problems, and how to make and interpret a scale drawing. In addition, you were introduced to some applications of similar figures and trigonometric ratios in problem solving.

The following list indicates the major skills, facts, and results you should have mastered in this chapter:

● Use properties of proportional segments and similar triangles to solve problems. (**10-1**, pp. 396–398)

● Use only a compass and straightedge to divide a segment into any given number of congruent parts. (**10-2**, pp. 399–401)

● Know and use the relationship among the ratios of lengths of corresponding sides, peimeters, and areas for any two similar polygonal regions. (**10-3**, pp. 402–404)

● Know and use the relationship among the ratios of lengths of corresponding edges, total areas, and volumes for any two similar prisms. (**10-4**, pp. 405–408)

● Make and interpret scale drawings. (**10-5**, pp. 409–411)

● Find the sine, cosine, and tangent ratio for any acute angle of a right triangle given the lengths of the sides of the triangle. (**10-6**, pp. 412–415)

● Use a table of trigonometric ratios to find a decimal approximation for the sine, cosine, or tangent ratio for any acute angle or to find the measure of the acute angle having a given sine, cosine, or tangent ratio. (**10-7**, pp. 416–419)

● Use trigonometric ratios to find the measure of each acute angle of a right triangle, given the lengths of any two sides and the length of each side of a right triangle, given the length of one side and the measure of one acute angle. (**10-7—10-8**, pp. 416–421)

Exercises

Find the value of each ratio. (10–1)

1. $\dfrac{AX}{AB}$ 2. $\dfrac{AY}{YC}$

3. $\dfrac{AY}{AC}$ 4. $\dfrac{XY}{BC}$

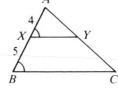

Find the value of each ratio. (10–1)

5. $\dfrac{BD}{DF}$

6. $\dfrac{AC}{AE}$

7. $\dfrac{BD}{BF}$

8. $\dfrac{DF}{BD}$

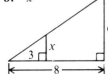

$AB \parallel CD \parallel EF$

Find each indicated measure. (10–1)

9. x

10. a. x
    b. y

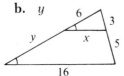

11. a. x b. RS
$\overline{XY}$ and $\overline{RS}$ are divided proportionally by points A and B, respectively.

12. x

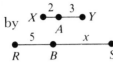

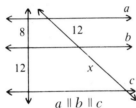

$a \parallel b \parallel c$

Draw $\overline{CD}$ at least 8 cm long. (10–2)

13. Use a compass and straightedge to divide $\overline{CD}$ into 3 congruent parts.

14. Construct a segment of length $\frac{2}{3} \cdot \overline{CD}$.

15. Construct a triangle similar to $\triangle GHI$ using $\frac{5}{3}$ as the constant of similarity. (**10-2**)

Each exercise concerns two similar two-dimensional figures. Copy and complete the table. (10–3)

	Constant of Similarity	Ratio of Perimeters	Ratio of Areas
16.	3:5	?	?
17.	?	1:3	?
18.	?	?	9:49

Find the indicated information.

19. Find the following information for $\triangle XYZ \sim \triangle ABC$ with $k = \frac{1}{2}$. (**10-3**)

    a. $XY:AB$

    b. If $AB = 10$ cm, $XY = $? cm.

    c. $\dfrac{\text{Perimeter of } \triangle XYZ}{\text{Perimeter of } \triangle ABC}$

    d. $\dfrac{\text{Area of } \triangle XYZ}{\text{Area of } \triangle ABC}$

    e. If the area of $\triangle ABC = 80$ cm², what is the area of $\triangle XYZ$?

Each exercise concerns two similar three-dimensional figures. Copy and complete the table. (**10–4**)

	Ratio of Lengths of Corresponding Edges	Ratio of Total Areas	Ratio of Volumes
20.	1:2	?	?
21.	?	9:25	?
22.	?	?	27:343

Find the indicated information.

23. Look at prisms X and Y. Find the following information. (**10–4**)

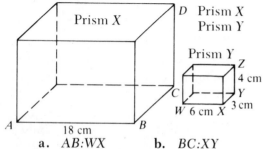

a. $AB:WX$ b. $BC:XY$

c. $\dfrac{\text{Total Area of prism } X}{\text{Total Area of prism } Y}$

d. $\dfrac{\text{Volume of prism } X}{\text{Volume of prism } Y}$

24. Assume that prism $A \sim$ prism B and $k = 2$.
Volume of $A = 80$ cm³
Volume of $B = ?$ cm³ (**10–4**)

25. Suppose a scale drawing has a scale of $\frac{1}{8}$ in. = 5 ft. Find the actual distance represented by each length on the drawing. (**10–5**)
a. $\frac{1}{2}$ in. b. 1 in. c. 2 in. d. $2\frac{1}{4}$ in.

Make a scale drawing of a 12-ft by 16-ft rectangle using each indicated scale. (10–5)

26. $\frac{1}{2}$ in. = 4 ft   **27.** $\frac{1}{8}$ in. = 2 ft
28. 1 cm = 4 ft

Find the indicated information.

29. Identify each of the following for $\triangle RST$. (**10–6**)
a. Hypotenuse
b. Leg opposite $\angle R$
c. Leg adjacent to $\angle R$
d. Leg opposite $\angle T$
e. Leg adjacent to $\angle T$

30. Look at $\triangle WXY$. Find each trigonometric ratio and express it in simplest fraction form. (**10–6**)
a. $\sin X$
b. $\cos X$
c. $\tan X$
d. $\sin Y$
e. $\cos Y$
f. $\tan Y$

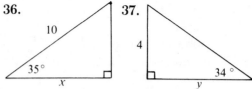

31. Use the table of trigonometric ratios on page 476 to find the value of each. (**10–7**)
a. $\sin 23°$ b. $\tan 32°$ c. $\cos 62°$

Find $m\angle A$ to the nearest degree. (10–7)
32. $\sin A = 0.899$ **33.** $\tan A = 5.000$
34. $\cos A = 0.850$ **35.** $\tan A = 0.340$

Find each indicated length to the nearest whole number. (10–8)
36.   **37.**

Find $m\angle A$ to the nearest degree. (10–8)
38.   **39.**

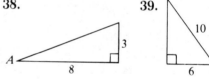

MAPPING IT OUT

Coordinate Systems and Linear Equations

11-1

Adding Integers

Some computational skills that will be helpful with the graphing you will do later in this chapter are reviewed in the next three lessons.

Opposites are the same distance from 0 on a number line but in opposite directions. If x represents some number, than ^-x is the opposite of x. If $x = 5$, then $^-x = ^-5$. If $x = ^-7$, then $^-x = ^-(^-7) = 7$.

The *integers* are the whole numbers and their opposites.

Integers: . . . , $^-4$, $^-3$, $^-2$, $^-1$, 0, 1, 2, 3, 4, . . .

The *absolute value* of an integer is its distance from 0 on a number line. For example, the absolute value of 3 is 3 and the absolute value of $^-4$ is 4.

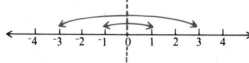

The opposite of 1 is $^-1$. $^-1$ is read "negative one."
The opposite of $^-3$ is 3.

The addition of integers can be shown on a number line:

$^-2 + 3 = 1$ $^-1 + ^-2 = ^-3$ $3 + ^-5 = ^-2$

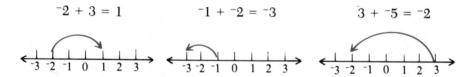

The following rules apply to the addition of integers, as well as other signed numbers:

> **The sum of two negative numbers is negative.**
> **The sum of a negative and a positive number is found by *subtracting* absolute values. The sum has the sign of the number with the greater absolute value.**

Here are some examples:

$$^-6 + ^-4 = ^-10 \qquad ^-6 + 4 = ^-2$$

$$^-9 + ^-7 = ^-16 \qquad 9 + ^-7 = 2$$

1. What is the sum of any number and its opposite?
2. Which integer is neither positive nor negative?

State the opposite of each integer.

3. 6   4. ⁻6   5. ⁻11

Find each sum.

6. ⁻3 + ⁻8   7. ⁻10 + 6   8. 7 + ⁻5   9. ⁻8 + ⁻4 + 5

EXERCISES

State the opposite of each integer.

1. 3   2. ⁻3
3. 10   4. ⁻10
5. ⁻7   6. 7
7. 5   8. ⁻13

Find each sum.

9. 6 + 5   10. 8 + ⁻7
11. ⁻5 + ⁻4   12. ⁻2 + 9
13. 0 + ⁻8   14. ⁻9 + 4
15. 3 + 2   16. ⁻3 + 2
17. 3 + ⁻2   18. ⁻3 + ⁻2
19. ⁻6 + 6   20. 6 + ⁻6
21. ⁻6 + ⁻6   22. 9 + ⁻3
23. ⁻6 + 5   24. ⁻3 + 4 + ⁻6
25. 6 + ⁻7 + 1   26. ⁻8 + ⁻1 + ⁻5
27. ⁻8 + 4 + ⁻5   28. 9 + ⁻1 + ⁻6

Classify each statement as true or false.

29. The sum of any two negative integers is negative.
30. The sum of any positive and any negative integer is negative.

Integers are often used to represent everyday situations and their opposites. Complete the following table.

	Situation and Its Opposite	Integers
31.	10° above zero	10
	10° below zero	?
32.	6-yard loss	⁻6
	6-yard gain	?
33.	50 miles east	50
	?	⁻50
34.	$500 profit	?
	$500 loss	⁻500
35.	?	⁻3
	Up 3 floors	3
36.	8 meters right	8
	?	⁻8

Complete each statement.

37. 11 + ⁻11 = ?
38. ? + 8 = 0
39. ⁻9 + ? = 0
40. ⁻5 + ⁻(⁻5) = ?
41. (14 − 6) + 6 = ?
42. (8 − 3) + ? = 8
43. (15 − ?) + 6 = 15
44. ? + 2 = ⁻10
45. (8 − 2) + 2 + ⁻2 = 8 + ?
46. 9 + ⁻2 = ? + 2 + ⁻2 = 7
47. ⁻11 + 5 = ? + ⁻5 + 5 = ⁻6

11-2

Subtracting Integers

Consider the following equations.

$$6 - 2 = 4 \qquad 6 + {}^-2 = 4$$
$$8 - 5 = 3 \qquad 8 + {}^-5 = 3$$
$$9 - 8 = 1 \qquad 9 + {}^-8 = 1$$
$$13 - 8 = 5 \qquad 13 + {}^-8 = 5$$
$$11 - 4 = 7 \qquad 11 + {}^-4 = 7$$

Compare the equations in the left-hand column with those in the right-hand column. Notice that the answers in the left-hand column are the same as those in the right-hand column.

The equations above suggest that subtracting an integer is equivalent to adding its opposite. The following EXPLORING investigates this.

EXPLORING

Defining Subtraction as Addition

1. Complete this statement: $(8 - 3) + \ ?\ = 8$
2. What is the opposite of 3?
3. Why is this statement true? $(8 - 3) + (3 + {}^-3) = 8 + {}^-3$
    How does it differ from the statement in step 1?
4. $3 + {}^-3 = \ ?$
5. Why is this statement true? $(8 - 3) + (3 + {}^-3) = (8 - 3) + 0$

$$= 8 - 3$$

6. Complete this statement: $8 - 3 = 8 + \ ?$
7. Repeat steps 1–6 above to show that ${}^-3 - 6 = {}^-3 + {}^-6$ and that $3 - {}^-6 = 3 + 6$. Do you get the same results in each case?

The preceding EXPLORING illustrates the following method for subtracting integers.

> **To subtract an integer, add its opposite.**
>
> $$a - b = a + {}^-b$$

Here are some examples using this rule.

$$8 - 6 = 8 + {}^-6 = 2 \qquad {}^-8 - 6 = {}^-8 + {}^-6 = {}^-14$$
$$6 - 8 = 6 + {}^-8 = {}^-2 \qquad 6 - {}^-8 = 6 + 8 = 14$$

$$8 - {}^-6 = 8 + 6 = 14 \qquad {}^-8 - {}^-6 = {}^-8 + 6 = {}^-2$$
$${}^-6 - 8 = {}^-6 + {}^-8 = {}^-14 \qquad {}^-6 - {}^-8 = {}^-6 + 8 = 2$$

CLASS PRACTICE

Write an addition problem that has the same answer as the given subtraction problem.

1. $8 - {}^-3$ **2.** $3 - 7$ **3.** $6 - 4$

4. ${}^-6 - 4$ **5.** ${}^-9 - {}^-5$ **6.** ${}^-7 - {}^-10$

Find each difference.

7. $9 - 3$ **8.** $3 - 9$ **9.** ${}^-9 - {}^-3$

10. ${}^-3 - {}^-9$ **11.** ${}^-9 - 3$ **12.** $3 - {}^-9$

EXERCISES

— A —

Find each sum.

1. $4 + {}^-9$ **2.** ${}^-6 + {}^-5$

3. ${}^-7 + 9$ **4.** ${}^-3 + 1$

5. ${}^-4 + {}^-8$ **6.** ${}^-6 + 9$

7. ${}^-6 + {}^-9$ **8.** $13 + {}^-8$

Write an addition problem that has the same answer as the given subtraction problem.

9. $9 - 2$ **10.** $10 - {}^-2$

11. $4 - 9$ **12.** ${}^-6 - 5$

13. ${}^-3 - {}^-1$ **14.** ${}^-7 - {}^-9$

15. $3 - 11$ **16.** $7 - {}^-5$

Find each difference.

17. $6 - 9$ **18.** ${}^-9 - 6$

19. ${}^-6 - 9$ **20.** ${}^-6 - {}^-9$

21. $13 - {}^-3$ **22.** ${}^-9 - {}^-2$

23. $13 - 5$ **24.** ${}^-4 - 8$

25. $0 - 5$ **26.** $2 - {}^-5$

27. $0 - {}^-3$ **28.** $2 - 8$

Classify each statement as true or false.

29. The difference of any two positive integers is positive.

30. The difference of any two negative integers is negative.

31. The difference of a positive and a negative integer can be negative.

32. The difference of a positive and a negative integer can be positive.

— B —

Complete each statement.

33. $13 - \;?\; = 8$

34. ${}^-7 - 0 = \;?$

35. $15 - {}^-9 = \;?$

36. $7 - {}^-2 = 7 + \;?$

37. ${}^-8 - 3 = {}^-8 + \;?$

38. $\;?\; - 6 = {}^-2$

39. $\;?\; - {}^-2 = 9$

40. $10 - \;?\; = 13$

41. $9 - {}^-5 = \;?$

42. ${}^-9 + \;?\; = 0$

Find each answer.

43. $(8 - 2) - 3$ **44.** ${}^-4 - (2 - 5)$

45. $9 - (3 - 7)$ **46.** $13 + (8 - 9)$

47. $({}^-6 - 2) - 5$ **48.** $(9 - 5) - 0$

49. $0 - (9 - 5)$ **50.** $11 + ({}^-3 + {}^-1)$

11-3
Multiplying and Dividing Integers

When multiplying two integers, there are four possible types of problems, as illustrated here:

$$4 \times 2 \qquad 4 \times {}^-2 \qquad {}^-4 \times 2 \qquad {}^-4 \times {}^-2$$

The first type of problem presents no difficulty since you already know how to multiply positive integers. Some multiplication problems, such as those of the second type, can be thought of as repeated addition. For example, the problem $4 \times {}^-2$ may be solved this way:

$$4 \times {}^-2 = {}^-2 + {}^-2 + {}^-2 + {}^-2$$
$$= {}^-8$$

Now consider a problem such as $^-4 \times 2$. The order of factors in a product can be reversed without changing the result (example: $6 \times 5 = 5 \times 6$). Therefore problems such as $^-4 \times 2$ may be solved this way:

$$^-4 \times 2 = 2 \times {}^-4$$
$$= {}^-4 + {}^-4$$
$$= {}^-8$$

Now consider a problem such as $^-4 \times {}^-2$. It is not possible to think of this problem as repeated addition. However, it can be shown that the product of any two negative integers is a positive integer, so $^-4 \times {}^-2 = 8$.

Here are some examples illustrating the rules for multiplication of integers.

$4 \times 5 = 20$	$9 \times 8 = 72$	$6 \times 9 = 54$
$4 \times {}^-5 = {}^-20$	$9 \times {}^-8 = {}^-72$	$6 \times {}^-9 = {}^-54$
$^-4 \times 5 = {}^-20$	$^-9 \times 8 = {}^-72$	$^-6 \times 9 = {}^-54$
$^-4 \times {}^-5 = 20$	$^-9 \times {}^-8 = 72$	$^-6 \times {}^-9 = 54$

The following statements summarize the rules for division as well as multiplication of integers. If $a \times b = c$, then $a = \dfrac{c}{b}$. Therefore division of integers follows the same pattern as multiplication. These rules apply to signed numbers that are not integers as well.

> **If two integers have the same sign, then their product or quotient is positive.**
>
> **If two integers have different signs, then their product or quotient is negative.**

Complete each statement.

1. $^-3 \times 7 = 7 \times$?
2. $3 \times {}^-5 = {}^-5 + {}^-5 + {}^-5 =$?
3. $4 \times$? $= {}^-5 + {}^-5 + {}^-5 + {}^-5 = {}^-20$
4. $^-6 \times 3 = 3 \times {}^-6 = {}^-6 + {}^-6 + {}^-6 =$?
5. Since $^-3 \times 6 = {}^-18$, then $^-18 \div 6 =$? .
6. Since $^-9 \times {}^-5 = 45$, then $45 \div {}^-5 =$? .
7. Since $8 \times {}^-7 = {}^-56$, then $^-56 \div {}^-7 =$? .

Find each product or quotient.

8. $9 \times {}^-4$	9. $^-9 \times {}^-4$	10. $12 \div {}^-4$	11. $^-12 \div {}^-4$
12. $^-5 \times 6$	13. $10 \div {}^-5$	14. $^-9 \div 3$	15. $^-4 \times {}^-3$
16. $(6 \times {}^-3) \times 2$	17. $({}^-4 \times {}^-2) \times {}^-3$	18. $^-5 \times 4 \times {}^-3$	19. $8 \times {}^-3 \times 0$

EXERCISES

_ A _

State whether each product or quotient is positive or negative.

1. $^-8 \times {}^-24$	2. $^-8 \times 24$
3. $^-24 \div 8$	4. $^-24 \div {}^-8$
5. $6 \times {}^-2 \times {}^-5$	6. $^-5 \times 14 \times 5$

7. $8 \times {}^-17 \times 13$
8. $^-3 \times {}^-5 \times {}^-18$
9. $^-9 \times {}^-7 \times 27$
10. $^-5 \times {}^-8 \times {}^-11 \times {}^-7$
11. $^-13 \times 8 \times {}^-10$
12. $^-18 \times 5 \times {}^-63 \times {}^-3$

Find each product.

13. $8 \times {}^-5$	14. $^-8 \times 5$
15. $^-8 \times {}^-5$	16. $^-3 \times 7$
17. $^-9 \times {}^-2$	18. $1 \times {}^-8$
19. $3 \times 5 \times {}^-2$	20. $6 \times {}^-6$
21. $8 \times 0 \times {}^-8$	22. $^-4 \times 7 \times {}^-2$
23. $^-3 \times {}^-2 \times {}^-5$	24. $^-3 \times {}^-2 \times 5$

Find each quotient.

25. $20 \div {}^-4$	26. $^-20 \div 4$
27. $^-20 \div {}^-4$	28. $^-28 \div 4$
29. $32 \div {}^-8$	30. $^-12 \div {}^-4$

Classify each statement as true or false.

31. The product of any two negative integers is positive.
32. The quotient of any two negative integers is positive.
33. If there are an even number of negative factors, then the product is positive.
34. If there are an odd number of negative factors, then the product is negative.

_ B _

Find each answer.

35. $8({}^-6) + 8(6)$	36. $^-3(5 + {}^-2)$
37. $9({}^-8 + 5)$	38. $5(6 - 10)$
39. $^-3(5) + {}^-3({}^-5)$	40. $^-2({}^-8 + 2)$
41. $7({}^-6 - {}^-2)$	42. $^-3({}^-5 + {}^-3)$
43. $3({}^-7 + {}^-2)$	44. $2({}^-3) + {}^-5$
45. $4 - 5({}^-2)$	
46. $^-3({}^-6 - 5)$	
47. $(16 \div {}^-4) \div {}^-2$	
48. $16 \div ({}^-4 \div {}^-2)$	
49. $({}^-30 \div {}^-3) \div {}^-2$	

11-4

Coordinate Systems and the Number Line

A *coordinate system* assigns a label, or *coordinates*, to an object or region so that it can be located. Various types of coordinate systems are used in everyday life. One example is the use of map coordinates—a letter and a number—to locate cities or towns on a road map.

Part of a map of Oregon and a part of its index of cities and towns are shown. To locate the town of Battin on the map, follow these steps:

First, find Battin in the alphabetical listing of cities and towns. Battin has coordinates E-7.

Second, follow across the horizontal band labeled E until you reach the vertical band labeled 7. Battin is located in this region.

Another well-known coordinate system is the 5-digit zip code system used by the United States Postal Service to identify regions of the country. Each state or possession is assigned to one of ten large geographic areas and identified by a whole number from 0 through 9. The first three digits of each zip code identify a sectional center or a metropolitan area. The last two digits identify a post office or delivery area.

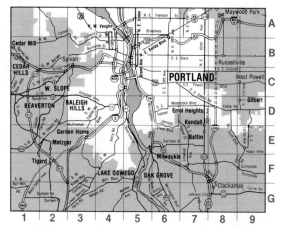

Index of Cities and Towns

Battin	E-7	Maywood Park	A-8
Clackamas	G-8	Russellville	B-8
Durham	G-2	West Powell	C-9
Kendall	E-7	West Slope	C-2

The numbering of points on a number line is also an example of a coordinate system. Once an *origin*, or zero point, and a scale have been selected, every number corresponds to exactly one point on the number line and every point on the number line corresponds to exactly one number.

On a horizontal number line, points to the right of the origin (zero) correspond to positive numbers and points to the left of the origin correspond to negative numbers. On a vertical number line, points above the origin correspond to positive numbers and points below the origin correspond to negative numbers.

Explain how each of the following is used as a coordinate system. (What is located? How is it located?)

1. House numbers on a street
2. Room numbers in a hotel
3. Dewey decimal or Library of Congress system in a library
4. Reserved-seat theater tickets
5. Class seating chart
6. Parking lot signs
7. Describe several other types of coordinate systems.
8. Suppose you wish to construct a number line and label it with the integers from ‾6 to 6 (‾6, ‾5, ‾4, . . . , 4, 5, 6).
   a. Describe, in order, the steps in the process.
   b. Is more than one solution possible? Why or why not?

CLASS PRACTICE

Look at the map and index shown on page 438.

1. Battin is located in region E-7. How many regions on this map have coordinates E-7?
2. Must the region containing Battin have coordinates E-7 on other maps of Oregon? Why or why not?

Use the index to find the coordinates of each indicated city or town. Locate each on the map.

3. West Powell
4. Russellville
5. Durham
6. West Slope
7. Clackamas
8. Maywood Park

The following cities and towns are not listed in the partial index. Locate each on the map and state its coordinates.

9. Gilbert
10. Tigard
11. Cedar Mill
12. Metzger

EXERCISES

_ A _

State the number corresponding to each labeled point.

1.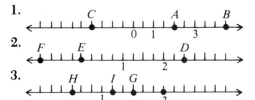

2.

3.

4.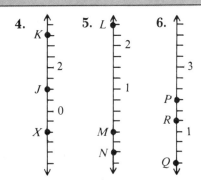

5. *L*

6.

Look at the partial map of South Carolina and index of cities and towns.

Use the index of cities and towns to find the coordinates of each of the following.

7. Andrews
8. Barnwell
9. Great Falls
10. Darlington
11. Camden
12. Bamberg
13. Chesterfield
14. Conway

The following cities and towns are not listed in the partial index. Locate each on the map and state its coordinates.

15. Walterboro
16. Olanta
17. Neeses
18. Holly Hill
19. Ruffin
20. Sumter
21. Lake City
22. Awendaw
23. Hampton
24. Swansea
25. Bethune
26. Myrtle Beach

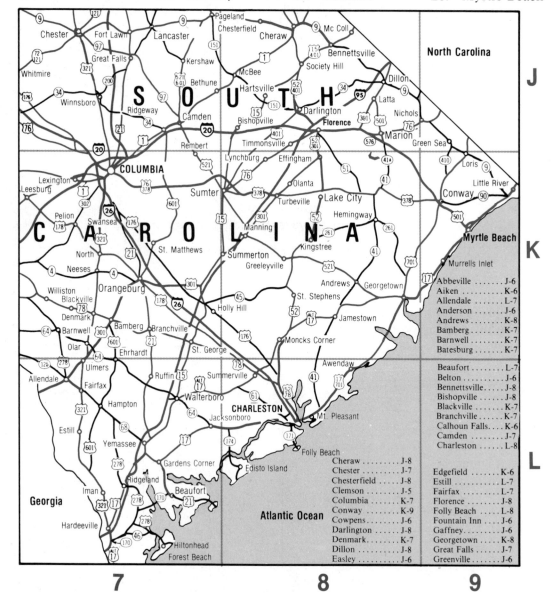

Abbeville	....	J-6
Aiken	....	K-6
Allendale	....	L-7
Anderson	....	J-6
Andrews	....	K-8
Bamberg	....	K-7
Barnwell	....	K-7
Batesburg	......	K-7
Beaufort	....	L-7
Belton	....	J-6
Bennettsville	....	J-8
Bishopville	.....	J-8
Blackville	....	K-7
Branchville	......	K-7
Calhoun Falls	....	K-6
Camden	....	J-7
Charleston	......	L-8
Cheraw	....	J-8
Chester	....	J-7
Chesterfield	.....	J-8
Clemson	....	J-5
Columbia	....	K-7
Conway	....	K-9
Cowpens	....	J-6
Darlington	......	J-8
Denmark	....	K-7
Dillon	....	J-8
Easley	....	J-6
Edgefield	....	K-6
Estill	....	L-7
Fairfax	....	L-7
Florence	....	J-8
Folly Beach	.....	L-8
Fountain Inn	....	J-6
Gaffney	....	J-6
Georgetown	.....	K-8
Great Falls	......	J-7
Greenville	......	J-6

Find the indicated information.

27. On the number line shown, x represents a number.
  - **a.** Is x a positive or negative number?
  - **b.** Are the numbers between x and 0 all negative, all positive, or of both types?

28. On the number line shown, b represents a number.
  - **a.** Suppose a represents a number such that $a > b$. Is a located to the right or left of b?
  - **b.** Suppose b is a number such that $b > 0$. Is 0 located to the right or left of b?

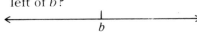

— **B** —

On the number line shown, p, q, and r represent numbers. For each statement, write *true*, *false*, or *not enough information*.

29. $p < q$ **30.** $r > p$

31. $q > r$ **32.** $r = 3q$

33. $r > 0$ **34.** $p < 0$

35. Describe how the point representing 1 can be located on the number line shown.

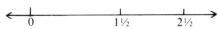

36. What is incorrect about the number line shown?

— **C** —

Look at the grid with perpendicular number lines. The letter O identifies the origin. Find the following information for each labeled point.

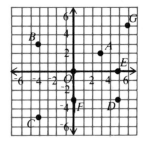

  - **a.** Number of units right or left of the origin
  - **b.** Number of units above or below the origin

Example: Point G is 6 units to the right and 5 units above the origin.

37. A **38.** B **39.** C

40. D **41.** E **42.** F

DID YOU KNOW THAT....

Coordinates in map-making were probably first used by the Greeks (perhaps as early as 320 B.C.). Early map makers used a variety of prime meridians (0° longitude)—often the one through the city of the map maker—before the Greenwich meridian became universally accepted.

Applications

Zip Code

Different coordinate systems are used for different purposes. For example, the 5-digit zip code is presently used by the United States Postal Service.

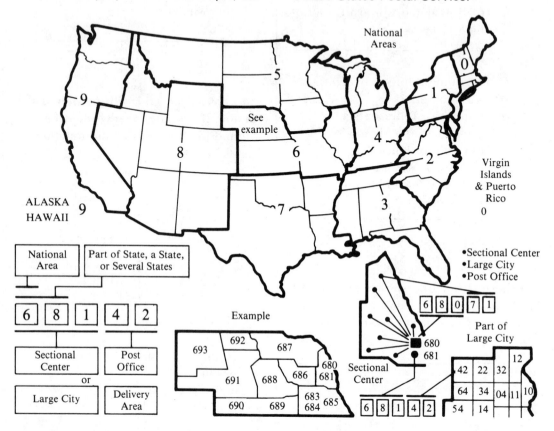

The Postal Service plans to put into use a new 9-digit zip code. The additional four digits are to be added to the right of the present zip code following a dash. The first two additional digits will identify a postal delivery route and the last two digits will identify a street or portion of a street. Use of the 9-digit zip code will eliminate some sorting and allow mail to be delivered to individual post offices already sorted by delivery route and street.

You might be interested in finding out some of the 5-digit zip codes and 9-digit zip codes used in your area and learning the sectional center, post offices, delivery routes, and streets they represent.

11-5

Locating Points in a Plane

Graphs are used to display a variety of information. The ability to locate and name points in a plane is useful for constructing many graphs. A pair of perpendicular number lines is used on a grid as a coordinate system to locate and name points in a plane. Each set of coordinates locates exactly one point.

Two points are located and named in the graph shown.

The horizontal number line is called the *x-axis*.

The vertical number line is called the *y-axis*.

The point where the two axes intersect is called the *origin*.

The two axes divide the plane into four regions called *quadrants*, which are numbered as shown.

Notice that the order in which the numbers are used to name each point is important. The coordinates of each point are an *ordered pair* of numbers. The first number is called the *x-coordinate*. The second number is called the *y-coordinate*. The coordinates of a point are always named in this order: (x, y).

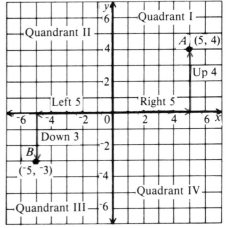

> When locating a point in a plane, the following rules apply:
>
> The *x*-coordinate is stated first. It tells how far right or left of the origin the point is.
>
> The *y*-coordinate is stated last. It tells how far above or below the origin the point is.

CLASS PRACTICE

Look at the graph.

1. What are the coordinates of the origin?
2. State the coordinates of each labeled point.
3. Which labeled points have the same *x*-coordinate?
4. Which labeled points have the same *y*-coordinate?

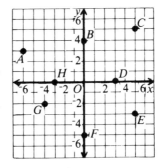

Look at the graph.

5. State the coordinates of five points in each quadrant.
6. State the coordinates of five points on each axis.
7. State the coordinates of a point that is on both the *x*-axis and the *y*-axis.

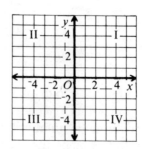

State the quadrant or axis in(on) which each point is located.

8. (6, 1)
9. (⁻5, ⁻2)
10. (0, 4)
11. (⁻6, 3)
12. (3, ⁻5)
13. (3, 4)
14. (⁻6, 0)
15. (0, ⁻2)
16. (5, ⁻1)
17. (2, 0)
18. (⁻4, 5)
19. (⁻3, ⁻6)

State the coordinates of point *C* in each right triangle. Each leg is parallel to one of the axes.

20.

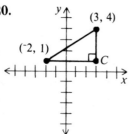

21.

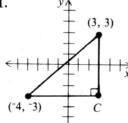

22.

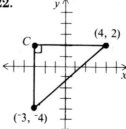

EXERCISES

— A —

Look at the graph. Find the coordinates of each point.

1. *A*
2. *B*
3. *C*
4. *D*
5. *E*
6. *F*
7. *G*
8. *H*
9. *I*
10. *J*
11. *K*
12. *L*

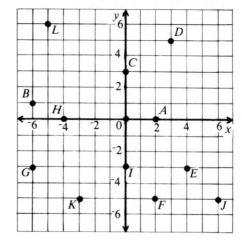

Draw a set of axes on graph paper. Locate each point with a dot and label each point with its coordinates.

13. (5, 2)
14. (2, 5)
15. (⁻3, 4)
16. (4, ⁻3)
17. (0, 8)
18. (8, 0)
19. (9, ⁻5)
20. (⁻5, 9)
21. (⁻10, 6)
22. (6, ⁻10)
23. (⁻7, 0)
24. (0, ⁻7)
25. (⁻10, ⁻10)
26. (⁻5, ⁻9)
27. (11, 6)
28. (11, ⁻6)

29. a. State the coordinates of four points that have an x-coordinate of 0.
    b. State the coordinates of four points that have a y-coordinate of 0.
    c. Points with an x-coordinate of 0 are on which axis?
    d. Points with a y-coordinate of 0 are on which axis?

State the coordinates of point C in each right triangle. Each leg is parallel to one of the axes.

30.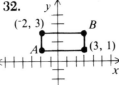

31.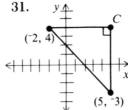

State the coordinates of points A and B in each rectangle. Each side is parallel to one of the axes.

32.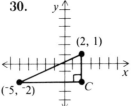

33.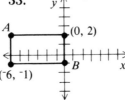

Find the distance between each pair of points. (A sketch may be helpful.)

34. (3, 0) and (12, 0)
35. (2, 0) and (⁻6, 0)
36. (0, 1) and (0, 7)
37. (1, 2) and (6, 2)
38. (⁻4, ⁻3) and (6, ⁻3)
39. (3, ⁻2) and (3, 9)

Use a separate set of axes for each of Exercises 40–46.

40. a. Locate and mark each of these points.
       (4, ⁻4) (2, ⁻2) (⁻1, 1) (3, 3)
       (⁻5, 5)
    b. Four of the points in part a are on the same line. Which one is not?
    c. Change one coordinate of the point in part b so that it is on the same line as the other four points.
    d. If the x-coordinate of a point on that line is 15, what is its y-coordinate?

41. a. Locate and mark each of these points.
       (⁻2, ⁻4) (⁻4, ⁻6) (0, ⁻2)
       (6, 4) (3, 1)
    b. The points in part a are all located on the same line. State the coordinates of three other points that are on that line.

42. a. Locate the following points and connect them in order.
       (⁻1, 1) (1, 5) (7, 5) (5, 1)
    b. What kind of figure is formed?
    c. Draw the diagonals of the figure. State the coordinates of the point of intersection of the diagonals.

43. a. Which points named below fit the following description? "The x-coordinate plus the y-coordinate is 6."

A(5, 1) B(⁻1, 7) C(⁻4, ⁻2)
D(0, 6) E(⁻3, 3)

b. Locate and mark the points you chose in part a. (You should be able to draw one line through all these points.)

c. State the coordinates of three other points that are on that line.

44. a. Locate and mark four points whose x-coordinate is 4. Draw a line through these points.

b. Locate and mark four points whose y-coordinate is ⁻3. Draw a line through these points.

c. State the coordinates of the point of intersection of these two lines.

45. a. Draw a vertical line through the point (5, 2).

b. State the coordinates of three other points on that line.

c. Which coordinate, x or y, is the same for all points on a vertical line?

46. a. Draw a horizontal line through the point (5, 2).

b. State the coordinates of three other points on that line.

c. Which coordinate, x or y, is the same for all points on a horizontal line?

— **C** —

Locate and mark the points in the order given. Then connect these points with segments in the order given. The direction "STOP" between two points means that you do not connect them.

47.	a.	(⁻9, 1)	b.	(⁻6, ⁻2)
	c.	(5, ⁻2)	d.	(10, 1)
	e.	(⁻9, 1)	f.	(1, 1)
	g.	(1, 13)	h.	(⁻5, 3)
	i.	(1, 3)		

48.	a.	(0, 13)	b.	(⁻1, 11)
	c.	(⁻1, 6)	d.	(⁻10, 0)
	e.	(⁻10, ⁻2)	f.	(⁻1, 0)
	g.	(⁻1, ⁻6)	h.	(⁻4, ⁻8)
	i.	(⁻4, ⁻9)	j.	(0, ⁻8)
	k.	(4, ⁻9)	l.	(4, ⁻8)
	m.	(1, ⁻6)	n.	(1, 0)
	o.	(10, ⁻2)	p.	(10, 0)
	q.	(1, 6)	r.	(1, 11)
	s.	(0, 13)		

49.	a.	(3, 5)	b.	(3, 6)
	c.	(1, 6)	d.	(1, 2)
	e.	(3, 2)	f.	(3, 3)
	g.	(2½, 3)	h.	(3½, 3) STOP
	i.	(6, 6)	j.	(4, 6)
	k.	(4, 4)	l.	(5, 4)
	m.	(4, 4)	n.	(4, 2)
	o.	(6, 2) STOP	p.	(9, 6)
	q.	(7, 6)	r.	(7, 2)
	s.	(9, 2)	t.	(9, 6) STOP
	u.	(12, 2)	v.	(12, 6)
	w.	(11, 4)	x.	(10, 6)
	y.	(10, 2) STOP	z.	(15, 6)
	aa.	(13, 6)	bb.	(13, 4)
	cc.	(14, 4)	dd.	(13, 4)
	ee.	(13, 2)	ff.	(15, 2) STOP
	gg.	(18, 6)	hh.	(16, 6)
	ii.	(17, 6)	jj.	(17, 2) STOP
	kk.	(19, 2)	ll.	(19, 6)
	mm.	(21, 6)	nn.	(21, 4)
	oo.	(19, 4)	pp.	(21, 2) STOP
	qq.	(24, 6)	rr.	(23, 4)
	ss.	(22, 6)	tt.	(23, 4)
	uu.	(23, 2) STOP		

50.	a.	(⁻4, 4)	b.	(⁻4, ⁻4)
	c.	(4, ⁻4)	d.	(4, 4)

e. (⁻4, 4)   f. (1, 7)
g. (9, 7)   h. (9, ⁻1)
i. (4, ⁻4)   j. (4, 4)
k. (9, 7)

Follow the indicated directions.

51. Shown at right is a drawing of a triangular prism. Write a set of directions like those for Exercises 47–50 that could be used to make a copy of this drawing.

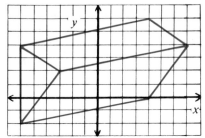

52. Draw a picture of your choosing on graph paper. Write a set of directions that could be used to make a copy of your drawing.

Test Yourself

1. State the number corresponding to each labeled point.

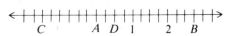

△ABC shown is a right triangle. Find the following information.

2. Coordinates of points A, B, and C
3. Length of segments AC and BC

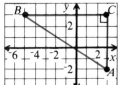

Draw a set of axes on graph paper. Locate and mark each point. Label each point with its coordinates.

4. (4, 3)   5. (⁻6, 2)
6. (0, ⁻5)   7. (2, 0)
8. (⁻4, ⁻3)   9. (5, ⁻4)

Perform the indicated computation.

10. ⁻8 + 3   11. ⁻6 + ⁻7
12. 6 − 11   13. 3 − ⁻2
14. ⁻6 − 4   15. ⁻8 − ⁻3
16. ⁻7 − ⁻10   17. 6 × ⁻4
18. ⁻3 × ⁻9   19. ⁻24 ÷ 6
20. ⁻27 ÷ ⁻9   21. 32 ÷ ⁻4

DID YOU KNOW THAT....

The use of the symbols + and − for addition and subtraction began in Germany in the last 20 years of the fifteenth century and they became widely used by the seventeenth century. The origin of these symbols is not certain but it is believed that the symbol + was derived as an abbreviation of the Latin word *et*, meaning "and."

11-6

Slope of a Line

The *slope* of a line is the measure of its steepness and is given by the ratio of rise to run. *Rise* is the amount of vertical movement and *run* is the amount of horizontal movement when going from one point to another on a line. Recall that in a plane, a move to the right or upward is positive and a move to the left or downward is negative.

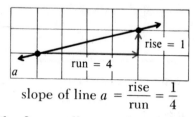

slope of line $a = \dfrac{\text{rise}}{\text{run}} = \dfrac{1}{4}$

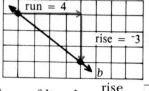

slope of line $b = \dfrac{\text{rise}}{\text{run}} = \dfrac{^-3}{4}$

The figures illustrate four ways to find the slope of line l shown.

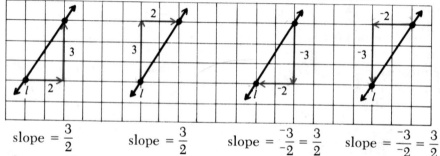

$\text{slope} = \dfrac{3}{2}$ $\qquad$ $\text{slope} = \dfrac{3}{2}$ $\qquad$ $\text{slope} = \dfrac{^-3}{^-2} = \dfrac{3}{2}$ $\qquad$ $\text{slope} = \dfrac{^-3}{^-2} = \dfrac{3}{2}$

The figures indicate that given two points on any line, you may start at either point and move in either a positive or negative direction in order to find the slope.

In the following figures, three points have been marked on line m. Different pairs of these points are used to find the slope of m.

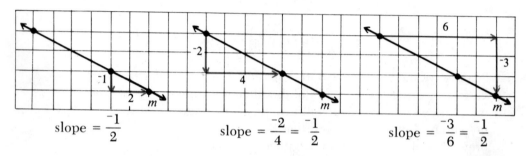

$\text{slope} = \dfrac{^-1}{2}$ $\qquad\qquad$ $\text{slope} = \dfrac{^-2}{4} = \dfrac{^-1}{2}$ $\qquad\qquad$ $\text{slope} = \dfrac{^-3}{6} = \dfrac{^-1}{2}$

The figures at the bottom of page 448 indicate that you may use *any* two points on a line when finding its slope. The slope of a line is constant—it is the same everywhere along its length.

Notice that line *l* (in the first set of figures) has a positive slope, while the slope of line *m* is negative.

Lines *a* and *b* shown both have a positive slope. A line will have a *positive* slope if it slants *upward* from left to right.

Lines *c* and *d* shown both have a negative slope. A line will have a *negative* slope if it slants *downward* from left to right.

Not every line has either a positive or a negative slope. There are two other possibilities. As indicated in the figures below, some lines have a slope of zero and for some lines the slope is undefined.

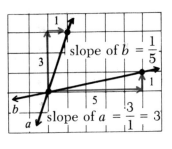

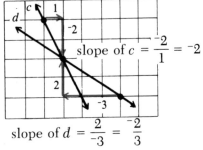

A horizontal line does not slant either upward or downward. The slope of any horizontal line is zero.

The ratio $\frac{2}{0}$ is undefined. Therefore the definition of slope has no meaning for a vertical line. The slope of any vertical line is undefined.

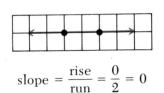

$$\text{slope} = \frac{\text{rise}}{\text{run}} = \frac{0}{2} = 0$$

$$\text{slope} = \frac{\text{rise}}{\text{run}} = \frac{2}{0}$$

The slope of any vertical line is undefined.

The slope of any nonvertical line is given by the ratio: $\frac{\text{rise}}{\text{run}}$.

The slope of any horizontal line is zero.

To find the slope of any line, you may use any two points on the line.

The slope of a line is positive if the line slants upward from left to right.

The slope of a line is negative if the line slants downward from left to right.

For each line, tell whether the slope is positive, negative, zero, or undefined.

1.

2.

3.

4.

Find the slope of each line.

5.

6.

7.

8.

Draw a set of axes on graph paper. Locate each pair of points and draw the line through them. Write the slope of each line in simplest form.

9. (⁻4, 0) and (⁻2, 5)   10. (3, 4) and (5, 1)   11. (⁻2, 4) and (3, 4)

EXERCISES

_ A _

1. For each line, tell whether the slope is positive, negative, zero, or undefined.

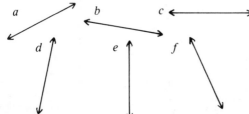

Find the slope of each line.

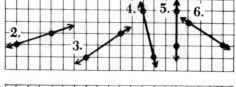

Look at the graph.

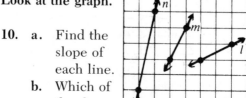

10. a. Find the slope of each line.
    b. Which of the three lines is steepest?
    c. As lines become steeper, how does slope change?

Draw a set of axes on graph paper. Locate each pair of points and draw the line through them. Write the slope of each line in simplest form.

11. (1, 3) and (5, 6)
12. (⁻3, 0) and ⁻1, 6)
13. (3, ⁻2) and (⁻2, 2)
14. (0, 2) and (3, ⁻1)
15. (⁻4, ⁻2) and (⁻6, ⁻3)
16. (0, 0) and (⁻3, ⁻2)

17. (‾3, 4) and (4, 2)

18. (‾4, ‾3) and (1, ‾3)

___ **B** ___

Find the missing coordinate. (A sketch may be helpful.)

19. The line through (2, ‾1) with a slope of $\frac{3}{2}$ also passes through the point (4, ?).

20. The line through (3, 2) with a slope of $-\frac{3}{4}$ also passes through the point (‾1, ?).

The *pitch* of a roof is a slope-related idea. It indicates the steepness of a roof and is defined as follows:

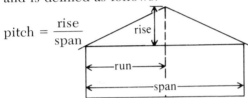

$$\text{pitch} = \frac{\text{rise}}{\text{span}}$$

Find the pitch of each roof described.

21. span = 30 ft, rise = 5 ft

22. span = 36 ft, rise = 6 ft

23. span = 40 ft, rise = 8 ft

24. run = 20 ft, rise = 8 ft

Use a separate set of axes for each of Exercises 25–27.

25. **a.** Locate and mark the point (3, 1).

    b. Draw the line through (3, 1) that has a slope of $\frac{2}{5}$.

26. **a.** Locate and mark the following points: $A(1, 1)$; $B(6, 2)$; and $C(3, 4)$.

    b. Connect points A, B, and C to form a right triangle with a right angle at C.

    c. Find the slope of each leg ($\overline{AC}$ and $\overline{BC}$) of the right triangle.

    d. Compare the slopes. How are they related?

27. **a.** Locate and mark the following points: $A(1, 2)$; $B(4, 4)$; $C(1, ‾1)$; and $D(4, 1)$.

    b. Draw the line through points A and B and the line through points C and D. ($\overleftrightarrow{AB}$ and $\overleftrightarrow{CD}$ are parallel.)

    c. Find the slope of $\overleftrightarrow{AB}$ and of $\overleftrightarrow{CD}$.

    d. Compare the slopes. How are they related?

═══════ *MORE EXPLORING* ═══════

Subtracting Coordinates to Find Slope

You have found the slope of a line by counting squares and using the ratio: $\dfrac{\text{rise}}{\text{run}}$.

The slope of a line may also be found by subtracting coordinates. For example, the slope of line l shown is $\frac{3}{2}$. Notice that the rise is found by subtracting the y-coordinates of the two points and the run is found by subtracting the x-coordinates.

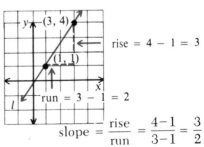

$$\text{rise} = 4 - 1 = 3$$

$$\text{run} = 3 - 1 = 2$$

$$\text{slope} = \frac{\text{rise}}{\text{run}} = \frac{4-1}{3-1} = \frac{3}{2}$$

Copy and complete the table on page 452 to find the slope of the line through each pair of points. The first row has been completed for you.

	(x_1, y_1)	(x_2, y_2)	Rise $(y_2 - y_1)$	Run $(x_2 - x_1)$	Slope
	$(0, 0)$	$(3, 2)$	$2 - 0 = 2$	$3 - 0 = 3$	$\frac{2}{3}$
1.	$(3, 2)$	$(0, 0)$	?	?	?
2.	$(3, 5)$	$(6, 3)$	?	?	?
3.	$(1, 2)$	$(3, 7)$	?	?	?
4.	$(0, 2)$	$(3, 6)$	?	?	?
5.	$(3, 0)$	$(1, 5)$	?	?	?

Your results should suggest the following conclusion:

> The slope of a line through two points with coordinates (x_1, y_1) and (x_2, y_2) is: $\text{Slope} = \dfrac{(y_2 - y_1)}{(x_2 - x_1)}$

The results in the first two rows of the table indicate that when using this formula, it does not matter which point you call (x_2, y_2).

Everyday Geometry

Slopes in Buildings

When doing home repair or improvement it must be noted that parts of a house exposed to the weather should be sloped to allow rainwater to run off. The *slope* is the ratio: $\dfrac{\text{rise}}{\text{run}}$.

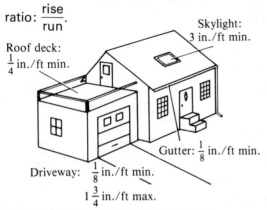

Skylight: 3 in./ft min.

Roof deck: $\frac{1}{4}$ in./ft min.

Gutter: $\frac{1}{8}$ in./ft min.

Driveway: $\frac{1}{8}$ in./ft min.
$1\frac{3}{4}$ in./ft max.

A driveway should be sloped, but not so steeply that cars slip in icy weather. Some recommended slopes are shown in the diagram.

EXERCISES

1. A roof deck 12 feet wide is to be built. What is the minimum rise?
2. A gutter 20 feet long is to be installed. What is the minimum rise?
3. A roof has a run of 15 feet and a rise of 4 feet. Can a properly sloped skylight be installed?
4. A driveway 30 feet long has a rise of 5 feet. Is its slope within the recommended range?

11-7

Slope of Parallel and of Perpendicular Lines

In the top figure, $a \parallel b$. Notice that the slopes of the lines are equal. Are the slopes of any two parallel lines equal? This question is investigated below.

In the bottom figure shown, $l \parallel m$. A vertical segment is drawn from the x-axis to each line, forming two right triangles with the lengths of the legs labeled as shown.

Since $l \parallel m$, $\angle 1 \cong \angle 2$ since they are corresponding angles. Therefore the two right triangles are similar by the AA Property.

Notice that $\dfrac{a}{c}$ is the ratio of the lengths of the legs of the first right triangle and $\dfrac{b}{d}$ is the ratio of the lengths of the corresponding legs of the other triangle. The ratios $\dfrac{a}{c}$ and $\dfrac{b}{d}$ represent $\dfrac{\text{rise}}{\text{run}}$ for the two parallel lines. Since the triangles are similar, these ratios are equivalent. So we can conclude: slope of l = slope of m.

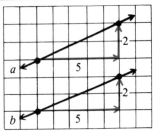

slope of $a = \dfrac{2}{5}$ slope of $b = \dfrac{2}{5}$

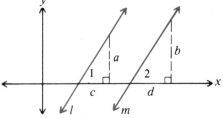

The preceding discussion indicates that nonvertical parallel lines have the same slope. The following two statements are true:

> If two nonvertical lines are parallel, they have equal slopes.
> If two lines have equal slopes, they are parallel.

EXPLORING
The Slope of Perpendicular Lines

1. Three pairs of perpendicular lines are shown. Find the slope of each line.

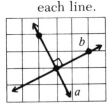

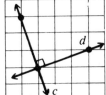

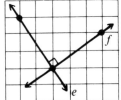

2. Find the following products: (slope of a)·(slope of b); (slope of c)· (slope of d); and (slope of e)·(slope of f). How are the products related?

If you did the preceding EXPLORING carefully, you discovered that the product of the slopes of two perpendicular lines is ⁻1. The following two statements are true:

> **If two nonvertical lines are perpendicular, the product of their slopes is ⁻1.**
>
> **If the product of the slopes of two lines is ⁻1, the lines are perpendicular.**

DISCUSS
---

1. As shown in the figure, a line perpendicular to a horizontal line is vertical. Why is it not possible to find the product of the slopes of lines l and m?

2. Will the product of the slopes of any two perpendicular lines always be equal to ⁻1? Why or why not?

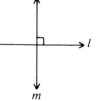

CLASS PRACTICE

Find the slope of each indicated line. Line l has a slope of $-\frac{3}{5}$.

1. Line parallel to l **2.** Line perpendicular to l

The slopes of two lines are given. Tell whether the lines are parallel, perpendicular, or neither.

3. $\frac{3}{4}$ and $\frac{4}{3}$ **4.** $\frac{3}{7}$ and $-\frac{3}{7}$ **5.** $\frac{2}{5}$ and $-\frac{5}{2}$

6. $\frac{2}{5}$ and $\frac{2}{5}$ **7.** 3 and ⁻3   **8.** 3 and 3

Draw lines to fit each description. Use a separate set of axes for each exercise.

9. Two different lines each with a slope of $-\frac{2}{5}$

10. Line with a slope of $\frac{2}{5}$ and a second line with a slope of $\frac{5}{2}$

11. Line with a slope of $\frac{2}{5}$ and a second line with a slope of $-\frac{5}{2}$

12. Line through (2, 1) with a slope of $-\frac{3}{4}$

— A —

1. Line l has a slope of $\frac{3}{4}$. Find the slope of each indicated line.
   a. Line parallel to l
   b. Line perpendicular to l
2. Line m has a slope of $^-4$. Find the slope of each indicated line.
   a. Line parallel to m
   b. Line perpendicular to m
3. Line x is vertical.
   a. What kind of line is perpendicular to x?
   b. What is the slope of x?

The slopes of two lines are given. Tell whether the lines are parallel, perpendicular, or neither.

4. $\frac{2}{3}$ and $\frac{6}{9}$ 5. 1 and $^-1$

6. 2 and $^-2$ 7. $\frac{3}{5}$ and $\frac{-5}{3}$

8. $\frac{4}{7}$ and $\frac{7}{4}$ 9. 1 and 1

10. $\frac{3}{5}$ and $\frac{-3}{5}$ 11. 0 and 0

— B —

12. $ABCD$ shown is a rectangle. The slope of $\overline{AD}$ is $\frac{1}{3}$. Find the slope of each indicated segment.
    a. $\overline{BC}$ b. $\overline{DC}$
    c. $\overline{AB}$

13. $WXYZ$ shown is a rhombus. The slope of $\overline{WZ}$ is $\frac{3}{4}$ and the slope of $\overline{ZX}$ is $^-2$. Find the slope of each indicated segment.
    a. $\overline{XY}$
    b. $\overline{WY}$

14. $LMNO$ shown is a square. The slope of $\overline{LN}$ is $\frac{2}{3}$ and the slope of $\overline{ON}$ is $-\frac{1}{5}$. Find the slope of each indicated segment.
    a. $\overline{OM}$
    b. $\overline{NM}$
    c. $\overline{LM}$
    d. $\overline{LO}$

Draw lines to fit each description. Use a separate set of axes for each exercise.

15. Three different lines each with a slope of $-\frac{3}{5}$

16. Three different lines each with a slope of $\frac{2}{7}$

17. Line with a slope of $\frac{3}{4}$ and a second line with a slope of $-\frac{4}{3}$

18. Line with a slope of $\frac{2}{3}$ and a second line with a slope of $\frac{3}{2}$

19. Two different lines each with a slope of 0

20. Two different lines each of whose slope is undefined

21. Line through (3, 2) that has a slope of $\frac{-3}{4}$

Find the indicated information.

22. The slopes of four lines are given:
    $a: \frac{3}{5}$; $b: \frac{-10}{6}$; $c: \frac{-5}{3}$; $d: \frac{9}{15}$
    Do these lines determine a rectangle? Why or why not?

23. The slopes of three lines are given:
    $l: \frac{5}{2}$; $m: \frac{3}{7}$; $o: \frac{-2}{5}$
    These lines determine a triangle. What kind of triangle is it? Explain.

11-8

Distance Between Two Points

The distance between any two points on either a horizontal or a vertical line can be found by counting squares. For example, in the figure shown, $AB = 4$ and $BC = 3$.

However, the length of $\overline{AC}$ cannot be found simply by counting. The Pythagorean Theorem may be used to find the length of $\overline{AC}$ since $\triangle ABC$ is a right triangle with $\overline{AC}$ as its hypotenuse.

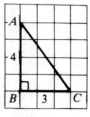

$$AC^2 = 3^2 + 4^2 = 9 + 16 = 25$$

$$AC = \sqrt{25} = 5$$

Notice that when computing distance, we are not concerned with direction, as we were when determining rise and run to find the slope of a line. We will treat all distances between points as positive.

Example: Find the distance between $A(^-3, ^-2)$ and $B(3, 1)$. Express the answer in simplest radical form.

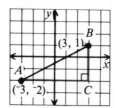

Solution:
Locate points A and B and draw $\overline{AB}$. Then draw vertical and horizontal segments to form $\triangle ABC$.

Count to find AC and BC.

$$AC = 6 \quad \text{and} \quad BC = 3$$

Use the Pythagorean Theorem to find AB.

$$d^2 = 3^2 + 6^2 = 9 + 36 = 45$$
$$d = \sqrt{45} = \sqrt{9} \cdot \sqrt{5} = 3\sqrt{5}$$

CLASS PRACTICE

For each right triangle, find the indicated lengths. Write the length of $\overline{AB}$ in simplest radical form.

a. AC b. BC c. AB

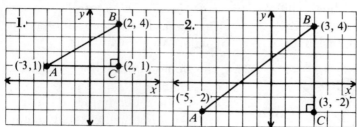

— A —

Draw a set of axes on graph paper and locate the indicated points. Find the length of $\overline{AB}$. Write answers in simplest radical form.

1. $A(3, 2)$ and $B(6, 6)$
2. $A(0, {}^-2)$ and $B(3, 3)$
3. $A({}^-4, {}^-2)$ and $B(1, 3)$
4. $A({}^-5, 2)$ and $B(0, 4)$
5. $A({}^-3, {}^-1)$ and $B(5, {}^-7)$
6. $A({}^-5, {}^-3)$ and $B({}^-3, {}^-5)$
7. $A(0, 1)$ and $B(2, 5)$
8. $A({}^-4, {}^-5)$ and $B({}^-1, 1)$
9. $A(2, 3)$ and $B(4, {}^-2)$
10. $A({}^-4, 2)$ and $B(3, 0)$

— B —

Write all answers in simplest radical form.

Find the following information about $\triangle ABC$.

a. AB b. BC c. AC
d. Perimeter e. Area

11.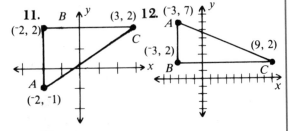

12.

Find the indicated information.

13. For $\triangle RST$ shown, find each measure.
    a. RS
    b. ST
    c. RT
    d. Area

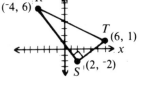

14. $ABCD$ shown is a square. Find each measure.
    a. AB
    b. BC
    c. Perimeter
    d. Area
    e. Slope of $\overline{AB}$
    f. Slope of $\overline{BC}$
    g. Slope of $\overline{DC}$

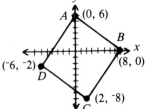

15. $WDIV$ shown is a parallelogram. Find each measure.
    a. WV b. WD c. IX
    d. Perimeter e. Area
    f. Slope of $\overline{ID}$ g. Slope of $\overline{VI}$

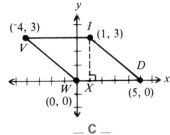

— C —

16. Look at $\triangle ABC$.
    a. Find AC, BC, and AB.
    b. Use slope to show that $\triangle ABC$ is a right triangle.
    c. Show that $\triangle ABC$ is isosceles.

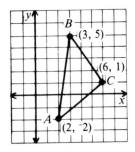

Draw a set of axes on graph paper. Locate each pair of points and draw the line through them. Find the following information. Write answers in simplest radical form.

a. Slope of $\overleftrightarrow{AB}$ b. Distance between points A and B

1. $A(1, 2)$ and $B(5, 5)$
2. $A(^-3, 4)$ and $B(3, 1)$
3. $A(^-3, ^-2)$ and $B(4, ^-2)$

Find the slope of each indicated line. Line m has a slope of $\frac{2}{3}$.

4. Line parallel to m
5. Line perpendicular to m

Draw lines to fit each description. Use a separate set of axes for each exercise.

6. Two different lines each with a slope of $\frac{1}{4}$

7. Line with a slope of $\frac{3}{4}$ and a second line with a slope of $^-\frac{4}{3}$
8. Line whose slope is undefined
9. Line through $(3, 2)$ with a slope of $\frac{2}{5}$

Look at the diagram. Find the following information. Write answers in simplest radical form.

10. Coordinates of point C
11. AC
12. BC
13. AB

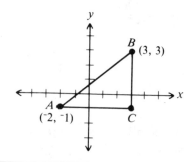

11-9

Equations of Lines

Points whose coordinates fit certain patterns will lie on the same line. The following points are marked on the line shown:

$$A(3, 0) \quad B(1, 2) \quad C(0, 3) \quad D(^-2, 5)$$

Notice that for each of these four points, the sum of the x-coordinate and the y-coordinate is equal to three. Therefore the following equations could be used to describe the relationship between the x-coordinate and the y-coordinate of every point on the above line:

$$x + y = 3 \quad\quad y = {}^-x + 3$$

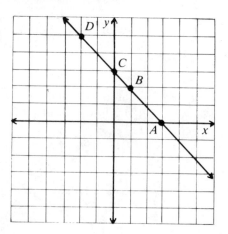

Points whose coordinates make the above equations true will lie on the line, while points whose coordinates do not make the equation true will not. Coordinates which make an equation true are said to *satisfy the equation*. The line determined by an equation is called its *graph*. In the figure above, the line is the graph of the equation $x + y = 3$.

The pattern describing the coordinates of the points on any line can always be given by one of the following types of equation:

$Ax + By = C$ where A, B, and C are constants and A and B are not both 0

$y = mx + b$ where m and b are constants

Therefore each of the following equations will determine a line.

$$2x + 3y = 12 \qquad y = 4x \qquad y = {}^-5$$

$$y = 3x + 1 \qquad x + 3y = 8 \qquad 3x + y = 12$$

$$x + y = 4 \qquad x = 6 \qquad {}^-2x + 4y = 10$$

EXPLORING
Equations of Lines

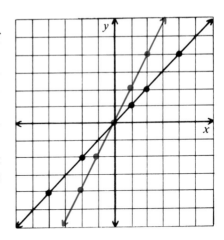

PART A
1. Look at the black line. State the coordinates of the five points marked on the line.
2. For each point in step 1, what is the relationship between the x-coordinate and the y-coordinate?
3. Write an equation that describes that relationship.
4. State the coordinates of four points that are not on the line. Do the coordinates of these points satisfy the equation of the line?
5. Repeat steps 1–4 for the other line shown.

PART B
1. Find five ordered pairs of numbers that satisfy the equation $x + 2y = 6$. (Hint: Replace y with 0, 1, 2, 3, 4 in order. What will the value of x be in each case?)
2. Draw a set of axes on graph paper. Locate and mark the five points with the coordinates in step 1. Are they on the same line?
3. Repeat steps 1 and 2 for these equations: $y = 3x$ and $y = 2x + 1$.

PART C

1. Find four ordered pairs of numbers that satisfy each of these equations: $y = 2x$ and $x + y = 3$.
2. Using the same set of axes, draw the line described by each equation.
3. What is the point of intersection of the two lines? Do the coordinates of the point of intersection satisfy both equations?
4. Repeat steps 1–3 for this pair of equations:
   $x - 3y = 0$ and $x - 2y = 3$.

If you did the preceding EXPLORING carefully, you discovered the following conclusions:

> **If a point is on a line, its coordinates must satisfy any equation describing the line.**
>
> **If the coordinates of a point satisfy an equation of a line, the point is on the line described by the equation.**
>
> **If the coordinates of a point satisfy equations of two different lines, then the point is the point of intersection of the two lines.**

Recall from Chapter 1 that any two points determine one line. The graph of any equation that may be written in the form $Ax + By = C$ or $y = mx + b$ can be drawn by following these steps:

Step 1. Find at least two ordered pairs of numbers that satisfy the equation.

Step 2. Draw a set of axes on graph paper and locate the points with these coordinates.

Step 3. Draw the line through the points.

Example: Draw the graph of $x + 4y = 10$.

Solution:

Step 1. Choose some values for y (or x). Find the corresponding values for x (or y).

Let $y = 0$.	Let $y = 1$.	Let $y = 2$.
$x + 4y = 10$	$x + 4y = 10$	$x + 4y = 10$
$x + 4(0) = 10$	$x + 4(1) = 10$	$x + 4(2) = 10$
$x + 0 = 10$	$x + 4 = 10$	$x + 8 = 10$
$x = 10$	$x = 6$	$x = 2$

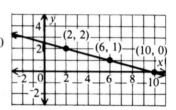

Step 2. Locate these points: (10, 0) (6, 1) (2, 2)

Step 3. Draw the line through the points.

1. It takes only two points to determine a line. Why might it be a good idea to find the coordinates of *more than* two points before drawing the line?

Tell how each equation may be viewed as an equation of the form $Ax + By = C$.

2. $x = 8$ 3. $y = {}^-5$

Select the coordinates that satisfy each given equation.

1. $y = 3x + 1$ a. $(0, 1)$ b. $({}^-1, 2)$ c. $(1, 4)$
2. $x + 3y = 8$ a. $(3, {}^-1)$ b. $(2, 2)$ c. $(8, 0)$
3. $y = {}^-1$ a. $(2, {}^-3)$ b. $({}^-1, 0)$ c. $(3, {}^-1)$
4. $x = 2$ a. $(2, 0)$ b. $(1, 1)$ c. $(0, 2)$

Find four ordered pairs of numbers that satisfy each equation.

5. $x + y = 5$ 6. $2x + y = 6$ 7. $x - 3y = 8$
8. $y = 3x + {}^-4$ 9. $x = 5$ 10. $y = 2$

11–16. Draw the graph of each equation in Exercises 5–10.

EXERCISES

_ A _

Select the coordinates that satisfy each given equation.

1. $y = 2x + 3$
   a. $(0, 3)$ b. $(1, 5)$ c. $({}^-2, 1)$
2. $x + 2y = {}^-3$
   a. $(3, 0)$ b. $({}^-1, {}^-1)$ c. $({}^-7, 5)$
3. $y = x$
   a. $({}^-3, {}^-3)$ b. $(0, 0)$ c. $({}^-2, 2)$
4. $y = {}^-2x$
   a. $(0, 0)$ b. $({}^-3, {}^-6)$ c. $({}^-6, 3)$
5. $x + 3y + 2 = 0$
   a. $(5, 1)$ b. $(1, {}^-1)$ c. $({}^-5, 1)$
6. $2x - 3y = 1$
   a. $(2, 1)$ b. $(8, 5)$ c. $(14, 9)$

7. $2x + y = {}^-5$
   a. $({}^-1, {}^-3)$ b. $(2, 1)$ c. $({}^-4, 3)$
8. $y = 3$
   a. $(0, 3)$ b. $(3, {}^-2)$ c. $(1, 2)$
9. $x = 2$
   a. $(0, 2)$ b. $(2, 0)$ c. $(1, 1)$
10. Select the equations that describe a line containing the point $({}^-2, 3)$.
    a. $2x + y = {}^-1$ b. $3x + 2y = 12$
    c. $x + 2y = 4$ d. ${}^-3x = 2y$
    e. $3y = 2x + 5$

Find four ordered pairs of numbers that satisfy each equation.

11. $x - y = 4$ 12. $x + {}^-2y = 8$

13. $y = 5x + 1$ **14.** $y = 2x$

15. $x = {}^-2$ **16.** $y = 4$

17–22. Draw the graph of each equation in Exercises 11–16.

— B —

23. The lines described by $y = 2x + {}^-5$ and $y = 5x + {}^-2$ intersect. Which of the following points is the point of intersection?

$(1, 3)$ $({}^-1, {}^-7)$ $(1, {}^-3)$

24. Use the same set of axes for all parts of this exercise.
a. Locate and mark three points that satisfy each equation.
$x + y = 4$ $x + y = 0$
$x + y = {}^-4$
b. Draw a line through each set of three points.
c. Describe the relationship among the three lines.

25. Use the same set of axes for all parts of this exercise.
a. Locate and mark three points that satisfy each equation.
$y = 2x$ $y = 2x + 4$
$y = 2x + {}^-4$

b. Draw a line through each set of three points.
c. State the coordinates of the point where each line crosses the y-axis.
d. Describe the relationship among the three lines.

Draw the graph of each equation on a separate set of axes.

26. $3x + 4y = 8$ **27.** $y + \frac{1}{2}x = 5$

28. $y = {}^-3x + 1$ **29.** $y = {}^-x$

30. $x - 2y = 6$ **31.** $y = 2x - 5$

32. $2x + y = 4$ **33.** $x = 3y$

34. $y = {}^-5$ **35.** $x = 3$

Write an equation that is satisfied by each set of five ordered pairs.

36. $({}^-5, 2)$ $(0, {}^-3)$ $(7, {}^-10)$, $(1, {}^-4)$, $({}^-3, 0)$

37. $(1, 2)$ $(3, 6)$ $({}^-2, {}^-4)$, $({}^-5, {}^-10)$, $(0, 0)$

38. $(5, 3)$, $(0, {}^-2)$, $(4, 2)$, $(2, 0)$, $({}^-5, {}^-7)$

39. $(4, 7)$, $(1, 4)$, $({}^-1, 2)$, $(0, 3)$, $({}^-3, 0)$

40. $(3, 7)$, $(0, 1)$, $(5, 11)$, $(1, 3)$, $({}^-2, {}^-3)$

DID YOU KNOW THAT....

Simon Stevin of Belgium (1548-1620) is credited with the introduction of decimal fractions. Stevin used the notation 5 3⓪1①4② for 53.14. The decimal point is thought to have been first used in 1608. Earlier notations used to express this same number included the following: 53,14; 53,1′4″; 53(14); and 53 ⌊14. The issue of notation for decimal fractions is still not settled today, as the United States uses 53.14 for 53 and 14 hundredths while this number is written as 53·14 in Europe.

11-10

Graphing Formulas

Scientific data obtained through measurement can often be described by formulas whose graph is a line. Such graphs give us a picture of the data.

Here are two examples. Notice that in both examples only quadrant I is used since the measurements involved are limited to positive numbers.

Example 1: Draw a graph of the formula $p = 1.15d$ that gives the water pressure in the ocean, where p = pressure in tons per square inch and d = depth in miles.

Solution:

Draw the axes.

Choose a convenient scale for each axis and label both axes.

Find values for p and d that satisfy the equation.

d	0	1	2	3	4
p	0	1.15	2.30	3.45	4.60

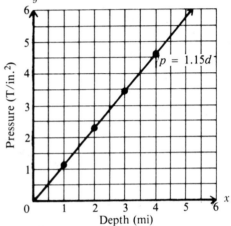

Each pair of values (d, p) represents the coordinates of a point. Locate the points and draw a line through them.

Example 2: Draw a graph of the formula for the recommended slope for drainage pipes. The formula is $d = \frac{1}{4}f$, where d = amount of drop in inches and f = length of pipe in feet.

Solution:

Some values of f and d that satisfy the equation are:

f	0	4	8	12	16
d	0	1	2	3	4

The completed graph is shown here.

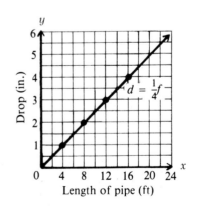

Coordinate Systems and Linear Equations   **463**

Look at Example 1.
1. Could different scales be used to label the x-axis and y-axis?
2. Could the x-axis have been labeled to represent pressure?
3. Which gives more accurate values for pressure and depth—the formula or the graph?
4. What could be done to improve the accuracy of the graph?
5. Why were only positive numbers used?

Look at Example 2.
6. Could different scales be used to label the x-axis and y-axis?
7. Could the x-axis have been labeled to represent drop?
8. Use the graph to find the drop for 6 ft of pipe and for 18 ft of pipe.
9. Why were only positive numbers used?

EXERCISES

For each formula, (a) find at least four pairs of values that satisfy the formula, and (b) draw a graph that represents the equation.

1. $15r = 22s$ or $r = \dfrac{22s}{15}$,

   where s = speed in feet per second
   r = speed in miles per hour

2. $h = \dfrac{w}{750}$,

   where h = approximate horse-power rating of an electric motor
   w = number of watts

3. $t = \dfrac{n}{4} + 40$,

   where t = temperature in degrees Fahrenheit
   n = number of cricket chirps per minute

4. $d = \dfrac{t}{5}$,

   where d = distance in miles from lightning flash
   t = time in seconds be-tween lightning flash and thunder clap

5. $A = 6h$,

   where A = area of a rectangle with base length 6
   h = height of the rectangle

6. $C = \pi d$,

   where C = circumference of a circle
   d = diameter of the circle

7. $C = 0.2 + 0.17\,(m - 1)$,

   where C = cost in dollars of phone call between two cities
   m = length of call in min-utes

Geometry on the Job

CARTOGRAPHER

Marguerite Wilkins is a *cartographer*, or map maker. Working from photographs taken from airplanes, as well as measurements made on the ground, she makes an accurate map of a region.

A map that shows the slope of the land at each point, called a *topographic* map, is used by hikers and builders. To make a topographic map like the one shown, Marguerite needs to know the altitude (distance above sea level) at each point. After choosing an interval curve such as 100 m, she draws a curve connecting all points with altitude 100 m, another curve connecting all points with altitude 200 m, and so on. Because the rise between two curves is always the same, the shorter the run, the greater the slope. So the closer together the curves, the steeper the land.

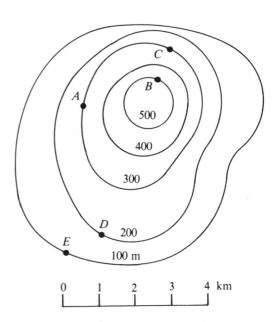

EXERCISES

1. The map shown is a topographic map of a hill. What is the altitude of point *A*? point *C*?

2. Which of the five points marked has the highest altitude?

3. At which of the marked points is the slope steepest?

4. What is the scale of this map?

5. What is the horizontal distance (the run) between *D* and *E*? What is the rise? What is the slope?

Coordinate Systems and Linear Equations   465

ARITHMETIC REVIEW — *Solving Percent Problems*

Shown below are three types of problems that can be solved with percents.

Examples:

1. 15 out of 20 is what percent?
    (15 is what percent of 20?)

    $$\frac{15}{20} = \frac{x}{100}$$ (Think: 15 out of 20 is what out of 100?)

    $20x = 1500$

    $x = 75$

    Answer: 75%

2. 15% of what number is 3?
    (3 is 15% of what number?)

    $$\frac{15}{100} = \frac{3}{x}$$ (Think: 15 out of 100 is 3 out of what number?)

    $15x = 300$

    $x = 20$

    Answer: 20

3. 15% of 40 is what number?
    (What number is 15% of 40?)
    (Two methods of solution are given:)
    Using proportions:

    $$\frac{15}{100} = \frac{x}{40}$$ (Think: 15 out of 100 is what out of 40?)

    $100x = 600$

    $x = 6$

    Answer: 6

Using multiplication:

$$15\% = \frac{15}{100} = 0.15$$

$$15\% \text{ of } 40 = \frac{15}{100} \times \frac{40}{1} = \frac{600}{100} = 6$$

or

$$15\% \text{ of } 40 = 0.15 \times 40 = 6.00$$

Answer: 6

EXERCISES
Solve.

1. 14 out of 40 is what percent?
2. 21 out of 30 is what percent?
3. 21 out of 60 is what percent?
4. 6 out of 9 is what percent?
5. 30 is what percent of 75?
6. 15 is what percent of 25?
7. 35% of what number is 7?
8. 30% of what number is 12?
9. 24% of what number is 6?
10. 45% of what number is 90?
11. 77 is 70% of what number?
12. 42 is 60% of what number?
13. 60% of 45 is what number?
14. 12% of 68 is what number?
15. 4% of 60 is what number?
16. 35% of 80 is what number?
17. What number is 75% of 8?
18. What number is 22% of 6.25?

Chapter 11 Review

Vocabulary

The following terms, abbreviations, and symbols were introduced in this chapter. You should be able to write a brief definition, draw a picture, or give an example to illustrate the meaning of each.

absolute value (p. 432)
axes (p. 443)
coordinate system (p. 438)
coordinates (p. 438)
graph of an equation (p. 459)
integers (p. 432)

opposites (p. 432)
ordered pair (p. 443)
origin (pp. 438, 443)
quadrant (p. 443)
rise (p. 448)
run (p. 448)

satisfy an equation (p. 459)
slope (p. 448)
x-axis (p. 443)
y-axis (p. 443)
x-coordinate (p. 443)
y-coordinate (p. 443)

Symbols (x, y) (point with coordinates x and y) (p. 443)

Skills Checklist

In Chapter 11 you learned how to compute with positive and negative integers, how to use ordered pairs of numbers to locate points in a plane, how to find the slope of a line, how to find the distance between two points, and how to draw the graph of an equation or formula describing a line. In addition, you were introduced to some applications of coordinate systems and graphs of lines.

The following list indicates the major skills, facts, and results you should have mastered in this chapter:

- Find the sum of any two or more integers. (**11-1**, pp. 432–433)
- Find the difference of any two integers. (**11-2**, pp. 434–435)
- Find the product or quotient of any two integers. (**11-3**, pp. 436–437)
- Use map coordinates to locate cities or towns on a road map. (**11-4**, pp. 438–441)
- State the coordinate of a point located on a number line. (**11-4**, pp. 438–441)
- Locate a point in a plane given its coordinates. (**11-5**, pp. 443–447)
- Find the slope of any nonvertical line. (**11-6**, pp. 448–452)
- Recognize whether the slope of a given line is 0, undefined, positive, or negative. (**11-6**, pp. 448–452)
- Find the slope of a line parallel to or perpendicular to a line with a given slope. (**11-7**, pp. 453–455)
- Draw a line with a given slope. (**11-6—11-7**, pp. 448–455)
- Find the distance between two points by using the Pythagorean Theorem. (**11-8**, pp. 456–457)

- Draw the graph of the line described by an equation and select ordered pairs of coordinates (x, y) that satisfy the equation. (**11-9—11-10**, pp. 458-464)
- Write an equation for a line when the coordinates of three or more points are known. (**11-9**, pp. 458-462)

Exercises

Find each sum or difference. (**11-1—11-2**)

1. $^-9 + 3$
2. $^-7 + {}^-6$
3. $^-8 + 8$
4. $6 + 2$
5. $6 - {}^-2$
6. $0 - {}^-10$
7. $^-5 - {}^-8$
8. $^-9 - {}^-5$
9. $^-5 - 7$
10. $^-11 - {}^-11$
11. $2 - 8$
12. $7 - {}^-1$

Find each product or quotient. (**11-3**)

13. $^-6 \times 2$
14. $3 \times {}^-5$
15. $^-8 \times {}^-2$
16. $^-6 \times {}^-3 \times {}^-2$
17. $^-6 \times {}^-3 \times 2$
18. $^-6 \times 3 \times 2$
19. $32 \div {}^-8$
20. $^-32 \div {}^-8$

Complete each statement. (**11-1—11-2**)

21. $9 - {}^-5 = 9 + $?
22. ? $- 7 = {}^-3$
23. $8 - $? $= 12$
24. $^-4 + $? $= 0$
25. $^-7 - $? $= {}^-2$
26. $^-8 + $? $= {}^-5$

Find the value of each expression. (**11-1—11-3**)

27. $13 - (2 - 5)$
28. $0 - (8 - 2)$
29. $^-3({}^-5 + 1)$
30. $6(4 - 7)$
31. $^-2(4) + {}^-2({}^-4)$
32. $(6 - 10) - 0$

For Exercises 33-40, look at the partial map of Indiana and partial index of cities and towns on page 469.

Use the index to identify the coordinates of each of the following cities and towns. (**11-4**)

33. French Lick
34. Crawfordsville
35. Bloomington
36. Columbus

The following cities and towns are not listed in the partial index. Identify the coordinates of each. (**11-4**)

37. Austin
38. Terre Haute
39. Madison
40. Muncie

State the number corresponding to each labeled point. (**11-4**)

41.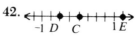
42.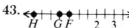
43.

44.

Draw a set of axes on graph paper. Locate each given point with a dot and label it with its coordinates. (**11-5**)

45. $(7, 3)$
46. $(3, 7)$
47. $(^-5, 4)$
48. $(4, {}^-5)$
49. $(0, 5)$
50. $(5, 0)$
51. $(0, {}^-5)$
52. $(^-5, 0)$
53. $(^-11, {}^-11)$
54. $(9, {}^-6)$
55. $(^-6, 9)$
56. $(^-6, {}^-9)$

Find the indicated information.

57. For each line, tell whether the slope is positive, negative, zero, or undefined. (**11-6**)

Find the slope of each line shown. (**11-6**)

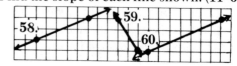

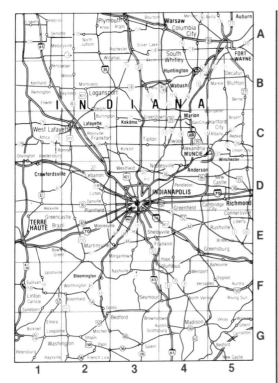

Index of Cities and Towns

Draw a set of axes on graph paper. Locate each pair of points and draw the line through them. Write the slope of each line in simplest form. (11-6)

61. (2, 3) and (5, 7)

62. (⁻5, ⁻2) and (⁻1, 1)

63. Line l has a slope of $\frac{3}{5}$. Find the slope of each indicated line. (11-7)

a. Line parallel to l

b. Line perpendicular to l

Draw lines to fit each description. Use a separate set of axes for each exercise. (11-7)

64. Two different lines each with a slope of $\frac{4}{7}$

65. Two different lines each with a slope of $-\frac{2}{3}$

66. Two different lines each with a slope of 0

67. Line with a slope of $\frac{3}{5}$ and a second line with a slope of $\frac{-5}{3}$

Find the distance between each pair of points. Use graph paper if needed. (11-8)

68. (⁻3, ⁻5) and (3, 3)

69. (1, 2) and (2, 5)

Classify each statement as true or false.

70. A line with a slope of $-\frac{1}{3}$ will slant upward from left to right. (11-6)

71. A horizontal line has an undefined slope. (11-6)

72. The line through (⁻3, 2) and (⁻3, ⁻1) is vertical. (11-6)

73. The line described by the equation $y = 2x + 1$ passes through the point (1, 0). (11-9)

Each equation describes a line. For each equation, (a) state coordinates of four points on the line, and (b) draw the graph of the equation. Use a separate set of axes for each exercise. (11-10)

74. $x + 3y = 9$

75. $y = 2x$

76. $y = 2x + 3$

77. $2x + 3y = 12$

78. $y = ⁻6$

79. $x = 5$

Cumulative Review — CHAPTERS 6-11

Classify each statement as true or false.

1. Polygonal regions with equal areas must have equal perimeters. **(6–14)**
2. If both the base length and height of a rectangular region are tripled, then its perimeter is tripled. **(6–11)**
3. If both the base length and height of a rectangular region are tripled, then its area is tripled. **(6–11)**
4. If all dimensions of a rectangular prism are multiplied by two, then its volume is doubled. **(7–9)**
5. A triangle with sides of length 2 cm, $4\sqrt{2}$ cm, and 6 cm will be a right triangle. **(8–3)**
6. Two figures that are similar will always also be congruent. **(9–5)**
7. Two figures that are congruent will always also be similar. **(9–5)**
8. $\sqrt{4} \cdot \sqrt{9} = \sqrt{36}$ **(8–2)**
9. $\sqrt{4} + \sqrt{9} = \sqrt{13}$ **(8–2)**
10. $\sin 35° = \cos 55°$ **(10–7)**
11. Any vertical line has a slope of zero. **(11–6)**
12. The line described by the equation $y = {}^-3x + 1$ passes through the point $(0, 1)$. **(11–9)**

Draw and label a figure or figures to fit each description.

13. Rectangular region with an area of 12 and a height of 2 **(6–3)**
14. Rectangular region with a perimeter of 12 and a base length of 4 **(6–3)**
15. Rectangular region with an area of 24 and a perimeter of 22 **(6–3)**
16. Nonrectangular parallelogram region with a base length of 10 and an area of 30 **(6–7)**
17. Acute triangular region with a base length of 6 and a height of 5 **(6–8)**
18. Triangular region with a base length of 6 and an area of 12 **(6–8)**
19. $\triangle RST \sim \triangle DEF$ **(9–6)**
20. Two rectangular regions that are not similar **(9–6)**

Convert each measurement to the unit indicated.

21. $36 \text{ ft}^2 = \ ? \ \text{yd}^2$ **(6–13)**
22. $5 \text{ m}^2 = \ ? \ \text{cm}^2$ **(6–13)**
23. $1 \text{ yd}^3 = \ ? \ \text{ft}^3$ **(7–11)**
24. $54 \text{ ft}^3 = \ ? \ \text{yd}^3$ **(7–11)**
25. $2 \text{ L} = \ ? \ \text{cm}^3$ **(7–11)**
26. $4000 \text{ mL} = \ ? \ \text{L}$ **(7–11)**

Find the indicated information.

27. Area = ? in.² **(6–8)**

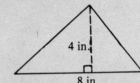

4 in.

8 in.

28. a. Perimeter = ? cm
    (6–7) b. Area = ? cm²

5 cm 4 cm

8 cm

29. a. Perimeter = ? m
    (6–9) b. Area = ? m²

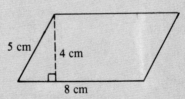

5 m

4 m

7 m

8 m

4 m

12 m

30. **a.** Circumference = ? cm
(6-10) **b.** Area = ? cm²

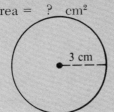

3 cm

31. Area = ? cm²
(6-13)

6 cm

4 cm

10 cm   4

32. Area = ? in.²
(6-13)

10 in.

6 in.

16 in.

33. **a.** Perimeter = ? ft
(6-4) **b.** Area = ? ft²

2 ft

1 yd

34. Area = 24 cm²
(6-8) h = ? cm

h

8 cm

Find the area of each shaded region.

35.

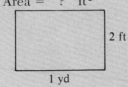

4 cm

4 cm

36. 6 cm

2 cm   2 cm   6 cm

Draw a triangle similar to but larger than each one shown. Draw the altitude to $\overline{AB}$.
(6-6)

37.

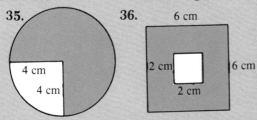

C

A   B

38.

A

C

B

Describe the size and shape of the faces of each prism. (7-1)

39.

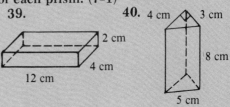

2 cm

12 cm   4 cm

40. 4 cm   3 cm

8 cm

5 cm

Find the indicated information.

41-42. Find the lateral area, total area, and volume of each prism in Exercises 39-40. (7-2, 7-3, 7-5, 7-6)

43. Find the lateral area, total area, and volume of the cylinder shown. (Use 3.14 for π.) (7-4, 7-7)

10 cm

3 cm

Find the volume of each figure. (7-10)

44.
Regular Square Pyramid

6 cm

5 cm

5 cm

45.

6 cm

4 cm

(Use 3.14 for π)

Find the indicated information.

46. Find the slant height, lateral area, and total area of the regular square pyramid shown. (7-10)

5 cm

4 cm

3 cm

6 cm

47. A cube has a total area of 96 cm². Find the area of each face and the length of each edge. (7-2)

48. A prism has a volume of 200 cm³ and a base area of 50 cm². Find its height. (7-6)

49. A regular pyramid has a volume of 100 cm³ and a base area of 50 cm². Find its height. (7-10)

Find the value of each expression. (8–1)
50. Square of 9   51. 9 squared
52. 9^2 53. $\sqrt{9}$

Use the table of squares and square roots on page 475 to find the value of each expression. (8–2)
54. $\sqrt{29}$ 55. $\sqrt{1444}$
56. 23^2 57. 3.5^2
58. Square root of 67   59. 67 squared

Express in simplest radical form. (8–5)
60. $(3\sqrt{5})^2$ 61. $3(\sqrt{5})^2$ 62. $(\sqrt{6})^2$
63. $\sqrt{6}\cdot\sqrt{3}$ 64. $\sqrt{45}$ 65. $\dfrac{2}{\sqrt{3}}$

Find the indicated length in each triangle. Express your answers in simplest radical form.

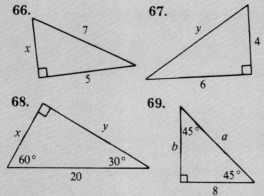

66.

67.

68.

69.

Find the indicated information.
70. If $\frac{3}{x} = \frac{5}{6}$, then $x = $? . (9–3)
71. On a certain scale drawing, 2 cm represents a distance of 30 m. Find the distance represented by 3 cm. (10–5)
72. Assume that $\triangle RST \sim \triangle XYZ$ and that $RS = \frac{3}{4}\cdot XY$ (9–6)
    a. $RS:XY = $?
    b. $XY = $? $\cdot RS$
    c. If $m\angle Y = 60°$, $m\angle S = $?° .

d. If $XY = 20$ cm, $RS = $? cm.
e. If $XZ = 32$ cm, $RT = $? cm.
f. What is the constant of similarity of $\triangle RST$ to $\triangle XYZ$?

73. Assume that $\triangle ABC \sim \triangle GHI$ as shown. (9–6)

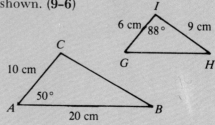

a. $BC = $? cm   b. $GH = $? cm
c. $m\angle C = $?°   d. $m\angle G = $?°
e. Constant of similarity of $\triangle ABC$ to $\triangle GHI = $?

Trace the figure shown. Use the point method to draw the indicated reduction or enlargement. (9–8)

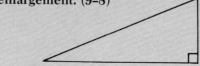

74. 1:2 reduction
75. 5:2 enlargement
76. Draw a segment. Use a compass and straightedge to divide the segment into 3 congruent parts. (10–2)

Construct a triangle similar to $\triangle DEF$ shown by using the indicated method and constant of similarity. (9–9, 9–10)
77. SSS $\sim$; 3   78. ASA $\sim$; $\frac{2}{3}$
79. SAS $\sim$; $\frac{3}{2}$ 80. ASA $\sim$; 1

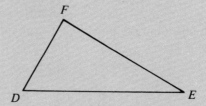

Find each indicated length. (10-1)

81.

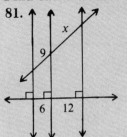

82.

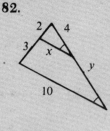

Find the indicated information.

83. Look at the triangle shown. Find the value of each ratio. (10-1)

a. $\dfrac{CX}{XA}$ b. $\dfrac{CY}{CB}$

c. $\dfrac{CX}{CA}$ d. $\dfrac{XY}{AB}$

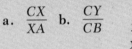

84. The ratio of the lengths of two corresponding sides of two similar figures is 3:4. Find the ratio of their perimeters and the ratio of their areas. (10-3)

85. The ratio of the lengths of two corresponding segments of two similar prisms is 2:3. Find the ratio of their total areas and the ratio of their volumes. (10-4)

86. Assume that prism A is similar to prism B with $k = 3$ and that the volume of prism B is 20 cm³. Find the volume of prism A. (10-4)

87. Look at $\triangle RST$. Find each trigonometric ratio in simplest fraction form. (10-6)
a. $\sin T$
b. $\cos T$
c. $\tan T$
d. $\sin S$

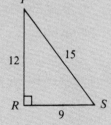

For Exercises 88-91, use trigonometric ratios.

Find each indicated length to the nearest whole number. (10-8)

88. **89.**

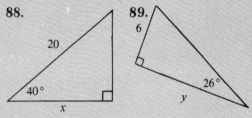

Find $m\angle A$ to the nearest degree. (10-8)

90. **91.**

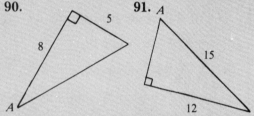

Find the indicated information.

92. Find the slope of the line through the points (3, 4) and (8, 6). (11-6)

93. Line l has a slope of $\frac{2}{3}$. Find the slope of a line parallel to l and the slope of a line perpendicular to l. (11-7)

94. Find the distance between the points (2, 3) and (5, 7). (11-8)

Draw a line to fit each description. Use a separate set of axes for each problem. (11-6)

95. Line through the point (3, 4) with a slope of $\frac{1}{2}$

96. Line with a slope of $-\frac{3}{4}$

Draw the graph of each equation. Use a separate set of axes for each problem. (11-9)

97. $x + 2y = 8$ **98.** $y = 2x + 3$

99. $y = 4$ **100.** $x = {}^-3$

SYMBOLS

∠ (p. 12) angle

≈ (p. 227) approximately equal to

A (p. 232) area

B (p. 290) area of the base

b (p. 232) base length

cm (p. 86) centimeter

⊙O (p. 42) circle with center at O

C (p. 226) circumference

≅ (p. 93) congruent to

k (p. 404) constant of similarity

cos (p. 413) cosine

° (p. 48) degree

d (p. 226) diameter

h (p. 232) height

km (p. 87) kilometer

AB (p. 42) length of $\overline{AB}$

$\overleftrightarrow{AB}$ (p. 6) line AB (A and B are points on the line.)

$\overset{\frown}{ABC}$ (p. 63) major arc

$m\angle ABC$ (p. 45) measure of angle ABC

$m\overset{\frown}{AB}$ (p. 63) measure of arc AB

m (p. 87) meter

mm (p. 86) millimeter

$\overset{\frown}{AB}$ (p. 63) minor arc

n^2 (p. 326) (number squared, or square of a number)

∥ (p. 9) parallel to

P (p. 222) perimeter

⊥ (p. 48) perpendicular to

π (p. 226) pi

(x,y) (p. 443) point with coordinates x and y

$\sqrt{n}$ (p. 326) positive square root of a number

r (p. 254) radius

$a{:}b$ or $\dfrac{a}{b}$ (p. 354) ratio of a to b

$\overrightarrow{AB}$ (p. 6) ray AB (A is the endpoint.)

$\overline{AB}$ (p. 6) segment AB (A and B are the endpoints.)

~ (p. 366) similar to

sin (p. 413) sine

tan (p. 413) tangent

△ (p. 93) triangle

V (p. 290) volume

SQUARES AND SQUARE ROOTS

n	n^2	$\sqrt{n}$	n	n^2	$\sqrt{n}$	n	n^2	$\sqrt{n}$
1	1	1.000	51	2601	7.141	101	10,201	10.050
2	4	1.414	52	2704	7.211	102	10,404	10.100
3	9	1.732	53	2809	7.280	103	10,609	10.149
4	16	2.000	54	2916	7.348	104	10,816	10.198
5	25	2.236	55	3025	7.416	105	11,025	10.247
6	36	2.449	56	3136	7.483	106	11,236	10.296
7	49	2.646	57	3249	7.550	107	11,449	10.344
8	64	2.828	58	3364	7.616	108	11,664	10.392
9	81	3.000	59	3481	7.681	109	11,881	10.440
10	100	3.162	60	3600	7.746	110	12,100	10.488
11	121	3.317	61	3721	7.810	111	12,321	10.536
12	144	3.464	62	3844	7.874	112	12,544	10.583
13	169	3.606	63	3969	7.937	113	12,769	10.630
14	196	3.742	64	4096	8.000	114	12,996	10.677
15	225	3.873	65	4225	8.062	115	13,225	10.724
16	256	4.000	66	4356	8.124	116	13,456	10.770
17	289	4.123	67	4489	8.185	117	13,689	10.817
18	324	4.243	68	4624	8.246	118	13,924	10.863
19	361	4.359	69	4761	8.307	119	14,161	10.909
20	400	4.472	70	4900	8.367	120	14,400	10.954
21	441	4.583	71	5041	8.426	121	14,641	11.000
22	484	4.690	72	5184	8.485	122	14,884	11.045
23	529	4.796	73	5329	8.544	123	15,129	11.091
24	576	4.899	74	5476	8.602	124	15,376	11.136
25	625	5.000	75	5625	8.660	125	15,625	11.180
26	676	5.099	76	5776	8.718	126	15,876	11.225
27	729	5.196	77	5929	8.775	127	16,129	11.269
28	784	5.292	78	6084	8.832	128	16,384	11.314
29	841	5.385	79	6241	8.888	129	16,641	11.358
30	900	5.477	80	6400	8.944	130	16,900	11.402
31	961	5.568	81	6561	9.000	131	17,161	11.446
32	1024	5.657	82	6724	9.055	132	17,424	11.489
33	1089	5.745	83	6889	9.110	133	17,689	11.533
34	1156	5.831	84	7056	9.165	134	17,956	11.576
35	1225	5.916	85	7225	9.220	135	18,225	11.619
36	1296	6.000	86	7396	9.274	136	18,496	11.662
37	1369	6.083	87	7569	9.327	137	18,769	11.705
38	1444	6.164	88	7744	9.381	138	19,044	11.747
39	1521	6.245	89	7921	9.434	139	19,321	11.790
40	1600	6.325	90	8100	9.487	140	19,600	11.832
41	1681	6.403	91	8281	9.539	141	19,881	11.874
42	1764	6.481	92	8464	9.592	142	20,164	11.916
43	1849	6.557	93	8649	9.644	143	20,449	11.958
44	1936	6.633	94	8836	9.695	144	20,736	12.000
45	2025	6.708	95	9025	9.747	145	21,025	12.042
46	2116	6.782	96	9216	9.798	146	21,316	12.083
47	2209	6.856	97	9409	9.849	147	21,609	12.124
48	2304	6.928	98	9604	9.899	148	21,904	12.166
49	2401	7.000	99	9801	9.950	149	22,201	12.207
50	2500	7.071	100	10,000	10.000	150	22,500	12.247

TRIGONOMETRIC RATIOS

$m\angle A$	$\sin A$	$\cos A$	$\tan A$	$m\angle A$	$\sin A$	$\cos A$	$\tan A$
0	0.000	1.000	0.000				
1	0.017	1.000	0.017	46	0.719	0.695	1.036
2	0.035	0.999	0.035	47	0.731	0.682	1.072
3	0.052	0.999	0.052	48	0.743	0.669	1.111
4	0.070	0.998	0.070	49	0.755	0.656	1.150
5	0.087	0.996	0.087	50	0.766	0.643	1.192
6	0.105	0.995	0.105	51	0.777	0.629	1.235
7	0.122	0.993	0.123	52	0.788	0.616	1.280
8	0.139	0.990	0.141	53	0.799	0.602	1.327
9	0.156	0.988	0.158	54	0.809	0.588	1.376
10	0.174	0.985	0.176	55	0.819	0.574	1.428
11	0.191	0.982	0.194	56	0.829	0.559	1.483
12	0.208	0.978	0.213	57	0.839	0.545	1.540
13	0.225	0.974	0.231	58	0.848	0.530	1.600
14	0.242	0.970	0.249	59	0.857	0.515	1.664
15	0.259	0.966	0.268	60	0.866	0.500	1.732
16	0.276	0.961	0.287	61	0.875	0.485	1.804
17	0.292	0.956	0.306	62	0.883	0.470	1.881
18	0.309	0.951	0.325	63	0.891	0.454	1.963
19	0.326	0.946	0.344	64	0.899	0.438	2.050
20	0.342	0.940	0.364	65	0.906	0.423	2.145
21	0.358	0.934	0.384	66	0.914	0.407	2.246
22	0.375	0.927	0.404	67	0.921	0.391	2.356
23	0.391	0.921	0.424	68	0.927	0.375	2.475
24	0.407	0.914	0.445	69	0.934	0.358	2.605
25	0.423	0.906	0.466	70	0.940	0.342	2.747
26	0.438	0.899	0.488	71	0.946	0.326	2.904
27	0.454	0.891	0.510	72	0.951	0.309	3.078
28	0.470	0.883	0.532	73	0.956	0.292	3.271
29	0.485	0.875	0.554	74	0.961	0.276	3.487
30	0.500	0.866	0.577	75	0.966	0.259	3.732
31	0.515	0.857	0.601	76	0.970	0.242	4.011
32	0.530	0.848	0.625	77	0.974	0.225	4.331
33	0.545	0.839	0.649	78	0.978	0.208	4.705
34	0.559	0.829	0.675	79	0.982	0.191	5.145
35	0.574	0.819	0.700	80	0.985	0.174	5.671
36	0.588	0.809	0.727	81	0.988	0.156	6.314
37	0.602	0.799	0.754	82	0.990	0.139	7.115
38	0.616	0.788	0.781	83	0.993	0.122	8.144
39	0.629	0.777	0.810	84	0.995	0.105	9.514
40	0.643	0.766	0.839	85	0.996	0.087	11.430
41	0.656	0.755	0.869	86	0.998	0.070	14.301
42	0.669	0.743	0.900	87	0.999	0.052	19.081
43	0.682	0.731	0.933	88	0.999	0.035	28.636
44	0.695	0.719	0.966	89	1.000	0.017	57.290
45	0.707	0.707	1.000	90	1.000	0.000	—

CONSTRUCTIONS

MAJOR CONCLUSIONS

If two lines intersect, their intersection is a point. (p. 9)

If two planes intersect, their intersection is a line. (p. 9)

The measure of a central angle is equal to the measure of its intercepted arc. (p. 64)

The measure of an inscribed angle is equal to one half the measure of its intercepted arc. (p. 70)

An inscribed angle that intercepts a semicircle is a right angle. (p. 70)

The measures of vertical angles are equal. (p. 77)

The corresponding parts of congruent polygons must also be congruent. (p. 94)

A line of symmetry divides a geometric figure into two congruent halves. (p. 98)

Every angle has exactly one line of symmetry and exactly one angle bisector. (p. 102)

For every angle, the angle bisector determines the line of symmetry. (p. 102)

Every segment has exactly two lines of symmetry. (p. 102)

The line passing through a segment and the perpendicular bisector of the segment are lines of symmetry. (p. 102)

Properties of an Isosceles Triangle (p. 110)
Exactly one line of symmetry.
The base angles are congruent.
The line of symmetry bisects the vertex angle and is the perpendicular bisector of the base.

Properties of an Equilateral Triangle (p. 111)
Exactly three lines of symmetry.

continued

continued

All angles are congruent.

Each line of symmetry bisects an angle of the triangle and is the perpendicular bisector of the side opposite that angle.

Properties of a Parallelogram (p. 114)

Opposite sides are congruent.

Opposite angles are congruent.

Consecutive angles are supplementary.

Diagonals bisect each other.

Properties of a Rhombus (p. 117)

Opposite angles are congruent.

Consecutive angles are supplementary.

Exactly two lines of symmetry.

Each diagonal bisects the angles whose vertices are its endpoints.

Each diagonal determines a line of symmetry.

Each diagonal is the perpendicular bisector of the other.

Properties of a Rectangle (p. 120)

Exactly two lines of symmetry.

Each line of symmetry is the perpendicular bisector of the sides it intersects.

Diagonals bisect each other and are congruent.

Properties of a Square (p. 122-123)

Exactly four lines of symmetry.

Two of the lines of symmetry are the perpendicular bisectors of the sides they intersect.

Two of the lines of symmetry bisect the angles they intersect.

Diagonals are the perpendicular bisectors of each other and are congruent.

Each diagonal determines a line of symmetry.

Side/Side/Side Property (SSS) (p. 134)

If three sides of one triangle are congruent to the corresponding sides of another triangle, the triangles are congruent.

The Triangle Inequality Property (p. 135)

The sum of the lengths of any two sides of a triangle is greater than the length of the third side.

Side/Angle/Side Property (SAS) (p. 142)

If two sides and the included angle of one triangle are congruent to the corresponding sides and angle of another triangle, the triangles are congruent.

Angle/Side/Angle Property (ASA) (p. 143)

If two angles and the included side of one triangle are congruent to the corresponding angles and side of another triangle, the triangles are congruent.

If two coplanar lines are perpendicular to the same line, then the two lines are parallel. (p. 148)

If a point is equidistant from the endpoints of a segment, then it lies on the perpendicular bisector of the segment. (p. 161)

If a point lies on the perpendicular bisector of a segment, then it is equidistant from the endpoints of the segment. (p. 161)

The perpendicular bisector of a chord contains the center of a circle. (p. 162)

The perpendicular bisectors of any two nonparallel chords intersect at the center of the circle. (p. 162)

The perpendicular bisectors of the three sides of any triangle meet at a single point. This point is called the *circumcenter*. (p. 162)

The three altitudes of any triangle meet at a single point. This point is called the *orthocenter*. (p. 168)

Each point on the bisector of an angle is equidistant from the sides of the angle. (p. 170)

The angle bisectors of any triangle meet at a single point. This point is called the *incenter*. (p. 170)

The three medians of any triangle meet at a single point. This point is called the *centroid*. (p. 172)

The tangent at a point on a circle is perpendicular to the radius drawn to that point. (p. 174)

Exactly two tangents can be drawn to a circle from an outside point. (p. 175)

The two segments tangent to a circle from an outside point are congruent. (p. 175)

If two parallel lines are cut by a transversal, then each pair of alternate interior angles are congruent. (p. 185)

If two parallel lines are cut by a transversal, then each pair of interior angles on the same side of the transversal are supplementary. (p. 185)

If two lines are cut by a transversal so that one pair of alternate interior angles are congruent, then the lines are parallel. (p. 186)

If two lines are cut by a transversal so that the interior angles on one side of the transversal are supplementary, then the lines are parallel. (p. 186)

If two parallel lines are cut by a transversal, each pair of corresponding angles are congruent. (p. 189)

If two lines are cut by a transversal so that one pair of corresponding angles are congruent, then the lines are parallel. (p. 190)

The sum of the interior-angle measures of any triangle is 180°. (p. 197)

In a triangle, the measure of each exterior angle is equal to the sum of the measures of its two remote interior angles. (p. 202)

A segment joining the midpoints of two sides of a triangle is parallel to the third side and one half its length. (p. 202)

The sum of the interior-angle measures of any quadrilateral is 360°. (p. 205)

The sum of the interior-angle measures of any polygon having n sides is $(n-2)180°$. (p. 206)

The sum of the exterior-angle measures, one at each vertex, of any polygon is 360°. (p. 206)

If the diagonals of a quadrilateral bisect each other, then the quadrilateral is a parallelogram. (p. 209)

If the diagonals of a quadrilateral are congruent and bisect each other, then the quadrilateral is a rectangle. (p. 209)

If the diagonals of a quadrilateral are the perpendicular bisectors of each other, then the quadrilateral is a rhombus. (p. 209)

If the diagonals of a quadrilateral are congruent and are the perpendicular bisectors of each other, then the quadrilateral is a square. (p. 209)

The formula for the circumference of any circle is $C = \pi d$. (p. 227)

To find the area of a rectangular region, multiply the base length by the height. $A = bh$. (p. 232)

To find the area of a parallelogram region, multiply the base length by the height. $A = bh$. (p. 242)

To find the area of a triangular region, multiply $\frac{1}{2}$ by the product of the base length and height. $A = \frac{1}{2}bh$. (p. 246)

To find the area of a circular region, multiply π by the square of the radius. $A = \pi r^2$. (p. 255)

If both the base length and height of a rectangular region are multiplied by n, its perimeter is multiplied by n and its area is multiplied by n^2. (p. 258)

If the radius of a circular region is multiplied by n, its circumference is multiplied by n and its area is multiplied by n^2. (p. 258)

The area determined by a rhombus is equal to one half the product of the lengths of the diagonals. $A = \frac{1}{2}d_1d_2$. (p. 263)

The area of any trapezoidal region is equal to one half the product of the height and the sum of the base lengths. $A = \frac{1}{2}h(b_1 + b_2)$. (p. 263)

To find the lateral area of a cylinder, multiply the circumference of the base by the height. L.A. $= \pi dh$. (p. 285)

To find the volume of any prism, multiply the area of the base by the height. $V = Bh$. (p. 290)

To find the volume of a cylinder, multiply the area of the base by the height. $V = \pi r^2h$. (p. 297)

If the length of each edge of a rectangular prism is multiplied by n, its total area is multiplied by n^2 and its volume is multiplied by n^3. (p. 303)

If both the radius of the base and the height of a cylinder are multiplied by n, its total area is multiplied by n^2 and its volume is multiplied by n^3. (p. 303)

The volume of a regular pyramid or a cone is given by the following formula. Volume $= \frac{1}{3} \times$ Area of base $\times$ Height, or $V = \frac{1}{3}Bh$. (p. 307)

The total area and volume of a sphere with radius r are given by the following formulas. T.A. $= 4\pi r^2$, and $V = \frac{4}{3}\pi r^3$. (p. 310)

If the lengths a, b, and c, where c is the longest of the three sides of a triangle, are related by the formula $a^2 + b^2 = c^2$, then the triangle is a right triangle. (p. 332)

Pythagorean Theorem (p. 333)
For any right triangle, the square of the length of the hypotenuse is equal to the sum of the squares of the lengths of the legs. $c^2 = a^2 + b^2$.

In every 30-60-90 triangle, (p. 344)
  the hypotenuse is twice as long as the side opposite the 30° angle (the shorter leg),
  the side opposite the 30° angle (shorter leg) is one half as long as the hypotenuse, and
  the side opposite the 60° angle (longer leg) is $\sqrt{3}$ times as long as the side opposite the 30° angle (shorter leg).

In every 45-45-90 triangle, (p. 345)
  both legs are the same length, and
  the hypotenuse is $\sqrt{2}$ times as long as each leg.

Properties of Similar Polygons (p. 370)
Corresponding angles are congruent.
The lengths of corresponding sides are proportional.

Side/Side/Side Property (SSS ~) (p. 384)
If the lengths of the corresponding sides of two triangles are proportional, the triangles are similar.

Side/Angle/Side Property (SAS ~) (p. 384)
If the lengths of two pairs of corresponding sides of two triangles are proportional and the corresponding included angles are congruent, the triangles are similar.

Angle/Angle Property (AA) (p. 385)
If two angles of one triangle are congruent to two angles of another triangle, the triangles are similar.

If a segment is parallel to one side of a triangle and intersects the other two sides, the following statements are true: (p. 396)
The triangle formed is similar to the original triangle.
The sides of the original triangle are divided proportionally.

If three or more parallel lines intersect two transversals, the segments cut off on the transversals are divided proportionally. (p. 397)

If three or more parallel lines intersect two transversals and cut off congruent segments on one transversal, the parallel lines cut off congruent segments on the other transversal. (p. 400)

If two polygonal regions are similar and the ratio of the lengths of a pair of corresponding sides is $a:b$, then the following statements are true: The ratio of their perimeters is $a:b$. The ratio of their areas is $a^2:b^2$. (p. 404)

If region X ~ region Y and k = the constant of similarity of region X to region Y, then the following statements are true: (p. 404)
Perimeter of region $X = k \cdot$ perimeter of region Y
Area of region $X = k^2 \cdot$ area of region Y

If two prisms are similar and the ratio of the lengths of a pair of corresponding segments is $a:b$, then the following statements are true: (p. 407)
The ratio of their total areas is $a^2:b^2$.
The ratio of their volumes is $a^3:b^3$.

If prism X ~ prism Y and k = the constant of similarity of prism X to prism Y, then the following statements are true: (p. 407)
Total Area of prism $X = k^2 \cdot$ Total Area of prism Y
Volume of prism $X = k^3 \cdot$ Volume of prism Y

The slope of any vertical line is undefined. (p. 449)

The slope of any nonvertical line is given by the ratio: $\frac{\text{rise}}{\text{run}}$. (p. 449)

The slope of any horizontal line is zero. (p. 449)

To find the slope of any line, you may use any two points on the line. (p. 449)

The slope of a line is positive if the line slants upward from left to right. (p. 449)

The slope of a line is negative if the line slants downward from left to right. (p. 449)

If two nonvertical lines are parallel, they have equal slopes. (p. 453)

If two lines have equal slopes, they are parallel. (p. 453)

If two nonvertical lines are perpendicular, the product of their slopes is $^-1$. (p. 454)

If the product of the slopes of two lines is $^-1$, the lines are perpendicular. (p. 454)

If a point is on a line, its coordinates must satisfy any equation describing the line. (p. 460)

If the coordinates of a point satisfy an equation of a line, the point is on the line described by the equation. (p. 460)

If the coordinates of a point satisfy equations of two different lines, then the point is the point of intersection of the two lines. (p. 460)

GLOSSARY

Many entries are informal definitions or descriptions. For formal definitions consult a mathematics dictionary.

acute angle *See* angle.

acute triangle (p. 107) A triangle in which all angles are acute angles.

adjacent angles (p. 76) Two angles in the same plane with a common vertex and a common side but no interior points in common.

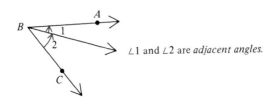

∠1 and ∠2 are *adjacent angles*.

alternate interior angles *See* transversal.

altitude of a parallelogram (p. 239) A segment from a point on one side perpendicular to the line containing the opposite side, called the *base*. The length of an altitude is called the *height* of the parallelogram.

altitude of a three-dimensional figure *See* prism, regular pyramid, right circular cone, and right circular cylinder.

altitude of a triangle (p. 167) A segment from one vertex perpendicular to the line containing the opposite side, which is called the *base*. The length of an altitude is called the *height* of the triangle.

amount of turn (p. 45) A unit of angle measure used when an angle is viewed as the figure formed by turning a ray about its endpoint.

angle (∠) (pp. 12, 42) An angle may be viewed as either two rays with a common endpoint, or the figure formed by turning a ray about its endpoint. The common endpoint of the rays is the *vertex* of the angle. The rays forming the angle are the *sides* of the angle. An angle can be named by the vertex (if only one angle pictured has that point as vertex), by the vertex and one point on each side, or by a lowercase letter or number written inside the picture of the angle. An *acute angle* (p. 74) is an angle with a measure less than 90°, or less than $\frac{1}{4}$ turn. An *obtuse angle* (p. 74) is an angle with a measure between 90° and 180°, or between $\frac{1}{4}$ and $\frac{1}{2}$

turn. A *straight angle* (p. 48) is an angle with a measure of 180°, or $\frac{1}{2}$ turn. A *right angle* (p. 48) is an angle with a measure of 90°, or $\frac{1}{4}$ turn.

angle bisector (p. 103) A ray that divides an angle into two congruent angles.

arc (⌒) (p. 63) A part of a circle determined by two points. An arc is named by its endpoints. A third point is used to name arcs larger than a semicircle.

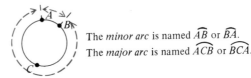

The *minor arc* is named $\overset{\frown}{AB}$ or $\overset{\frown}{BA}$.
The *major arc* is named $\overset{\frown}{ACB}$ or $\overset{\frown}{BCA}$.

area (A) (p. 229) The amount of surface of any two-dimensional region. Area is usually measured in square units.

base of a parallelogram (p. 239) Any side of a parallelogram can be considered the base. This is true for all parallelograms including rectangles, rhombuses, and squares.

base of a three-dimensional figure *See* prism, regular pyramid, right circular cone, and right circular cylinder.

base of a triangle (p. 167) Any side of a triangle may be called the base. In an isosceles triangle, it is usually the side opposite the vertex angle.

bearing (p. 60) The direction of one point or location with respect to another point or location. A bearing is measured in degrees from north in a clockwise direction. Bearings are expressed with three digits.

bisector of a segment (p. 6) Any line or part of a line that contains the midpoint of a segment. A segment has infinitely many bisectors. A *perpendicular bisector* (p. 103) is a line which is perpendicular to a segment and divides the segment into two congruent parts (bisects the segment).

capacity (p. 289) A concept closely related to volume. Capacity is the amount of fluid substance that a container will hold. Some commonly used units of capacity are the pint, quart, gallon, liter, and fluid ounce.

central angle (p. 45) An angle whose vertex is at the center of a circle. (See figure on next page.)

$\angle ABC$ is a *central angle.*

chord *See* circle.

circle (⊙) (p. 42) All points in a plane which are the same distance from some point called the *center*. A circle is named by its center. A *chord* (p. 42) is a segment whose endpoints are any two points of a circle. A diameter is a special type of chord. A *radius* (*r*) (p. 42) is a segment joining the center of a circle and any point on the circle. Also, the distance from the center of a circle to any point on the circle. A *diameter* (*d*) (p. 42) is a chord that passes through the center of a circle. Also, the length of a chord that passes through the center of a circle. A *semicircle* (p. 70) is half a circle.

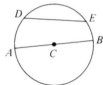

C is the center of ⊙C.
$\overline{DE}$ and $\overline{AB}$ are *chords* of ⊙C.
($\overline{AB}$ is also a *diameter.*)
$\overline{AC}$ and $\overline{CB}$ are radii of ⊙C.
$\overparen{ADB}$ is a semicircle.

circumference (**C**) (p. 226) The distance around (perimeter of) a circle.

circumscribed circle (p. 159) A circle is circumscribed about a polygon if every vertex of the polygon is on the circle.

⊙O is *circumscribed* about $\triangle ABC$.

circumscribed polygon (p. 159) A polygon is circumscribed about a circle if every side of the polygon is tangent to the circle.

Quadrilateral *DEFG* is *circumscribed* about ⊙P.

collinear points (p. 2) A set of points all on the same line.

common tangent (p. 159) A line that is tangent to two or more circles.

complementary angles (p. 76) Two angles whose measures add up to 90°.

congruent figures (≅) (p. 93) Figures that have the same size and shape.

cosine *See* trigonometric ratios.

constant of similarity (**k**) (p. 371) The ratio of the lengths of any two corresponding sides of two similar figures. It is the number by which the length of each segment in one figure is multiplied to find the length of the corresponding segments in a similar figure.

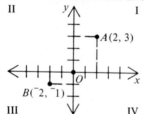

$\triangle ABC \sim \triangle DEF$

Since $BC = \frac{1}{2}EF$, the *constant of similarity* of $\triangle ABC$

to $\triangle DEF$ is $\frac{1}{2}$. $AB = \frac{1}{2}DE$ and $AC = \frac{1}{2}DF$.

construction (p. 132) A geometric drawing made with only straightedge and compass.

coordinate axes (p. 442) The pair of perpendicular number lines used to name points on a plane with ordered pairs of numbers. The horizontal axis is called the *x-axis* and the vertical axis is called the *y-axis*. The point where the axes intersect is called the *origin*. A *quadrant* (p. 442) is one of the four regions, labeled I-IV, into which the coordinate axes divide the plane.

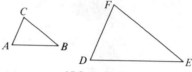

Point O is the *origin for coordinate axes* x and y.

coordinate (p. 438) A number used to name (locate) a point on a number line. An *origin* (p. 439) is the zero point on a number line.

The *coordinate* of point A is 2.

coordinates (**x, y**) (p. 438) An ordered pair of numbers used to name (locate) a point in a plane. The *x-coordinate* (p. 442) is the distance of a point right or left of the origin. In an ordered pair, it is always stated first. The *y-coordinate* (p. 442) is the distance of a point above or below the origin. In an *ordered pair*, it is always stated second. The *x*-coordinate is always listed first and the *y*-coordinate second.

coplanar points (p. 2) A set of points all in the same plane.

corresponding angles *See* transversal.

corresponding parts *See* similar figures.

cube (p. 26) A rectangular prism in which all faces are congruent squares.

degree (p. 48) A unit of angle measure equivalent to $\frac{1}{360}$ turn.

diagonal of a polygon (p. 18) A segment joining a pair of opposite vertices.

$\overline{AD}$ and $\overline{AC}$ are some *diagonals* of *ABCDE*.

diameter *See* circle.

divided proportionally (p. 396) Segments are said to be divided proportionally when the ratios of corresponding lengths are equivalent.

edge (p. 25) A segment formed by the intersection of two faces of a three-dimensional figure.

equiangular triangle (p. 107) A triangle with three congruent angles. Every equiangular triangle is also equilateral.

equidistant (p. 161) The same distance. If *AB* = *AC*, then *A* is equidistant from *B* and *C*.

equilateral triangle (p. 107) A triangle with three congruent sides. Every equilateral triangle is also equiangular.

equivalent ratios (p. 357) Ratios which make the same comparison (have the same value).

exterior angles *See* transversal.

exterior angle of a triangle *See* interior angles of a triangle.

face (p. 25) A part of a plane forming a side of a three-dimensional figure.

graph of an equation (p. 459) Line determined by an equation that can be written in the form $y = mx + b$.

height (*h*) (p. 232) The measure of an altitude of a figure.

hexagon *See* polygon.

included angle of a triangle (p. 141) For two sides of a triangle, the angle formed by those sides.

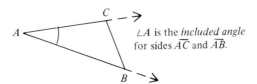

∠*A* is the *included angle* for sides $\overline{AC}$ and $\overline{AB}$.

included side of a triangle (p. 141) For two angles of a triangle, the side of the triangle that is a side of both angles.

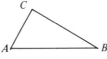

Side $\overline{AB}$ is the *included side* for ∠*A* and ∠*B*.

inscribed angle (p. 69) An angle whose vertex is on a circle.

∠*ABC* is an *inscribed angle*.

inscribed circle (p. 159) A circle is inscribed in a polygon if every side of the polygon is tangent to the circle.

inscribed polygon (p. 159) A polygon is inscribed in a circle if every vertex of the polygon is on the circle.

integers (p. 432) The set of all whole numbers and their opposites. Integers: . . . , -3, -2, -1, 0, 1, 2, 3, ... *Opposites* (p. 432) are two numbers whose sum is zero. The opposite of -3 is 3 because -3 + 3 = 0.

intercepted arc (p. 63) An arc determined by the points of intersection of a circle and the sides of a central or inscribed angle.

$\overset{\frown}{BC}$ is *intercepted* by the central ∠*BAC*.

$\overset{\frown}{BC}$ is *intercepted* by the inscribed ∠*BAC*.

interior angles *See* transversal.

interior angles of a triangle (p. 201) The angles formed by the sides of a triangle. An *exterior angle of a triangle* (p. 197) is an angle formed by one side of the triangle and the extension of the adjacent side. A triangle has six exterior angles, two at each vertex. For each exterior angle, the interior angle to which it is adjacent is called the *adjacent interior angle* (p. 201) and the two interior angles to which it is not adjacent are called the *remote interior angles* (p. 201).

Exterior Angle: ∠1
Adjacent Interior Angle: ∠2
Remote Interior Angles: ∠3 and ∠4

isosceles triangle (p. 107) A triangle with at least two congruent sides. The two congruent sides are called the *legs*. The *vertex angle* is the angle formed by the legs. The *base angles* and *base* are the other angles and side. An equilateral triangle is a special type of isosceles triangle.

lateral area (p. 281) The area of all faces of a three-dimensional figure except the bases.

lateral face (p. 25) Any face of a three-dimensional figure that is not a base.

line of symmetry (p. 98) A line that divides a figure into two parts that match exactly.

median of a triangle (p. 171) A segment joining a vertex and the midpoint of the opposite side.

meter (m) (p. 86) The basic unit of length in the metric system. A meter is about the height of a doorknob from the floor. A *centimeter* (cm) (p. 86) is equivalent to $\frac{1}{100}$ or 0.01 of a meter (1 m = 100 cm or 1 cm = 0.01 m). A *millimeter* (mm) (p. 86) is equivalent to $\frac{1}{1000}$ or 0.001 of a meter (1 m = 1000 mm or 1 mm = 0.001 m). A *kilometer* (km) (p. 86) is equivalent to 1000 meters (1 km = 1000 m or 1 m = 0.001 km).

midpoint of a segment (p. 6) A point that divides a segment into two congruent segments. Each segment has exactly one midpoint.

oblique prism *See* prism.

obtuse angle *See* angle.

obtuse triangle (p. 107) A triangle that contains one obtuse angle.

octagon *See* polygon.

opposite rays (p. 6) Two rays that have a common endpoint and form a line.

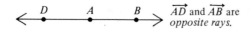

$\overrightarrow{AD}$ and $\overrightarrow{AB}$ are *opposite rays*.

origin *See* coordinate and coordinate axes.

parallel lines (∥) (p. 9) Two or more lines in the same plane that do not intersect.

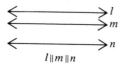

$l \parallel m \parallel n$

parallel planes (p. 9) Two or more planes that do not intersect.

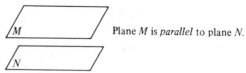

Plane *M* is *parallel* to plane *N*.

parallelogram (p. 21) A quadrilateral with two pairs of opposite sides parallel. Rectangles, rhombuses, and squares are special types of parallelograms.

pentagon *See* polygon.

perfect square *See* square root.

perimeter (P) (p. 222) The distance around a two-dimensional figure.

perpendicular bisector *See* bisector of a segment.

perpendicular lines (⊥) (p. 48) Two lines that meet to form four right angles.

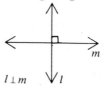

$l \perp m$

perspective drawing (p. 34) The use of a special technique, involving a *horizon line* and *vanishing point(s)*, to represent a three-dimensional object on a flat surface.

pi (π) (p. 226) The ratio of the circumference of a circle to its diameter. The most commonly used approximations for π are $\frac{22}{7}$ and 3.14.

polygon (p. 15) A simple closed two-dimensional figure formed only by line segments that meet at points called *vertices*. The segments are called *sides*. *Consecutive (adjacent) angles of a polygon* (p. 18) are a pair of angles that have one side containing the same side of the polygon. *Consecutive (adjacent) sides of a polygon* (p. 18) are a pair of sides that intersect. *Consecutive (adjacent) vertices of a polygon* (p. 18) are a pair of vertices that are endpoints of the same side of a polygon. *Opposite (nonconsecutive) angles of a polygon* (p. 18) are a pair of angles whose sides contain different sides of the polygon. *Opposite (nonconsecutive) sides of a polygon* (p. 18) are a pair of sides that do not meet. *Opposite (nonconsecutive) vertices of a polygon* (p. 18) are vertices that are not endpoints of the same side. A *quadrilateral* (p. 18) is a polygon with four sides. A *pentagon* (p. 18) is a polygon with five sides. A *hexagon* (p. 18) is a polygon with six sides. An *octagon* (p. 18) is a polygon with eight sides.

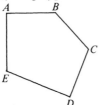

Vertices: *A, B, C, D, E*   Sides: $\overline{AB}, \overline{BC}, \overline{CD}, \overline{DE}, \overline{EA}$

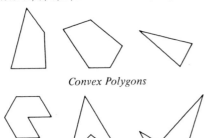

Convex Polygons

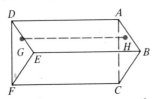

Concave Polygons

prism (p. 25) A three-dimensional figure that has two parallel congruent polygonal regions as bases and lateral faces that are parallelogram regions. Prisms are named by the shape of their *bases*. An *edge* of a prism is a segment formed by the intersection of two faces and a *vertex* is a point formed by the intersection of two edges. Any segment perpendicular to both bases and with one endpoint in each base is an *altitude* of the prism. A *right prism* (p. 26) is a prism in which all lateral faces are rectangles. An *oblique prism* (p. 26) is a prism that is not a right prism.

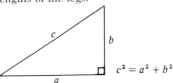

protractor (p. 51) An instrument used to measure angles.

proportion (p. 361) A statement that two ratios are equivalent.

extremes $\dfrac{5}{4} \diagup \diagdown \dfrac{9}{12}$ *means*

proportional (p. 371) When numbers can be arranged so that a true proportion can be written, the numbers are said to be proportional.

Pythagorean theorem (p. 332) For any right triangle, the square of the length of the hypotenuse is equal to the sum of the squares of the lengths of the legs.

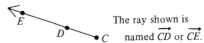

$$c^2 = a^2 + b^2$$

quadrant *See* coordinate axes.

quadrilateral *See* polygon.

radius *See* circle.

ratio (p. 354) A comparison of two numbers by division. If $b \neq 0$, the ratio of a to b is denoted by $\frac{a}{b}$, $a{:}b$, or a to b.

ray ($\overrightarrow{AB}$) (p. 6) Part of a line with one endpoint. A ray is named by its endpoint and any other point on the ray. The endpoint is named first.

The ray shown is named $\overrightarrow{CD}$ or $\overrightarrow{CE}$.

rectangle (p. 21) A parallelogram with four right angles. A square is a special type of rectangle.

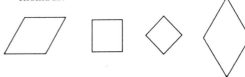

regular polygon (p. 22) A polygon in which all sides are congruent and all angles are congruent.

regular pyramid (p. 306) A three-dimensional figure formed by joining the vertices of a regular polygon (*base*) to a point (*vertex*) that is not in the same plane as the base and that lies directly above the center of the base. A segment from the vertex perpendicular to the base is an *altitude* of the pyramid. The *slant height* (p. 306) in a regular pyramid is the length of an altitude of a lateral face.

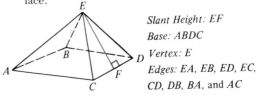

Slant Height: *EF*
Base: *ABDC*
Vertex: *E*
Edges: *EA, EB, ED, EC,*
CD, DB, BA, and *AC*

rhombus (p. 21) A parallelogram with four congruent sides. A square is a special type of rhombus.

right angle *See* angle.

right circular cone (p. 306) A three-dimensional figure formed by joining a circle (*base*) to a point (*vertex*) that is not in the same plane as the base and that lies directly above the center of the base. A segment from the vertex perpendicular to the base in an *altitude* of the cone.

$\overline{AB}$ is the *altitude.*

right circular cylinder (p. 285) A three-dimensional figure having two parallel congruent circular bases and a curved lateral surface connecting them. The bases are directly above or opposite each other. Any segment perpendicular to both bases and with one endpoint in each base is an *altitude* of the cylinder.

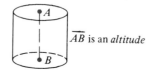

$\overline{AB}$ is an *altitude*

right triangle (p. 107) A triangle that contains one right angle. The side opposite the right angle (longest side) is the *hypotenuse* of the right triangle. The sides forming the right angle are the *legs* of the right triangle.

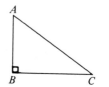

Hypotenuse: $\overline{AC}$
Legs: $\overline{AB}$ and $\overline{BC}$

right prism *See* prism.

scale (p. 409) Ratio of a dimension of a scale drawing to the actual dimension of the object being represented. A *scale drawing* (p. 409) is an enlargement or reduction.

scale drawing *See* scale.

scalene triangle (p. 107) A triangle with no congruent sides.

segment ($\overline{AB}$) (p. 6) Part of a line with two endpoints. A segment is named by its endpoints.

similar figures (~) (p. 366) Figures that have the same shape but not necessarily the same size. Congruent figures are also similar. A *similarity statement* (p. 366) is a statement asserting that two figures are similar. *Corresponding parts* (pp. 93, 366) are any pair of sides or angles in two

congruent or similar polygons having the same relative position.

simplest radical form (p. 342) A square root expression is said to be in simplest radical form if there are no perfect-square factors other than 1 under a radical sign and there is no radical sign in a denominator.

sine *See* trigonometric ratios.

slant height *See* regular pyramid.

slope (p. 448) The measure of the steepness of a line. It is the ratio of *rise* to *run*.

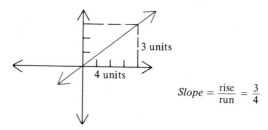

$$Slope = \frac{rise}{run} = \frac{3}{4}$$

sphere (p. 310) The set of all points in space that are the same distance from some point called the *center*.

Points *A*, *B*, *C*, and *D* are all equidistant from center *O*.

square (p. 21) A parallelogram with four right angles and four congruent sides. A square may also be defined as a parallelogram that is both a rectangle and a rhombus.

square of a number (n^2) (p. 326) A number multiplied by itself. The exponent 2 is used to represent the multiplication. For example, "3 squared" can be written 3^2 and $3 \cdot 3 = 9$.

square root ($\sqrt{\ }$) (p. 326) The positive number which when squared gives the original number as a product. The square root of 25 is 5 because $5 \cdot 5 = 25$. A *radical sign* (p. 326) is a symbol used to indicate the positive square root of a number. A *perfect square* (p. 326) is a number that can be written as the product of two equal factors. For example, 16 is a perfect square because $4 \cdot 4 = 16$.

straight angle *See* angle.

supplementary angles (p. 76) Two angles whose measures add up to 180°.

symmetric figure (p. 98) Any figure which has at least one line of symmetry. If a symmetric figure is folded over a line of symmetry, the two halves will match exactly.

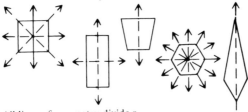

All lines of symmetry divide a figure into two congruent parts.

tangent *See* trigonometric ratios.

tangent (p. 159) A line is tangent to a circle if it is coplanar with the circle and intersects the circle in exactly one point. This point is the *point of tangency.* Such a line is called a *tangent line* or *tangent.*

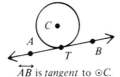

$\overset{\leftrightarrow}{AB}$ is *tangent* to $\odot C$.

total area (p. 279) The sum of the areas of all faces of a three-dimensional figure.

transversal (p. 182) A line intersecting two or more lines, each at a different point. *Alternate interior angles* (p. 185) are a pair of angles formed by a transversal and the two lines it intersects. Alternate interior angles have different vertices and are located on opposite sides of the transversal and inside, or between, the two lines the transversal intersects. *Corresponding angles* (p. 182) are a pair of angles formed by a transversal and the two lines it intersects. Corresponding angles have different vertices and are located in corresponding positions with respect to the two lines. *Exterior angles* (p. 182) are four angles that are located outside the two lines crossed by a transversal. *Interior angles* (p. 182) are four angles located inside, or between, the two lines crossed by a transversal.

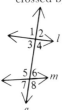

Alternate Interior Angles: ∠3 and ∠6, ∠4 and ∠5
Corresponding Angles: ∠2 and ∠6, ∠4 and ∠8, ∠1 and ∠5, ∠3 and ∠7
Exterior Angles: ∠1, ∠2, ∠7, ∠8
Interior Angles: ∠3, ∠4, ∠5, ∠6

trapezoid (p. 21) A quadrilateral with exactly one pair of opposite sides parallel.

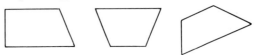

triangle (p. 18) A polygon with three sides. The point of intersection of two sides is a *vertex.*

trigonometric ratios (p. 412) Ratios of corresponding sides in similar right triangles. The *cosine* (cos) is the ratio of the length of the leg adjacent to an acute angle of a right triangle to the length of the hypotenuse. The *sine* (sin) is the ratio of the length of the leg opposite an acute angle of a right triangle to the length of the hypotenuse. The *tangent* (tan) is the ratio of the length of the leg opposite an acute angle of a right triangle to the length of the adjacent leg.

vertical angles (p. 76) Two angles whose sides form two pairs of opposite rays. Vertical angles are congruent.

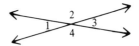

Vertical Angles: ∠1 and ∠3
∠2 and ∠4

volume (p. 289) The amount of space within, or occupied by, a three-dimensional figure. Volume is usually measured in cubic units.

x-coordinate *See* coordinates.

y-coordinate *See* coordinates.

INDEX

SELECTED ANSWERS

(to odd-numbered CLASS PRACTICE exercises and all TEST YOURSELF exercises)

Lesson 1-1
Class Practice (p. 3) **1.** collinear **3.** collinear **5.** B, C, D, G, H **7.** C, D, G **9.** coplanar
11. coplanar **13.** coplanar **15. a.** yes **b.** 1 **c.** none

Lesson 1-2
Class Practice (p. 7) **1.** The endpoint is not named first. **3.** $\overline{CM}, \overline{MD}$ **5.** 1; infinitely many
7. Each is determined by 2 points and extends indefinitely in 0, 1, or 2 directions depending on the
number of arrowheads. **9.** no

Lesson 1-3
Class Practice (p. 9) **1.** *See figure.* **3.** 1; 3 noncollinear points (point of intersection and one other
point on each line) determine a plane. **5.** hidden edges Answers to Ex. 7 and 9 will vary. For
example: **7.** wall and floor (or ceiling) **9.** ceiling and floor **11.** line
Figure

1.

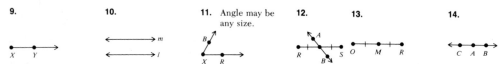

Lesson 1-4
Class Practice (p. 12) **1.** $\angle R, \angle 1, \angle SRT, \angle TRS$ **3.** $\overrightarrow{RS}$ and $\overrightarrow{RT}$ **5.** Answers will vary. For example:
corner of a room
Test Yourself (p. 14) **1.** A, E, B **2.** D, A, E (also, D, A, C; or D, A, B; or D, E, C; or D, E, B; or
D, B, C; or A, E, C; or A, B, C; or E, B, C) **3.** A, B, C, E **4.** $\overleftrightarrow{AB}$ **.5.** T **6.** T **7.** T **8.** F
9-14. *See figure.*
Figures

| 9. | 10. | 11. Angle may be any size. | 12. | 13. | 14. |

Lesson 1-6
Class Practice (p. 18) **1. a.** A, B, C, D **b.** $\overline{AB}, \overline{BC}, \overline{CD}, \overline{DA}$ **c.** $\overline{AB}$ & $\overline{BC}$ (also, $\overline{BC}$ & $\overline{CD}$, or $\overline{CD}$ & $\overline{AD}$,
or $\overline{AD}$ & $\overline{AB}$) **d.** $\overline{AB}$ & $\overline{CD}$ (also, $\overline{AD}$ & $\overline{BC}$) **e.** A & B (also, B & C, or C & D, or D & A) **f.** A & C
(also, B & D) **g.** $\angle A$ & $\angle B$ (also, $\angle B$ & $\angle C$, or $\angle C$ & $\angle D$, or $\angle D$ & $\angle A$) **h.** $\angle A$ & $\angle C$ (also, $\angle B$ & $\angle D$)
i. $ABCD, ADCB$ (also, $BADC$, or $BCDA$, or $CDAB$, or $CBAD$, or $DABC$, or $DCBA$) **j.** 1 **3. a.** F, G, H, I, J, K
b. $\overline{FG}, \overline{GH}, \overline{HI}, \overline{IJ}, \overline{JK}, \overline{KF}$. **c.** `$\overline{FG}$ & $\overline{GH}$ (also, $\overline{GH}$ & $\overline{HI}$, or $\overline{HI}$ & $\overline{IJ}$, or $\overline{IJ}$ & $\overline{JK}$, or $\overline{JK}$ & $\overline{KF}$, or $\overline{KF}$ & $\overline{FG}$)
d. $\overline{FG}$ & $\overline{HI}$ (also, $\overline{FG}$ & $\overline{IJ}$, or $\overline{FG}$ & $\overline{JK}$, or $\overline{GH}$ & $\overline{IJ}$, or $\overline{GH}$ & $\overline{JK}$, or $\overline{GH}$ & $\overline{KF}$, or $\overline{HI}$ & $\overline{JK}$, or $\overline{HI}$ & $\overline{KF}$, or
$\overline{IJ}$ & $\overline{KF}$) **e.** F & G (also, G & H, or H & I, or I & J, or J & K, or K & F) **f.** F & H (also, F & I, or F & J,
or G & I, or G & J, or G & K, or H & J, or H & K, or I & K) **g.** $\angle F$ & $\angle G$ (also, $\angle G$ & $\angle H$, or $\angle H$ & $\angle I$,
or $\angle I$ & $\angle J$, or $\angle J$ & $\angle K$, or $\angle K$ & $\angle F$) **h.** $\angle F$ & $\angle H$ (also, $\angle F$ & $\angle I$, or $\angle F$ & $\angle J$, or $\angle G$ & $\angle I$, or $\angle G$
& $\angle J$, or $\angle G$ & $\angle K$, or $\angle H$ & $\angle J$, or $\angle H$ & $\angle K$, or $\angle I$ & $\angle K$ **i.** $FGHIJK, FKJIHG$ (also, $GHIJKF$, or $GFKJIH$,
or $HIJKFG$, or $HGFKJI$, or $IJKFGH$, or $IHGFKJ$, or $JKFGHI$, or $JIHGFK$, or $KFGHIJ$, or $KJIHGF$) **j.** 3

Lesson 1-7
Class Practice (p. 22) **1.** parallelogram **3.** parallelogram, rectangle **5.** parallelogram, rhombus
7. parallelogram **9.** parallelogram **11.** For the rhombus, all angles are not the same size; for others,
all sides are not the same length.

494

Lesson 1-8

Test Yourself (p. 28) **1.** $\overline{BC}, \overline{CD}$ **2.** A, D **3.** $\overline{BE}, \overline{BD}$ **4.** F **5.** T **6.** F **7.** (drawing of any convex quadrilateral) **8.** (drawing of any 6-sided polygon) **9.** (drawing of any polygon with both equal-length sides and equal-size angles) **10.** (drawing of any 4-sided polygon with segments connecting the two pairs of opposite vertices)

Lesson 1-9

Class Practice (p. 29) **1.** A—head on; B—right; C—above and directly in front **3.** Without dashed edges, cube will seem to move and change its orientation; Which edges are dashed depends on point of view. **5.** Only difference is that in Steps 1–2 rectangles are not squares. **7.** Draw triangular bases so they point to the back rather than the front. **9.** In Steps 1–2, reduce distance between triangles. **11.** Replace triangles with pentagons that are the same size and shape.

Lesson 2-1

Class Practice (p. 42) **1.** $\overline{AX}, \overline{XB}, \overline{XC}$ **3.** $\overline{AC}$ **5.** 8

Lesson 2-2

Class Practice (p. 46) **1.** $\frac{3}{8}$ **3.** $\frac{1}{4}$ **5.** $\frac{1}{6}$ **7.** $\angle 2, \angle 4; \angle 1, \angle 3, \angle 5, \angle 6$ **9.** $\frac{3}{4}$

Lesson 2-3

Class Practice (p. 49) **1.** 4; 2 **3.** $\frac{1}{9}$ **5.** $\frac{3}{8}$ **7.** 144°

Lesson 2-4

Class Practice (p. 53) **1.** Answers will vary depending on size of angles drawn and on estimating skill. **3.** yes; The scale on each type divides a semicircle into 180 equal parts.
Test Yourself (p. 54) **1.** $\overline{XC}, \overline{YC}, \overline{ZC}$ **2.** $\overline{RS}, \overline{XY}$ **3.** $\overline{XY}$ **4.** 5 **5.** $\frac{1}{360}$ **6.** $\frac{1}{6}$ **7.** $\frac{5}{12}$ **8.** 360
9. 36 **10.** 135 **11. a.** Answers will vary. **b.** 60° **12. a.** Answers will vary. **b.** 135
13. (drawing of a circle with a 120°-degree angle whose vertex is at its center) **14.** (drawing of a 90° angle) **15.** (drawing of a 180°-angle—a straight line)

Lesson 2-5

Class Practice (p. 56) **1.** 20° **3.** 100° **5.** 50° **7.** 125° **9.** 40° **11.** 110°

Lesson 2-6

Class Practice (p. 58) **1.** 95 **3.** 70 **5.** 145

Lesson 2-7

Class Practice (p. 61) **1.** direction angle measured in degrees clockwise from north; radar location and navigation **3.** 180° **5.** 045° **7.** 225°

Lesson 2-8

Class Practice (p. 65) **1.** $\overarc{XY}, \overarc{YZ}$ **3.** $\angle XCY, \angle YCZ, \angle XCZ$ **5.** $\overline{XZ}$ **7.** 115° **9.** 65° **11.** 180°
13. a. 180 **b.** 180 **15. a.** 70 **b.** 70 **17. a.** 40 **b.** 70 **c.** 110 **d.** 250 **e.** 110 **19.** 90°
21. progressively greater **23.** The 24 equally-spaced markings on the face can be located by drawing adjacent central angles of measure 15° using the center of the face as the vertex. **25.** Answers will vary depending on particular dials and gauges used.

Lesson 2-9

Class Practice (p. 70) **1.** $\angle WCX, \angle XCY, \angle WCY$ **3.** $\overarc{YZW}, \overarc{YXW}$ **5.** $\overarc{ZY}$ **7.** 100° **9.** 25°
11. 130° **13.** 280° **15.** 90 **17.** 280 **19.** 80 **21.** 180
Test Yourself (p. 73) **1.** $\angle CXD, \angle DXA, \angle CXA$ **2.** $\angle BAC$ **3.** $\overarc{ABC}, \overarc{ADC}$ **4.** $\overarc{AB}, \overarc{BC}, \overarc{CD}, \overarc{DA},$ $\overarc{BD}$ **5.** $\overarc{BAD}, \overarc{BAC}, \overarc{ADB}$ **6.** $\overarc{BC}$ **7.** 60 **8.** 60 **9.** 220 **10.** 300 **11.** 110 **12.** 220 **13.** 35
14. 180 **15.** 90 **16.** 110

Lesson 2-10

Class Practice (p. 75) **1.** acute **3.** obtuse **5.** obtuse **7.** $\angle DOE, \angle AOB, \angle BOC$ **9.** $\angle AOE,$ $\angle AOC$ **11.** 40° **13.** 140° **15.** 130°

Lesson 2-11

Class Practice (p. 77) **1.** no; They have interior points in common. **3.** ∠ARC & ∠BRC, ∠CRD & ∠DRE; 2 **5.** yes; no—If one is acute, the other must be obtuse. **7.** no; Their measures must add up to 90°. **9.** no; Their measures must add up to 180°. **11.** ∠EOD, ∠BOC **13.** yes **15.** 25 **17.** 65

Lesson 3-1

Class Practice (p. 87) **1.** 100 **3.** 10 **5.** $\frac{1}{10}$; $\frac{1}{1000}$ **7, 9.** Answers will vary with estimating skill. (Actual lengths are: **7.** 4.2 cm **9.** 5.8 cm) **11. a.** 3 **b.** 27 **13, 15.** See figure. **17.** m (or cm) **19.** m **21.** ruler, tape measure

Figures

13.

14.

15.

Lesson 3-2

Class Practice (p. 91) **1. a.** 43 **b.** 4.3 **3. a.** 22 **b.** 2.2 **5, 7.** See figure. **9.** 89 **11.** 63 **13.** 5.4

Figures

5.

7.

Lesson 3-3

Class Practice (p. 95) **1.** $\overline{JK}$; $\overline{KL}$; $\overline{JL}$ **3.** $\overline{DF}$ **5.** $\overline{EF}$ **7.** E **9.** FED **11.** EDF **13.** $\overline{RS}$ & $\overline{GH}$; $\overline{ST}$ & $\overline{HI}$; $\overline{TR}$ & $\overline{IG}$

Lesson 3-4

Class Practice (p. 99) **1.** yes **3.** no **5.** no **7.** ABC **9.** B **11.** $\overline{CB}$

Test Yourself (p. 101) **1. a.** 4 **b.** 42 **2. a.** 2 **b.** 18 **3. a.** 6 **b.** 57 **4–6.** See figure. **7.** 68 **8.** 8.0 **9.** 700 **10.** 400,000 **11.** 8 **12.** 170 **13.** congruent **14.** not congruent **15. a.** yes **b.** no **16. a.** yes **b.** no

Figures

4.

5.

6.

Lesson 3-5

Class Practice (p. 103) **1.** 2; infinitely many **3.** (copy of angle with line determined by angle bisector) yes **5.** no **7.** (copy of figure with perpendicular bisector of top and bottom sides and with line determined by horizontal diagonal) yes

Lesson 3-6

Class Practice (p. 107) **1.** $\overline{EF}$, $\overline{DF}$ **3.** ∠F **5.** △ABC **7.** △RST, △XYZ, △HIG **9.** △ABC, △LMN, △PQO, △HIG **11.** △RST **13.** △RST, △XYZ **15.** yes **17.** no

Lesson 3-7

Class Practice (p. 111). **1.** (drawing of any triangle with at least two congruent sides and including line through vertex angle that bisects and is perpendicular to the third side (base)) **3.** 60 **5.** 6 **7.** 65 **9.** 20 **11.** 5 **13.** 30 **15.** 4 **17.** 8

Test Yourself (p. 113) **1.** (copy of angle with line determined by angle bisector) **2.** (copy of segment with perpendicular bisector and line determined by the segment) **3.** (copy of equilateral triangle with lines determined by all three angle bisectors) **4.** (copy of isosceles triangle with line determined by perpendicular bisector of base) **5.** (copy of rectangle with perpendicular bisectors of both pairs of opposite sides) **6.** none **7.** ADCB ≅ WZYX, BCDA ≅ XYZW (also, BADC ≅ XWZY, or CDAB ≅ YZWX, or CBAD ≅ YXWZ, or DABC ≅ ZWXY, or DCBA ≅ ZYXW) **8.** $\overline{ZW}$ **9.** $\overline{XW}$ **10.** ∠XYZ

11. $\angle G$ & $\angle J$, $\angle H$ & $\angle K$, $\angle I$ & $\angle L$ **12.** $\overline{GH}$ & $\overline{JK}$, $\overline{HI}$ & $\overline{KL}$, $\overline{IG}$ & $\overline{LJ}$ **13.** (drawing of any triangle with one angle that measures more than 90°) **14.** (drawing of any size triangle with one 90° angle and with two congruent sides) **15.** (drawing of any triangle with three angles that all measure less than 90°) **16.** (drawing of any triangle with three noncongruent sides) **17.** $\overline{RT}$ & $\overline{ST}$ **18.** $\angle R$ & $\angle S$ **19.** 24 **20.** 90 **21.** 66 **22.** 10

Lesson 3–8
Class Practice (p. 115) **1.** 140 **3.** 140 **5.** 6 **7.** 7 **9.** 14

Lesson 3–9
Class Practice (p. 117) **1.** 25 **3.** 65 **5.** 130 **7.** 3 **9.** 8 **11.** 7

Lesson 3–10
Class Practice (p. 120) **1.** 6.5 **3.** 13 **5.** 12 **7.** 65 **9.** 25 **11.** 50

Lesson 3–11
Class Practice (p. 123) **1.** 8.5 **3.** 17 **5.** 12 **7.** 45 **9.** 45 **11.** 90

Lesson 4–1
Class Practice (p. 135) Length of two segments for Ex. 1, 3, and 5 will vary. **1.** (copy of segment constructed with Construction 1) **3.** (copy of segment constructed twice with Construction 1) **5.** (copy of longer segment constructed with Construction 1 first and then copy of shorter segment constructed with Construction 1 starting at right end of copy of longer segment) **7.** yes **9.** yes **11–19.** ex. 12, 14, 15, 17, and 19, since in the other sets the sum of the lengths of one pair of sides is less than or equal to the length of the third side.

Lesson 4–2
Class Practice (p. 140) **1.** Measure of angle drawn will vary. See Construction 3.

Lesson 4–3
Class Practice (p. 143) **1.** $\overline{XZ}$, $\overline{XY}$ **3.** Y **5.** (copy of $\triangle RST$ constructed with Construction 5) **7.** $\overline{XY}$; $\overline{YZ}$; Y

Lesson 4–4
Class Practice (p. 149) **1.** Length of segments drawn may vary. See Construction 7. **3.** Length of segment and position of point will vary. See Construction 9.
Test Yourself (p. 151) **1.** (triangle constructed with Construction 2) **2.** (triangle constructed with Construction 5) **3.** (triangle constructed with Construction 6) **4.** a & c **5.** (See Construction 4.) **6.** (See Construction 7.) **7.** (See Construction 8.) **8.** (See Construction 9.)

Lesson 4–5
Class Practice (p. 153) **1.** SAS **3.** SSS **5.** $\overline{YZ}$ & $\overline{DR}$, $\overline{ZX}$ & $\overline{RP}$, $\angle Z$ & $\angle R$ (also, $\overline{ZX}$ & $\overline{RP}$, $\overline{XY}$ & $\overline{PD}$, $\angle X$ & $\angle P$; or $\overline{XY}$ & $\overline{PD}$, $\overline{YZ}$ & $\overline{DR}$, $\angle Y$ & $\angle D$) **7.** $\angle B$ & $\angle S$, $\angle C$ & $\angle T$, $\overline{BC}$ & $\overline{ST}$ (also, $\angle C$ & $\angle T$, $\angle A$ & $\angle R$, $\overline{CA}$ & $\overline{TR}$; or $\angle A$ & $\angle R$, $\angle B$ & $\angle S$, $\overline{AB}$ & $\overline{RS}$) **9.** $\angle N$ & $\angle M$, $\angle NPO$ & $\angle MPO$, $\overline{NP}$ & $\overline{MP}$ (also, $\angle NPO$ & $\angle MPO$, $\angle PON$ & $\angle POM$, $\overline{OP}$ & $\overline{OP}$; or $\angle PON$ & $\angle POM$, $\angle N$ & $\angle M$, $\overline{ON}$ & $\overline{OM}$) **11.** $\triangle AEC$ & $\triangle BED$ (also, $\triangle ACB$ & $\triangle BDA$) **13.** $\triangle AEC$ & $\triangle BED$ **15.** $\triangle AEC$ & $\triangle BED$ (also, $\triangle ACB$ & $\triangle BDA$) **17.** F **19.** T

Lesson 4–7
Class Practice (p. 159) **1.** A **3.** $\overleftrightarrow{AB}$ **5.** $\triangle EDC$ **7.** $\overline{OE}$ & $\overline{OC}$

Lesson 4–8
Class Practice (p. 164) **1.** (drawing containing points A and B and points on the perpendicular bisector of $\overline{AB}$) **3.** 6 **5.** isosceles
Test Yourself (p. 166) **1.** $\overline{GH}$ & $\overline{XY}$, $\overline{HI}$ & $\overline{YZ}$, $\overline{IG}$ & $\overline{ZX}$ **2.** $\overline{GH}$ & $\overline{XY}$, $\overline{HI}$ & $\overline{YZ}$, $\angle H$ & $\angle Y$ (also, $\overline{HI}$ & $\overline{YZ}$, $\overline{IG}$ & $\overline{ZX}$, $\angle I$ & $\angle Z$; or $\overline{IG}$ & $\overline{ZX}$, $\overline{GH}$ & $\overline{XY}$, $\angle G$ & $\angle X$) **3.** $\angle G$ & $\angle X$, $\angle H$ & $\angle Y$, $\overline{GH}$ & $\overline{XY}$ (also, $\angle H$ & $\angle Y$, $\angle I$ & $\angle Z$, $\overline{HI}$ & $\overline{YZ}$; or $\angle I$ & $\angle Z$, $\angle G$ & $\angle X$, $\overline{IG}$ & $\overline{ZX}$) **4.** (drawing of any triangle with one

angle that measures more than 90° and with all 3 vertices on a circle) **5.** (drawing of any triangle with a circle tangent to all 3 sides) **6.** (drawing of any size circle with a line intersecting it at one point only) **7.** (drawing of any triangle with 3 angles that all measure less than 90° and with all 3 vertices on a circle constructed with Construction 10) **8.** 10 **9.** 8 **10.** 86 **11.** 43

Lesson 4–9
Class Practice (p. 168) **1.** $\overline{CB}$ **3.** $\overline{RE}$ **5.** (copy of triangle with line through C perpendicular to $\overline{AB}$ constructed with Construction 9) **7.** (drawing of any shape triangle with base length and height as specified and with 3 angles that all measure less than 90°) **9.** (drawing of any shape triangle with base length and height as specified and with one angle that measures more than 90°)

Lesson 5–1
Class Practice (p. 183) **1.** t **3.** $\angle 1, \angle 2, \angle 7, \angle 8$ **5.** $\angle 1$ & $\angle 5, \angle 3$ & $\angle 7, \angle 2$ & $\angle 6, \angle 4$ & $\angle 8$ **7.** $\angle 3$ & $\angle 5, \angle 4$ & $\angle 6$ **9.** n & p **11.** $\angle 10, \angle 12, \angle 13, \angle 15$

Lesson 5–2
Class Practice (p. 187) **1.** $\angle 3$ **3.** $\angle 1$ & $\angle 3$ **5.** 50° **7.** 130° **9.** 90° **11.** 90° **12.** 90°

Lesson 5–3
Class Practice (p. 190) **1.** $\angle 1$ & $\angle 5, \angle 4$ & $\angle 8, \angle 2$ & $\angle 6, \angle 3$ & $\angle 7$ **3.** $\angle 7, \angle 1, \angle 3$ **5.** 55° **7.** 55° **9.** 55° **11.** 90°

Lesson 5–4
Test Yourself (p. 196) **1.** $\angle 1$ & $\angle 6, \angle 2$ & $\angle 5$ **2.** $\angle 1$ & $\angle 5, \angle 2$ & $\angle 6$ **3.** $\angle 7$ & $\angle 2, \angle 6$ & $\angle 3, \angle 8$ & $\angle 1, \angle 5$ & $\angle 4$ **4.** $\angle 2, \angle 4, \angle 5, \angle 7$ **5.** $\angle 3, \angle 6, \angle 8$ **6.** 60, 120, 60 **7.** 115° **8.** 65° **9.** 115° **10.** Use Constructions 14 & 15, or 15 & 16, or 14 & 16.

Lesson 5–5
Class Practice (p. 198) **1.** 60° **3.** 126° **5.** 60° **7.** 40° **9.** 45° **11.** 70°

Lesson 5–6
Class Practice (p. 202) **1.** $\angle 5; \angle 4$ **3.** $\angle 5$ **5.** $\angle 1; \angle 2$ **7.** 66° **9.** 110° **11.** 70° **13.** 80° **15.** 145°

Lesson 5–7
Class Practice (p. 207) **1.** 900° **3.** 1440° **5. a.** 45° **b.** 8 **7.** 108°
Test Yourself (p. 208) **1.** 95 **2.** 40 **3.** 5 **4.** 360° **5.** 720° **6.** 60° **7.** 120° **8.** 150° **9.** 40° **10.** 150° **11.** 35° **12.** 145° **13.** 60° **14.** 49°

Lesson 6–1
Class Practice (p. 223) **1.** 20 cm **3.** 22 cm **5.** 6 **7. a.** 12 **b.** 10 **9.** $P = 2x + y$

Lesson 6–2
Class Practice (p. 227) **1.** 16 **3. a.** 12π cm **b.** 37.68 cm **5. a.** 12π cm **b.** 37.68 cm **7.** 11 cm

Lesson 6–3
Class Practice (p. 230) **1.** 12 **3.** 3 **5.** 10 **7.** (drawing of a 4 × 2 rectangle) **9.** (drawing of any triangle for which $bh = 8$)

Lesson 6–4
Class Practice (p. 233) **1.** 24 cm² **3.** 1 cm² or 100 mm² **5.** $A = 64$ cm²; $P = 32$ cm **7.** 4 **9.** $P = 40$ cm; $A = 70$ cm²

Lesson 6–5
Test Yourself (p. 239) **1.** $P = 28$ cm; $A = 45$ cm² **2.** $P = 32$ cm; $A = 64$ cm² **3.** $P = 10$ ft or $3\frac{1}{3}$ yd; $A = 6$ ft² or $\frac{2}{3}$ yd² **4.** $7\frac{1}{2}$ **5. a.** 56 **b.** 132 **6.** 12 **7.** 5 **8.** 5 **9. a.** 10π cm **b.** 31.4 cm **10.** (drawing of a 6 × 6 square)

Lesson 6–6
Class Practice (p. 240) **1.** (copy of $\triangle ABC$ with segment from C perpendicular to the extension of side AB) **3.** (copy of rectangle $ABCD$ with segment from any point on DC perpendicular to AB) **5, 7.** *See figure.*

Figures

5.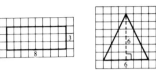

7.

Lesson 6–7
Class Practice (p. 243) **1.** T **3.** T **5.** $P = 26$ cm; $A = 24$ cm² **7.** $P = 28$ cm; $A = 40$ cm² **9.** 6

Lesson 6–8
Class Practice (p. 247) **1.** 17.5 cm² **3.** 12 cm² **5.** 27 ft² **7.** 6 **9.** *See figure.*
Figure

9. Shapes may vary.

Lesson 6–9
Class Practice (p. 251) Answers to Ex. 1 and 3 will vary. For example: *See figure.* **5.** 104 cm² **7.** yes
Figures

1.

3.

Test Yourself (p. 253) **1.** 4 **2.** 60 **3.** 38 cm **4.** 24 **5.** 24 **6.** 20 **7.** 6 **8.** 108 **9.** (drawing of any quadrilateral with both pairs of opposite sides parallel and with a height of 3 and a base length of 4) **10.** (drawings of any two quadrilaterals with both pairs of opposite sides parallel and with a height of 3 and a base length of 6) **11.** (drawing of any shape triangle with a base length of 6 and a height of 4)

Lesson 6–10
Class Practice (p. 256) **1. a.** 16π cm² **b.** 50.24 cm² **3. a.** 16π cm² **b.** 50.24 cm²

Lesson 6–13
Class Practice (p. 264) **1.** 3 **3.** 288 **5.** 30,000 **7.** (drawing of any 3 rectangular regions for which $bh = 144$ in.²) **9.** 24 cm² **11.** 50 cm²

Lesson 7–1
Class Practice (p. 276) **1.** *See figure.* **3.** 2 rectangular—10 cm × 5 cm; 2 rectangular—10 cm × 6 cm; 2 rectangular—5 cm × 6 cm **5.** 2 rectangular—10 ft × 6 ft; 1 rectangular—14 ft × 6 ft; 2 triangular—14 ft × 10 ft × 10 ft **7.** rectangular **9.** triangular **11.** T **13.** T
Figure

1.

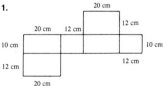 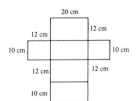

Lesson 7-2
Class Practice (p. 280) **1.** 8 cm **3.** 4 cm **5.** 12 cm **7.** 12 cm **9.** 4 cm **11.** 4 cm × 8 cm
13. 4 cm × 5 cm **15.** 5 cm × 12 cm

Lesson 7-3
Class Practice (p. 282) **1.** L.A. = 300 cm²; T.A. = 360 cm² **3.** yes; no; L.A. changes because a different pair of faces are used as the bases of the prism.

Lesson 7-4
Class Practice (p. 287) **1. a.** 44 in. **b.** 880 in.² **c.** 154 in.² **d.** 1188 in.² **3.** 8 cm
Test Yourself (p. 288) **1.** 2 trapezoidal—6 cm × 10 cm × 7 cm × 8 cm; 1 rectangular—6 cm × 10 cm;
1 rectangular—8 cm × 10 cm; 1 rectangular—7 cm × 10 cm; 1 square—10 cm × 10 cm
2. 2 rectangular—3 in. × 5 in.; 2 rectangular—3 in. × 12 in.; 2 rectangular—5 in. × 12 in. **3.** 2
triangular—4 cm × 8 cm × 9 cm; 1 rectangular—4 cm × 6 cm; 1 rectangular—8 cm × 6 cm; 1
rectangular—9 cm × 6 cm **4.** 310 cm² **5.** 192 in.² **6.** 126 cm² **7.** 212 in.² **8.** L.A. = 113.04 in.²;
T.A. = 169.56 in.² **9.** L.A. = 130 cm²; T.A. = 202 cm² **10.** L.A. = 120 cm²; T.A. = 132 cm² **11.** 54 in.²
12. 17 cm

Lesson 7-5
Class Practice (p. 291) **1. a.** (drawing of a 3 cm × 4 cm rectangle) **b.** 12 cm² **c.** 144 cm³ **3.** 140
5. 5

Lesson 7-6
Class Practice (p. 295) **1. a.** (drawing of a right triangle with $h = 4$ cm and $b = 6$ cm, or *vice versa*)
b. 12 cm² **c.** 144 cm³ **3.** 128 **5.** 6

Lesson 7-7
Class Practice (p. 297) **1. a.** 44 cm **b.** 440 cm² **c.** 154 cm² **d.** 748 cm² **e.** 1540 cm³
3. 128 cm³ **5.** 6
Test Yourself (p. 301) **1. a.** (drawing of a 6 cm × 16 cm rectangle) **b.** 96 cm² **c.** 768 cm³
2. a. (drawing of a right triangle with $b = 6$ cm and $h = 6$ cm) **b.** 18 cm **c.** 270 cm³ **3. a.** (drawing
of a circle with radius of 4 cm) **b.** 50.24 cm² **c.** 401.92 cm³ **4.** 8 cm **5.** 15 cm²

Lesson 7-11
Class Practice (p. 310) **1.** $\overline{XW}, \overline{XY}, \overline{XZ}$ **3.** 4 cm **5.** 200.96 cm² **7.** $r = 3$ cm, $d = 6$ cm

Lesson 7-12
Class Practice (p. 313) **1.** 108 ft³ **3.** 2 yd³ **5.** 5000 **7.** 4 **9.** Answers will vary. In centimeters, the product of the dimensions must be 1000. For example: 100 cm × 10 cm × 1 cm, or 100 cm × 5 cm × 2 cm

Lesson 7-13
Class Practice (p. 317) **1.** 3 **3.** 16 **5.** 48 **7.** 16 **9.** 32 **11.** 2 **13.** Answers will vary. For example: cooking, buying and selling fruits and vegetables, the beverage industry

Lesson 8-1
Class Practice (p. 327) **1.** 16 **3.** 2 **5.** 10 **7.** 47.61 **9.** 4; 5 **11.** 6; 7

Lesson 8-2
Class Practice (p. 330) **1.** none **3.** 9 **5.** 4, 16 **7.** yes **9.** no **11.** no **13.** $\sqrt{64} = 8$; $\sqrt{18} = 3\sqrt{2}$; $\sqrt{32} = 4\sqrt{2}$; $\sqrt{8} = 2\sqrt{2}$ **15.** 5184 **17.** 21 **19.** 54 **21.** 9.644 **23.** 120

Lesson 8-3
Class Practice (p. 334) **1.** 16 + 9 = 25 **3.** 225 + 400 = 625 **5.** yes **7.** no **9.** yes **11.** 9

Lesson 8-4
Class Practice (p. 338) **1.** $\sqrt{21}$ **3.** 24 **5.** 48
Test Yourself (p. 341) **1.** 7.810 **2.** 32 **3.** 6889 **4.** 324 **5.** 324 **6.** 4.243 **7.** $4\sqrt{2}$ **8.** $3\sqrt{7}$
9. $5\sqrt{10}$ **10.** yes **11.** yes **12.** no **13.** yes **14.** 4 **15.** $\sqrt{41}$ **16.** 8

Lesson 8-5

Class Practice (p. 343) **1.** $\left(\dfrac{\sqrt{2}}{\sqrt{2}}\right)$ that is a name for the number one. **3. a.** $\dfrac{\sqrt{30}}{6}$ **b.** 2 **c.** $\dfrac{2\sqrt{21}}{3}$ **d.** $\dfrac{\sqrt{65}}{5}$

Lesson 8-6

Class Practice (p. 346) **1.** Ex. 3: $3^2 + 3^2 = c^2$, $c^2 = 9 + 9 = 18$, $c = \sqrt{18} = 3\sqrt{2}$ Ex. 4: $d^2 + d^2 = 5^2$, $2d^2 = 25$, $d^2 = \dfrac{25}{2}$, $d = \dfrac{5}{\sqrt{2}} = \dfrac{5\sqrt{2}}{2}$ **3.** 45 **5.** $8\sqrt{2}$; $8\sqrt{2}$ **7.** 5; $5\sqrt{3}$

Lesson 9-1

Class Practice (p. 354) **1.** 5 **3.** 5 to 4 **5.** (for example, a drawing of a rectangle divided into 12 congruent squares, 5 of which are shaded) **7.** 21 to 13 **9.** 21 to 8 **11.** 8 to 13

Lesson 9-2

Class Practice (p. 359) **1.** (for example, drawing of two congruent rectangles, the first of which is divided into 3 congruent parts, 2 of which are shaded; and the second of which is divided into 6 congruent parts, 4 of which are shaded) **3.** $\dfrac{2}{9}$ **5.** 3:4 **7.** 2 to 5 **9.** 3 to 1 **11.** 1 to 2

Lesson 9-3

Class Practice (p. 362) **1. a.** x **b.** 2 **c.** 5 **d.** 7 **e.** 2, 5 **f.** x, 7 **3.** $\dfrac{4}{16} = \dfrac{5}{20}$ **5.** T **7.** 24 **9.** $\dfrac{24}{5}$, or $4\dfrac{4}{5}$

Lesson 9-4

Class Practice (p. 363) **1.** $\dfrac{30}{45} = \dfrac{44}{x}$, $30x = 44 \times 45$, $x = 66$; yes **3. a.** $\dfrac{\frac{1}{2}}{1} = \dfrac{x}{5}$, or $\dfrac{\frac{1}{2}}{x} = \dfrac{1}{5}$ **b.** $2\dfrac{1}{2}$

Test Yourself (p. 365) **1.** (for example, two rectangles, the first of which is divided into 3 congruent parts, 2 of which are shaded; and the second of which is divided into 12 congruent parts, 8 of which are shaded) **2.** $\dfrac{3}{5}$ **3.** $\dfrac{2}{3}$ **4.** $\dfrac{6}{5}$ **5.** $\dfrac{1}{3}$ **6.** $\dfrac{9}{12} = \dfrac{15}{20}$ **7.** $y = 12\dfrac{1}{2}$ **8.** $x = 20$ **9.** $c = 7$ **10.** $10\dfrac{1}{2}$ Tbsp

Lesson 9-5

Class Practice (p. 367) **1.** $\overline{XY}$ **3.** $\angle Z$ **5.** $\overline{PO}$ **7.** $\angle T$ **9.** STO **11.** OTS **13.** $\overline{BI}$ **15.** OTP

Lesson 9-6

Class Practice (p. 372) **1.** They are equal. **3.** $\dfrac{3}{5}$ **5.** $\dfrac{3}{5}$ **7.** 12 **9.** $\dfrac{5}{3}$ **11.** 15 **13.** $\dfrac{3}{5}$ **15.** 4 **17.** 4 **19.** $\dfrac{1}{4}$ **21.** Y **23.** WXYZ

Lesson 9-7

Class Practice (p. 375) **1.** 5×20 **3.** 4, 4, 6 **5.** (drawing of figure with same shape as original and dimensions of 3 (top), 3 (right), 6 (bottom), 3 (left)) **7.** (drawing with same shape as original and $h = 2$ and $b = 4$)

Lesson 9-8

Class Practice (p. 379) **1, 3.** *See figure.*

Figures   **1.** Shown
                   half-scale

3. Shown
half-scale.
Location of P
may vary.

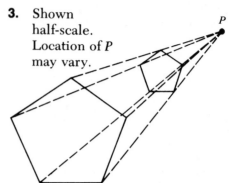

Test Yourself (p. 381)   **1.** $\angle N$ & $\angle D$, $\angle M$ & $\angle F$, $\angle O$ & $\angle E$ **2.** $\triangle DFE \sim \triangle NMO$, $\triangle FED \sim \triangle MON$ (also, $\triangle EDF \sim \triangle ONM$, or $\triangle DEF \sim \triangle NOM$, or $\triangle EFD \sim \triangle OMN$, or $\triangle FDE \sim \triangle MNO$)   **3.** $\frac{1}{3}$ **4.** $\frac{1}{3}$
5. $\frac{1}{3}$ **6.** $\frac{1}{3}$ **7.** 6   **8.** 30   **9.** 39   **10.** $\frac{1}{3}$ **11–12.** *See figure.*

Figures   **11.** Location of P
                   may vary.   **12.**

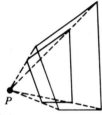

Lesson 9-9
Class Practice (p. 383)   **1.** (copy of angle constructed with Construction 3)   **3.** (copy of segment constructed 3 times with Construction 1)   **5.** (copy of $\frac{1}{2}AB$ (constructed with Construction 7) copied 3 times with Construction 1)   **7.** (drawing of triangle same shape as $\triangle ABC$ and with each side twice as long constructed by Construction 18)

Lesson 9-10
Class Practice (p. 386)   **1.** no   **3.** no   **5.** yes; SSS~   **7.** 50°   **9.** 45°   **11.** 10   **13.** $\frac{BC}{NO}$, $\frac{CA}{OM}$
15. $M; O$

Lesson 10-1
Class Practice (p. 398)   **1.** YR   **3.** PR   **5.** QR   **7.** $\frac{5}{3}$ **9.** $\frac{5}{8}$ **11.** $\frac{5}{8}$ **13.** $\frac{4}{5}$ **15.** $\frac{4}{9}$ **17.** $\frac{5}{9}$
19. 6   **21.** 9

Lesson 10-2
Class Practice (p. 401)   **1.** (drawing of line through P parallel to $\overline{AB}$ constructed with Construction 14, 15, or 16)   **3.** (drawing of segment made up of 3 congruent segments constructed by dividing $\overline{CD}$ into 4 equal lengths with Construction 20)

Lesson 10-3
Class Practice (p. 404)   **1.** 3:7; 9:49   **3.** 5:8; 5:8   **5.** 4   **7.** 4   **9.** 16

Lesson 10-4
Class Practice (p. 407)   **1.** 1   **3.** 4   **5.** 9   **7.** $\frac{1}{4}$ **9.** $\frac{1}{9}$ **11.** $\frac{1}{16}$ **13.** $\frac{8}{27}$ **15.** $\frac{4}{25}$ **17.** 9:25; 27:125
19. 4:3; 16:9   **21.** $\frac{3}{4}$ **23.** $\frac{3}{4}$ **25.** 160 cm²   **27.** $\frac{9}{16}$ **29.** 128 cm³   **31.** $\frac{27}{64}$

Lesson 10-5
Class Practice (p. 410) **1.** 8 cm **3.** 24 cm **5.** 12 ft **7.** 30 ft **9.** 9 ft **11.** 8 ft; 30 ft **13.** 12 ft; 16.2 ft

Test Yourself (p. 412) **1.** 8 **2.** 10 **3.** 9 **4.** $7\frac{1}{2}$ **5.** (drawing of segment made up of 4 congruent segments constructed by dividing $\overline{AB}$ into 5 equal lengths with Construction 20) **6. a.** $\frac{2}{3}$ **b.** $\frac{4}{9}$ **7.** 20 **8.** $3.\overline{3}$ **9.** $\left(2\frac{1}{2}\text{-in.} \times 1\frac{1}{2}\text{-in. rectangle}\right)$

Lesson 10-6
Class Practice (p. 414) **1.** $\overline{AB}$ **3.** $\overline{AC}$ **5.** $\overline{BC}$ **7. a.** $\frac{15}{17}$ **b.** 0.882 **9. a.** $\frac{15}{17}$ **b.** 0.882 **11. a.** $\frac{15}{8}$ **b.** 1.875 **13.** a number

Lesson 10-7
Class Practice (p. 418) **1.** 0.139 **3.** 0.956 **5.** 0.625 **7.** 52° **9.** 60° **11.** 27° **13.** 17° **15.** $4\sqrt{3}$

Lesson 10-8
Class Practice (p. 420) **1.** tan **3.** sin **5.** sin **7.** 37° **9.** 62

Lesson 11-1
Class Practice (p. 433) **1.** 0 **3.** ⁻6 **5.** 11 **7.** ⁻4 **9.** ⁻7

Lesson 11-2
Class Practice (p. 435) **1.** 8 + 3 **3.** 6 + ⁻4 **5.** ⁻9 + 5 **7.** 6 **9.** ⁻6 **11.** ⁻12

Lesson 11-3
Class Practice (p. 437) **1.** ⁻3 **3.** ⁻5 **5.** ⁻3 **7.** 8 **9.** 36 **11.** 3 **13.** ⁻2 **15.** 12 **17.** ⁻24 **19.** 0

Lesson 11-4
Class Practice (p. 439) **1.** 1 **3.** C-9 **5.** G-2 **7.** G-8 **9.** D-9 **11.** B-1

Lesson 11-5
Class Practice (p. 443) **1.** (0, 0) **3.** B & F; C & E **5.** Answers will vary. I—any point with two positive coordinates. II—any point with a negative x-coordinate and a positive y-coordinate. III—any point with two negative coordinates. IV—any point with a positive x-coordinate and a negative y-coordinate **7.** 0, 0 **9.** III **11.** II **13.** I **15.** y-axis **17.** x-axis **19.** III **21.** (3, ⁻3)

Test Yourself (p. 447) **1.** A—0; B—$2\frac{3}{4}$; C—$1\frac{1}{2}$ **2.** A(3, ⁻2); B(⁻5, 3); C(3, 3) **3.** AC = 5; BC = 8 **4-9.** *See figure.* **10.** ⁻5 **11.** ⁻13 **12.** ⁻5 **13.** 5 **14.** ⁻10 **15.** ⁻5 **16.** 3 **17.** ⁻24 **18.** 27 **19.** ⁻4 **20.** 3 **21.** ⁻8
Figure

4-9.

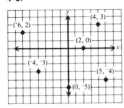

Lesson 11-6
Class Practice (p. 450) **1.** 0 **3.** — **5.** $\frac{3}{2}$ **7.** $\frac{-5}{2}$ **9.** slope $= \frac{5}{2}$ **11.** slope = 0

Lesson 11-7
Class Practice (p. 454) **1.** $\frac{-3}{5}$ **3.** neither **5.** perpendicular **7.** neither **9, 11.** *See figure.*

Figures

9. Any lines paral-
lel to those
shown

11. Any lines
parallel to
those shown

Lesson 11–8

Class Practice (p. 456) **1. a.** 5 **b.** 3 **c.** $\sqrt{34}$

Test Yourself (p. 458) **1. a.** $\frac{3}{4}$ **b.** 5 **2. a.** $\frac{^{-}1}{2}$ **b.** $3\sqrt{5}$ **3. a.** 0 **b.** 7 **4.** $\frac{2}{3}$

5. $\frac{^{-}3}{2}$ **6–9.** *See figure.* **10.** $(3, ^{-}1)$ **11.** 5 **12.** 4 **13.** $\sqrt{41}$

Figures

6. Any lines paral-
lel to those
shown

7. Any lines paral-
lel to those
shown

8. Any vertical
line

9.

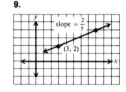

Lesson 11–9

Class Practice (p. 461) **1.** a, c **3.** c Answers to Ex. 5, 7, and 9 will vary. For example: **5.** (0, 5),
(1, 4), (2, 3), (3, 2) **7.** (8, 0), (5, $^{-}$1), (2, $^{-}$2), ($^{-}$1, $^{-}$3) **9.** (5, 0), (5, 1), (5, 2), (5, 3) **11, 13, 15.** *See figure.*

Figures

11.

13.

15.

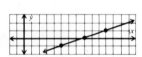